PRICING AND TRADING INTEREST RATE DERIVATIVES

A PRACTICAL GUIDE TO SWAPS

THIRD EDITION

J H M Darbyshire

BSc. Mathematics, University of Nottingham, '06.
MSc. Mathematics, The Open University '15.
MSc. Computational Science, Uppsala University '19.

This third edition published by Aitch & Dee Limited 2022.
Printed by CreateSpace.

ISBN: 978-0-9954555-4-2

Dedicated to my wife, Sanna, without whom I would never have had the time to start, let alone finish, this.
Less so, my daughters, Isla and Lily, who did their best to command all of my spare time!

And thanks and much credit to those that introduced me to IRDs and the nuances of specific markets;

Kilian Murray,

John Mann,

Trevor Pugh,

Aiden Buckley,

Ian Horsely,

Nat Tyce,

Lyndon Drake,

David Brown,

Jon Desler,

Lauri Snäll,

Kasper Korgaard,

Lars Hesstvedt Olson,

Ralph Beckers, and

Damien Leculee.

List of acronyms

Acronym	Description
1D	One day
1M, 3M, 1Y, etc.	One month, three month, one year etc.
ASF	Available stable funding
AT1	Additional Tier 1 Capital
ATM	At-the-money
BBA	British Banker's Association
b.d.	Business day
BoE	Bank of England
bp	Basis point
CC	Continuously compounded
CCP	Centrally cleared counterparty
CCR	Counterparty credit risk
CCVA	Cleared counterparty valuation adjustment
CE	Credit exposure
CEM	Current exposure method
CET1	Common Equity Tier 1 Capital
CFTC	Commodity Futures Trading Commission
c.i.	Confidence interval
CLOB	Central limit order book
CME	Chicago Mercantile Exchange
CoVaR	Variance-covariance VaR
CSA	Credit support annex
CTD	Cheapest to deliver
CVA	Credit valuation adjustment
(CVA)	(Collateral valuation adjustment)
DCF	Day count fraction
DCM	Designated contract market
DF	Discount factor
DMO	Debt management office
EAD	Exposure at default
ECB	European Central Bank
EDSP	Exchange delivery settlement price
EE	Expected exposure
EEE	Effective expected exposure
EEPE	Effective expected positive exposure
EPE	Effective potential exposure
EMMI	European Money Markets Institute
ES	Expected shortfall
Excel	Microsoft Excel
FCA	Futures convexity adjustment
FED	Federal Reserve System
FRA	Forward rate agreement
FRTB	Fundamental review of the trading book
FVA	Funding valuation adjustment
fwd	Forward (derivatives starting on future dates)
FX	Foreign exchange
GDP	Gross domestic product
G-SIB	Global systemically important bank
HQLA	High quality liquid asset

IBOR	Interbank offered rate
i.i.d.	Identical and independently distributed
IR	Interest rate
IRD	Interest rate derivative
IRR	Internal rate of return
IRS	Interest rate swap
ICMA	International Capital Market Association
IMM	International Monetary Market
ISDA	International Swaps and Derivatives Association
ISMA	International Securities Market Association
ITM	In-the-money
LCH	London Clearing House
LCR	Liquidity coverage ratio
LGD	Loss given default
MAT	Made available to trade
MTM	Mark-to-market
NCB	National central bank
NFC	Non-financial corporation
NSFR	Net stable funding ratio
OIS	Overnight index swap
O/N	Overnight
OTC	Over-the-counter
OTM	Out-the-money
par	Par tenor (standard maturity derivatives starting imminently)
PC	Principal component
PCA	Principal component analysis
PD	Probability of default
PFE	Potential future exposure
PnL	Profit and loss
PV	Net present value
pv01	Present value of a basis point
QE	Quantitative easing
RFR	Risk free rate, e.g. ESTR, SOFR, SONIA etc.
RSF	Required stable funding
RV	Relative value
RW	Risk weight
RWA	Risk weighted asset
SA-CCR	Standardised Approach (to CCR)
SBS	Single currency basis swap
s.d.	Standard deviation
SEF	Swap execution facility
STIR	Short term interest rate
T1	Tier 1 Capital
T2	Tier 2 Capital
VaR	Value at risk
VBA	Visual Basic for Applications (Microsoft)
XCS	Cross-currency swap
ZCA	Zero coupon swap convexity adjustment
ZCS	Zero coupon swap

List of mathematical symbols and notation

Symbol	Description
	Generic symbols
$(h), i, j, k, l$	typical counting indices.
T_x	terminal number for counting index, usually time or date dependent.
δ_i^j	equal to one if, $i = j$, otherwise zero.
α_i^j	equal to one if, $i \leq j$, otherwise zero.
$\boldsymbol{\delta}$	vector with all elements equal to one, sometimes labelled $\mathbf{1}$ in wider literature.
$\mathbf{diag}(\mathbf{x})$	creates a diagonal matrix from 1-d vector $\mathbf{x}$.
$\mathbf{diagonal}(\mathbf{x})$	creates a 1-d vector from the diagonal elements of a matrix $\mathbf{x}$.
	Yield curve pricing
m_i	a specific date, or maturity, where $m_i < m_{i+1}$.
d_i	DCF between dates, m_{i-1} and m_i.
D_i	DCF between today (or m_0) and date, m_i.
$\bar{Z}_i$	CC zero-rate applicable over period, D_i.
$N_{(i)}$	notional amount (over period , d_i) .
r_i	floating forecast rate fixing applicable over period, d_i (e.g. 3M-IBOR).
$\bar{r}_i$	CC floating forecast rate over period, d_i, associated to r_i.
s_i	bp spread over r_i (over period, d_i) to attain discount rate.
$\bar{s}_i$	CC bp spread over $\bar{r}_i$ to attain continuously compounded (CC) discount rate.
z_i	bp spread over r_i (over period, d_i) to obtain another forecast rate.
$\bar{z}_i$	CC bp spread over $\bar{r}_i$ to attain another CC forecast rate.
R_i	fixed rate applicable over period, d_i.
C_i	a cashflow receivable on date, m_i.
Z_i	fixed bp spread over r_i over period, d_i
v_i	DF for date, m_i.
w_i, x_i	DF referencing an alternate method, CSA, or adjustment to v_i (context dependent).
F_i	market FX rate on any date, m_i.
f_i	FX rate fixings applicable to date, m_i.
$r_i^*, d_i^*, v_i^*, w_i^*$	for XCSs, respective variables of the domestic currency (e.g. the EUR leg of a EUR/USD XCS).
P	PV of a derivative asset, or portfolio.
θ_P	Sharpe ratio of a trade, or portfolio.
	Risk notation
A_i	analytic delta risk of instrument, i.
$\mathbf{Q}(\mathbf{x})$	covariance matrix of the instruments in vector $\mathbf{x}$.
$\mathbf{S_A}$	numeric risk strip obtained for risk model, A, directly from the portfolio's trades.
S_A^i	specific risk bucket, i, of $\mathbf{S_A}$.
$\mathbf{S_A^*}$	numeric risk strip obtained for risk model A by a Jacobian transformation from another risk model.
$\widetilde{\mathbf{S_A}}$	PC risk representation of $\mathbf{S_A}$ generated through PCA.
$\mathbf{S}$	in chapters 11, 12 and 19 this represents the known swap rates that parametrises an iteratively solved curve. Risk of a portfolio relative to this curve is expressed as $\boldsymbol{\nabla_S} P$

$\mathbf{G_A}$	analytic cross-gamma grid, expressed in terms of risk model A's instruments, of a trade or portfolio.
$G_{\mathbf{A}}^{jk}$	specific cross-gamma risk element of $\mathbf{G_A}$.
c	value at risk (VaR) multiplier of a portfolio (representing 1 s.d. of VaR).
$\mathbf{J_{A \to B}}$	Jacobian transformation matrix from risk model A to model B.
$\mathbf{J_{A \to B}^{-1(+)}}$	inverse (or pseudo-inverse) transformation of $\mathbf{J_{A \to B}}$.

Swaption pricing

$O_{\{p,\,r,\,s\}}$	Swaption price of payer, receiver, and straddle (bps×100 relative to analytic pv01 of underlying).
F	mid-market rate of the underlying derivative price (%).
K	strike rate of the swaption's underlying (%).
σ_{N}	normal volatility of underlying (bps per period /annum).
σ_{LN}	log-normal volatility of underlying (% per period /annum).
σ_{N}^*	normalised vol estimated from the log-vol (bps).
T	decimalised number of periods /years until expiry.
$\Phi(x)$	cumulative standard normal distribution evaluated at x.

Swap and swaption terminology

(0Y)5Y	a 5Y swap starting imminently.
1Y5Y	a 5Y swap forward starting after 1Y (or a swaption on a 5Y swap with 1Y expiry).
1Y2Y5Y	a swaption on a 2Y5Y swap with a 1Y expiry.
1Y5Y_2Y	used to express volatility on a 1Y5Y swaption after 2Y.
2s5s	represents a spread trade of 2Y versus 5Y.
2s5s10s	represents a butterfly trade of 5Y versus 2Y and 10Y.
2s3s4s5s	represents a pascal trade of 2s3s4s versus 3s4s5s.
2s3s/4s5s	represents a condor trade of 2s3s versus 4s5s.
EURUSD	domestic versus foreign FX rate (1 EUR = F USD).
EUR/USD	XCS with bp spread attached to domestic currency (EUR $+z$ bps = USD $+0$ bps).

Market-maker pricing (all in basis points, chapter 18 only)

X	margin to mid-market of a quotation shown by market-maker.
C	presumed cost of hedging a quoted trade.
Z	value that is greater than C by the minimum marketable increment.
T	s.d. of non-transparency of a quoted trade price.
I	informational value associated with a trade request.

Risk terminology

Interest rate derivative (IRD) risks are not consistent in their conventions from user to user. In this book we adopt the conventions stated below. This is done to; provide clarity across as many sections and examples as possible, support the true mathematical derivations, and align with terminology of trading in the interbank market.

Outright delta risk: +'ve risk prefers interest rates to increase (per bp)

SBS basis risk: +'ve risk prefers the rates of the longer tenor index to increase, relative to the shorter tenor index (per bp)

XCS basis risk: +'ve risk prefers the XCS basis attached to the domestic currency to increase (per bp)

FX risk: +'ve risk indicates a long domestic position and prefers the foreign exchange (FX) rate to increase (notional exposure).

Segregating the IR curveset

Figure 1 shows one way of segregating an interest rate (IR) curveset into consecutive forward starting (referring to derivatives starting on future dates) (fwd) instruments, for the purpose of referencing variables in the pricing formula of IRDs. Other ways are possible but we choose this as it has a clear definition, and is very useful for mathematical formula manipulation in subsequent chapters.

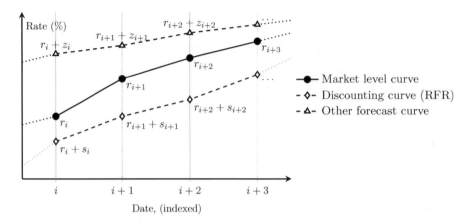

Figure 1: Illustrating the symbols used to describe the make up of the IR curveset.

Each part of any curve is indexed and independent from any other. One curve, the **outright** market level curve, is chosen to denote that which identifies the overall level of the IR market, and given the symbols, r_i. The value of r_i defines a zero coupon deposit rate between the date m_i and m_{i+1}. The spacing of these dates is often chosen to suit the mathematical purpose of analysis.

All the other curves are dependent upon the outright curve by means of **spread** levels; in the case of the discounting curve the symbols used are, s_i, and for another, forecasting, curve the symbols used are, z_i. A positive spread value always places a new curve above the level of the outright curve, and a negative spread level below.

Prior to the transition from IBOR this was an important distinction. After the transition the risk free rate (RFR) curve in a single currency typically acts as both the forecasting curve for settling cashflows, **and** the discount curve for discounting cashflows. From this perspective it is therefore sensible to establish the outright market level curve, r_i, as those RFR curve rates, and since the forecasting curve is identical to those RFRs:

$$z_i \equiv 0 \quad \forall i \quad \text{in an RFR only single currency framework}$$

and since the discounting curve is also identical to those RFRs:

$$s_i \equiv 0 \quad \forall i \quad \text{in an RFR only single currency framework}$$

Since z_i and s_i are always zero in the RFR framework this does not mean that their associated risk calculations are not worthwhile. Calculations can still be made and are still relevant.

Preface

to the third edition...

It has been over five years since the publication of the revised edition. In that time IR markets have undergone **a large transition - from IBOR to RFRs**. As a response, to stay current and preempt the future of a completely IBOR free market, this new edition has, too, eliminated IBOR. Some sections remain for historical context but otherwise the practical focus has completely shifted to use RFRs.

Additionally, in that intervening time while on sabbatical from markets, I attended and taught at university again and was quite shocked to see such high level of knowledge in programming these days, as opposed to when I originally attended university almost twenty years ago. My first time around I distinctively remember coding classes to learn the basic loops and logic statements in Fortran 95. Recently I took part in mathematics courses which assumed students had a coding knowledge and allowed them to source public code libraries to support their projects. Some of those projects were very imaginative with marvellous results that might have utilised the pre-trained TensorFlow models or a variety of other tools widely publicised. For this reason, and after some inspirational feedback received from Kristofer Spinka, Michael Vaiana and Artagan Malsagov, I chose to adapt to **a much more electronic focus in this edition**. An entire code repository has been uploaded with working examples providing a sandbox environment to experiment and learn in almost every chapter in the book. All the code commits have been indexed making it great to follow along and understand all of the implementations. Additionally, all of this includes my own implementation of automatic differentiation, giving readers a chance to fully understand one of the more powerful developments in the modern era. Lastly, the material goes into greater quantitative detail ensuring readers have everything they need to get going on either, a fixed income trading, or quantitative analyst career.

I was unsure whether I would ever update the previous edition but the two changes above are so significant that I hope they extend the impact that this book can have, now and into the future.

to the first and revised editions...

When I first stepped onto a trading floor, the world of derivatives was a different place to where it is today. The financial crisis that began midway through '07 was the precursor to a whole host of new and technical developments. Why? Because it highlighted flaws in many of the pricing models. Flaws which were only ever going to be noticed (or at least corrected) with such an incentive as to protect financial institutions from complete collapse, as was the fate of many around that time. As well, information technology had a huge impact and continues to drive forward every day, influencing more efficient trading and demanding greater and greater understanding of the interconnectivity of the financial world. In one way I was very fortunate to have entered the industry at the time I did. It gave me enough time to understand the old models, but not enough to take them for granted, and I was then ideally positioned to follow the analytical developments which occurred in the subsequent decade, with an unprejudiced mind and keen curiosity.

When I sat down to write this book I had two guiding objectives. I wanted to update the fixed income literature in light of these progressive developments, and I also wanted to explain the important and practical concepts of trading IRDs. This is important because anyone new to the industry today is often expected to be up-to-speed within months, if not weeks, of starting out. Without coherent, concise and consistent tutelage this task is next to impossible with all of the modern complexities. The first edition was guided by four overarching questions it sought answers to:

What makes up the set of linear IRD products?

How does one trade IRDs physically, practically and sensibly?

How are each of the IRDs priced and what factors influence their prices?

What are the risks of trading IRDs and how are they risk managed?

It sufficed that these leading questions were enough to provide the basic structure of that first edition. They captured the technical and advisory knowledge I had acquired in my tenure of trading so far, and that which I wished to impart on any aspiring or experienced practitioners alike.

The feedback I received for that first edition was highly complimentary, from both those aspiring traders and experienced ones. But the readers wanted more. Specifically, they said they wanted the material to be put more in a context of the wider financial industry. This gave me two ideas. Firstly, I drew up some additional questions to steer new material, and secondly, it gave me the idea to create a map of useful reading material to enhance the capabilities of any trader. The additional questions I posed and answered in this edition of the book are:

Who trades IRDs, and why?

What are the drivers of IR markets at large?

What does the future hold for IRD risk management and trading?

So this revised edition took on a new persona to the first. Not only does it strive to be directly practical, with clear and simple instruction, but it serves to point readers in the right direction for expanding their knowledge in specific areas. Hunting other material can be a time consuming task, but, with references included here and there, a reader can quickly learn his way around wider literature available.

I emphasise that I did not want to spend time writing a book that has already been written. The reason this book exists is because it fills a niche gap in the fixed income literature market. There are some very popular, well known books in existence; *Options, Futures, and Other Derivatives* by J Hull, *Interest Rate Swaps, and Other Derivatives* by H Corb, and *Interest Rate Modeling* by a former colleague of mine at Barclays, V Piterbarg and L Andersen. The first two are generalist derivatives books. Hull, at least in my copy of his fifth edition, dedicates only roughly fifty pages to linear IRDs, describing some of their properties and general features. The majority of his fine work is dedicated to option pricing theory, and products outside of fixed income. Corb, takes a similar approach, and although his focus is more toward the interest rate market, the number of exotic variant products he discusses satiates his pages. Neither book is especially trading oriented from the point of view of actively managing portfolios and market-making or price-taking. Piterbarg and Andersen write for quantitative analysts. They produce a comprehensive text, requiring a high level mathematical knowledge and write in a style suitable for mathematical essays.

The book I have chosen to present here is different, albeit with some minor overlap. It positions itself as a specific guide from the point of view of trading and risk managing. It covers every topic I have encountered trading IRD specific markets. The only point of replicating material is to maintain an instructive flow of text in my own book, ensuring the reader is suitably armed with knowledge to progress to subsequent chapters. Very often material might be presented from a different perspective to make it relevant to the trader, rather than the quant, generalist or risk supervisor.

I chose to include a chapter on swaptions and volatility in this revised edition. A reader will recognise my attempts in those chapters to convey relevant concepts, ideas and terminology. All the mathematics and stochastic differential equations are left to other books to explain. Linear rates traders simply benefit from the knowledge of how to price swaptions, what are the important assumptions made about their prices, and what are the inferences to wider interest rate markets.

I would very much like this book to be accessible to all but alas the fixed income and currencies realm relies upon mathematical consistency to function. As such many of the techniques are inherently mathematical. However, I have purposefully sought to avoid a mathematical essay style of prose, and have even substituted mathematical formality at times for a presentation style that is just easier to follow. Of course, not to undermine those who do enjoy a proof here and there, the relevant mathematics are included in appendices, placed there to maintain the overall flow of text and provide clarity for those sections that deserve it. The notation used is developed to be as clear and simple as possible and is completely consistent throughout the book. Certainly complicated symbols and mathematics is avoided everywhere to present a practical text that can be read and used with minimal 'deciphering', for want of a better term. The order of all the material has been carefully constructed in the hope that readers benefit to the fullest.

The difficulty I encountered in writing this book was really trying to maintain a constant level of experience or knowledge of the reader. Some facets of derivative pricing and some aspects of risk management are highly nuanced and require a level of experience and of understanding beyond the basics to appreciate it in a practical sense. Ultimately, I had to make a decision and opted to structure the book so that each chapter generally becomes more and more complex. With novices in mind they can progress through earlier chapters to gain a solid grounding, and seasoned professionals can refer to ad-hoc chapters as reference and as new material. Unfortunately, the revised edition highlighted the nature of the information being grossly interconnected. This meant a linear progression of chapters was impossible, but, in fact, the reader is probably better off for it as a means relating all concepts.

Finally it is worth noting that every reader who picks up this book will subjectively expect a certain level of detail. I have struck a balance between a progressive pace and an amount of knowledge that covers a lot, but doesn't labour the point. Trading is one of the most time sensitive disciplines after all. Individual examples have been included to demonstrate topics but multiple examples, for instance, were deemed excessive. The appendix does expand, particularly mathematically, many of the topics. I think it adds just that extra level of detail that takes an informative, broad text into one that really probes and makes readers think deeply about their subject.

This book is about trading IRDs, specifically for traders (or aspiring traders), written by a trader. The principles here are what I have used day in, day out in my whole career. What is included is what has been important to my job and not theoretical material just to fill pages. It is my sincere hope that you find it helpful and informative.

Contents

Chapter

1

Mathematical Review

There is an underlying objective of this book to avoid complicated notation and mathematics in favour of practical application. But, that doesn't mean critical items have been overlooked or omitted, in fact they certainly have not. The reviewed items in this chapter are not complicated. Many are high school grade, others are early undergraduate. In my experience it is not necessarily the mathematics itself that confounds some fixed income students but the process of applying traditional mathematical techniques in a fixed income context. That is why I begin with this review; to highlight some of the mathematics that will be used, and also to then show readers how it is often applied in a fixed income context. It doubles as useful information for those traders who have not studied degrees with much mathematical content.

1.1 Calculus

Basic calculus is frequently used in upcoming chapters, notably partial differentiation. I regret that I can't really recommend any basic books on calculus but [1] is useful in general. It is more advanced than necessary for our purposes but at least covers all areas.

Stochastic calculus is another branch of mathematics widely used throughout finance in general. It is highly useful but more complicated, often found in quantitative based research for option and volatility based products. With that in mind, it is avoided completely in this book, replaced instead by qualitative reasoning and numerical models where necessary. Other popular texts which demonstrate its use in fixed income calculations, however, are [2] and [3].

1.2   Linear algebra and matrices

To handle the information about portfolios and market movements the data is often arranged into arrays and matrices. Calculations on matrices are frequent, meaning the reader must understand matrix multiplication. Since the focus of this book is on the so-called 'linear IRDs' then a knowledge of linear algebra is incredibly useful across all areas. The specific results in this book might be intuitive or perhaps taken for granted by some readers, but I still recommend [4] highly as being the most concise and introductory but complete text.

For general purposes of data analysis, either historical or aggregating a lot of information, linear algebra and vectorisation is a very efficient means of performing calculations. A lot of programming code and theory, is based around linear algebra techniques and methods.

Within this book any code that is written often makes use of Python's NumPy library and its linear algebra functions. It should be assumed that all code imports this as,

```
1  import numpy as np
```

1.3   Random variables and statistical distributions

I think the area of mathematics most likely to be unknown to readers is this third topic on random variables and statistics. General information on the topic might be easily researched, but I think its application to a fixed income context is the most useful, and most difficult to research, so I will expand this topic directly.

These are the mathematical techniques that traders use for modelling outcomes and events. We can class it as a series of processes; defining some unknown quantities or variables to be predicted, analysing how the defined variables might move (and move together) and producing some statistical tests for the likelihood of different outcomes. Each stage is outlined, although not necessarily separately.

Where code that is written it may make use of Python's SciPy library and its statistical functions. It should be assumed that all code imports this in a manner similar to,

```
1  from scipy.stats import norm
```

1.3.1   Defining random variables

Random variables represent unknown quantities which will be determined at some point in the future. They are often denoted by a symbol in capitals. They are frequently used in trading to model profit and loss (PnL) and future market prices, and to derive statistical inferences from them. Random variables have to be used in conjunction with a statistical distribution. The statistical distribution parametrises the variable so that some values are more likely to occur than others. For example consider an infant whose height at adulthood is modelled as a random variable. It is very unlikely that the infant will grow to be about 1m or 2.5m tall, but around 1.75m is much more likely. Natural processes, such as this, and many other types of process, can be shown to have what is called a 'normal' (or 'Gaussian') distribution. The shape of this distribution is well known and often referred to as a 'bell' curve. But in finance the statistical distribution is often unknown, which means it has to be guessed, or modelled. The naturalness of the normal distribution makes it a prime model for economical events, particularly those in derivatives pricing. An adjustment to this distribution leads to a second distribution called the 'log-normal' distribution. This is also widely used throughout finance to model certain events. Below we describe both these distributions which are well referred to in the main text of this book.

Normal distribution

When describing a normal distribution one must give the mean, μ, of the distribution and the variance, σ^2, and then X, the random variable adhering to this distribution, is expressed as,

$$X \sim N(\mu, \sigma^2) .$$

The probability density function of X:

$$p_X(x) = \frac{1}{\sigma\sqrt{2\pi}} e^{-\frac{(x-\mu)^2}{2\sigma^2}}$$

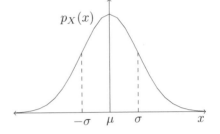

Figure 1.1: The probability density function and graphical illustration of $X \sim N(\mu, \sigma^2)$.

The probability density function is a statistical measure of how likely a certain outcome is relative to the overall space of possible outcomes.

Log-normal distribution

A log-normal distribution is one where the natural logarithm of a variable is normally distributed. A mean is given, μ_{LN}, and the variance also, σ_{LN}^2. In finance the standard deviation (s.d.) is often interpreted as the percentage of the underlying[1]. Y, the random variable adhering to this distribution, is expressed as,

$$Y \sim lognormal(\mu_{\text{LN}}, \sigma_{\text{LN}}^2) , \quad \text{or equivalently,} \quad \ln Y \sim N(\mu_{\text{LN}}, \sigma_{\text{LN}}^2) .$$

Random variables with a log-normal distribution can never be negative, making that an attractive property for modelling prices of some financial instruments. A graphical representation is shown in figure 1.2. The log-normal distribution is used predominantly in two specific chapters

The probability density function of Y:

$$p_Y(y) = \frac{1}{y\sigma_{\text{LN}}\sqrt{2\pi}} e^{-\frac{(\ln y - \mu_{\text{LN}})^2}{2\sigma_{\text{LN}}^2}}$$

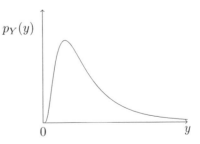

Figure 1.2: The probability density function and graphical illustration of $Y \sim lognormal(\mu_{\text{LN}}, \sigma_{\text{LN}}^2)$.

of this book, 20 on swaptions and 8 on the term structure of interest rate curves.

The normal distribution is used much more frequently, though, also being included in those same chapters. So the following sections specifically relate to normal random variables only.

---

[1]chapter 20 expands more on this as it arises, although this is only an approximation

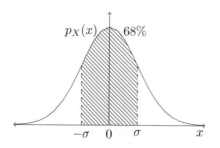

(a) Approximately 68.3% of values lie within one s.d. of the mean.

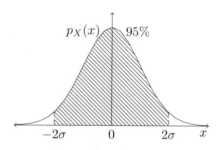

(b) Approximately 95.4% of values lie within two s.d.s of the mean.

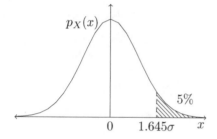

(c) 5% of values lie beyond approximately +1.645 s.d.s from the mean.

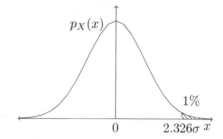

(d) 1% of values lie beyond approximately +2.326 s.d.s from the mean

Figure 1.3: Frequently used and quoted c.i.s of normal random variables. Plotted is $X \sim N(0, \sigma^2)$.

1.3.2   Confidence intervals (c.i.s)

One of the most useful statistical inferences from a random variable is to assign probabilities of likely (or unlikely) ranges of outcomes. For this task the graph of the probability density of a random variable is useful. The area beneath it, within a specific range, determines the percentage chance of the actual value falling within that range. For normal random variables this is always characterised in terms of s.d.s from the mean.

Figure 1.3 highlights a series of confidence intervals (c.i.s) that are frequently used. VaR calculations often involve characterising risk into c.i.s and for these purposes I prefer to use, particularly, the rightmost 5% measure, which typically indicates a loss level exceeded only 5% of the time. Calculating intervals analytically is very difficult but, helpfully, is easily implemented in Microsoft Excel (Excel), using the NORMDIST() and NORMINV() functions. The equivalent in Python, using the `scipy.stats` module are `norm.pdf`, `norm.cdf`, `norm.ppf` methods.

Confidence intervals have other uses too. One is in statistical tests. A test involves forming a hypothesis and determining whether that hypothesis is true and should be accepted or is false and can be rejected. As an example, a trader might have the last year's worth of data on the price of oil. He might have a hypothesis that it is mean reverting. He could choose to commit a statistical test with a specific c.i. to assess if his hypothesis is supported by the data to the level of deterministic accuracy he requires.

1.3.3 Use of standardised normal random variables

To perform mathematical analysis it is often much simpler to convert a non-standardised random variable to one that is standardised, since it is often much easier to research results on standardised variables. A standardised normal random variable, Z say, has the specific mean and variance, zero and one respectively:

$$Z \sim N(0,1) \, .$$

All other normal random variables can be expressed in terms of Z, so that if,

$$X = \mu + \sigma Z, \quad \text{then} \quad X \sim N(\mu, \sigma^2) \, .$$

Additionally a log-normal random variable can be expressed in terms of Z also so that,

$$X = e^{\mu_{\mathrm{LN}} + \sigma_{\mathrm{LN}} Z}, \quad \text{then} \quad X \sim lnN(\mu_{\mathrm{LN}}, \sigma_{\mathrm{LN}}) \, .$$

1.3.4 Combining normal random variables

A special property of independent normal random variables[2] is that their sum can be expressed as a single normal random variable with defined mean and variance:

$$\text{for} \quad X_1 \sim N(\mu_1, \sigma_1^2), \ \ X_2 \sim N(\mu_2, \sigma_2^2), \quad \text{and} \quad Y = X_1 + X_2 \, ,$$

then,

$$Y \sim N(\mu_1 + \mu_2, \sigma_1^2 + \sigma_2^2) \, ,$$

This is easily extended for, $Y = X_1 + \ldots + X_k$.

Example 1.1.
A trader models tomorrow's basis point (bp) change in the 10Y interest rate swap (IRS) rate as $X \sim N(0, 16)$. He wishes to calculate the distribution of the total change in the 10Y IRS rate, Y, over the five day week. He further assumes that each day's moves are independent and identically distributed except for Friday, when US non-farm payrolls data is released, which he thinks is twice as volatile as usual. He calculates as follows:

$$Y = X_1 + X_2 + X_3 + X_4 + 2X_5, \quad \text{for} \quad X_i \sim N(0, 16) \, ,$$

$$Y \sim N(0, 16 + 16 + 16 + 16 + 2^2 \times 16) = N(0, 128) \, .$$

Example 1.2.
The trader wishes to know to a 95% c.i. the maximum bp change in 10Y IRS rates over a five day week, having modelled it as, $Y = N(0, 128)$. He calculates as follows:

$$Y = \sqrt{128} \, Z, \quad \text{for} \quad Z \sim N(0, 1) \, ,$$

with a 95% c.i. $Z \leq 1.645$ from standard results, hence $Y \leq 18.6$ bps market move.

---

[2]the proof is omitted but widely available online.

1.3.5   Correlation and covariance

In trading there are often many random variables, of many different prices that can change. And when one attempts to model multiple random variables they can be dependent upon one another, and this occurs very frequently in financial markets. For example if one were to model the bp change in both 5Y and 10Y IRS rates tomorrow as two random variables they would be expected to show some positive correlation meaning they tend to move in the same direction as one another; one bp higher in both rates would be a more likely outcome than one bp higher in 5Y and one bp lower in 10Y for example. We emphasise that this correlation is always measured in a **linear** sense, defining the accuracy of a purported linear relationship between variables.

Correlation and covariance matrices are frequently used to express properties of the random variables. Correlation depicts how similarly one variable changes relative to another with correlation ranging from -1 to +1, and zero representing no correlation whatsoever. Covariance matrices are then constructed using the variance of each variable and their correlation. Suppose $X_1 \sim N(\mu_1, \sigma_1^2)$ and $X_2 \sim N(\mu_2, \sigma_2^2)$ with, $Corr(X_1, X_2) = \rho$, then:

$$\rho_X = \begin{bmatrix} 1 & \rho \\ \rho & 1 \end{bmatrix}, \quad \mathbf{Q_X} = \begin{bmatrix} \sigma_1^2 & \rho\sigma_1\sigma_2 \\ \rho\sigma_1\sigma_2 & \sigma_2^2 \end{bmatrix}.$$

This is, of course, similarly extended in the case of multiple random variables.

One property to highlight is that correlation matrices are not arbitrary, and not all combinations of values are valid. This particular property is called 'positive definiteness', and it is due to this property that variance-covariance VaR (CoVaR) multipliers (see chapter 14) will always be positive when covariance matrices are used in their calculation. As an intuitive example suppose the amount of water collected in a bottle is almost perfectly correlated with the amount of rainfall, and the amount of water available to drink is perfectly correlated with the amount of water collected in the bottle. It is then impossible to imagine a scenario where the amount of rainfall is negatively correlated with the amount of water available to drink.

Covariance matrices are often constructed from sample historical data. In Excel this task is simplified with the native functions but to be precise, from a given set of N sample data points, $\mathbf{X} = [X_{ij}]$, equation 1.1 defines the unbiased estimate of covariance, q_{jk}, between two variables, X_j and X_k. The s.d. of each random variable is the square root of its variance (its covariance with itself).

$$q_{jk} = \frac{1}{N-1} \sum_{i=1}^{N} (X_{ij} - \bar{X}_j)(X_{ik} - \bar{X}_k) \tag{1.1}$$

Chapter 14 explores constructing covariance matrices further in the context of the material on VaR.

1.3.6   Expectation

The expected value of a random variable is the same as its mean, and is the probability weighted average value. In the course of many chapters the expectation of variables arises in formulae for prices. Often, in the case of applying the *no arbitrage principle*, the expectation is set equal to zero. This is sensible because in the event that the same product, or scenarios, were played out many, many times over, one would expect, when the no arbitrage principle applies, to have zero value at the end, and neither result in profit nor loss.

When two or more variables influence a pricing formula the following identity is very useful to be aware of,

$$E[X_1 X_2] = E[X_1]E[X_2] + Cov(X_1, X_2).$$

1.4   Optimisation

I find that many problems encountered within trading can often be reduced to optimisation problems, where one is typically searching for a minimum (or maximum) of some function by varying a multitude of search variables. Chapter 11 and the section on curve solving uses these techniques intensively, as well as others. This is a wide field with a vast array of potential approaches and classes of problems. The general formulation of an optimisation problem is to **minimise an objective function** of variables and parameters expressed as,

$$\min_{\mathbf{x}} f(\mathbf{x}, \mathbf{u})$$

where $\mathbf{x}$ is a vector of multiple variables to solve for simultaneously and $\mathbf{u}$ is a vector of parameters that are fixed during optimisation. If not unconstrained, then the solution will be subject to a number of constraints, usually classed as equality constraints such as,

$$g_i(\mathbf{x}, \mathbf{u}) = 0$$

and/or inequality constraints such as,

$$h_i(\mathbf{x}, \mathbf{u}) \leq 0$$

Depending upon the form of f and the types of constraints, if any, there will be different methods which are generally acknowledged as being the best approaches to find solutions. The Karush-Kuhn-Tucker conditions generalise the method of Lagrange multipliers, which allows only equality constraints, providing an approach to non-linear programming allowing inequality constraints. These are first-order necessary conditions for a solution to be optimal, provided that some regularity conditions (which we rarely need to be concerned with for our purposes) are satisfied.

Really excellent resources for optimisation can be found in [5] and [6].

Interest Rates

This chapter introduces the reader to simple aspects of interest rates. In the case that these are already understood, it is still not recommended to skip this chapter because subsequent chapters rely on the information and terminology contained within. In particular, after reading it, one should know;

- an interest rate is only useful when its associated conventions are applied for calculations,

- what day count conventions are and how to apply them,

- how to consider business days and holidays when applying modifiers,

- what impact the frequency of payments has when comparing interest rates,

- the difference between per annum and annualised interest rates,

- what CC interest rates are and why they are useful,

- how to calculate discount factors and understand the time value of money concept,

- what interest rate indexes are and the distinctions between different types of index.

2.1 Interest rates

An interest rate defines the amount of money charged to a borrower for the provision of a loan of a sum of money by a lender. Normally, interest rates are expressed in percentage terms making reference to the original sum of any loan, usually termed the notional (or principal) amount.

In practice, uncertainty can often arise due to the different ways that interest rates can be expressed. This might even be the case when descriptions appear to be straightforward. In many cases mistaken conventions lead to miscalculations of interest payments.

Example 2.1.
Alpha lends $100mm to Bravo for three months at a rate of 5%.
Bravo lends $100mm to Charlie for three months at a rate of 10%.

One would be forgiven for assuming that Bravo stands to make a profit in example 2.1. However, if the terms of each loan are not identical (and unclear) then it is impossible to make any such determination without clarification.

Example 2.2.
Alpha lends $100mm to Bravo from 1st Jun to 1st Sep at a rate of 5%, expressed in absolute interest rate terms, that is, with a 1/1 day count convention, payable at maturity.
Bravo lends $100mm to Charlie from 1st Jun to 1st Sep at a rate of 10% per annum under a 30/360 day count convention, payable at maturity.

Example 2.2 serves to make the terms of the loans clear. It can now be seen and calculated that Bravo will be liable to pay interest in the amount of $5mm to Alpha on 1st Sep, and that Charlie is liable to pay interest in the amount of $2.50mm on 1st Sep to Bravo. This results in an apparent loss for Bravo of $2.50mm.

These trivial examples have been included to highlight that interest rates must always be considered with reference to their calculation conventions. Here, we have highlighted the concept of day count convention but there are also other important factors. Scheduling of payments, such as whether interest is paid at maturity or after certain periods of time, is one other good example.

2.2   Day count conventions

Day count conventions define the rules for calculating the amount of interest that is accrued between any two given dates on any interest rate product, e.g. a loan. It is permissible for any product, in its documentation, to specify its own, custom day count convention. Although, it is typical that products of the same type share a standard convention[1], even if that standard convention differs by currency associated with the product. The most standard day count conventions for financial products are defined by international associations such as the International Swaps and Derivatives Association (ISDA), International Securities Market Association (ISMA), and International Capital Market Association (ICMA). Note also that similarly named conventions can differ across associations so it is important to always understand which one is actually being used. This is confusing even for experienced practitioners.

Day count conventions give rise to the related concept of **day count fractions (DCFs)**. These are the decimalised determination of the number of years over which interest has accrued, using the appropriate day count convention to define the calculation. In turn DCFs allow the calculation of the amount of interest payable on the specific interest rate product:

$$interest\ payable = notional \times DCF \times interest\ rate\ per\ annum\ .$$

We highlight, to the reader, the previous footnote which contains a wealth of information on specific day count conventions. It is not the intent here to go through all of the calculations for all commonly used conventions, but we must at least define one convention that will be

---

[1]see 'OpenGamma Interest Rate Instruments and Market Conventions Guide'[7]

used as the primary for this book. This, we choose to be the 'ACT/365F' or 'Actual 365 Fixed' convention, defined as:

$$DCF_{ACT/365F} := \frac{accrual\ end\ date - accrual\ start\ date}{365}\ .$$

Expanding on example 2.2 we do give an illustration of the interest payable by Charlie in the case of a variety of day count conventions in example 2.3.

Example 2.3.

Day count convention (from ISDA)	DCF from 1st Jun '16 to 1st Sep '16	Interest payable on $100mm notional at 10% per annum
1/1	1/1 = 1.000000000	$10,000,000.00
ACT/ACT	92/366 = 0.251366120	$2,513,661.20
30/360	90/360 = 0.250000000	$2,500,000,00
ACT/365F	92/365 = 0.252054795	$2,520,547.95

2.3 Frequency of payments

As well as day count conventions being a key component to the terms of a loan or an interest rate product to define calculation of interest, so too is the frequency of interest rate payments. In the case of, for example, the ACT/ACT(ICMA) day count convention the frequency of payments is also, in point of fact, a required input for the calculation of the DCF.

Example 2.4.
Charlie lends £10mm to Delta from 1st Jan '16 to 1st Jan '17 at 10% per annum with an ACT/365F convention. The table shows a variety of possible frequency of interest payments.

Frequency	Interest paid on 1st Apr '16 (£)	Interest paid on 1st Jul '16 (£)	Interest paid on 1st Oct '16 (£)	Interest paid on 1st Jan '17 (£)
1-Annual	0.00	0.00	0.00	1,002,739.73
2-Semi	0.00	498,630.14	0.00	504,109.59
4-Quarterly	249,315.07	249,315.07	252,054.79	252,054.79

In example 2.4 the total amount of interest payable is the same for all frequencies, which begs the question which is the most profitable loan for Charlie? Although it is possible to give examples of scenarios in which any one of the above loans is theoretically the most profitable, it will normally be the case that the quarterly loan will be the most profitable.

Generally, a loan with a higher frequency of payments compared against one with a lower frequency, but the same per annum rate, will be more profitable. This is because the more frequent interest payments received can often be reinvested earning 'compound interest', what is essentially interest on interest. This also comes from the 'time value of money principle' where it is normally better to receive money sooner than later. In negative interest rate environments this, unfortunately, reverses and can introduce confusion in this regard.

2.4   Business day calendars and modified following

As well as defining frequency of payments and methods of interest calculation, the specific dates themselves (of accrual start and end dates, payment dates and fixing dates) must be accurately defined. This is where the concept of business days is introduced.

Scheduling is a process which requires *two features*; **a business day (or holiday) calendar** distinguishing business days from non-business days (holidays), and **a rule for modifying the date** schedule if the date in question happens to land, unfeasibly, on a holiday.

Calendars are plentiful. The London business day calendar is different to the New York calendar, or the Target calendar (used for financial transactions denominated in EUR) or the Tokyo calendar, etc.. Calendars can be combined also. For two calendars a holiday in either of them becomes a holiday in the combined calendar, and a business day will only be such if it is a business day in both calendars. This should not be overlooked as it can often have quite a large impact on the pricing of IRDs.

The day modifier rule is usually fairly straightforward also, but does have variations. The most simple day rules are those which say if the date in question falls on a holiday then either go forward to the following business day or backwards to the preceding business day. Usually denoted 'F' and 'P' respectively.

These rules are often applied with an additional modifier preventing a movement into another month and thus switches to the alternative 'P' or 'F' style at the end or start of the month respectively. These are often denoted by 'MF' and 'MP' with the 'M' standing for 'Modified'. For example 2M starting on Sep 30th has an unadjusted end date of 30th Nov, which happens to fall on a Sunday (a holiday). The day rule to apply is 'MF', but in this case moving forward moves the date to Mon 1st Dec, a new month, so instead the modifier kicks in and the adjusted date is actually set to be Fri 28th Nov, which of course precedes the 30th.

A further modifier used in some cases and some products is to make an additional rule for dates that start on a month end, and ensure that they always end on a month end. For example a 6M tenor that begins on 28th Feb (not in a leap!) will end on 31st Aug (or the nearest date in Aug to it that is a business day). Under just the 'MF' rule, without month-end adjustment, the 28th Aug would be a perfectly valid end date if it was a business day since it still fell within the month of August.

For payment dates and fixing dates some of this information is determined by default. For example payments made in London for GBP cashflows must often be made on (at least) a London business day calendar since it might be impossible to make a payment on a London holiday. Fixing (or reset) date calendars for EUR IRSs must follow at least a Target calendar because EUR rate indexes are not set on those specific holidays. But calendars for accrual dates can be flexible. Since accrual dates only define the DCF it does not necessarily matter if they start or end on holidays as defined by some calendars. Sometimes dates are said to be 'unadjusted' meaning they are not modified even if they fall on a holiday as defined by a given calendar. Semantically this is the same as adjusting the date under a calendar which has no holidays in it at all. In that case every date is classed as a valid business day so no valid adjustments would ever occur even though they were permitted.

2.5   Per annum interest rates and annualised interest rates

In the above examples the interest payable has been shown to be calculated from a given **per annum rate**. This is by far the most utilised type of interest rate quoted across financial institutions today, with the frequency and day count convention being assumed to be standardised for each product, unless specified otherwise.

It is often useful to make generalised, simple comparisons across interest rates expressed in different frequencies, however. To do this the concept of annualisation is used. Annualisation is a calculation transformation applied to per annum rates. Annualisation essentially approximates the amount of interest if it were to be paid in a single amount as with any typical annual frequency. Be aware that an annualised rate is *never* used for the calculation of interest payments, rather the underlying per annum rate is still used, and it only serves for the purpose of comparison between products of differing payment frequencies.

As a point of reference to consumer finance, it is very common for banks and credit card companies to publicly display their APRs (Annual Percentage Rates) as they are bound by consumer rights statutes to do so. Although these annualised rates provide a basis for consumer comparison, different jurisdictions can define terms differently. This means that across countries and even across companies it can be difficult to know if you truly are comparing like for like. But, at least considering APRs (defined differently) will lead to a better comparison than to look at any of the other headline rates.

The standard method of annualisation of per annum interest rates adopted in the financial industry is the following:

$$annualised\ rate = \left(1 + \frac{per\ annum\ rate}{frequency}\right)^{frequency} - 1\ .$$

Example 2.5.
Annualisation of rates from example 2.4

Frequency	Per annum rate	Annualised rate
1-Annual	10%	10%
2-Semi	10%	10.25%
4-Quarterly	10%	10.381%

In example 2.5 the annualised rate gives a clear indication that the quarterly rate is more profitable for Charlie. As with comments made before about consumer finance, though, using annualised rates as anything other than a 'quick and easy', broad comparison is unwise as they don't take account of all of the accurate economics involved. For readers with a broad fixed income understanding, this is akin to comparisons drawn on yield-to-maturity calculation on bonds.

Unless otherwise stated **all interest rates quoted in this book are given on a per annum basis**, with a frequency and day count convention either specified or inherently assumed from context.

2.6   Continually compounded (CC) interest rates

While annualisation attempts to rationalise per annum interest rates of a given frequency into a yearly comparison rate, CC rates essentially seek to go the other way. They do this by defining a rate for smaller and smaller time periods. CC rates are really a hypothetical construct - no one will ever have a continually changing balance in a bank account that accrues and pays a minuscule amount of interest each instant - and due to that, their definition can vary across authors and literature. I have personally found the following definition to be the most useful:

$$e^{DCF \times CC\ rate} = 1 + DCF \times per\ annum\ rate\ .^2$$

To be dutifully clear, and to put this formula in context with its intended usage, what CC rates seek to express is the rate, which, if it were to pay and compound interest on a notional amount at every instant continuously, between the start of an accrual period and the end of the accrual period, then it would produce the same total interest amount as that given by the traditional calculation of discrete interest for the per annum rate accrued over the same period.

It is the case that, **for each per annum rate applied to an accrual period with given DCF there is a specific and unique CC rate** that would, theoretically, produce the same interest amount as the usual calculation.

Example 2.6.

Per annum rate	Frequency	Typical DCF	Associated CC rate
5%	2-Semi	0.495890..	4.939020%
5%	2-Semi	0.50	4.938523%
5%	12-Monthly	0.082191..	4.989754%
6%	12-Monthly	0.082191..	5.985254%

The use of CC rates is really in manipulation of mathematical formulae and taking derivatives for delta and gamma calculations of IR products. It is easier in many cases to work with CC rates due to the exponential term which differentiates directly. This theoretical construct helps enormously to advance pricing theory, and will often be found in other financial literature and especially in relation to bonds. But besides the mathematical side, CC rates do not really have any other practical use.

2.7   Time value of money and discount factors (DFs)

Interest rates are very important for considering what money is worth at different times in the future. The time value of money principle is a practical application of the 'no arbitrage principle', where no one should be able to obtain a free lunch, so to speak. In a more formal manner the no arbitrage principle can be described as follows;

Where two or more equivalent financial scenarios exist, they will have the same value, otherwise the least costly will be in such demand and the most costly in such supply that the prices will adjust accordingly, in a dynamic market, to become equal.

The time value of money principle underpins the financial industry. To demonstrate how time value of money is an application of the no arbitrage principle, consider two financial scenarios relating interest payments;

1. You receive \$1,000 today and invest it (risk free) for one year accruing some interest at 5%.

2. You receive \$1,000 in one year (guaranteed).

The terms of equivalence of the scenario is that you are guaranteed, without risk, an amount of money after one year. It is obvious that the first scenario is preferred and would be in much

---

^{2}see the appendix for a derivation of this formula

greater demand than the latter scenario. The scenarios would only become equivalent in value if (using ACT/365F and not being in a leap year) scenario two was changed to receive precisely $1,050 after one year.

Specifically, **the time value of money principle asserts the value today of a nominal amount of money receivable (or payable) on some date in the future**. When that future amount is deemed to be a nominal $1, £1, €1, ¥1, etc. this leads to the concept of discount factors (DFs) for each currency. For example if £1 receivable in one year is deemed to be worth £0.97 today, akin to the manner above, then the discount factor for that date in one year's time is 0.97.

The existence of interest rates establishes the mathematical basis for all interest rate products across the financial industry. On the face of it, time value of money is a simple concept, but delve into details and its scope broadens dramatically. Much of this scope is a core component of what this book aims to explain. I think it highly likely that less than half of all financial institutions have the understanding and system development to apply principles consistently across the extent of their operations, and to obtain 'true' valuation of their assets and liabilities, when factoring all the technicalities of the underlying transactions.

The knowledge of the DF for every future date in a single currency is the complete make-up of the information contained in, what is typically termed a 'discount curve'. This is frequently referred to on trading floors as it allows one to value any, and a series of, cashflows in the future. The aggregate sum of discounted cashflows is the amount which is universally termed the net present value (PV).

All of the fundamental concepts mentioned in this chapter are obviously further utilised or explored in later chapters. With discount curves it is important to realise that there are potentially hundreds of valid ways to discount a future cashflow on a single date, in a single currency, dependent upon underlying assumptions or inherent terms associated with that particular cashflow[3]. Fortunately, as will be shown, there are also market standards and generally consistent contract terms which typically allow the concept of a consistent discount curve across all financial institutions.

The notation which is adopted in this book is to denote by, v_i, the discount factor (with the currency and any other specifics taken from context) applicable to a specific future date, m_i, aligned with index, i. Then for a set of n future cashflows, say C_i, receivable on specific future dates their PV is:

$$P = \sum_{i=1}^{n} C_i v_i \ .$$

Other notation can be seen in the list of mathematical symbols.

2.8 Interest rate indexes

Official interest rates, often called indexes (indexes to distinguish between different types of index, and indices to denote the plural of the same type of index), are the reference rates used by governments, financial institutions, corporates, and individuals across the world, not only in decision making but also in the settlement of trillions of dollars worth of notional interest rate products on a daily basis. Below we present the most commonly cited indexes[4].

---

[3]see relevant sections on credit support annexs (CSAs), cheapest to deliver (CTD) pricing and multi-currency curve modelling

[4]see 'OpenGamma Interest Rate Instruments and Market Conventions Guide'[7]

Central bank rates

The dominant influence on interest rates in any single currency is that exerted by the central reserve bank of that currency. The operations of central banks are subject to change and do so as they seek to exert further influence on their economy other than that affected by changing the domestic base interest rate level. Details of central bank operations runs to thousands of pages, which I will leave the central banks to best describe on their own websites[5].

In USD the Federal Reserve System dictates the Discount Rate and the Federal Funds Target Rate, the level at which is decided in monthly meetings held by the Federal Open Market Committee (FOMC).

In EUR the European Central Bank (ECB) sets the Marginal Lending Facility Rate, the Main Refinancing Operations Rate, and the Deposit Facility Rate, which are decided in monthly meetings held by the Governing Council.

In GBP the Bank of England (BoE) sets the Bank Base Rate, decided in monthly meetings held by the Monetary Policy Committee (MPC).

In YEN the Bank of Japan (BoJ) sets the Basic Discount Rate and Basic Loan Rate decided on an ad hoc basis at meeting held by the Policy Committee.

Overnight indexes and Risk Free Rates (RFRs)

Overnight indexes are very different to central bank rates because they are completely market dependent and transaction based. Since around 2017 many central banks established working groups to discuss the introduction of RFRs, such as SOFR, SONIA, ESTR, NOWA etc.. As of mid 2022 these have been fully implemented in some currencies and swap markets have either fully transitioned to these new rates or are in the process of doing so. In other markets these rates are still being developed. The specifications of the determining factors for each RFR differs but the overall aim is for them to be transparently transaction based on overnight financing with a 1 business day (b.d.) term. The relevant central bank and publishing authorities release materials based on each index.

In parallel, other such indexes known as overnight index swap (OIS) rates are calculated and these rates are/were based on data from officially recognised money brokers, or central banks, who recorded certain unsecured lending transactions between counterparties on any given day, and then average the transactions, in a notionally weighted manner. The resulting value is/was published as the daily overnight index in the specific currency. The previously specified footnote highlights the details for the precise calculation of these indexes. OIS rates will or have been superseded by RFRs.

These rates are important for a second reason; they are often used as the rate which determines the amount of interest payable on cash posted between institutions for the purpose of collateralising secured liabilities.

	RFR	OIS
USD	SOFR (Secured Overnight Funding Rate)	FOIS (Effective Fed Funds Rate)
EUR	ESTR (Euro Short Term Rate)	EONIA (obsolete since 2018)
GBP	SONIA (Sterling Overnight Index Average)	SONIA (now reformed)
JPY	TONA (Tokyo Overnight Average)	TONA
SEK	SWESTR (Swedish Krona Short Term Rate)	STINA
NOK	NOWA (Norwegian O/n Weighted Average)	-
CHF	SARON (Swiss Average Rate Overnight)	TOIS (discontinued 2017)
DKK	DESTR (Denmark Short Term Rate)	-
CAD	CORRA (Canadian O/n Repo Rate Avg.)	

[5]see relevant listings in the bibliography - USD[8], EUR[9], GBP[10] and JPY[11]

Interbank offered rate indexes

An IBOR index is a proxy for unsecured interbank lending. IBOR indexes are being globally phased out through official transition and cessation programmes. Therefore this book will avoid any reference to trading IBOR products, but will include definitions and information to give context, since IBOR has played a part in the development of the IRD market since the late 1980s.

There are a number of IBOR indices for a set of given maturities, between one day and one year. They differ from the OIS index in the way that each is based on estimated tradable levels, as opposed to physically executed and recorded financial transactions. The calculation process is different across different currencies. Previous general principles of the calculation were that financial institutions, within a recognised collective, submit their estimate of where they either expect to be able to, or have borrowed money on an unsecured basis in the interbank market for the given range of maturities. From a trimmed set of these submissions an average is taken and published as the index, or fixing, for that specific maturity in the currency specified. Traders also colloquially refer to the fixing rate as the reset rate, because once published it resets cashflows on trades that were floating to being fixed.

The London Interbank Offered Rate (LIBOR) is historically published on behalf of the British Banker's Association (BBA) for a range of tenors for USD, EUR, GBP, JPY, and CHF. Recently, there has been a change in the benchmark administrator and these rates are now collated and published by Intercontinental Exchange (ICE)[12]. The European Money Markets Institute (EMMI), formerly known as Euribor-EBF, are responsible for the publication of EU-RIBOR indices and the EONIA index[13].

It is worth highlighting that some currencies have, what is called, a fixing lag. This is the number of days ahead of time that a benchmark fixing rate is published for specific value dates, unto which interest is calculable. Figure 2.1 below makes this clear, by outlining the value dates applicable to a specific rate, and also the fixing date when the rate is physically published. As an example GBP is a currency where IBOR rates are published without a lag, so the 3M IBOR rate for value dates 3rd Feb to 3rd May is published on precisely 3rd Feb. EUR is a currency with a 2 b.d. lag so for the same value dates the publication of the rate would be made on 1st Feb.

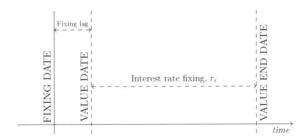

Figure 2.1: Highlighting the distinction between fixing dates and value dates.

Fallback Method

With the cessation of IBOR indexes in different currencies a fallback method of publication was required in order to continue to settle the trillions of dollars worth of outstanding derivatives contracts which settled against IBOR. The fallback method, which may differ for different currencies, is now to use compounded RFR rates, plus a fixed spread determined by the official IBOR cessation notice, to derive the equivalent IBOR rate that is published in its place.

This has one key major change. IBOR goes from being a look-forward rate (one which is published and fixed ahead of the value period with its start and end dates) to a look-back rate (where the final known value of the fallback rate can only be known after every daily RFR fixing has been published for the period over which the IBOR rate extends). For regular IRSs which pay in arrears this does not necessarily matter since the payments can still go ahead with known data by the time they need to be made. For unconventional, in advance IRS this poses a problem since the payment cannot be made as it is not known at the time it is scheduled to be made. These transactions are likely to have been restructured before the transition from IBOR.

2.9 Foreign exchange (FX) rates

FX rates, labelled for example EURUSD, where EUR is the domestic currency and USD the foreign currency, detail the amount of USD one can acquire for a single EUR. Or equivalently how many USD one must pay to acquire a single EUR. Typically, FX transactions are executed on a spot basis (trade date plus two (t+2) b.d.) time frame. Of course FX rates also exist for any date of scheduled exchange and these form part of, what is termed the forward FX curve.

For the settlement of cross-currency derivatives officially published FX fixings, or resets, are released which defines the spot FX rate of a pair of currencies at a particular time on a specific date.

2.10 Appendix

2.10.1 Derivation of CC rates formula

Continuously compounded interest rates are the result of taking the limit of more and more discrete interest payments over shorter and shorter time intervals, but all yielding the same total at maturity. Mathematically then;

$$\lim_{n\to\infty}\left(1 + DCF \times \frac{CC\ rate}{n}\right)^n = 1 + DCF \times per\ annum\ rate\ .$$

Let,

$$L = \lim_{n\to\infty}\left(1 + DCF \times \frac{CC\ rate}{n}\right)^n,$$

$$log(L) = \lim_{n\to\infty} nlog\left(1 + DCF \times \frac{CC\ rate}{n}\right),$$

$$\sim \lim_{n\to\infty} n\left(0 + DCF \times \frac{CC\ rate}{n} + O\left(\frac{1}{n^2}\right)\right),$$

$$= DCF \times CC\ rate.$$

Thus,

$$L = e^{DCF \times CC\ rate}\ .$$

Basics of Interest Rate Derivatives

Whether to present the basics of IRDs before constructing interest rate curves was a question of structure for this book. Each topic requires knowledge of the other. In the end, though, I opted to present the products first. This only needs the reader to assume that a set of curves can be constructed that will predict any interest rate index for any specific date in the future. It also means that all possible DFs will be available to value cashflows. With this assumption, the mathematical formulation of all the following derivative products can be shown and they can all be accurately priced. The products presented here are not an exhaustive list by any means. Over the years there have been spin-offs and exotic structured variants but they tend to be isolated endeavours. This list is that of regularly traded, key products that are of suitable variety for the reader. More importantly, the products explained here are key to the development of the pricing of the interest rate market and in the construction of curvesets. They also represent those that are traded in major interbank markets.

This chapter outlines;

- how any IRD can be physically traded and the associated mechanisms,

- each of the basic interest rate products including their mathematical pricing formulae.

3.1   Trading mechanics

To trade an IRD two counterparties must firstly be able to communicate, and secondly have some form of legal acknowledgement in place to recognise a trade and stipulate ongoing obligations. Considering the legal element in the first instance, there are the cases of trading on exchanges or off exchanges.

3.1.1   On exchange

An exchange is a recognised legal entity which defines the rules of trading a certain product, that, in some cases the exchange itself has created, and is specific only to that exchange. Some products are generic or universally defined and available to trade on multiple exchanges. Exchanges are regulated for the protection of all parties, according to their type and jurisdiction. An exchange is a broad term encompassing different types of entity.

Futures and options exchange

A party wishing to trade a future or an option on an exchange must have formal accounts set up with that exchange, and the ability to submit orders to it, e.g. 'sell 1 lot @ price of 10'. Nowadays orders and exchanges are conducted electronically but historically these contracts were traded visually with hand signals in a specified trading 'ring' or 'pit'. When another party submits a matching order, e.g. 'buy 1 lot @ price of 10', then a trade will take place on the exchange; 1 lot is exchanged at a price of 10, and it becomes public record that one lot has traded at this price at this particular time. The counterparties trading with each other will not be publicly disclosed or disclosed to each other on electronic exchanges. This will result in an account being held with the exchange recording the traded positions, until such time as the open positions are closed (traded in the opposite direction) or cash settled or physically settled, again done directly between the exchange and the individual parties.

Being a member of an exchange can be costly in terms of capital so some institutions operate as clearing brokers / prime brokers, which means that other companies can effectively trade with the exchange on their own behalf via the account of their broker, who then administer the position management, and charge a fee for this service.

Swap execution facility (SEF)

A swap execution facility (SEF) is simpler construct. It represents a legal entity that has agreed to record and publish the required details of certain swap transactions according to the Dodd-Frank rules. It is not a fully fledged exchange because it does not service accounts or maintain margin. It is as the name suggests only facilitatory. Transactions can be informally agreed or brokered outside of the SEF but the execution is made binding and legal by committing the details electronically to the SEF trading platform. SEFs exist because the mandatory transparency of tradable markets and recording of trading information to a public ledger needs to be done by a recognised, registered entity.

Designated contract market (DCM)

A designated contract market (DCM) is similar to a SEF in as much as the swaps executed that fall under the jurisdiction of the Dodd-Frank rules can be traded on a DCM rather than a SEF, and that DCM will record and publish the swap's details. Specific differences between SEFs and DCMs highlight the manner in which they are permitted to display and service liquidity. They are both subject to different, technical, regulatory requirements - the nature of which is outside the scope of this book.

Made available to trade (MAT)

The Commodity Futures Trading Commission (CFTC) defines a narrow set of benchmark swaps which are those that are required to be traded on a SEF or DCM. These are the most liquid, and most often traded swaps in the interbank and institutional client market, for specific major currencies. Any made available to trade (MAT) swap executed on a SEF or DCM is mandated to be cleared through a clearing house. The clearing house operates as the controller of margin and positions, in a similar way that a futures and options exchange maintains margin and reconciles futures and options positions.

3.1.2 Off exchange

A trade that is executed off exchange is a transaction that has been agreed directly between two parties, or has been brokered between the two by an intermediary broker, and is not legally required to be on SEF or put through a clearing house. For two parties to trade they must have pre agreed and signed a document outlining the terms of their engagements. This is typically referred to as an ISDA master agreement. When trades take place off exchange they can be settled **bilaterally**, meaning directly between the counterparties themselves[1], or through a clearing house.

Regulators around the globe are actively trying to force all trading to take place on exchange in some fashion, due to its increased level of transparency. In particular the earliest set of rules, which leads the way towards this form of trading, was created by the Dodd-Frank Act[2], which has been mentioned above. Failing the practicalities of forcing all trades onto exchanges, regulators are pushing for all off exchange trades to be mandated to clear. It is an evolving regulatory landscape for IRDs at time of publication of this book.

3.1.3 Clearing house

Trades can be executed on some form of exchange or off exchange, and then settled through a clearing house. This means that the clearing house, which is a legal entity, steps in to be the legal counterparty to each of the two original counterparties, who executed the trade. The clearing house essentially enters into two opposing trades, one with each of the original parties, so the clearing house will never, by choice, have a risky position in the sense of market risk. Each counterparty to the clearing house will also be bound by the same benchmark CSA of the given product type, so the clearing house will also never be exposed to any form of collateral mismatch[3].

---

[1]see chapter 5 on collateral and credit risk to describe this form

[2]officially the Dodd-Frank Wall Street Reform and Consumer Protection Act signed into US federal law on July 21st 2010

[3]also see chapter 5 for further information in this regard

Clearing houses are designed to be centralised trade depositories which mitigate credit risk for every counterparty who clears their trades through the clearing house. In theory a clearing house will never default because it has no overall market risk, since each trade is necessarily offset by another. The only event that poses a risk to the clearing house defaulting is if a counterparty defaults, and then the loss to the clearing house is so great that it cannot cover its ongoing obligations to the remaining counterparties. Given the dangerous outcome of a clearing house failing they aim to be well capitalised, and, in a sense, insured. This is what leads to margining accounts.

3.1.4 Margin

Clearing houses, and futures and options exchanges, demand that each counterparty, with whom they have open, at risk, traded positions, post an amount of cash, termed margin. Margin is an insurance policy for the clearing house. It reflects the value of loss that the clearing house perceives it can lose if a counterparty defaults and market rates change. Margin calculations can be based on many factors, but certainly the volatility of the market and the level of risk that the counterparty is exposed to will be factored in. As well as thinking of margin as insurance from the clearing house's perspective it can also be thought of in this way from a counterparty's perspective. By using a clearing house, or exchange, any counterparty's credit risk is vastly reduced and thus this service should necessarily warrant some form of fee or ongoing capital expense.

Be it an individual investor's personal trading account or a large financial institution's, margin works in the same manner and comes in two forms; initial margin and variation (sometimes called maintenance) margin. Initial margin is an amount of cash required to be posted to allow new positions and new trades to be executed. Of course the amount of initial margin needs to be enough to cover regular trading activity by the specific party, meaning financial institution's initial margin will be far larger than any individual investor's. Variation margin is cash posted to maintain the open, at risk, positions, so the amount is also related to the scale of trading activity. Variation margin needs to be sufficient to cover large adverse market movements of open, risky positions. The required variation margin is calculated by the clearing house every day. If positions move adversely for a counterparty in any day and the mark-to-market (MTM) value of the trades falls then the clearing house will make a margin call to the counterparty to request them to post more variation margin to reach the required level. Particularly with exchanges and trading in liquid products, if the counterparty cannot afford the margin call then their open positions will be automatically stopped out for a loss to protect the exchange from assuming any loss themselves. If the opposite occurs and market rates move favourably and the open positions make a daily MTM profit then the exchange or clearing house will pay back some of the posted variation margin to the counterparty.

3.1.5 Mid-market price

When trading any product the idea of the mid-market price is always needed. This is the price of any IR product where its PV is deemed to be zero. That means is it is neither in-the-money (ITM) nor out-the-money (OTM).

Although this might seem like a very simple concept, financial markets are not always black and white. One individual might record the mid-market price as the last traded price, and another individual might call it the middle of the bid and offer price currently available (see chapter 19, for example). Another perspective might be to say that the mid-market price reflects the most up to date assessment of that price at which an IR product will next trade in the interbank market. This definition, though, is subjective and statistical in nature. Particularly with obscure, non-benchmark IR products this can lead to quite some discrepancy, alongside other factors, some of which will be discussed in chapter 6. The concept of mid-market will in fact be revisited numerous times at various points in the book.

Where mid-market prices differ across different parties, it will still always be true that an IR product executed at a price, or rate, the same as the assumed mid-marked will have a PV of zero, measured by that respective party.

Some products, for example basis swaps, will often quote prices in bps. One bp represents one hundredth of a percentage rate. They are useful measurements because daily market movements are often of this order of magnitude. Market risks are always quoted in bp terms. Bps will often be used in reference and in the examples in this book.

3.1.6 Reviewed products

The following lists the reviewed products in this chapter and their current status (as of 2022). Different currencies are at different stages of the transition.

Product	Status
FRA	Obsolete after transition from IBOR
STIR future (IBOR)	Obsolete after transition from IBOR
STIR future (RFR)	Active, or in development
IRS (IBOR)	Obsolete after transition from IBOR
IRS (RFR) and OIS	Active, or in development
SBS	Obsolete after transition from IBOR
ZCS	Same status as IRS
IRS future	Same status as STIR futures
Non-MTM XCS	Same status as IRS
MTM XCS	Same status as IRS
FX Swaps	Active, unaffected by IBOR transition

3.2   Forward rate agreements (FRAs)

**Note: This is an obsolete or becoming obsolete product depending upon currency.
This description is maintained for historical context.**

A forward rate agreement (FRA) is a cash for difference derivative contract. It is settled against
a particular IBOR index of some future, benchmark interest rate fixing, for example 6M EURI-
BOR or 3M LIBOR. Any individual FRA can only be settled against one index on one future
date, and this makes it one of the simpler IRDs. The cash difference settled is the difference
between the initial rate, or price, agreed, and the future, officially published interest rate fixing.
The cash amount is paid on the value start date of the FRA but is discounted by the published
fixing rate for the tenor of the index. This artificial discounting acts as a proxy for the payment
being paid at the end of the period instead, which would be more typical on a loan, for example.
The agreed notional and DCF are also factors which determine the ultimate settlement amount.

Mathematical formulation:
The PV of a FRA (from the point of the view of the buyer /payer of the contract) is:

$$P = v_{i-1} \frac{N d_i (r_i - R)}{(1 + d_i r_i)} \; .$$

The mid-market price, R^{mid}, of a FRA is equal to the expected published fixing for the given
value date, r_i. The v_{i-1} DF is required to discount the forward settlement of the FRA to the
present day.

Quoting convention:
'Currency, Index, Start-month × End-month, Roll-date.'
E.g. 'GBP, LIBOR, 5 × 8, 23rd, FRA.'
Usually the currency and index can be omitted if they are obvious from the context. The start
and end-months are determined as the number of months from the current month, and the
roll-date simply determines the start day of the interest rate period, e.g. if the current month
is March a '5×8 23rd FRA' is one for the period whose value dates run from 23rd August for
three months to November.

Example 3.1.
*A trader buys a $100mm LIBOR 2×3 10th FRA @ 0.95%. To PV this contract the trader is
required to predict two variables; the expected 1m $LIBOR rate for the 10th day in two month's
time, and the discount factor for that same payment date of the contract. Suggest these are
1.00% and 0.9984 respectively, then the PV of the contract is (with convention 30/360):*

$$PV = 0.9984 \times \frac{\$100mm \times \frac{1}{12} \times (1\% - 0.95\%)}{1 + \frac{1}{12} \times 1.00\%} = \$4,157 \; .$$

3.3 Short term interest rate (STIR) futures on IBOR

Note: This is an obsolete or becoming obsolete product depending upon currency. This description is maintained for historical context.

Short term interest rate (STIR) futures based on IBOR are a product similar to FRAs in the sense they are cash settled against a future benchmark interest rate, but differ in a set number of ways;

  (i) STIR futures are traded on exchanges, FRAs are off exchange,

 (ii) the size of a single contract on a STIR future is a set notional according to the exchange rules (typically 0.5mm or 1mm), as opposed to FRAs which can have bespoke notionals agreed between the counterparties,

(iii) STIR futures are quoted in price terms, whereas FRAs are quoted in yield terms,

 (iv) STIR futures settle against specific dates set according to the exchange rules, FRAs can be contracts written for any set of business dates.

Expanding on the last item, STIR futures settle only against 3M-IBOR tenors and only for value start dates that fall on International Monetary Market (IMM) dates. IMM dates are defined to be the third Wednesday of any month. And, in fact, many currencies permit STIR futures with an IMM settlement date in only the months of March, June, September and December. In this way, for a year of around 252 b.d.s and that many possible 3M-IBOR fixings (and FRAs), only four of these are relevant to the IMM settlement dates of the futures contracts of these four months.

Usually the first four contracts spanning the first year, known as the front or white contracts, are very liquid. The next four contracts spanning the subsequent year, known as the red contracts, are also liquid. Liquidity tapers off after the whites and reds, but certainly contracts with longer maturities do trade. The names of other contracts are given in table 3.1.

#	Months of IMM dates	Name	#	Months of IMM dates	Name
1-4	Sep '16, Dec, Mar, Jun '17	Whites	21-24	Sep '21, .., Jun '22	Purples
5-8	Sep '17, Dec, Mar, Jun '18	Reds	25-28	Sep '22, .., Jun '23	Oranges
9-12	Sep '18, Dec, Mar, Jun '19	Greens	29-32	Sep '23, .., Jun '24	Pinks
13-16	Sep '19, Dec, Mar, Jun '20	Blues	33-36	Sep '24, .., Jun '25	Silvers
17-20	Sep '20, Dec, Mar, Jun '21	Golds	37-40	Sep '25, .., Jun '26	Coppers

Table 3.1: Grouped naming convention for STIR futures contracts with an assumed present date of 1st July 2016.

Specific contracts are also given individual names to identify them. This is done with a letter for the month and the year of settlement. The letters assigned to the months of March, June, September and December are H, M, U, and Z, so for example the STIR futures contract settling to the March 2017 IMM 3M-IBOR fixing would be denoted the H17 contract. Note that this naming convention applies to all kinds of product futures, like oil futures, stock index futures etc. and not just STIRs. From January through to December the full set of letter descriptors is { F, G, H, J, K, M, N, Q, U, V, X, Z }.

Mathematical formulation:

The 3M-IBOR fixing rate implied by a STIR future[4] is:

$$r_i = 100 - q_i \ ,$$

where q_i is the price of the future.

The PV of a **single** STIR future contract (from the point of view of the buyer of the contract) is:

$$P = N(q_i - Q_i) \ ,$$

where N is the value of one lot per unit increment, and Q_i the originally traded price.

Example 3.2.

A trader buys a single lot of Z16 £LIBOR STIR future at a price of 99.01. The price rises to 99.28. The value of one lot set by the exchange per percentage point is £1,250. His total PnL is:

$$P = 1250 * (99.28 - 99.01) = £337.50 \ .$$

Settlement:

Since STIR futures are traded on an exchange the margining process is applicable. MTM gains or losses are recognised daily through the receipt of surplus variation margin or the payment of additional variation margin respectively, measured against the daily official closing price. When a futures contract expires on the IMM date the final variation margin adjustment is measured between the previous close and the exchange delivery settlement price (EDSP). Although EDSPs might differ slightly across different exchange rules the most common is to take:

$$EDSP = 100 - 3\text{M-IBOR fixing} \ ,$$

where the 3M-IBOR fixing is rounded to 3 decimal places and if the fixing is an exact multiple of 0.0005 then it is rounded lower, so for example a 3M-IBOR of 1.6155% would be rounded to 1.615%, and thus the EDSP is 98.385. In effect by rounding down the fixing rate the EDSP is rounded up in these specific cases.

---

[4]see chapter 21 for a precise relationship between implied rates of STIR futures and their respective IMM FRAs, which differ by an amount known as the futures convexity adjustment (FCA)

3.4 Short term interest rate (STIR) futures on RFR

These products have similar properties as STIR futures on IBOR. They were designed as replacements and they have the same properties with respect to IMM dates, fixed notional and pricing conventions etc, so the previous section is relevant. However, they have the same difference with respect to all products under the IBOR transition which is that the settlement of, say, the March contract cannot, unlike IBOR futures, be settled in March. Instead all fixings within the period must occur before the EDSP can be produced, either in April (for the one month contract) or June (for the three month contract).

As of this book's publication the most common STIR futures on RFRs are SONIA futures, SOFR futures and SARON futures. These come in two varieties; one month tenors, and three month tenors. The one month tenor typically settles to an EDSP of the arithmetic average of the RFR fixing in the one month period,

$$EDSP \ one \ month \ rate = 100 \times \left(\frac{1}{d_1} \sum_{k=1}^{T_1} (r_k d_k) \right)$$

where T_1 is the number of fixings that make up the period.

The three month tenor settles to a compounded rate, albeit both of these definitions are at the discretion of the exchange specifying the contracts and they may differ,

$$EDSP \ three \ month \ rate = 100 \times \left(\frac{1}{d_1} \prod_{k=1}^{T_1} (1 + r_k d_k) - 1 \right)$$

Since the front month contract does not settle until all the RFR fixings are published this means that it continues to trade mid period. This of course reduces its volatility substantially midway through its period since a proportion of the EDSP rate is already known, and with each published fixing becomes less variable.

RFR STIR futures also experience convexity adjustments as with IBOR STIR futures. The settlement process and margining process is also as described in the previous section.

3.5   Interest rate swaps (IRSs) and Overnight Index Swaps (OIS)

IRSs are one of the most frequently traded IRD contracts. An IRS represents an agreement to exchange a series of fixed rate payments (often termed the fixed leg) for a series of floating rate payments (the floating leg) based on an IBOR index, historically, but presently by an RFR index. Traditionally IRSs was the name for swaps against an IBOR index whereas OIS was the name for swaps against an overnight index. Since the transition from IBOR, IRS and OIS are semantically now the same, and we will refer to swaps as essentially IRSs based on RFRs. The receiver of the fixed leg is at the same time the payer of the floating leg and of course vice versa.

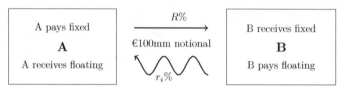

Figure 3.1: A flows diagram of a standard IRS between two counterparties, Alpha and Bravo.

The main component of any IRS is its date schedule. The date schedule outlines; when payments are to be made, accrual periods for calculating DCFs, fixing dates for determination of floating interest rates, and even notional amounts per period so that any cashflow can be calculated. Example 3.3 highlights this in a practical sense for a simple, small IRS.

Example 3.3.
Example cashflows of a standard 6M semi-quarterly IRS starting on 8th February '16 and ending on 8th August '16. It details one fixed cashflow and two floating cashflows.

Notional	Accrual date	Accrual end date	Fixing date	Value date	Value end date	Payment date	Rate	Cashflow
€100mm	8/2/16	8/8/16	-	-	-	8/8/16	2.025	€1,009,726
€100mm	8/2/16	9/5/16	4/2/16	8/2/16	9/5/16	9/5/16	1.961	€-488,907
€100mm	9/5/16	8/8/16	5/5/16	9/5/16	9/8/16	8/8/16	2.061	€-513,838

To obtain the PV of the IRS in example 3.3 one must simply multiply the cashflows by the appropriate DF relevant to the payment date. The floating payments are, of course, unknown until all of the relevant fixing publications have been made, so market movements will cause valuation changes to the projected cashflows.

Standard (or vanilla) IRSs adopt standard conventions for the above scheduling rules. In particular, a standard IRS has;

(i) the same notional, N, for every individual period of the IRS either on the floating or fixed leg,

(ii) a consecutive structure so that each period comes immediately after another without overlapping or creating gaps,

(iii) an alignment between the fixed and floating legs (subject to the frequency) so that accrual periods and payment dates on each are the same,

(iv) an alignment of the fixing date and floating rate tenor to the given accrual schedule and payment schedule for the floating leg. Payments are made in arrears, that is, at the end of each period, usually on the accrual end date,

(v) standard day count conventions and fixed leg frequency in each specific currency.

The IRS of example 3.3 is standard and highlights all of these properties.

Customisation:
IRSs are bespoke derivatives meaning they can be customised between parties in a host of different ways, for example payment dates for calculated cashflows can be adjusted, the notional in any particular period can be altered or amortised (which is common for using swaps to hedge loans), or the start and end dates of the entire IRS can be specified with no apparent relationship.

When start and end dates are specified without an associated relationship it creates what are called 'stub' periods. **Stub periods** are those placed within the IRS either at the start, end, or both, so that the remaining part of the leg follows the specified frequency and reverts to the form of a standard IRS. Usually called short-front, short-back, long-front or long-back, figure 3.2 illustrates graphically the purpose of stubs to create exterior periods which are necessarily out-of-sync with the rest of the IRS's structure.

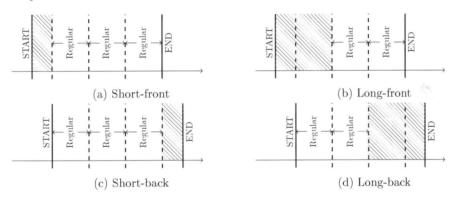

(a) Short-front   (b) Long-front

(c) Short-back   (d) Long-back

Figure 3.2: Showing short and back stub types (which can be combined) either side of swap periods which take place with regular frequency, such as annual, semi-annual, quarterly or monthly.

Historically, stub periods, being non-standard tenors, meant that they had to settle against **interpolated IBOR fixings**. For example, if a stub period had a tenor of, say, just over five months, it would settle to a fixing linearly interpolated between the published three month and six month IBOR fixing, and is measured by value end date. Since the introduction of RFRs the settlement process is the same as with any other period and the individual daily RFR fixings are compounded up over the stub period, there will simply be fewer or more fixings than in a regular period.

Mathematical formulation:
The formula below presents the PV of an IRS, from the point of view of the payer of the contract. It is important that the direction (whether one is the payer or receiver) is always quoted in terms of the fixed leg. This is the universal market convention.

$$P = N\left(-R\sum_{i=1}^{T_1} d_i v_i + \sum_{j=1}^{T_2} d_j r_j v_j \right) \quad \text{(standard IRS)}$$

$$P = -R\sum_{i=1}^{T_1} N_i d_i v_i + \sum_{j=1}^{T_2} N_j d_j r_j v_j \quad \text{(customised IRS)}$$

where T_1, T_2 = the number of period in the fixed and float leg respectively

In the case of OISs and compounded RFRs the period floating rates, r_j, are determined by each daily published fixing, r_k, in the period so that:

$$r_j = \frac{1}{d_j} \prod_{k=1}^{T_j} (1 + d_k r_k) - 1, \qquad T_j = \text{number of business days in period, } j \qquad (3.1)$$

Example 3.4.
Suppose that just three RFR fixings make up a single OIS period and that on Thursday, Friday and Monday the fixings are published at 2.00%, 2.10% and 2.15%. Then the compounded rate over the period from Thursday to Tuesday, which represents the part of the formula, $\left(\prod_{k=1}^{T_j} (1 + d_k r_k) - 1 \right) (\times \frac{1}{d_j})$, *is:*

$$\left((1 + \frac{1}{365} 2\%)(1 + \frac{3}{365} 2.1\%)(1 + \frac{1}{365} 2.15\%) - 1 \right)(\times \frac{365}{5}) = 2.0902\% \ .$$

In this example Friday's OIS fixing has been applied over the weekend days, so that the DCF becomes effectively longer. Very often in OISs, particularly for those with short maturities these fixings can dominate the equation and become important considerations. Even more so around holiday periods such as Easter and Christmas do certain fixings have greater impact.

Mid-market pricing:
Pricing the mid-market rate for any IRSs of course relies on rearranging the equation to solve for, R^{mid}, when the PV is zero. Given that one can use a curveset to forecast each r_i, v_i or v_j, we do just that below. Additionally, in the case of IRSs against RFRs, the discounting curve and the rates forecasting curve (often) depend upon the same forecast fixing rates so we may have a direct relationship between the two such that,

$$r_j = (\frac{v_{j-1}}{v_j} - 1)\frac{1}{d_j}$$

Thus in the case of a standard IRS (the day count fraction of the floating leg and the floating rate are consistent) we have:

$$R^{\text{mid}} = \frac{\sum_{j=1}^{T_2} d_j r_j v_j}{\sum_{i=1}^{T_1} d_i v_i} = \frac{\sum_{j=1}^{T_2} (v_{j-1} - v_j)}{\sum_{i=1}^{T_1} d_i v_i} = \frac{v_0 - v_{T_2}}{\sum_{i=1}^{T_1} d_i v_i}$$

where v_0 is the DF at the start of the IRS and v_{T_2} is the DF at the end.

Quoting convention:
'Currency, Start-date, End-date, Fixed-frequency, Float-frequency, Roll-date, Stub-type.'

E.g. 'EUR ESTR, 1st Feb '16, 10th Feb '24, Semi, Quarterly, 10th, Short-front, IRS.' This represents a EUR IRS with a floating leg that settles against ESTR for periods with start dates as of the 10th of each month of Feb, May, Aug, Nov. There is a stub period at the start of the swap on both legs which runs between the 1st and 10th Feb. The fixed leg has a semi-annual frequency, so each regular fixed period spans two of the regular quarterly periods on the floating leg.

E.g. 'USD SOFR, 3rd Jun '18, 29th Jul '28, Annual, Semi, 15th, Long-front short-back, IRS.' This is a USD IRS with a floating leg that settles against SOFR for periods with start dates as the 15th of each month of Jan and Jul. The long-front stub on the floating leg runs from 3rd Jun '18 to 15th Jan '19, and the short-back stub from 15th Jul '28 to 29th Jul '28. The fixed leg's long-front stub is slightly different to account for the different frequency and runs from 3rd Jun '18 to 15th Jul '19.

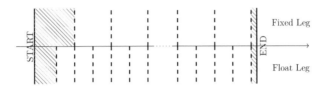

Figure 3.3: Depicting the schedule of a 'USD SOFR, 3rd Jun '18, 29th Jul '28, Annual, Semi, 15th, Long-front short-back, IRS'.

3.6 Single currency basis swaps (SBSs)

Note: This is an obsolete or becoming obsolete product depending upon currency. This description is maintained for historical context.

A single currency basis swap (SBS), or often just basis swap, is an agreement to exchange a series of floating cashflows, almost exclusively of one index against another, for example one might swap 3M-IBOR cashflows for 6M-IBOR, or 1M-IBOR. A bp spread amount (or annuity) is attached to one of the legs to ensure the contract at inception is valued at zero. This spread amount is the effective mid-market price. Usually the spread is added to the index of the shortest tenor of either of the legs often resulting in a positive spread. It is also possible, and common, to exchange an IBOR index for an OIS index, in which case the compounding of the OIS rate fixings means it becomes easier to attach the spread to the IBOR leg.

In all other ways these swaps behave similarly to IRSs /OISs, being simply two floating legs, rather than a fixed and floating leg. All of the date scheduling is done in the same way.

Mathematical formulation:
The PV of a basis swap (from the point of the view of the buyer /payer of the spread) is (where r^1, r^2 refer to different IBOR tenors or indexes):

$$P = -\sum_{i=1}^{T_1} N_i d_i (r_i^1 + Z) v_i + \sum_{j=1}^{T_2} N_j d_j r_j^2 v_j \quad \text{(IBOR/IBOR)}$$

$$P = -\sum_{i=1}^{T_1} N_i d_i (r_i^1 + Z) v_i + \sum_{j=1}^{T_2} N_j v_j \left(\prod_{k=1}^{T_j} (1 + d_k r_k^2) - 1 \right) \quad \text{(IBOR/OIS)}$$

As with IRSs and OISs to determine the mid-market price Z^{mid}, it simply requires manipulation of the formulae setting $P = 0$, so that for a standard IBOR/IBOR SBS (one with constant notional in every period):

$$Z^{\text{mid}} = \frac{\sum_{i=1}^{T_1} d_i r_i^1 v_i - \sum_{j=1}^{T_2} d_j r_j^2 v_j}{\sum_{i=1}^{T_1} d_i v_i} .$$

Quoting convention:
'Currency, Index(es), Start-date, End-date, Float-frequency[1], Float-frequency[2], Roll-date, Stub-type.'
This is the same as for IRSs and OISs.

3.7 Zero coupon swaps (ZCSs)

A zero coupon swap (ZCS) is similar to an IRS, except that payments are not made after each accrual period. Instead, payments due for each period, on each leg of the swap, are compounded up to be paid as a single cashflow at the maturity of the swap. In this manner the fixed leg has a single cashflow, and the floating leg has a single cashflow, payable on the same day in the future for standard ZCSs. After netting, then, this results in only one payment regardless of the maturity or tenor of the ZCS.

The fixed leg's single cashflow can be specified in different ways. Being only a single cashflow means the simplest method is often to specify the actual fixed amount of cash. However, to appear more alike other instruments it can be quoted in rate terms as what is called an internal rate of return (IRR) (the mathematical formulation below also shows this approach). But IRRs can sometimes be misleading; firstly they require a frequency, f, to make sense, and secondly the DCF which are applied to them are sometimes exact and sometimes rounded to a whole number of years. Each method produces different results so a prudent trader will always make it clear which is being used.

The floating leg is uniquely defined. A ZCS compounds all of the relevant index fixings (be it RFR or now obsolete IBOR) to make a single payment at maturity. This is the same compounding methodology that is applied to RFRs over their single swap periods. The mathematical formulation below makes this apparent.

Mathematical formulation:
The PV of a ZCS (from the point of the view of the payer) is, firstly with the fixed leg specified as an interest cashflow on top of notional and secondly in IRR terms:

$$P = -(N + C)v_{T_1} + Nv_{T_1} \prod_{i=1}^{T_1}(1 + d_i r_i) \quad \text{(RFR or IBOR)}$$

$$P = -Nv_{T_1}\left(1 + \frac{R^{\text{IRR}}}{f}\right)^{f(D_{T_1} - D_0)} + Nv_{T_1}\prod_{i=1}^{T_1}(1 + d_i r_i) \quad \text{(RFR or IBOR)}$$

Quoting convention:
'Currency, Index(es), Start-date, End-date, IRR-frequency, Float-frequency, Roll-date, Stub-type.'

Example 3.5.
A trader has received a 20Y ZCS at a semi-annual IRR of 2.40% on a notional of €100mm. He calculates the single, fixed interest cashflow payable after 20Y as:

$$C = \text{€100mm} \times \left(\left(1 + \frac{2.40\%}{2}\right)^{2(20-0)} - 1\right) = \text{€}61,146,360.$$

The next 5Y worth of RFR fixings are forecast to be 2.10% and any subsequent fixing is forecast to be 2.15%. The floating leg's forecast interest cashflow, payable in 20Y is calculated (ignoring business day calendars) as:

$$C = -\text{€100mm} \times \left(\left(1 + \frac{2.10\%}{360}\right)^{1827}\left(1 + \frac{2.15\%}{360}\right)^{5479} - 1\right) = -\text{€}54,307,963.$$

The DF for the payment date, $v_{40} = 0.6690$, and thus the PV of the ZCS is:

$$P = 0.6690 \times (61,146,360 - 54,307,963) = €4,574,888 \ .$$

The current mid-market IRR can also be determined from the floating leg's forecast interest cashflow. If we assume the fixed leg has the equal and opposite cashflow then the semi-annual IRR that will return this cashflow is 2.1807%. This has an effective day count convention of act/act ICMA, whilst the ESTR leg has act/360 are not directly comparable.

3.8   Interest rate swap (IRS) futures

IRS futures are similar to STIR futures in that they trade on exchanges in price terms, with margining principles applied, and a single contract is a predetermined notional (typically 0.1mm) set by the exchange. They also have standard IMM only settlement days, frequently for March, June, September and December. These contracts are, however, physically settled, which means that counterparties which hold open positions at expiry of the future will enter into an over-the-counter (OTC) IRS with all of the swap parameters (that is the start-date, end-date, fixed-frequency, float-frequency, index, roll-date, conventions, and fixed rate) as specified by the terms of the specific futures contract. For example one might trade the USD 0.1mm Z16 10Y SOFR IRS 2.0% contract in which case the swap is fully specified.

In order to complete the action of settlement at expiry counterparties either pay or receive an amount of cash to the clearing house dependent upon the EDSP of the contract, and the direction (whether they bought or sold the futures contract). The EDSP is often determined as the final trading price of the contract before its expiry. At the time of publication IRS futures are not particularly liquid or well traded, if at all.

Mathematical formulation:
Where a party has bought an IRS future, that translates to the direction of receiving fixed on the physically settled IRS. The amount of cash payable to the exchange on settlement of **a single contract** is:

$$P = \frac{EDSP - 100}{100} N, \quad \text{where } N \text{ is a single contract notional} \ .$$

Similarly the live price of an IRS future is determined by the market PV of the contract specified IRS (from the point of view of the receiver) as:

$$q = 100 + 100 \times \frac{P}{N}$$

Example 3.6.
A trader buys 10 {USD 0.1mm Z16 10Y SOFR IRS 1.5%} IRS futures contracts at a price of 100.00.
The market rallies and yields fall by 15bps from 1.5% to 1.35% so that the PV of the IRS representing a single contract is now $1,386.
The price of the IRS future is then 101.39 (or quoted in 32nds 101-12+). To reflect the MTM the exchange credits the trader's account with $10 \times \$1,386 = \$13,860$.
The future expires with an EDSP of the same price and the trader's open position is physically settled. He pays $13,860 to the exchange and enters an IRS for $1mm notional with the clearing house which necessarily possesses a PV of $13,860. The clearing house posts this amount to the trader as collateral.

3.9   Non-MTM cross-currency swaps (XCSs)

A non-MTM cross-currency swap (XCS)[5] is a swap similar to single currency basis swaps, except instead of swapping different tenor indices or different indexes in the same currency, the counterparties exchange indexes (usually RFRs) in two different currencies. To balance the legs so that, at mid-market, the sum of each is zero requires a fixed spread (or annuity) to be attached to one of the floating legs. Usually the non-USD leg or least liquid currency is where the spread is added. In this book we will use the convention that the domestic currency is the one to which the spread is attached, e.g. in a EUR/USD it is the EUR leg and a USD/EUR it will be the USD leg.

Additionally, XCSs involve a notional exchange at the start and end of the swap in the two currencies, which in the case of non-MTM XCSs will always be the same value. The exchange of notional is transacted based on an initially agreed FX rate usually the spot FX at the time of executing the transaction.

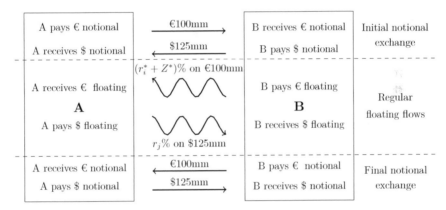

Figure 3.4: A flows diagram of a €100mm EUR/USD non-MTM XCS with initial EURUSD FX fixing of 1.25.

Mathematical formulation:
The PV of, for example, a EUR/USD non-MTM XCS from the point of view of the payer of the spread (B in figure 3.4) is:

$$P(\$) = NF_0 w_0^* - NF_0 \sum_{i=1}^{T_1} (r_i^* + Z^*) d_i^* w_i^* - NF_0 w_{T_1}^*$$

$$- N f_0 v_0 + N f_0 \sum_{j=1}^{T_2} r_j d_j v_j + N f_0 v_{T_2} \,,$$

where v_i represents the discount factor of a USD cashflow and w_i^* the discount factor for a EUR cashflow. f_0 represents the FX rate which was fixed at the time of execution and F_0 represents the current spot FX rate. N is the notional of the domestic currency where the bp spread is attached, so in this case is in EUR. It is also usual (although not strictly necessary) to assume that $f_0 = F_0$ when pricing a new trade. The rates r_i^*, r_j are determined according to equation 3.1 when RFRs are the leg indexes.

---

[5]chapter 7 explains multi-currency IR products in more detail

Customisation:

The above describes one of the more common floating-floating swaps but since these swaps are also completely bespoke much can be customised. The date schedule, including fixing schedule and the day count conventions can all be changed, similar to IRSs.

It is also possible, and quite common in fact, to have one or two fixed legs, where in the formula the respective r_i^*, r_j are replaced by R^*, R. This creates a swap where counterparties exchange a fixed series of payments in one currency for a floating series of payments in another.

Notionals can also, of course, be varied each period, and variable across each leg. Amortisation in the case of swaps hedging loans is a practical example where variable notionals are used.

Quoting convention:

'Currencies, Index(es), Start-date, End-date, Frequency1, Frequency2, Fixed /Floating1, Fixed /Floating2, Roll-date, Stub-type, MTM or non-MTM.'

As with any other product many conventions are omitted if the intention is clear. The simplest XCSs will be quoted as, for example, 'EUR/USD 5Y non-MTM', where the start date and indexes are implied by market conventions. This swap would be assumed to be a floating/floating ESTR/SOFR XCS since these are the standard interbank products.

3.10 MTM cross-currency swaps (XCSs)

A MTM XCS is the most common form of XCS. It is the standard XCS product traded in the interbank market. Its purpose, and its difference to non-MTM XCSs is to reduce credit exposure (CE) to counterparties by continually 'resetting' the notional on one leg throughout the length of the swap, in light of fluctuating exchange rates. What this does, is help to mitigate the overall PV of the derivative by restricting the impact of FX fluctuations. In non-MTM XCSs, FX fluctuations can have a far greater impact on the PV of those derivatives than the actual underlying XCS market prices, and hence the affinity toward MTM XCSs[6].

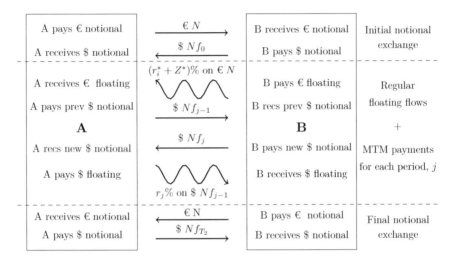

Figure 3.5: A flows diagram of a €N EUR/USD MTM XCS with initial EURUSD FX fixing of f_0.

Mathematical formulation:
The PV of, for example, a EUR/USD MTM XCS from the point of view of the payer of the spread is:

$$P(\$) = NF_0 w_0^* - NF_0 \sum_{i=1}^{T_1} (r_i^* + Z^*) d_i w_i^* - NF_0 w_{T_1}^*$$
$$- Nf_0 v_0 + N \sum_{j=1}^{T_2} f_{j-1} r_j d_j v_j + N \sum_{j=1}^{T_2} (f_{j-1} - f_j) v_j + Nf_{T_2} v_{T_2} .$$

It is common that one might seek to determine a mid-market spread, $Z^{*\mathrm{mid}}$, for a XCS. To do this the forecast rates and DFs in each currency need to be obtained from a multi-currency curveset. The PV can then be set to zero and the formula rearranged in terms of $Z^{*\mathrm{mid}}$ [7].

The same types of **customisations** are available as for non-MTM XCSs as are the **quoting conventions**.

---

[6]see chapter 7 for a more detailed explanation of the difference between non-MTM and MTM XCSs in the context of other chapters on credit risk and collateral

[7]the appendix for chapter 7 shows an application of this for simple XCSs

3.11   FX Swaps

FX swaps (alternatively called currency swaps) are agreements to complete two, offsetting FX exchanges: one exchange on a particular date and a re-exchange at a future date for an agreed price difference. For example one counterparty might agree to sell EUR100mm for USD at spot at an exchange rate of 1.2500 and then after one month purchase EUR100mm from USD at an exchange rate of 1.2480.

Mathematical formulation[8]

Suppose the example from above: *buying 1M €100mm EURUSD FX Swap at -20 points, i.e. EURUSD rates of 1.2500 and then 1.2480.* This equates to the following simple cashflows defined by the notional, initial FX rate and swap price:

Date	USD	EUR
1st Jan 2022	+$125mm	-€100mm
1st Feb 2022	-$124.8mm	+€100mm

FX swaps are **economically equivalent to single period, fixed-fixed XCSs** where the fixed rate on one currency is set to 0%, and the other currency is determined by a specified rate defined by the swap price.

Quoting convention:

Currency pair, start date, tenor, notional, swap points (the price) and an agreed initial FX rate.

3.12   Swaptions

Swaptions are not classed as linear IRD products. Chapter 20 exclusively outlines these products and their pricing formulae.

---

[8]chapter 7 covers FX swaps formulae in more detail

Chapter

4

Users of Interest Rate Derivatives

Every person and corporation might have cause to trade, or at least utilise, some form of IR product. Often one might even trade an IRS indirectly. In this chapter we seek to build up an understanding of who trades IR products, including derivatives, and why. This is good for the narrative because it places the need for IRDs in the wider context of the financial markets. This is certainly not an exhaustive list but it lays the foundations for understanding these markets from a trader's perspective.

4.1   Household sector and general banking

We begin with the driving force of the economy, its people. In life, any individual will be expected at some point to do all of the following; take out a loan, or a mortgage, borrow on a credit card, save some money in a bank account or pension fund, and finally monetise their pension fund. These all involve derivatives activities.

Banks (or similar financial institutions) can be expected to facilitate all of these services. To understand how a bank does this we point out that, on a rolling basis, the way a bank can source funds is dependent upon prevailing market interest rates. For example if a bank plans to raise cash in two years time then the rates it will be liable to pay to investors or creditors will be dependent upon what the rates are at that time. This makes a bank's funding rate floating, and this is a bank's reference point when considering all the services it offers to retail customers.

When a bank issues a loan or a mortgage to a customer it must do so by funding it in some way, and it benchmarks the cost of the loan against floating rates. Due to a psychological bias and general risk aversion, private individuals are commonly fearful of floating rate debt. They often prefer fixed rate mortgages and fixed rate loans. Bank's facilitate this by embedding IRSs into the structure, so that a customer ends up paying a fixed rate without the specific documentation of having actually traded an IRD. The bank would hedge this exposure by paying fixed on an IRS in the interbank market. An IRS portfolio of a bank will always contain IRSs directly relating to the issue of retail loans and mortgages, often these will be customised IRSs with amortising notionals.

The impact of this is that the fixed rates available to retail customers will fluctuate with general interest rate markets. In January, say, a 10Y fixed rate mortgage might be offered at 3.0% but in March it might be offered for 2.9%. This is likely due to IRSs, that the bank will use to hedge itself, having a lower mid-market rate as a result of interbank market movements between January and March.

Credit cards are a similar example. Banks usually offer these to customers for inflexible fixed rate APRs. But of course a bank must fund the customer's purchases. In order to match the fixed rate interest received with the floating interest on the funding, a bank must again hedge by paying fixed on IRSs.

Current deposits are of a different variety. Usually a bank pays a nominally small amount of interest on the money deposited in a current account, or checking account, e.g. 0.1%. This does not typically change whether market interest rates rise or fall. But it will impact a bank's profitability. The difference between the current account rate and the prevailing central bank deposit rate is sometimes referred to as the marginal rate. A bank's profit is larger for a higher marginal rate and less when it falls. Thus, a bank can hedge the marginal rate by receiving fixed on an IRS, to profit on the derivative instead when market rates fall and the marginal rate shrinks.

Hedging of this sort, executed by a bank's treasury department is an actuarial assessment. Current account deposits differ from loans and mortgages in that they are instant access, whereas the latter have defined repayment profiles. But it is not expected that all depositors would, all at the same time, choose to withdraw their deposits (this would amount to a run on the bank and likely collapse it). So, a model is drawn up to conservatively estimate how long the deposits will be expected to be maintained and hedge marginal rates according to that maturity profile.

In a similar vein, a bank will have to receive IRSs to hedge other fixed rate savings products that it offers to retail investors.

If the time comes for a pensioner to cash in his pension for an annuity the onus will fall on the pension provider to pay an income to him over time. In order to do this the pension provider will have to generate a return on the underlying cash over a period of years to pay out the income amount. It does this by investing the cash, exchanged for the annuity, in equities or other securities. If the future expectation of interest rates fall then the implicit amount of growth assumed over many years might not be sufficient to pay the annuity income that pensioner has purchased. Thus, a pension fund may choose to hedge long dated interest rates by receiving fixed on IRSs as a risk management device.

4.2   Central governments

The treasury and debt management office (DMO) of a central government are responsible for the public finances. This means they raise money through taxes and issuing sovereign bonds, to pay for public services. Issuing sovereign bonds is the primary way a government has of raising money, outside of taxes. This is important to the IR market because the sale of bonds represents a supply of fixed rates. Nominal sovereign debt is commonly issued as a fixed coupon which is paid to investors.

If a fixed coupon bond is issued, but the respective DMO believes that rates will fall, then it will, in turn, hedge the bond issuance by receiving fixed on an IRS. At the appropriate time, when market rates fall to target levels, that IRS will be unwound for a profit.

Conversely a DMO, which believes rates will rise, might pre-empt a government's requirement of funding and prematurely pay fixed on an IRS, until such a time when the bonds are issued. The IRS could at that time then be unwound, hopefully those market rates had risen in the meantime to recognise a profit. This activity is sometimes referred to as **rate locking**, since the level of rates at which an upcoming issue is effectively subject to has already been 'locked in' by the time of the issuance.

This slightly complicates the narrative as hedging bonds with IRSs is not a one-for-one hedge. In fact this is known as an **asset swap**, and along with it comes a type of basis risk termed **asset swap spread risk**. Asset swap spread risk is not dissimilar to single currency basis risk between two indexes. But instead, it is the risk that IRS rates will move more or less than the yields on the bonds to the same respective maturity that they are designed to hedge. This type of risk and trading bonds relative to swaps is very common. So much so that it is a valid criticism of this book that bonds are not mentioned in greater detail.

Some DMOs do not engage in this type of hedging. Their issuance profile, that is how much money they will raise in a year, might be sufficiently large that engaging in this type of activity would dominate a domestic market. It might also mean that the necessitated smaller hedging activity would be of negligible consequence, and thus avoided altogether. A DMO might also take the view that issuing on a continual basis, spaced throughout the year, provides an effective average of market rates over time, neither benefiting nor losing from market yield changes. A large enough issuance profile also provides enough flexibility on an on going basis to alter average portfolio duration and other interest rate risk measures. Thus it might perceive an unhedged strategy to be at least sufficient, if not optimal. A good example of a DMO which engages an unhedged strategy is the United Kingdom's[14].

On the other hand, smaller countries often have the unhindered ability, and need, to more actively manage their debt portfolio. This means having a more active decision making process, with respect to market rates. In turn they utilise IRSs as the instrument to hedge market risks. A good example of a DMO which engages this strategy is that of the Republic of Finland[15].

A treasury does not necessarily have to raise money in the domestic currency of their land. Using Finland as an example again, it could choose to issue sovereign debt in USD, widening its pool of potential investors. In this case, though, the DMO will want to hedge all market risk exposures so that its overall exposure is to its domestic currency, EUR, only. Therefore it will need to execute a fixed/fixed EUR/USD XCS. We look at this type of hedging in detail with respect to corporate issuance.

4.3 Central banks

Central banks preside over their own domestic currency. As a defensive measure to the world economy at large, central banks build up **foreign reserves**. This is where they purchase foreign currency, selling their own domestic currency in the process. This act (if done in enough nominal size) will weaken the domestic currency. This is usually supportive of inflation for two core reasons; firstly import prices rise, and secondly the economy can be stimulated by foreign investment increasing growth and wages. When the domestic currency is considered too weak a central bank will deplete its foreign reserves and buy back its own currency to counteract the weakness. Good examples of central banks that actively engage this activity are the Swiss National Bank (SNB)[16] and the Danish Central Bank (DNB)[17], which has maintained a stable rate of DKKEUR for many years.

The above is not derivative activity, but it places the following derivative activity in context. In order to facilitate a functional (and not dysfunctional) financial system, any domestic central bank is expected to provide liquidity to its domestic banks in some fashion, via standing facilities. Given the globalised nature of modern day finance activities, domestic banks often need to access liquidity in currencies other than their own. For the central bank to provide this liquidity it must have the currency available. But, central banks are not necessarily keen to offer this from their variable foreign exchange reserves. Therefore, central banks have created **swap lines** between themselves to exchange each other's domestic currency. Swap lines represent XCSs, so by utilising these derivatives a central bank gains access to a foreign currency but does not change the FX exposure of their foreign exchanges reserves account. This is more convenient since then neither central bank is exposed to the movement of FX rates via the transaction.

The management of foreign exchange reserves is also an active area of IR portfolio management. A central bank with the 'correct' perceived FX exposure, invested in the government bonds of the foreign currency might believe interest rates in that foreign currency will rise. Rather than sell the FX reserves it might be better to hedge using IRSs.

As an interesting aside, in 2022 in the Russo-Ukrainian war sanctions were imposed on Russia's central bank by the US, Japan and European Union countries freezing its built up foreign currency reserves held as government bonds in those respective countries. This amounted to about 50% of its $600bn reserves. This was made possible by the centralised clearing and settlements systems based in the relevant jurisdictions. Since the clearing and settlements houses were prohibited from dealing with Russia's central bank it was impossible for it to sell these assets to any other counterparty and monetise their value. This significantly weakened Russia's ability to defend its weakening currency at the time.

4.4   Non-financial corporations (NFCs)

Although non-financial corporations (NFCs) can have numerous reasons to access financial markets, be it surplus cash management, revenue smoothing or hedging, tax optimisation strategies, etc. **their primary action in the IR market is to issue debt**. Otherwise, this is known as raising financing, similar to the actions of DMOs. Given the impact that NFC issuance has on markets we will expand our focus here.

Sovereign debt is usually easier to issue than NFC debt because the credit quality of sovereign bonds is usually superior, or at least good. The size of the market is also usually larger attracting a more active secondary market and improving liquidity conditions. Liquidity conditions are important for any issuer because a lack of liquidity in a market costs that issuer more as investors demand supplementary premiums for holding the bonds, which they may not be able to resell very easily.

NFCs are therefore concerned with, and sensitive to, a number of factors when it comes to debt issuance. Firstly we can consider the headline influencer of an NFC's bond's price - its **credit spread**. The credit spread is the measured difference between the yield to maturity on the credit bond and some conventional benchmark reference rate. In different countries the benchmark changes. In the UK, for example, a common convention is to measure the credit spread relative to UK government bonds, where there is wide selection of maturities. In the Euro area the convention is to benchmark relative to IRSs, because of the complication of multiple countries' sovereign bonds having quite different overall yield levels and representing poor choices for benchmarks. In Sweden the convention is also to measure against IRSs because the number of available Swedish government bonds is too limited to always provide maturity matching benchmarks.

An NFC will be concerned that it can issue its bonds with as small a credit spread as possible, particularly relative to its peer NFCs. This suggests two observable markets; the **relative credit spread** of peer companies, and that of **domestic credit spreads** in general taken across all domestic NFCs. These levels will be constantly monitored and issuance initiated when they are perceived to be favourable.

To expand on **liquidity**, an NFC would generally like to issue bonds with a reasonable issuance size, to promote a broader secondary market. **Past performance** of successful, and oversubscribed, issuance carries psychological benefits. This can create positive momentum and further demand allowing issuers to charge higher prices (lower credit spreads) on new or tapped[1] issues. On the other hand issuers would like to avoid scenarios where their bonds are shunned, having adverse effects for future issuance. In cases where secondary market trading is very limited, past performance of issuance might be the only available information, on which to form any opinions and base conclusions, so can be very influential.

A third point, most relevant to our focus on IRDs, is that an NFC must pay attention to **international IRD rates and international credit spreads**. It may be that issuing in a foreign currency is cheaper for the issuer and allows the possibility of expanding to a wider pool of investors. We expand directly on this with an example below. We also highlight similar material in section 8.2.2 describing supply and demand factors of XCS markets.

Example 4.1.
Suppose Alpha Corp., a EUR domesticated NFC, is considering issuing a bond. It considers either domestic issuance or foreign issuance, in USD, swapped back to EUR. If Alpha swaps the issuance it will execute IRDs. The IRDs have three purposes; switch the USD that investors pay for the bonds to EUR for Alpha, allow Alpha to pay fixed EUR interest while the investors receive USD interest cashflows, and at maturity permit Alpha to pay back the original EUR sum whilst the investors receive the original USD sum, all without exposing any party to FX risk.

Figure 4.1 demonstrates netted legs from the point of view of Alpha Corp. if it pursues foreign issuance. The rightmost legs of the figure do not net and reflect outstanding commitments; a fixed EUR interest outflow and EUR notional exchanges, as required.

If Alpha chooses to issue domestically then it pays a fixed rate equal to EUR IRS rate (RFR benchmark) + EUR credit spread. Say these were 1% and +40bps respectively to give a total of 1.4%. For foreign issuance the figure demonstrates the net payment is equal to EUR IRS rate (RFR) + USD credit spread + EUR/USD XCS spread (non-MTM). Supposing the two spreads were +50bps and -30bps respectively then the overall fixed rate for comparison is 1.2%. So it is advantageous for Alpha to consider swapped foreign issuance even though the US market for credit spreads is higher than in EU.

It is common for a bank to facilitate this service to NFCs by providing them with a single non-MTM fixed /fixed XCS that replaces the three individual IRDs. Upon hedging the bank will usually expose itself to cross-gamma risks due to different terms of the CSAs of the interbank trade hedges, and due to the build up of non-MTM XCSs hedged with interbank MTM XCSs. This is explored further in chapter 21.

NFCs do not always desire to have fixed rate exposure on their bonds. Investors generally prefer fixed rate bonds, which are more common, so it makes sense to issue fixed rate. But, if the issuer were to receive fixed on an IRS then this would convert the issue to floating rate

---

[1]a tapped issuance is one where existing bonds are re-issued increasing to total size outstanding

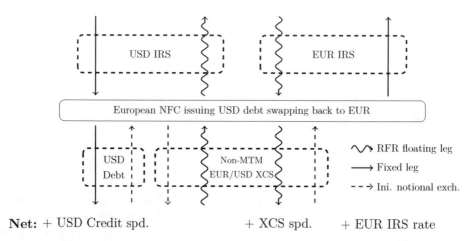

Figure 4.1: Transaction details of a 'swapped' foreign issuance back to domestic currency (the final notional exchange and repayment of principal to investors is not shown - it is the opposite of all initial exchanges).

(from only the issuer's perspective). In figure 4.1, for foreign issuance, this could be achieved by omitting to pay fixed on the EUR IRS. For domestic issuance there would be the requirement to receive on a stand-alone EUR IRS. Since issuance swaps are one of the largest, most common, types of swapping activity we expand details on their pricing below.

Issuance swaps

A domestic issuer chooses to 'swap to floating' its issuance by receiving fixed on an IRS. The issuer, however, does not just execute a benchmark interbank IRS to hedge its market risk exposure. Instead it executes an IRS that precisely matches the dates and specific cashflows of its bond. It does this in order to classify its issuance and derivative under the IFRS9 cash flow hedge accounting designation. Since the transactions are large, with the IRS notional being the same as that as the issue size, there is often the requirement for a third party validation of the pricing given by a market-maker. This validation comes in the form of, what are called, 'screen references'. A screen reference uses interbank brokers' electronically published prices to validate the mid-market of benchmark swaps. Since these benchmark swaps do not precisely match the issuer's customised IRS there are also adjustments that need to be agreed. We give an example of these adjustments showing how these transactions are organised in practice.

Example 4.2.
Alpha Corp. decides to issue domestically. It chooses to issue a new 7Y fixed rate bond, with settlement T+5 b.d.s, and swap it to floating RFR. With everything complete, Alpha Corp. will have issued bonds priced at some yield to maturity and received fixed on an IRS with the same fixed rate and conventions as the bond cashflows to pay RFR plus a bp spread. We outline the process of calculation of that spread.

*The bond is typically priced by specifying its yield to maturity as the forward adjusted, mid-market 7Y RFR IRS rate plus a credit spread. We begin by spotting the standard 7Y RFR IRS from some official screen source, say that this value is 0.995%. The fact that the bond settles T+5 means the dates on the swap are customised. The standard 7Y RFR IRS has a fixed rate 0.5bp lower that the equivalent IRS starting T+5. This is called the **forward adjustment**.*

*Thus, the referenced mid-market rate for the purpose of pricing the bond is equal to **screen price plus the forward adjustment** of 0.5%, making 1.00%. We now add the **credit spread**, which is agreed between the investors, the issuer and the syndicate banks organising the deal in advance, say 40bps, making a priced yield to maturity of 1.40%.*

Description	Value
Screen reference 7Y mid swap	0.995%
T+5 forward adjustment	0.005%
Bond credit spread	0.400%
Priced yield to maturity	1.400%

If the coupon on the bond were matched at 1.400% the bond would price at par. If Alpha Corp received 1.400% on the IRS with standard conventions the RFR floating rate spread would match the credit spread at 40bps. However, there are three adjustments which might exist which can result in that spread that the issuer pays differing from 40bps;

  *i) **convention adjustments**: if the fixed leg and float leg have different conventions, e.g. day count conventions or different frequencies, the same basis point spread on one leg is not equivalent to the same spread on the other.*

 *ii) **coupon adjustment**: if the coupon on the bond is not set to be the same as the priced yield to maturity then the bond price is not exactly par. Usually the coupon is set to be lower than the yield to maturity and the bond prices at a discount. The issuer typically wants to receive par however, so an economic upfront payment value known as the make to par is embedded into the swap. The lower coupon rate applied to the fixed rate of the swap offsets this in part but the economics are not exact.*

*iii) **market-maker's margin**: this is a fee for facilitating the transaction embedded into the issuer swap.*

The coupon is set at 1.375% and the issuer receives a T+5 7Y RFR fixed at 1.375% with conventions, Annual ACT/ACT ICMA, and pays floating rate plus 38.1bps, which equates to 37.5bps standard spread plus 0.3bps convention adjustment minus 0.2bps make to par coupon adjustment plus a market maker fee of 0.5 bps. The swap includes an upfront make to par payment.

4.5 Asset managers

Wealth management funds and pension fund providers need to hold physical products such as bonds, as an investment of their capital. They utilise IRDs to fine tune their IR risk exposure, either directly hedging their existing IR exposure or creating IR exposure, correlated with other assets, to diversify their portfolios. Diversified portfolios reduce overall risk and in turn this can increase Sharpe ratios.

An asset manager will typically utilise the full suite of IRDs, especially if it is a cross-asset, cross-currency management company.

A common example of an asset manager utilising IRDs is to gain specific exposure to **credit risk**. For example, an asset manager can invest their funds in a credit bond, say a 10Y bond issued by Volvo, or a 5Y bond issued by Apple. This exposes the fund to the credit rating of

Volvo or Apple and also exposes the fund to IR delta risk. If market interest rates fall or rise then the fund will earn PnL respectively. This is because the prices of those Volvo and Apple bonds will have changed alongside the overall IR market. In order to eliminate the IR delta risk a fund can pay an IRS. This means the fund will accrue PnL only if the market assessed credit rating on the bond changes and its yield adjusts accordingly, **relative** to the IR benchmark.

As has been mentioned already, though, this hedging strategy introduces asset swap spread risk. Another option the asset manager might consider would be to sell a benchmark government bond in order to eliminate the IR delta risk. Both options can be used, and leaves the asset manager with the credit risk exposure to the individual issuing corporation, without an element of IR delta risk. There are three reasons the asset manager might prefer paying IRSs then selling government bonds. The first is that short selling government bonds means that they must be sourced using repo transactions. This is an overhead operationally and at certain times can become expensive if those bonds go 'special'. This type of transaction is subject to rollover risk, where short tenor repos prove difficult to repeat for an extended period of time. Secondly, the underlying credit bond might be benchmarked against IRSs rather than government bonds. In the Euro area this is particularly common because the EUR currency spans many different countries whose domestic government bond yields can vary significantly. To compare corporations in the Euro area benchmarking tends to be done against a common ESTR index. Thirdly, the asset manager might be comfortable to own the swap spread risk, particularly if initiated at historically favourable levels.

For this type of bond hedging there are three specific types of IRS that are often chosen.

(i) **Matched maturity or yield-yield asset swap:** these are two names for the same IRS. It is a swap which has a maturity date that matches the maturity date of the bond. It has a front stub on both fixed and floating legs until the next bond coupon payment, and the rate will be the same as the mid-market rate as with any other IRS. The notional on the swap is chosen to match the IR delta on the bond, so is often not the same notional as that on the bond. The conventions of a yield-yield swap are typical of standard IRSs of the given currency.

(ii) **Par-par asset swap:** this is more complicated than the above, but its name is at least descriptive. An investor pays a price of par (i.e. 100) for the bond (either including accrued interest or, less commonly, excluding it by choice) and pays the fixed leg on an IRS with notional and convention to match the bond coupon cashflows. The floating leg has a short front stub with maturity mimicking the bond's, and the same notional as the fixed leg (and therefore the bond also). A bp spread is applied to the floating leg to equate the economics.

(iii) **Net proceeds swap:** probably the most complicated swap to execute against a bond. In this case the investor pays the dirty price (i.e. the clean price plus accrued interest) of the bond. The fixed leg of the IRS is the same as with the par-par swap, whereby the bond's cashflows are replicated. But, the floating leg is different in one respect - the notional is set to be reflective of the dirty price $\left(\frac{\text{dirty price}}{100} \times \text{fixed notional}\right)$, with a bp spread applicable to the floating RFR component to equate the economics.

Why are three forms of asset swap used? The first is the easiest measure, for calculation and tracking. The second and third provide measures designed to see the actual floating interest rate payments received relative to RFR, albeit on marginally different terms, and can be representative of accounting structures. It is an example of subjectivity of trade construction and risk management. Note that the notionals are different meaning the delta risks of the IRSs are also different. The different volatilities of the bond assets relative to associated swaps will result in one type providing the best delta hedge than the others, although it will likely differ which in different market conditions.

Example 4.3.
Two different investors of Alpha Corp.'s domestic issuance choose to purchase the bond on asset swap in €50mm each. At pricing, Alpha Corp.'s bond was in fact issued with a 1.375% coupon against a yield to maturity struck at 1.4%. This means that the new bond priced at €99.85, instead of par.

*The first investor enters a **yield-yield asset swap**. He pays fixed at 1.000% and receives RFR floating leg. The yield-yield asset swap spread is defined as 40bps. The only adjustment factored here relative to the benchmark mid-market 7Y is the forward adjustment (+0.5bps on fixed leg). The notional on the IRS is €49.6mm to give analytic delta neutrality.*

*The second investor enters a **par-par asset swap**. The investor pays a fixed leg of 1.375% replicating the bond cashflows and receives RFR + 37.6bps. The adjustments that have been factored here on the RFR leg are the standard spread (+37.5bps), convention adjustment (+0.3bps) and make to par coupon adjustment (-0.2bps). The notional on this IRS is €50mm and the analytic delta is not neutral.*

Since no market-maker fee was added in either case each swap has a MTM value of zero at inception. Even though their terms are different, their initial value is equivalent.

4.6   Hedge funds and speculators

Hedge funds and speculators use derivatives to create leverage. With relatively small amounts of capital they can offer large returns, if the market moves the right way! Funds exist in many shapes and sizes with countless investment strategies and styles. They will transact in both directions of IRDs depending on their specific view of the market and economy. They might often employ complicated strategies which utilise IRDs to gain very specialised financial exposures. Much like the example given for asset managers credit risk exposure.

One particular type of speculator, called a commodity trading account (CTA), trade exclusively on exchanges. STIR futures are an example of a product they would treat as a 'commodity' and engage in buying and selling of its contracts, possibly as part of larger strategies involving non-IR products such as equities or agriculture futures. As swap futures become more liquid in exchanges it is likely that the CTAs will also expand, applying their algorithmic trading strategies to these products too.

4.7   Banks

Banks doubtless have the most use of IRDs. Notwithstanding the fact they often facilitate all of the above counterparties' actions but they also have their own risks to manage. They undertake the same kind of debt issuance as non-financial corporations, so the above section is relevant too, but they also undertake many more activities alongside. A cross-asset bank, and one acting as market-maker, will accrue multiple IR risks from countless areas, and activities, of finance and financing. Some of these risks might be straightforward but many will be of a complex nature. This book aims to explain some of these risks and some appropriate risk management techniques.

Cash, Collateral and Credit

Derivatives portfolios are by no means defined simply by the types of products and trades contained within. Other aspects of the trades such as how they are collateralised, and who the counterparty, or credit, is are also of utmost importance. Even the treatment of an outstanding cash balance must be done properly to ensure consistency and accurate accounting of the portfolio. This chapter presents;

- what a cash balance is and why it is important in the context of an IRD portfolio,

- how accounting principles work to record trading profits and not cash balance interest profits,

- what collateral is, and how the terms are legally set out in CSAs,

- how and why CSAs must be considered in the accurate pricing of IRDs and the concept of the CTD collateral,

- why the counterparty of a trade is an important consideration,

- in what ways the credit risk of a counterparty can be expressed,

- what credit valuation adjustments (CVAs) and funding valuation adjustments (FVAs) are.

5.1   Cash balances

5.1.1   Introduction

Cash balances form an important part of any derivatives portfolio. Before engaging a more detailed discussion consider a simple example:

Example 5.1.

   (i) *A trader creates an empty IRDs portfolio, **initially with no cash nor any trades**.*

  (ii) *He executes a single trade, paying fixed on $100mm 1Y semi-semi IRS at the mid-market rate of 1.0%, and records the PV of the trade as zero.*

 (iii) *The compounded RFR fixings during the 6M period yield 1.1% exactly as initially forecast. This determines that at the 6M point the trader receives a cashflow (net of the fixed and floating legs) of $50,000.*

 (iv) *The second 6M period experiences RFR fixings, again exactly as was originally forecast at execution, compounding to give 0.8996%. This determines a net payment of $50,200 that the trader must pay at the 1Y point.*

At first glance example 5.1 suggests a contradiction. The RFR rates were published exactly as originally forecast, when the trade was executed at mid-market with zero PV. Yet, the trader received $50,000 after 6M and then paid $50,200 at the 1Y point. It would appear that he has lost $200 at maturity of the trade even though the original PV suggests he should have neither gained nor lost any money.

Time value of money is the key here. The additional $200 that the trader had to pay was recouped from interest he received at a specific rate of 0.8% on his cash balance of $50,000 over the period between the 6M point and the 1Y point. The result is that the trader is left with no cash and the trade has matured.

This example highlights the importance of cash balances when considering the physical settlement activities of derivatives. Derivatives are always priced assuming cash can be funded or invested at a specific rate of interest. This is the rate that determines the DF for any given day. For an IRD valued at zero to actually recognise no gain or loss at its ultimate maturity, two events must occur;

   (i) the originally forecast floating rates must publish as predicted, and

  (ii) the DFs used for the initial pricing must be attained when funding or investing real cash balances.

It is easy to see that had the cash balance of $50,000 not accrued interest at 0.8% over the latter six months of the IRS in the example, then the trader's final cash balance would not have been precisely zero and would have resulted in either a gain or a loss. Make a point of noticing that the example interest rate of 0.8% here is **not** the same as the RFR period rate published at 0.8996%. This is a very important distinction. For cleared and regularly collateralised derivates these will be the same rates, but in this specific contract's case 0.8% reflects the physically attainable rate of interest on the cash balance over the term, for example there is a non-standard remuneration agreement on collateral here, which we will come on to.

5.1.2   Cash balance profiles

A cash balance profile details the expected cash balance of a portfolio at differing future dates. It is measured by aggregating all cashflows on a given day including accumulated interest amounts from previous days' balances. Sometimes it is useful to consider the cash balance profile of a single trade, and at other times analysis of a portfolio of trades is necessary.

Example 5.1 (being a portfolio of one trade) had a relatively simple cash balance profile, with three important dates worth considering;

  (i) an initial cash balance of $0 as there were no fees or cashflows exchanged at the inception of the mid-market trade,

 (ii) then a balance of +$50,000 after consideration of the first netted cashflow at the 6M date,

(iii) finally a balance of $0 after consideration of the accumulated interest (+$200) on the previous balance and the final netted cashflow (-$50,200) at the 1Y date.

It is of course possible to calculate the cash balance of a derivative for any given date, for example the cash balance at the 9M point would be c.$50,100 after the accrual of some interest each day after the initial receipt of $50,000. However, the three dates above represent the important dates where significant change occurs due to cashflows being exchanged in this example.

For simple, mid-market IRDs the **expected** cash balance profile is often easy to qualitatively describe. Firstly, for any derivative which has only a single cashflow date there will never be any expectation of any cash balance. This is because any floating or fixed cashflows paid or received will be priced to net to zero, and therefore no net cashflows will ever be forecast to be exchanged. This is true, for example, with mid-market FRAs or ZCSs or single period IRSs or OISs. The trades still have risk, of course, and net cashflows will arise as market movements give rise to MTM PnL; we are simply highlighting the expected nature of a zero cash balance profile for certain trade types executed at mid-market.

Secondly, where derivatives have multiple cashflows there is generally a particular structure to the IR curve that allows a qualitative assessment, whether it be flat, upward sloping, downward sloping, or bowing. Figure 5.1 gives an example of an IRS in an upward sloping IR curve environment.

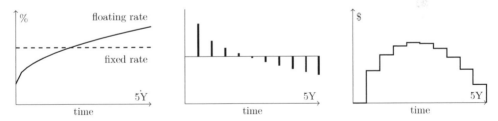

(a) Fixed rate and forecast com- (b) Forecast net cashflows due (c) Forecast cash balance of
pounded RFR rates.   on IRS payment dates.   portfolio due to the IRS.

Figure 5.1: Cash analysis of receiving a $ 5Y semi-semi IRS with initial PV of zero, in an upward sloping rates curve environment.

It is worth remembering that **any derivative whose initial PV is zero will always have an expected final cash balance of zero**. This is because a derivative with zero PV cannot be expected to gain or lose an amount of cash after its maturity. The interim, forecast, cash balance, however can feasibly have any pattern. These depend on the structure of all of the interim cashflows that take place and is the reason figure 5.1 was included to highlight this.

Cash balances are central to considering future discounting risk and the impact to PnL if discounting basis changes or the terms of a CSA is restructured. These items will become more clear as the reader progresses through various chapters of the book, but it is often useful to think about trades in context of their cash balance profile. It can be very illuminating and is often misunderstood, or ignored, by many traders.

5.1.3   Daily PnL accounting

IRDs are unlike securities in the sense that at inception you do not expect them to yield any return. For example if you buy a security, say a bond with one year maturity and with a 2% coupon, then after one year you expect it to have generated a 2% return. On the other hand, say, if you receive a mid-market 1Y IRS @ 2% then you do not expect to make any return at all. In fact, based on the expectation of future forecast floating rates you expect that the IRS will mature with zero PnL.

Derivatives are risk management and speculative, leveraged instruments. Trading them results in PnL but only when the market rates change and deviate from those originally forecast. This speculative nature must be taken into consideration in the context of cash balances for accounting purposes. To explain this simply, suppose a derivatives portfolio has a very large, positive cash balance, generated perhaps by previous successful trading. Suppose also that it is without any open derivative positions, and that it also refrains from executing any further derivative trades. The value of this portfolio will naturally increase via accrued interest on its cash balance[1], but the increase in value of the portfolio would not actually be due to any derivative trading whatsoever. This presents a conflict of interest because a derivative portfolio should be reporting only derivative trading profits and losses, and the interest accrued on previous profits should not be permitted.

This means that a method is needed to separate the difference between cash balances generated through previous trading profits (or losses) and cash balances required to fund future derivative cashflows. In the context of running a business owned by shareholders and a need to accurately report the derivative trading activity, the profit and loss statement and the balance sheet of a derivative portfolio are both important. **One should be aware that the cash balance of a derivative portfolio is necessarily made up of these two components, expressly;**

(i) **the PV of future cashflows,** where the cash balance either funds or recoups, negative or positive cashflows respectively, and,

(ii) **PnL,** where a positive or negative cash balance has been generated as the result of successful or unsuccessful trading, respectively.

Good accounting practice isolates the PnL component of any cash balance so that it cannot accrue any further interest gains or losses that would be misrepresented as derivative trading PnL (the definition of PnL here is MTM PnL, which is the sum of realised plus any unrealised PnL). An actual example of how daily derivative portfolio balance sheets and profit and loss statements function is in my opinion the best way to illustrate this concept. Do not confuse this, however, with quarterly or year end financial statements produced by a financial institution. The following is designed for monitoring a derivatives portfolio on a daily basis, only.

Example 5.2.
We outline a sample balance sheet and profit and loss statement of a derivatives portfolio.

---

[1]in a positive interest rate environment

BALANCE SHEET (000's)	Day 1	Day 2	Day 3
Previous closing values			
[A1=previous(E1)] PV of previous derivative contracts	80,000	75,711	76,635
[A2=-A1=previous(E4)] Total cash balance*	-80,000	-75,711	-76,635
Day's scheduled cashflow exchange			
[B1=αA2] O/N interest on previous cash balance*	-2	-2	-2
[B2] Net previous derivative contracts' cashflows*	5,000	-1,000	7,000
[B3=-B2] PV change of previous derivative contracts	-5,000	1,000	-7,000
Previous derivative contracts' valuation changes			
[C1$\approx$-B1] O/N carry from previous close to open[2]	2	2	2
[C2] PV due to market movements from open to close	965	-110	30
New trading activity			
[D1] PV of derivative contracts acquired /disposed	-256	33	612
[D2] Day's cash payments due to [D1]*	354	-10	-432
[D3] Other imposed cost-of-carry[3]	0	0	0
Closing values			
[E1=A1+B3+C1+C2+D1] PV of all derivative contracts	75,711	76,636	70,279
[E2=A2+B1+B2+D2] Intermediate cash balance*	-74,648	-76,723	-70,069
[E3=-(E1+E2)+D3] Balancing PnL cash transfer* (Dividend)	-1,063	87	-210
[E4=E2+E3] Total cash balance carried forward*	-75,711	-76,636	-70,279

PROFIT AND LOSS STATEMENT (000's)	Day 1	Day 2	Day 3
PnL itemised			
[F1=B1+C1] Funding inconsistencies (interest vs carry)	0	0	0
[F2=C2] Market movements from open to close	965	-110	30
[F3=D1+D2+D3] New daily activity	98	23	180
Total			
[G1=F1+F2+F3=-E3] Recorded PnL	1,063	-87	210

In example 5.2 most line items are self evident, with specific items related to cash balances highlighted with *. The *day's scheduled cashflow exchange* lists payments and receipts that are written into the derivative contracts and already known on the previous day. If cash is exchanged, then the value of the derivatives must move in the opposite direction. The *previous derivative contracts' valuation changes* determines the change in the value measured between the *previous close* to *today's close*. This period is subdivided into two line items; *previous close* to *today's open*, and *today's open* to *today's close*. How the open curves are produced differs across institutions. If the open curves are produced as explained in section 6.1.10 then the overnight carry value is synonymous with interest and reflects the fact that each future cashflow is one day closer to realisation and therefore each future cashflow is valued with a slightly different DF. *New trading activity* captures all of the items associated with actions of entering or terminating trades on the given day. And *closing values* are determined as the sums of the items above.

We highlight the transfer of PnL as an effective dividend to a governing entity. This is the isolation step and ensures that any profits or losses made do not generate interest directly for the derivatives portfolio. Profits paid as cash sums to the governing entity can generate interest instead for the governing entity, but, in practice, these profits will likely end up paying for staff wages or other administrative costs, shareholder dividends, and other corporate investments, as the business sees fit to optimally allocate its capital.

---

[2] see section 6.1.10 for important information about open and close curves
[3] see example 23.6 for an imposed cost–of–carry item

5.2 Collateral

5.2.1 Introduction

Collateral is an obligation attached to some derivative contracts. It is done so with the expressed purpose of mitigating one party against loss in the event of a default by the counterparty. The party holding the collateral is protected or insured, for want of a better term. In practical terms collateral means the cash or other financial asset that one party, with the liability side of the derivative, posts to the respective counterparty, possessing the equivalent asset side. The amount of collateral posted depends on the PV of the IRD between those parties, and the terms of the contract as to how much collateral should be posted, and in what form.

An important and historically significant development, that became apparent during the financial crisis that began in 2007, was that of collateral management. Assets and liabilities needed more accurate valuation in terms of their true attainable value other than inherent assumptions. Consider the following example to put this in context.

Example 5.3.
Day 1: Alpha reports a PnL of $710,000 due to the following two trades.
Alpha pays $100mm 5y IRS @ 2.0% to Bravo collateralised with USD cash.
Alpha receives $100m 5y IRS @ 2.15% from Delta, uncollateralised.

Day 2: Global event moves rates 100 bps lower.
Alpha records the IRS with Delta as an asset worth $5.51mm.
Alpha records the IRS with Bravo as a liability of $4.8mm.

Although accounting wise Alpha still records the same profit it cannot source funds to post $4.8mm collateral to Bravo, because the asset with Delta is specifically uncollateralised. Alpha defaults on its obligations, which could lead to bankruptcy, and lead to subsequent problems for Bravo.

Example 5.3 is simplified but demonstrates how a destructive chain of events can start. One party, who is unable to meet their contract obligations, may force another party to fail to meet their own obligations and thereby creating the collapse of multiple entities. The expression *too big to fail* was coined in the crisis and simply means that an entity's influence over others is so great that its failure could create a catastrophic chain of failures leading to the collapse of the financial system. Since 2007, regulators and governments have imposed much stricter controls in the hope of limiting such eventualities. Clearing is now much more prevalent and, specifically, banks must hold sufficient capital to be able to weather such incidents, measured in terms of accounting ratios and satisfying defined stress tests. This is expanded in chapter 17.

5.2.2 Credit support annexes (CSAs)

A CSA is a legal document which regulates collateral posting for derivative transactions. It is one of the four parts that make up an ISDA master agreement drawn up between two counterparties, but it is not mandatory. It is possible to have an ISDA agreement without a CSA but normally not a CSA without an ISDA agreement. The terms of a CSA usually specify all of the following criteria:

Type of collateral: cash, bonds (government or corporate), strips, bills, stocks, etc.

Currency of collateral: EUR, USD, GBP, JPY, etc.

Country of collateral (if applicable): UK, DE, US, JP, etc.

Thresholds: the asset value above that whereby parties exchange collateral.

Frequency of exchange: daily, weekly, monthly revaluations etc.

Bilateral or unilateral: whether only one party is required to post collateral.

Remuneration: the rates of interest paid for cash collateral. Where unspecified in this book assume local currency RFR rates.

Haircuts: the additional collateral required above the asset value when posting value-at-risk securities such as bonds and stocks.

Other clauses: such as the permissibility of the posting counterparty to switch collateral type or post multiple types of collateral. Or, the permissibility of the receiving counterparty to re-use, or rehypothecate, the collateral to satisfy their own collateral obligations on other trades.

5.2.3 Pricing derivatives with different CSAs

If all derivative contracts with the same headline parameters were valued equivalently, irrespective of their CSA agreements, this would lead to a concept of collateral arbitrage. By means of an example we seek to make this statement much clearer.

Example 5.4. *Derivative contract: €5bn IRS @ 1.5% start-1w tenor-3m*
Alpha has bought and sold this contract with Bravo and Charlie respectively, and current market rates are 1.0%.

Counterparty	Direction	Asset PV	CSA
Bravo	Paid fixed	€-6.23mm	Cash(EUR,USD)@OIS, weekly
Charlie	Received fixed	€ 6.23mm	Cash(EUR)@OIS, weekly

The t+0 EURUSD FX rate is 1.2500 and the 1w XCS EUR/USD OIS spread is +22bps.

*The terms of the CSAs for each contract are different. The collateral received by Alpha from Charlie will necessarily be EUR cash. But with respect to Bravo, Alpha has two choices; either Alpha can post the same €6.23mm as collateral, leaving a net zero position and no PnL at the end of one week **or** Alpha can receive €6.23mm 1W XCS trade at +22 bps and post $7.7875mm. This latter case is more complicated but if executed Alpha's cashflows would all net to give rise to a €260.5 profit. The table below documents each stage.*

Date	Ccy	Amount	Description
t+0	EUR	€ 6.23mm	Charlie posts to Alpha
t+0	EUR	€-6.23mm	XCS notional exchange
t+0	USD	$ 7.7875mm	XCS notional exchange
t+0	USD	$-7.7875mm	Alpha posts to Bravo
t+1w	EUR	€-X	Alpha pays €OIS interest to Charlie
t+1w	EUR	€ (X+260.5)	Alpha receives €OIS+22bps on XCS
t+1w	USD	$ Y	Bravo pays $OIS interest to Alpha
t+1w	USD	$-Y	Alpha pays $OIS on XCS
t+1w	EUR	€ 6.23mm	XCS notional exchange
t+1w	EUR	€-6.23mm	Alpha returns to Charlie
t+1w	USD	$ 7.7875mm	Bravo returns to Alpha
t+1w	USD	$-7.7875mm	XCS notional exchange

The arbitrage in the example came about because it proved to be better for Alpha to post USD cash collateral to Bravo, having swapped it from EUR. We say that USD cash is the **CTD collateral**. In order to adhere to the *no arbitrage principle*, the valuation of these example IRSs have to become CSA aware, so the IRS with Bravo should be valued €260.5 higher. More generally, the valuation of derivative contracts, to be measured accurately, must be dependent on the terms of the associated CSAs. It should also be assumed that a counterparty will always post, where one has an option, the CTD collateral, being the most economic choice.

Consider another example to highlight this topic.

Example 5.5.
Delta has a derivative liability valued at £100mm and £100mm in cash. The terms of the CSA on the derivative require GBP cash (remunerated at RFR) or UK gilts to be posted as collateral. The specified haircuts set by the CSA are 2% for gilts less than 5Y in maturity and 6% for gilts greater than 5Y in maturity.

The market repo rate on any gilt is RFR+8bps with no haircut and the RFR rate is 0.75%. Delta can, however, only borrow unsecured cash at a rate of 2.5%, which creates borrowing costs.

Delta's Strategy	Posted	Remuneration	Costs	1D Total
Post GBP cash	£100mm	@0.75% is £2055	£0	£2055
Borrow £2mm & reverse repo any gilt < 5Y maturity	3Y gilt £102mm	@0.83% is £2319	£-137	£2182
Borrow £6mm & reverse repo any gilt ≥5Y maturity	15Y gilt £106mm	@0.83% is £2410	£-411	£1999

The CTD is gilts less than five year maturity even with the inclusion of a haircut specified in the terms of the CSA.

5.2.4   Cheapest to deliver (CTD) discount curves

We have now observed that to satisfy the no arbitrage principle, the valuation of any derivative must be calculated using discount factors built specifically for the type of collateral under the terms of the CSA. Example 5.4 highlights the importance of XCSs when making this assessment for CSAs which permit different currencies, and example 5.5 highlights the importance of prices which allow comparison of different types of collateral within the same currency. In chapter 7 we discuss how to construct the individual discount curves for each collateral currency or type (otherwise termed single-CSA discount curves), which is quite an involved process.

Here, we *suppose* the existence of single-CSA discount curves and illustrate a way to combine these individual curves. By combining the individual curves we create a discount curve for a CSA that permits multiple choices (otherwise termed a **multi-CSA discount curve**). Combining single-CSA curves is the less difficult process of selecting the cheapest daily rate from any of the individual curves, and progressively building up a new one. This is essentially a bootstrapping process constructed one day after the next.

Example 5.6.
*Suppose that two single-CSA discount curves exist, containing DFs for any **JPY cashflow** under the terms of either a JPY cash only, or a USD cash only CSA. Then, we form the multi-CSA discount curve for a choice of either JPY or USD cash by taking the highest attainable daily rate each day:*

Date	JPY CSA. DF	JPY CSA. O/N Rate	USD CSA. DF	USD CSA. O/N Rate	JPY+USD. DF	JPY+USD. O/N Rate
t+0	1.000000	2.00%	1.000000	**2.10%**	1.000000	**2.10%**
t+1	0.999945	2.05%	0.999942	**2.10%**	0.999942	**2.10%**
t+2	0.999889	**2.15%**	0.999885	2.10%	0.999885	**2.15%**
t+3	0.999830	**2.20%**	0.999827	2.10%	0.999826	**2.20%**
t+4	0.999770	etc.	0.999769	etc.	0.999766	etc.

In order for the collateral posting institution to achieve the cheapest rate it will either; have USD cash available initially and post that for two days, then request its return, swap it for JPY cash via a XCS (or practically an FX swap) and then post JPY for the last two days, or, it will have JPY cash available initially but swap it for USD cash via a XCS (or FX swap) and post that for two days, then request its return, complete the XCS and post the remaining JPY for the final two days. The no arbitrage principle and pricing methodologies ensure that these two scenarios are equivalent.

In this example two single-CSA discounting curves for JPY cashflows have produced a third *basic* or *intrinsic* multi-CSA discount curve for JPY cashflows. The necessary assumption is that of executing XCS transactions to secure the prevailing rates. Expanding, we would see that three single-CSA curves could combine in four different ways and ten could produce a total of one thousand and twelve possible multi-CSA curves. Clearly for any institution to value its derivatives properly it must be able to;

(i) automate construction of all single-CSA curves for use with cashflows of a particular currency, JPY say in the above example,

(ii) have automated processes to combine single-CSA curves to produce new, required multi-CSA curves for cashflows in that same currency,

(iii) extract information about specific CSAs on individual derivative contracts to determine which discount curve to use to value and price that derivative contract accurately.

Actually doing all of the above is an operationally difficult task for financial institutions, which is why true valuations of all derivative assets and liabilities are potentially inaccurate or subject to some form of collateral valuation adjustments, as a way of approximating their true value. These types of adjustments are created usually when computer systems are not sophisticated enough to handle all of the information in real time or in an integrated way. Notwithstanding the complexity of valuation, practical collateral management is also an operationally challenging endeavour, as was highlighted in example 5.6. Thus, some theoretic asset values might not necessarily be completely attainable. Nor, might a liability realise its theoretic loss value, particularly if the counterparty is unable to practically post the supposed CTD collateral.

Traders, however, should be expected to be aware of all of these issues and produce accurate and timely valuations even when systems are inferior. They must be confident in their own models and calculations as this is often a large source of variation of pricing derivatives from institution to institution or trader to trader. Sometimes estimation and judgement is required which, in turn, requires a fundamental understanding of how cheaper or more expensive collateral assumptions will affect the PV of certain derivatives.

5.2.5   Standard CSAs for benchmark valuation

Against a backdrop of potentially thousands of discount curves to value derivatives, it is sensible to choose one as a benchmark. Preferably, this should be the one that is the attached CSA to the majority of derivatives in any portfolio.

Handily, all cleared trades will have the same CSA by product and it is very sensible to use this as the benchmark CSA because clearing of trades is prevalent for many counterparties, and encompasses the vast majority of traded derivatives. The standard terms of these CSAs are:

Type of collateral: cash.

Currency of collateral: locally specific to the product, e.g. a GBP IRS will be GBP.

Thresholds: zero, exchange on any liability.

Frequency of exchange: daily.

Bilateral or unilateral: bilateral.

Remuneration: RFR.

Having a benchmark makes it easier to compare between non-standard and standard CSAs. In turn this allows measures of CSA risk and CSA PnL, separable from other types of market risk and market PnL.

It is worth highlighting that the valuation difference between non-standard CSA trade valuations and benchmark CSA valuations is sometimes called the CVA, standing for collateral valuation adjustment. Whilst this may be appropriate terminology in certain contexts it should not be confused with the same acronym commonly used to describe credit valuation adjustment. In this book any reference to CVA is specifically for credit valuation adjustments.

5.2.6   Optionality

When a CSA exists that allows one or both parties to post multiple currencies or multiple types of collateral, and switch the collateral at any time, there exists an inherent option available to the institution that is posting. This is the same as the institution who holds the liability side of the derivative.

Example 5.7.
Consider a scenario where one party has a derivative liability and has a CSA which allows the posting of cash collateral in any of the currencies, GBP, EUR or USD. Suppose that all currencies are as cheap as each other, and to the benchmark, to post initially, but that after a period of time, due to market movements, they are either cheaper (+) or more expensive (-) than the benchmark collateral to post. The likelihood of any individual currency becoming cheaper or more expensive relative to the benchmark is the same.

Currency	1	2	3	4	5	6	7	8
GBP	+	+	+	+	-	-	-	-
EUR	+	+	-	-	+	+	-	-
USD	+	-	+	-	+	-	+	-
CTD	+	+	+	+	+	+	+	-

This simple probability grid outlines eight possibilities, all equally likely in which seven of them result in cheaper collateral and only one in more expensive collateral relative to the benchmark.

The example demonstrates an asymmetric bias for the poster of the collateral. Where one has an option to post multiple currencies or types of collateral then there is a greater chance that market movements will give rise to a cheaper scenario, because one is always able to select the cheapest option regardless of which it is. When this book was first printed in 2016 the pricing of this kind of optionality was a relatively new concept, and as such had not adapted a common pricing or risk management approach across many institutions. In the subsequent years I have not closely followed the developments, albeit I know for a fact that, as of 2022, many organisations still do not recognise this at all. It is quite a complicated problem dependent upon many variables which we outline below:

Expected value: a derivative whose expected value is around zero, that is one party could equally be ITM as opposed to OTM will have minimum optionality because the option of choice is as likely to be owned by one counterparty as the other.

A derivative which is deeply OTM, and with a one-sided expected value, will have a higher optionality because the collateral choice favours the poster much more than the asset holder.

Collateral choice & time: the more choices of collateral one can post will generally increase the value of optionality, as will time to maturity because with more time usually comes a greater chance that market movements will permit a cheaper option of collateral for the poster.

Expected CTD: as well as expected value of the derivative the expected CTD collateral has an impact on the value of optionality. If the current CTD is by far the cheapest then it may be unlikely that any other type of collateral included in the CSA will ever become cheaper decreasing the value of optionality. If the choices of collateral are broadly the same cost then the optionality will be, equivalently, increased.

Market volatilities: as with any option price the expectation of more volatile market movements and the probability of changing CTDs increases the optionality value.

Frequency of exchange /switch: There can only be optionality value if the terms of the CSA permit switching of collateral to monetise changes in CTD.

Practical expectations: the posting institution has to have the practical ability to react to changes in CTD. It's all well and good having theoretically accurate pricing but if an institution does not have the systems to minimise liability values in a practical sense, then perhaps it shouldn't measure them where it does. Transaction costs will also decrease the value of optionality as the necessary hedging costs to pursue a theoretical CTD strategy may exceed the benefits of the strategy, thus must be a consideration.

Modern approaches toward CTD optionality pricing will run a simulated environment approach (Monte Carlo analysis) and assume a statistical price, with input parameters estimated for all of the above points.

To conclude this section we present table 5.1 with hypothetical assessments as qualitative illustration.

Asset PV	Tenor	CSA specification	Optionality	Reason
Zero	5y	USD+EUR cash	Zero	Expected (futute) PV $\approx$ zero
\$ 100mm	5y	USD cash	Zero	No choice of collateral
\$ 100mm	5y	USD+JPY cash	Low	e.g. JPY is clear CTD here
\$ 100mm	5y	USD+EUR cash	Medium	Optionality exists where no clear CTD
\$ 100mm	5y	USD+SEK cash	Low/Medium	Optionality exists with higher transaction costs
\$ 100mm	5y	USD+EUR+SEK	Medium/High	Greater optionality
\$ 100mm	30y	USD+EUR+SEK	High	Time to maturity

Table 5.1: A qualitative example of the valuation of optionality attached to CSAs in different scenarios.

5.2.7   Unilateral CSAs

Occasionally CSAs exists which specify only one counterparty that needs to post collateral to the other. This creates a peculiar pricing dynamic. For assets like this which are heavily ITM then it is more statistically certain that the asset is either collateralised or uncollateralised (as standard market movements are unlikely to alter this binary determination). Its value can then be assumed to be broadly equivalent to the discounting of the cashflows assumed in either the case of a collateralised derivative or an uncollateralised one.

For assets with values close to zero then the impact of a unilateral or 'one-way' CSA becomes very significant, because the binary determination is potentially subject to fluctuate with market movements. This represents a different kind of option held by the counterparty who never needs to post collateral. Modern derivative pricing should take this into account, again through scenario analysis, but it is very complex. In fact it is so asymmetric that ideas of eradicating, or renegotiating, these types of CSA often circulate so we focus no further on this topic.

5.3   Credit risk

Counterparty credit risk (CCR) and CVAs is a broad topic. Usually institutions have teams of people dedicated to understanding and managing these specifically. The quantitative literature on the topic is also detailed and broad. Good examples, which extensively expand the topics we will review are [18] and [19]. The point of this section is to give the reader a sound grasp of the principle of CCR and CVA, with examples suggesting how simple models and simple calculations would arrive at values. It is important that an all-round trader can understand how derivative pricing can be affected by the exogenous factor of counterparties defaulting.

Most importantly though, this section aims to complete the trilogy of this chapter by placing everything in context with the cash and collateral sections already explained, giving the reader an all-encompassing view on the lifecycle of derivatives and their day to day operations. It is also fundamental information needed to comprehend regulatory capital and risk weighted assets (RWAs) in chapter 17.

5.3.1 Credit exposure (CE)

CE (sometimes also called current exposure), in reference to derivatives, is defined as the immediate potential loss in the event of a counterparty defaulting on its obligations. Exchange traded or cleared derivatives can be said not to possess CE because the legal counterparty of those trades is a clearing house, and not the direct counterparty who took the other side of the trade originally. This is valid only under the assumption that a clearing house cannot default.

For bilateral trades, that is those that face the counterparty directly, there is an important difference between collateralised and uncollateralised derivatives in the context of CE. As discussed previously, collateral obviously mitigates against loss by providing security for assets, but there are a few elements which are not protected by collateral. These can be stated as follows;

(i) **collateral valuation lag.** Even the most frequent collateral exchanges can only be posted one day in arrears, after the previous day's closing valuations have been exchanged and agreed between counterparties. This lag represents the time period between the date of the valuation for the most recently submitted collateral posting and the notice of bankruptcy filing, with a potential market move in between,

(ii) **uncollateralised valuation adjustment through period of transition.** When a counterparty defaults the fair value of the asset must be ascertained by the aggrieved party, which is usually done by using official daily closing curves to provide a legal demonstration of validity ahead of liquidation proceedings. This creates a period of time where valuation changes will occur without being collateralised any further, and is taken to be the period of time between notice of bankruptcy filing and final derivative valuation, upon which a claim is submitted in the bankruptcy proceedings,

(iii) **replacement cost of risk,** which is required as the defaulted derivative contract effectively ceases to exist. The cost of replacement can be made up of bid /offer spread and misaligned timing with respect to the formalisation of the fair value claim on the original derivative, particularly if it is expected to take a reasonable amount of time to execute suitable replacement trades. Basel II and III regulations are particularly keen to stress this factor when measuring the risks on derivative assets for the purpose of regulatory reporting[2].

Basel calls the above components (in a broad sense) the **margin period of risk** [20, Annex 4].

Example 5.8.
Alpha has a collateralised derivative with Lima, hedged by collateralised derivatives with other counterparties. On the open of day zero (i.e. after the close of day -1) Lima files for bankruptcy and makes no further collateral exchanges or payments. The table illustrates a possible scenario:

STATEMENT of VALUATION close on:	Day -2	Day -1	Day 0
PV of Lima derivatives	7,100,000	8,600,000	13,100,000
Collateral posted by Lima	6,900,000	7,100,000	7,100,000
PV of replacement derivatives	-	-	-600,000
PV of other derivatives	-7,100,000	-8,600,000	-13,100,000
Collateral posted by others	-6,900,000	-7,100,000	-8,600,000
Daily market move	-1bp	-7bp	-21bp

---
[2]see chapter 17 for details of RWAs and the Basel Accords

Alpha will submit a claim to Lima's bankruptcy administrators for a total of 6mm, which represents the claim of 13.1mm minus the kept collateral of 7.1mm. The 6mm is made up of a 1.5mm collateral lag and a 4.5mm uncollateralised valuation adjustment on the day of the declared bankruptcy. In addition Alpha suffers a loss of 0.6mm due to risk replacement. If recovery rates are, for example 30% then Alpha's loss may be finalised as 4.8mm, ignoring any other costs (such as legal, operational or administrative).

A brief point for portfolios containing multiple trades with a single counterparty is that they are often subject to **netting agreements** which state that the aggregate PV of all derivatives is the value used in legal claims. Without a netting agreement the CE is usually far higher because each derivative is treated individually and a different treatment of assets compared to liabilities has large impact.

Additionally it is worthwhile noting that an institution may choose to model the valuation lag and the valuation change through transition in slightly different ways. Before notification of bankruptcy, financial markets will typically be operating normally, but after an announcement panic and consolidation may impact the liquidity of markets meaning a more conservative approach would be to consider the volatility after the notification as having increased. However, this is usually only reserved for larger, more influential organisations, such as global systemically important banks (G-SIBs) or lesser relatives.

Calculating CE becomes a task synonymous with VaR. It requires statistical analysis to make predictions about viable market movements and then to ascertain values deemed to be expected within a specific c.i.. Suppose we wish to calculate the CE which is expected to be exceeded only $\alpha\%$ of the time, that is to a $(1-\alpha)\%$ c.i., then:

$$CE_{\alpha\%} = RC_{mtm} + C_{lag,\alpha\%} + C_{tran,\alpha\%} + RC_{risk,\alpha\%} \,,$$

where,

$$RC_{mtm} := \begin{cases} 0, & \text{(if collateralised)} \\ \max\{\text{asset PV}, 0\}, & \text{(if uncollateralised)} \end{cases}$$

$$C_{lag,\alpha\%} := \begin{cases} \text{the cost of collateral lag}, & \text{(if collateralised)} \\ 0, & \text{(if uncollateralised)} \end{cases}$$

$$C_{tran,\alpha\%} := \text{the cost of valuation change through transition},$$

$$RC_{risk,\alpha\%} := \text{the replacement cost of risk},$$

with all statistical values measured to a $(1 - \alpha)\%$ c.i..

Example 5.9.
Continuing from example 5.8, at the close of day -1 Alpha considers its CE with a 95% c.i. to Lima, and calculates it to be, $CE_{5\%} = 9,200,000$:

$$RC_{mtm} := 0 \text{ (the asset is collateralised)},$$
$$C_{lag,5\%} = 1,500,000 \text{ (is an observed value)},$$
$$C_{tran,5\%} = 6,500,000 \text{ (through statistical model)},$$
$$RC_{risk,5\%} = 1,200,000 \text{ (through expected charges)},$$

At this point it is well worth flagging **recovery rates** and **loss given default (LGD)** (which are terms for the same concept). Some of the CE will generally be expected to be recovered via the liquidation of assets of the defaulting entity, and this does play a part in CVA and regulatory reporting. But, as a value, CE seeks to indicate the immediate risk to a counter-party defaulting on its obligations and it is useful as an individual metric to compare exposure on different trades or portfolios to different counterparties, without specifically factoring in or estimating the LGD.

5.3.2 Potential future exposure (PFE)

Where CE is a metric for the immediate credit exposure the potential future exposure (PFE) seeks to present a metric considering exposure in the future. The calculation of PFE requires more simulation than that necessary for CE. If one considers a specific future date, m_i, then we obtain the future CE by considering:

$$CE_{\alpha\%}(m_i) = [RC_{mtm,\alpha\%} + C_{lag,\alpha\%} + C_{tran,\alpha\%} + RC_{risk,\alpha\%}](m_i) ,$$

where the major difference is that the uncollateralised asset value, $RC_{mtm,\alpha\%}$, has to be statistically modelled as its future value is dependent upon the unknown progression of market rates. Minor differences being that the other three elements of the formula need to be statistically modelled in the context of future volatilities. For example, if one were trying to calculate the CE of a trade five years into the future then one might choose to use higher volatilities which are more conservative than those used to calculate today's CE. Once enough future dates have been assessed the reported PFE is simply the maximum of any values:

$$PFE_{\alpha\%} = \max_i \{CE_{\alpha\%}(m_i)\} .$$

We highlight to the reader that the future CE values are indeed that. We have not expressly used DFs to attain any 'present value', since it is the future value that is assessed. This is a rare instance in pricing or determining properties of derivatives where the PV of such is not necessarily the most important figure. Different institutions may express this differently.

Example 5.10.
Alpha executes a collateralised £100mm 10Y IRS with Bravo and analyses the PFE. Alpha uses the following parameters in the model;
(i) five sampled future dates as well as the immediate CE,
(ii) the expected future delta risk of the remaining swap at each date,
(iii) a predicted market volatility for the remaining swap at each date
(iv) a multiplier, DM, for the consideration of distressed markets to estimate $C^{1D}_{tran,5\%}$,
(v) no expected cost of risk replacement but a variance of 1bp of delta risk to this variable, in respect of when the replacement trade might be executed,
(vi) a c.i. of 95%.

m_i	$E[pv01]$	$Vol^{1D}_{1s.d.}$	$C^{1D}_{lag,5\%}$	DM	$C^{1D}_{tran,5\%}$	$RC_{risk,5\%}$	$CE(m_i)$
0y	£92,000	4.5bp	681,000	1.5	1,021,000	151,000	£1,853,000
2y	£75,000	5.5bp	679,000	1.5	1,018,000	123,000	£1,820,000
4y	£57,000	6.5bp	609,000	1.5	914,000	94,000	£1,617,000
6y	£38,000	6.5bp	406,000	1.5	609,000	63,000	£1,078,000
8y	£19,000	6.5bp	203,000	1.5	305,000	31,000	£539,000
10y	£0	0bp	0	0	0	0	£0
						PFE	£1,853,000

In example 5.10 the PFE is the same as the CE. This is often the case with collateralised swaps, whose delta risk profile typically declines as the swap progresses through its life. However, changing the parameters can, of course, influence the results. Fwd swaps, whose risk increases as the swap start date becomes ever closer, is another example where this is not necessarily true. Once the swap begins, though, the risk starts to decrease with each passing swap period and falls back to the above case.

Example 5.11.

Alpha pays an uncollateralised £100mm start-2Y tenor-8Y IRS with Bravo, and analyses the PFE. Alpha uses the following model parameters;

(i) five sampled future dates as well as the immediate CE,

(ii) the expected future delta of the remaining swap at each date,

(iii) Monte Carlo analysis to produce $RC_{mtm,5\%}$,

(iv) a predicted market volatility for the remaining swap at each date to estimate $C^{1D}_{tran,5\%}$,

(v) no expected cost of risk replacement but a variance of 1bp of delta risk to this variable, in respect of when the replacement trade might be executed,

(vi) a c.i. of 95%

m_i	$E[pv01]$	$RC_{mtm,5\%}$	$Vol^{1D}_{1s.d.}$	$C^{1D}_{tran,5\%}$	$RC_{risk,5\%}$	$CE(m_i)$
0y	£73,000	540,000	4.5bp	540,000	120,000	£1,200,000
2y	£75,000	12,500,000	5.5bp	679,000	123,000	£13,302,000
4y	£57,000	17,800,000	6.5bp	609,000	94,000	£18,503,000
6y	£38,000	15,200,000	6.5bp	406,000	63,000	£15,669,000
8y	£19,000	9,000,000	6.5bp	203,000	31,000	£9,234,000
10y	£0	0	0bp	0	0	£0
					PFE	£18,503,000

In example 5.11 the effect of the valuation of the swap has significant and the dominant impact. With respect to PFE the key term is **potential**. The swap is clearly not expected to have greater than £17.8mm PV four years into its life, but the potential for that to happen exists 5% of the time. If the counterparty were then to file for bankruptcy in this circumstance it would be quite unfortunate. This impact to the credit risk consideration highlights the difference between collateralised and uncollateralised derivatives. Regulators aim to capture all of these aspects when assessing RWA values for derivative trades.

5.3.3   Expected exposure (EE)

Calculating PFE required the determination of $CE_{\alpha\%}(m_i)$, which is a specific type of statistical metric of exposure at a future date measured with a specific c.i.. Another frequently used metric is to consider the expected exposure (EE) which determines the average exposure on a specific date, m_i of all simulated scenarios. Where the PFE aims to provide a kind of worst case analysis, the EE gives a more typical exposure value.

In calculations, if the exposure in a scenario is assessed to be negative, that is the derivative is in fact a liability, then the exposure in that scenario is set to be zero. This ensures that EE values always express some credit risk, and is representative of the fact that if a counterparty were to file for bankruptcy and that counterparty be owed money then that would be collected in full by the bankruptcy administrators (subject to the aforementioned netting agreement). On the other hand if the counterparty owed money itself then only a proportion might be recovered depending upon the LGD and distributed amount by the bankruptcy administrators.

Conservatively[3] speaking, we can write EE as:

$$EE = E^+[RC_{mtm}] + E^+[C_{lag}] + E^+[C_{tran}] + E^+[RC_{risk}] ,$$

---

[3]conservative since the linear addition of each element assumes no netting of individual terms

where $E^+[..]$ represents the expectation of the random variable whose value is taken to be zero if negative. Note that for a normal distribution (as an approximation) $X \sim N(0, \sigma^2)$, $E^+[X] = \frac{\sigma}{\sqrt{2\pi}}$.

Example 5.12.
For the same trade in example 5.10 Alpha assesses its EE under the same parameters;

m_i	$E[pv01]$	$Vol_{1s.d.}^{1D}$	$E^+[C_{lag}]$	DM	$E^+[C_{tran}]$	$E^+[RC_{risk}]$	$EE(m_i)$
0y	£92,000	4.5bp	165,000	1.5	248,000	37,000	£450,000
2y	£75,000	5.5bp	165,000	1.5	248,000	30,000	£443,000
4y	£57,000	6.5bp	148,000	1.5	222,000	23,000	£393,000
6y	£38,000	6.5bp	99,000	1.5	149,000	15,000	£263,000
8y	£19,000	6.5bp	49,000	1.5	74,000	8,000	£131,000
10y	£0	0bp	0	0	0	0	£0
						max EE	£450,000

Example 5.13.
For the same trade in example 5.11 Alpha assesses its EE under the same parameters;

m_i	$E[pv01]$	$Vol_{1s.d.}^{1D}$	$E^+[RC_{risk}]$	$E^+[C_{tran}]$	$E^+[RC_{mtm}]$	$EE(m_i)$
0y	£73,000	4.5bp	29,000	197,000	131,000	£357,000
2y	£75,000	5.5bp	30,000	248,000	3,000,000	£3,278,000
4y	£57,000	6.5bp	23,000	222,000	4,800,000	£5,045,000
6y	£38,000	6.5bp	15,000	149,000	3,900,000	£4,064,000
8y	£19,000	6.5bp	8,000	98,000	1,100,000	£1,206,000
10y	£0	0bp	0	0	0	£0
					max EE	£5,193,000

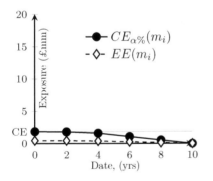
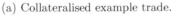

(a) Collateralised example trade.

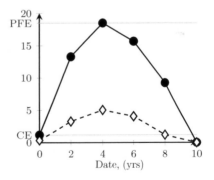

(b) Uncollateralised example trade.

Figure 5.2: Plots of the exposure data of the collateralised and uncollateralised example trades.

5.3.4 EPE, EEE and EEPE

To be consistent with the Basel III terminology [20, Annex 4], we must include three more terms.

(i) **Effective expected exposure (EEE):** on any date is the highest EE that has occurred at any point until that date.

(ii) **Effective potential exposure (EPE):** is the average across all time horizons of the EEs.

(iii) **Effective expected positive exposure (EEPE):** is the average across all time horizons of the EEEs.

The reason that these additional credit measures are used by Basel is because they believe they characterise better the risk of transactions which are subject to **rollover risk**. This incorporates a sense that transactions are likely to be extended into the future through new, on-going business.

5.3.5 Credit valuation adjustment (CVA)

With credit exposure in mind, financial institutions seek to calculate an adjustment to the market valuation of trades to reflect the chance of a counterparty defaulting and generating a loss in that scenario. Again, it is highlighted that many methods exist in practice for the determination of these adjustments. Some are more complicated and detailed than others. We can consider a standard simple model which help to present the overall idea of CVAs. Suppose that $p(m_i)$ is the modelled probability of default of the counterparty between dates m_i and m_{i+1}, then the CVA can be estimated as,

$$CVA = LGD \sum_{i=1}^{T} p(m_i) EE(m_i) v_i ,$$

where this model has chosen to adopt the EE as it base credit metric. We have also incorporated the probability of default and the LGD (or recovery ratio), which is another important estimation in the final assessment of ultimate loss if a counterparty defaulted.

Example 5.14.
Alpha calculates the CVA adjustment of both the collateralised (1) and uncollateralised (2) trades from previous examples using the suggested model, with the parameters;

m_i	0Y	2Y	4Y	6Y	8Y
(1) $p(m_i)$	0.1%	0.1%	0.1%	0.1%	0.1%
(2) $p(m_i)$	1%	0.4%	0.1%	0.1%	0.1%
v_i	1.000	0.963	0.928	0.906	0.856

Using LGD as 100%, for the collateralised trade the CVA adjustment is calculated as £1,592. In the case of the uncollateralised trade the CVA adjustment is, unsurprisingly, determined to be the much higher value of £25,593.

If a standard 40% recovery ratio, i.e. 60% LGD, were applied to these values then they might arguably be reduced by 40%.

CVAs are usually made at a counterparty level and not by each individual trade. If a counterparty were to default then the complete set of trades owned by an institution facing that counterparty would be affected simultaneously. A new trade (or an early termination of an old trade) should always be considered in the context of how it will affect the overall credit exposure of the institution to the counterparty as a whole (assuming netting set rules apply). Thus, the impact of a single trade could increase or decrease exposure dependent upon the other, current trades within the set. This is precisely the same concept as with the impact of new (or terminated) trades to RWA values of specific counterparties, which is covered in chapter 17.

The above examples all presented the information assuming that the trade in question was isolated and was the only trade in the set. Be aware that in practice, credit exposure increases or decreases might be unintuitive, as might also be the CVA, particularly without important knowledge of all of the other trades facing that same counterparty.

5.4 Funding valuation adjustment (FVA)

FVAs are the final adjustment types we discuss in this chapter. FVAs are not at all like CVAs in the sense that they have no dependence on the credit of the counterparty. Rather they are completely dependent upon the institution's own funding ability. So CVAs depend on the counterparty, factoring in the economics of what happens if they were to default, and FVAs depend on the institution, factoring in the economics of how it will manage its own funding obligations on the trade. Similar to CVAs there is a grave distinction between collateralised and uncollateralised trades when considering FVAs. Collateralised trades have little consideration because the funding of these trades is implicit. Net cashflows that are paid to one counterparty as part of regular, intermediate settlement of derivatives will necessarily be returned, by that same counterparty, to the other due to the PV of the derivative changing by the same amount. This is essentially a collateral flux. Uncollateralised trades, however are completely different; net cash outflows have to be funded and cash inflows provide an effective surplus.

When pricing an uncollateralised trade, the discount curve used to discount the cashflows is dependent upon an institution's ability to borrow or utilise cash. For example, suppose rates are very low at 0.5% and an institution is about to execute a 10Y receiver IRS at 3%. This will result in the institution getting an inflow of cash every accrual period until rates move higher nearer the maturity of the IRS when the cash starts being transferred back to the counterparty (to equate to an initial PV of zero). The cash balance profile of this trade becomes positive, much like that in figure 5.1. What does the institution do with this received cash in the meantime? Can it be invested or utilised and if so at what rate of return? This information is of the precise nature required in order to discount the IRS cashflows to price the IRS accurately. On the other hand, what if the institution were to enter the same IRS but as a payer rather than a receiver. In that instance it will give rise to a negative cash balance throughout the life of the IRS. In that scenario how will the institution raise the cash to fund the trade and at what expected cost? Again this is precisely the information needed to make a decision on how to discount the cashflows.

In practice for any large institution the rates at which it could borrow or fund cash will likely differ from those rates of return where it can utilise cash (albeit an efficient organisation might converge on an equilibrium). This creates asymmetry. It is not sensible to price an uncollateralised IRS with just one discount curve because it depends upon the direction of the trade. And, for more complicated IRSs it may depend on more parameters than even the direction.

The solution to the slightly complicated scenario is to invent the FVA. The technique allows an uncollateralised trade to be priced using a single, benchmark uncollateralised discount curve and then the FVA is an after pricing adjustment which takes account of the likely cash balance of the institution and its applicable rates of funding. All institutions will manage this differently and have a specific way of pricing the flows in conjunction with all of the ways cash is managed as part of on going business.

It is advantageous to have offsetting positions, for example paying uncollateralised cash on some derivatives and receiving uncollateralised cash on others. This reduces funding risk and allows an institution to be in a position of engaging new business in either direction. If an institution is heavily prepositioned in one direction their FVAs will be skewed to promote new business that mitigates the current trades and essentially prohibits new business that adds to the existing stock of similar trades[4].

---

[4]see chapter 18 on pricing trades for more information on this type of effect

Single Currency Curve Modelling

Curves make viable, and are the backbone of all derivative pricing techniques. Previous chapters have assumed that curves exists for their practical uses but this chapter explores how one goes about creating them. This chapter is more about explaining the concepts and chapters 11 and 12 demonstrate some quantitative implementations, involving the mathematical issues that arise.

It is important to make one general distinction early on. The term *curve modelling* can have slightly different meaning in different contexts; either it means **establishing the mechanical process** that will generate RFR rates used for the pricing of linear IRDs, *or* **constructing approximate, analytical mathematical models** (of which there are many varieties) aimed at reflecting or proxying the movement in rates, often for use with deriving solutions to stochastic differential equations (when pricing swaptions or other structured products), or more theoretical financial applications.

This chapter *does not* discuss this analytical side of constructing mathematical models to represent curves. This aspect has been well covered in the material [3], and therefore is not replicated. The focus here is on practical construction and the decisions involved in determining the mechanical process. It is worth highlighting that the mathematical models aim to reflect the movement of these true mechanically generated curves, which themselves reflect the market prices of basic IRDs.

Complacency tends to exist in this field because it is quite easy to generate curves poorly, without being able to observe their weaknesses. It is rather much more difficult to design curves well and that permit accurate interbank trading. In this chapter the items covered are;

 (i) underlying properties, or foundations, of IR curves,

 (ii) what types of curves are produced and the need for synchronous relationships,

 (iii) degrees of freedom and calibrating parameters,

 (iv) interpolation techniques for unspecified points of curves,

 (v) practical considerations of the curve's use affecting its design,

 (vi) trader's considerations when relying on curves to price derivatives.

6.1   General curveset construction

6.1.1   Introduction and principles

Curves exist to provide interested parties with the knowledge of, for any date in the future, both of the following; the DF for that date (using a particular CSA for discounting) or a forecast RFR rate (which can be compounded together to produce an RFR tenor period). This is their basic, simple premise.

In this chapter we will examine the most important points when creating curves for use in only a single currency, and do *not* consider the implications of the XCS market, nor of CSAs in alternate currencies. This we leave to chapter 7. Since the transition from IBOR creating curvesets has become simpler since the task involves the construction of only a single curve, the RFR curve. Previously *curveset* referred to the collection of OIS and IBOR curves for all tenors of IBOR index (e.g. 1M, 3M, 6M, 12M etc. which were all distinct curves with their own inherent basis). Here *curve* and *curveset* are semantically the same and we should technically only use the word *curve* in this reformed chapter.

Readers completely new to the concept of curve construction and trading IRDs with respect to them will do well to consider the below list of requirements, or design parameters included in figure 6.1 .

A curve should...

(i) be **time synchronised** with the instruments that parametrises it and with other relevant curves, see section 19.2,

(ii) be **calibrated to market instruments** and be able to replicate any mid-market price, see section 11.3,

(iii) be **numerically efficient** to calculate and derive, for an example see section 12.7,

(iv) be **practically maintainable** and **transparent** so that a trader can, for example, manually update it in markets that are less liquid and so that a trader is aware of its limitations and control structure, see chapter 19,

(v) consider **means of hedging** with respect to risk and profit and loss management, see section 9.3.2,

(vi) possess **inherent structure** to minimise internal volatility, i.e. 6Y expected to be proportional to 5Y and 7Y as an example, see section 12.3,

(vii) be **useful for market analysis** and not just for pricing, e.g. to provide valid historical data for chapters 14 and 15,

(viii) be **robust to the passage of time**, i.e. if a week passes the interpolation structure should still yield consistent interpolated values for the equivalent input parameters, see section 12.5.2.

Figure 6.1: Considerations for the construction of a curve.

6.1.2 Foundation of a curve

The foundation of any any single curve within a set of curves establishes how we are going to represent it mathematically. It can be designed with one of only two sensible bases; **DFs** and **forecast rates.** For RFRs, actually the two foundations are the same since there is a one-to-one equivalence, but for previous IBOR curves this was not the case. The material here is maintained for historical significance, and to illustrate the point.

DF based curves

This is the oldest and traditionally used approach. This type of curve will assign a DF for each future date on the curve and then, from that information, an appropriate rate can be determined between two given dates. This means that there is a mathematical equivalence between the rates implied by the curve and the DFs it contains.

In order to derive an implied rate from a DF based curve use the following formula;

$$r_i = \frac{1}{d_i} \left(\frac{v_{i-1}}{v_i} - 1 \right) ,$$

for m_{i-1}, m_i the value start date and value end date respectively of the appropriate tenor rate under consideration. To calculate, for example the forecast RFR for a particular day one need only take that day's DF and the subsequent DF (not on a holiday) and derive the rate. **We will use this DF based approach for our RFR curve construction.**

Forecast rate based curves

Forecast rate based curves are entirely different and designed for IBOR indexes. They produce only a specific index rate attributable for any future date, with that rate being the designated purpose of the curve. For example a 3M-$LIBOR curve will produce the set of all 3M-$LIBOR rates. This type of curve cannot have any DFs, due to mathematical inconsistencies. Consider the example:

Value Date	Value End Date	Rate	Start DF	End DF (implied)
12-Dec-2016	Mon 13-Mar-2017	1.6100%	0.99500	0.99102
13-Dec-2016	Mon 13-Mar-2017	1.6120%	0.99495	0.99101 !

The mathematical inconsistency here arises due to weekends and holidays which affect value end dates so that sometimes two or more forecast rates have the same end date and there is **not** a unique DF which, given their start DF, satisfies all. Implementing forecast rate based curves negated the problem of resulting in spurious IBOR rates derived from those *repeated* DFs.

6.1.3 Collection of curves

A curveset contains more than one curve, all of which need to be synchronised with each other according to the specified market data. Synchronisation is an important property of a curveset because without it pricing of derivatives will be timing inconsistent and will result in inaccurate prices. A typical curveset in a single currency for use in general trading will contain the following curves;

  (i) RFR curve,

 (ii) discounting curves: benchmark CSA, and uncollateralised or other forms.

(iii) central bank rate curve,

(iv) (**obsolete** IBOR curves: 1M, 3M, 6M, 12M)

6.1.4 Market data and knots

Building a curveset that is accurate to the market requires knowledge of some of the market prices as inputs to the curveset. One must be careful which prices to choose as inputs. If too many inputs are chosen the curveset risks being overspecified and it can be very difficult to calibrate the curve if some of these inputs have to be manually and synchronously updated, such as those prices which are voice brokered. If too few inputs are chosen, as in the curve is underspecified, then parts of the curve may be subject to other model assumptions and might not reflect the prices of real market trades.

The preferred, modern day method is to numerically solve curvesets. The 'bootstrapping' method (which we don't discuss) is particularly old and although a useful exercise for those new to the concept is, in my opinion, obsolete. This is because for implementing the more complicated features and flexibility of a curveset it is either impossible or far more complicated than a numerically iterative solution. To solve numerically then, our curve must have what are termed *knots, nodes, or pillar dates* depending upon author, with each knot typically representing a degree of freedom on a specific date of a curve for the numerical solver. Knots do not have to be positioned in exactly the same location as that implied by the calibrating input instruments but it is known that some general knot placements can lead to ill-constrained curves[1]. In chapter 12 we will cover this in greater detail, and better define our terms *nodes* and *knots* in that chapter. Prior to that chapter, knots and nodes are treated synonymously, but following that chapter knots are referenced only in the context of spline interpolators.

The below is a list of guidelines that would be expected of any curveset design, following the design parameters of figure 6.1;

(i) the most liquid, interbank products should be included as benchmarks (these make up the majority of the important input prices),

(ii) exchange traded products should be included (these usually fall in the above category as being the most liquid and they are also electronic which allows immediate and automatic feedback),

(iii) the further the maturity of the curve the sparser the inclusion of inputs becomes (because more products are usually traded at the shorter end of the curve requiring it to be calibrated to a greater degree),

(iv) each currency will usually have its own nuances meaning each curve design in each currency may have to be different to be optimally suited,

(v) the RFR curve will serve as the forecast curve and default curve for discounting benchmark CSA cashflows,

6.1.5 Interpolation styles of a curve

Between the knots, we must use interpolation techniques to derive all of the other values on all other dates that make up the curve. Additionally one may choose to employ one style of interpolation for one part of the curve, for example the first year, and then switch to use another, which is what we construct in chapter 12. Here we outline some of the most commonly used interpolation styles, and have neglected what are, in my opinion, outdated styles. Interested readers could readily research other interpolation styles online or design new ones which may very well be equally valid.

DF interpolation: log-linear or log-cubic

The common approach here is to either linearly interpolate the logarithm of DFs between knot dates or create a cubic spline function between the logarithm of the DFs. If a log-linear approach is adopted it results in constant overnight (O/N) rates for that curve between knot dates, and also produces curves whose tenor forecast rates have an approximate linear interpolation between knot dates, provided they are tightly spaced.

A log-cubic spline approach, which has the additional constraint that the first and second derivatives of the $log(DF)$ function are also required to be continuous at each knot produces a much smoother curve. The resulting O/N rates are smooth throughout and do not have discontinuous jumps at knot points unlike the case with log-linear. But this smoothness comes with a caveat; it also means that the curve becomes globally dependent so that changes to any input parameters may impact the interpolation of any part of the global curve.

6.1.6 Numerical solver

In order to generate a curve where the position of each knot is such that all of the input prices are returned exactly or as closely as possible, requires a numerical solver. In institutions, any numerical solver will have been specifically created and coded for the specific task of solving

---

[1] see for example section 12.9.2

curvesets, with speed and accuracy of pivotal importance in equal measure. Numerical solvers rely on techniques to iterate through multiple solutions (or guesses) trying to improve the accuracy each time and can be complex and specific. We build our own curve solver using various iterative algorithms such as gradient descent, Gauss-Newton and Levenberg-Marquardt in section 11.3.

6.1.7   Risk consideration

One of the major considerations to modelling and constructing a curveset is hedging. If any curve is so complicated in its design that priced and traded products cannot be confidently or knowingly hedged with liquid, benchmark interbank trades then the curveset is not really fit for the purpose of trading. In that case, the determination to produce such an accurate pricing curve has sacrificed the ability to risk manage traded products. Certain curve properties, such as turns (explained later), are examples of items that are complicated and difficult to hedge but must be captured by a pricing curve. This was much more important for obsolete IBOR curves and the impact to RFRs is more muted. Other complicated effects become subjective assessments by traders, whether they feel it is better to price and sacrifice the hedging ability, or neglect them to provide risk models which better capture the PnL of market movements. Chapter 9 seeks to expand on this from the point of view of introducing the concept of risk.

6.1.8   Practical example

[2]To bring together all of the previous aspects to demonstrate the concepts of curve design we use a numerical example. The curves here demonstrate, nicely, the differences when the different interpolation styles are used. Table 6.1 outlines all of the parameters that are used in this specific curveset.

Model consideration	Details
Curves in set:	RFR which also serves as the benchmark CSA DF curve.
Foundation:	DF based.
Input instruments:	3M RFR tenor rate starting t+0, IMM RFR IRSs on next 8 IMM dates, 3Y, 5Y, 7Y, 10Y IRS rates
Knot placement:	9 knots at start and maturity of IMM IRSs, 4 knots at the maturity of each IRS.
Interpolation style:	One curve created with log-linear, another curve created with log-cubic, a final curve with a mixed interpolation.
Numerical solver:	Chapter 11 and 12's Python solver.

Table 6.1: An overview of the model parameters for a simple dual curveset.

Table 6.2 shows all of the numerical data including the solved knots and plots the resultant curves of each curveset. The curvesets are distinctly different but all are equally valid since they reprice their inputs completely. This of course raises the question as to which is the better

---

[2]the code repository[21] contains a notebook which replicates the example here for the market data given in table 6.2

Input instruments and market prices

Deposit		IMM Swaps		IRSs	
Start	Rate	Start	Rate	Tenor	Rate
1-Jan-22	1.00%	15-Mar-22	1.05%	3Y	1.68%
		15-Jun-22	1.12%	5Y	2.10%
		21-Sep-22	1.16%	7Y	2.20%
		21-Dec-22	1.21%	10Y	2.07%
		15-Mar-23	1.27%		
		21-Jun-23	1.45%		
		20-Sep-23	1.68%		
		20-Dec-23	1.92%		

Curve knots and numerically solved values

	RFR DFs		
Date	Log-Lin	Log-Cub	Mixed
1-Jan-22	1.000000	1.000000	1.000000
15-Mar-22 $v_1 =$	0.998028	0.998014	0.998028
15-Jun-22 $v_2 =$	0.995393	0.995379	0.995393
21-Sep-22 $v_3 =$	0.992409	0.992391	0.992409
21-Dec-22 $v_4 =$	0.989547	0.989530	0.989547
15-Mar-23 $v_5 =$	0.986809	0.986785	0.986809
21-Jun-23 $v_6 =$	0.983455	0.983420	0.983455
20-Sep-23 $v_7 =$	0.979919	0.979881	0.979919
20-Dec-23 $v_8 =$	0.975832	0.975794	0.975832
15-Mar-24 $v_9 =$	0.971539	0.971426	0.971537
1-Jan-25 $v_{10} =$	0.950978	0.950978	0.950978
1-Jan-27 $v_{11} =$	0.900403	0.900403	0.900383
1-Jan-29 $v_{12} =$	0.857393	0.857432	0.857419
1-Jan-32 $v_{13} =$	0.814368	0.814484	0.814464

RFRs for each curve interpolation style

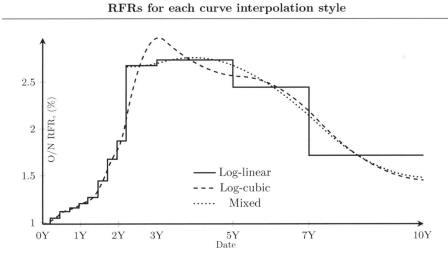

Table 6.2: Data for the modelled curveset and numerically solved values.

curveset to adopt, considering each's implication on the accuracy of risk and the accuracy of pricing. I prefer the mixed style for reasons explained in chapter 12.

6.1.9 Accuracy and value considerations

Since there are a variety of approaches and potential model choices, (e.g. interpolation styles, knot points, calibrating instruments etc.) there is a degree of **model uncertainty**. Some prices, or curve segments, will be subject to more model uncertainty than others. For example it is almost assured that a liquid 10Y IRS rate is an input to any curve model and therefore, with clarity over the market price, it will differ only marginally, if at all, across models.

Confidence in a curve might give a trader an edge to take advantages of market prices he perceives to be inaccurately priced by others. On the other hand, a trader whose prices are outliers because his curve model, even due to sound reasoning, is considerably different to all of the other traders in the market might find himself at a disadvantage.

Curve models tend to have the greatest model uncertainty at points which are about local maxima or minima, or the midpoint of convex or concave sections between knots. Figure 6.2 illustrates this, as well as the previous example of our constructed curves. Chapter 18 explores the theoretical impact of this non-transparency of prices in terms of market-maker margins, and also of prices amidst the context of the market.

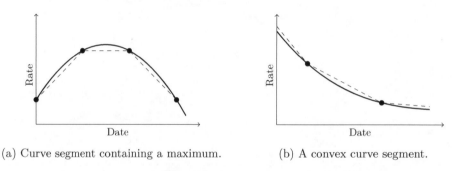

(a) Curve segment containing a maximum.   (b) A convex curve segment.

Figure 6.2: Highlighting common points of variation across curve models.

6.1.10 Opening and closing curvesets

Opening (or open) curvesets and closing (or close) curvesets are at least two curvesets that are generally saved each trading day. They represent 'snapshots' of curvesets at pre-determined times. The closing curveset of a given currency is usually measured at 1615hrs local time. The time synchronicity of all currencies and all other instruments is important to provide a consistent measure of cross market hedges. We won't expand much on the closing curveset in this section. Although the closing curveset is the most important curveset from the point of view of assessing the daily MTM value and collateral exchange of the traded positions in trading books[3], it is only a copy of the live pricing curveset measured at a certain instant in time. This means its construction is precisely the same as the theory laid out in this chapter so, in essence, this entire chapter so far provides information relevant to constructing closing curvesets. It is often benchmarked against broker screens to assure that its accuracy falls within a tolerance to interbank traded market levels. It is especially important from a regulator's and accountant's perspective emphasised at quarter and year ends.

The opening curveset, on the other hand, is less well defined and not benchmarked. The opening curveset is usually constructed from the previous day's closing curveset but structurally altered to represent the start of the next trading day. Opening and closing curvesets are fundamentally different from each other in their purpose and important for reliable calculations

---

[3]see example 5.2 to demonstrate the line item entries in daily PnL reports that are impacted

of PnL . It is more an internal design choice and is different across financial institutions. This section is specifically about generating opening curvesets - what is correct and what is incorrect regarding their construction.

In my experience there are two common approaches to building opening curvesets. One of which is flawed and should be replaced by the other more robust method. We discuss the flawed method first since it is older, simpler and surprisingly common.

An opening curveset constructed from the previous close's input prices

This is the simplest method because it does nothing more than generate an opening curveset by taking, for the input instruments, the same prices as were used for the input instruments to generate the previous day's closing curve. This introduces two sources of inconsistency:

(i) **Misaligned date schedule:** the specification of the input instruments from one day to the next is different (i.e. a 10Y IRS today does not have the same accrual, reset, or payment schedule as a 10Y IRS defined as of the previous day). This adjustment inherently introduces an amount of roll-down[4], albeit it is erroneously introduced due to the nature of ignoring the change in accrual schedule.

(ii) **An unintended distinction between fwd and par tenor (referring to derivatives starting imminently with standard tenors) (par) instruments:** if all the input instruments' prices are reused then par instruments suffer the above problem but certain fwd instruments, like IMM rates, do not, because their date schedule specification does not change from day to day. This means that *this* opening curve inconsistently treats some sections of the curve differently to other sections, by inherently introducing roll-down or not doing so.

The result of this means that *this* opening curveset can lead to bad decisions when it is assumed to be accurate. Consider the fact that introducing any arbitrary intermediate curveset between the closing curvesets of one day and the preceding day will not affect the total daily MTM change between those two closing measurements. But, labelling that arbitrary curve as the opening curveset creates two PnL numbers; an *overnight carry* (between the previous close and today's open), and a *daily market movement* (between today's open and close). These two components sum to give the total. Unfortunately in this instance these two components contain sizeable amounts of offsetting stochastic noise attributable to the two above issues. The size of this noise is often large and obfuscates any meaningful information from either component.

Maintaining constant fwd rates

This second method of construction creates an opening curveset where all of the rates are set to be those that were forecast, for the appropriate dates, by the previous day's closing curveset. This is a pricing consistent approach and it assumes that, between the previous day's closing curve and today's open curve, the market remains exactly the same. In particular there is **no inherent introduction of roll-down**.Technically, there may be two ways this type of opening curveset can be numerically generated. Either **DFs are scaled** or **instruments are repriced**.

When DFs are scaled the chosen input instruments are ignored completely in the process and the opening curveset is generated precisely by sampling every possible DF from the previous day's curveset and reinserting them into the opening curveset appropriately. Mechanically

---

[4]see section 23.2.2 for a description of roll-down

speaking, to preserve fwd rates on a curve that has been constructed using DFs, one must divide all of the DFs of the previous closing curve by the DF attributable to today's date (which was tomorrow's DF measured yesterday). This method also preserves the precise interpolation under the closing curves knot choices.

When instruments are repriced, the precise input instruments' prices, needed to generate the opening curveset, are calculated from the previous day's closing curveset, taking into account the different date schedules and other nuances of moving from one day to the next. This method uses the new day's interpolation scheme which may include a possible adjustment of knot points, see section 12.5.2.

As outlined, in the case where there are minor interpolation fluctuations moving from the previous day's *close* to today's *close*, because knot points or datasites have shifted, these fluctuations will either be,

i) **not** captured in opening curveset since DFs are scaled, so the attributed interpolation fluctuation PnL must be allocated to the daily market movement component, or,

ii) captured in opening curveset since instruments are repriced and the curve rebuilt, meaning the attributed interpolation fluctuation PnL is allocated to the overnight carry component.

Which way is better is subjective. I prefer allocation to overnight carry because it often permits a distinction useful for extracting information, that is impossible in the alternate (because market movements are often so large that they dominate the component in this case). This distinction is highlighted most prominently on an IMM roll, or when an input instrument is added or subtracted from the set of input instruments. On those rare, but important, days the interpolation fluctuation is greatest and the curve can also shift if the new instrument is priced differently to the previous close's estimate of the instrument's price.

6.2   Centrally cleared counterparty (CCP) adjustments

A notable evolution in recent years (post 2012) has been the development of a basis market for IRDs, and more prominently IRSs, which face one centrally cleared counterparty (CCP) versus another. The three largest CCPs being the London Clearing House (LCH), the Chicago Mercantile Exchange (CME) and the Eurex Exchange.

The form that this basis market takes is a bp spread price assigned to par tenor IRSs. One counterparty will execute an IRS with one CCP in one direction versus the same IRS in the opposite direction with another CCP: the fixed rates differing by the agreed spread price.

Example 6.1.
The table identifies some example CCP basis prices for EUR IRSs. These prices are both referenced versus LCH mid-market IRS rates, since that is (at the time of publication) the dominant clearing house for this product. IRS rates in the other two clearing houses have fixed rates higher than the LCH mid-market rate in this example.

At first glance the reader would be forgiven for considering this a rather odd notion. Why should an IRS with similar institutions, all of negligible credit risk, have significantly different prices? One might suspect that the collateral terms are different (given each CCP operates in a different country and different reporting currency) and that that effect should explain the difference, solely by the concept of CSA aware pricing. But this is, in fact, not the case at all. IRSs executed in a given currency cleared with any of the respective CCPs *have the same*

Tenor	CCP Basis (bp)
2Y	0.70
5Y	1.60
10Y	2.70

(a) EUR IRS Eurex/LCH price.

Tenor	CCP Basis (bp)
2Y	0.10
5Y	0.20
10Y	0.35

(b) EUR IRS CME/LCH price.

collateral terms (normally cash local to the product remunerated at RFR). So, again, why do they exhibit different pricing, and doesn't it breach the no arbitrage principle?

Assuming zero costs of trading this would breach the no arbitrage principle, but it does not breach the no arbitrage principle in practice because there are other costs of trading; respective costs-of-carry of each IRS[5] facing each CCP. Specifically, the margin payments that are required to be posted to each CCP. Each CCP defines their own methodology for calculating the margin amounts that any of their counterparties must post. Generally speaking these tend to be very similar, however what is noticeable are the so called "concentration charges". For example if a financial institution has a large net risk position facing the CCP (i.e. a risk position that is multiple times the expected daily executable and hedgeable volume) then that counterparty may be charged significantly higher margin amounts than would be expected through linear scaling. This is done to protect the CCP from significant losses in the event that counterparty were to default. There are also regulatory capital charges that should be considered also.

If the basis differential reached a quantity that overcame these specific costs-of-carry it would represent a genuine arbitrage opportunity so there is a limit, or a pricing window, within which these basis differentials must trade.

6.2.1 Impact of CCP basis on curve construction

The swaps traded at the different clearing houses settle against the same RFR fixing rates. It therefore warrants the question that if their mid-market prices are different how should that value be quantifiably represented, and how should one price the effect into non-observable prices like bespoke swaps or fwd swaps.

The solution is to utilise a **curve modelling approach**, where a separate curveset is created for the instrument prices derived from each CCP, acknowledging that the forecast RFRs will be different.

Suppose we are creating an ESTR curve in EUR. To do this we use the same set of calibrating instruments with their relevant prices at the different CCPs. This will produce three different curves; *EUR:1D.ESTR-LCH, EUR:1D.ESTR-EUREX, EUR:1D.ESTR-CME.*

Instrument	LCH Price	Eurex Price	CME Price
...	...	...	...
5Y	2.10%	2.116%	2.102%
...	...	...	...
10Y	2.07%	2.096%	2.0735%
...	...	...	...

We then use each of the curves to price trades designated to the respective CCPs. At the current time the LCH is by far the largest CCP in terms of traded volumes and therefore

---

[5]the reader is referred to section 23.2.1 for a full definition of costs-of-carry in the context of this book

must be assumed that this is the **source of truth**, for the true forecast RFR fixings, and will therefore be used to price generic trades outside of CCPs. The other prices are understood to suffer biases created by the cost of capital and execution charges incurred when settling through those CCPs. We discuss this a little more in the context of the market in section 18.1.

6.3 Appendix

6.3.1 Summary of interpolation styles

For an overview of the interpolation styles mentioned in this book see table 6.3.

Style	Details
DF log-linear	$log(v_i) = \left(\frac{D_{k+1}-D_i}{D_{k+1}-D_k}\right) log(v_k) + \left(\frac{D_i-D_k}{D_{k+1}-D_k}\right) log(v_{k+1})$ Constant O/N rates between knots. Locally stable and easily implemented.
DF log-cubic	$log(v_i) = \left(\frac{D_{k+1}-D_i}{D_{k+1}-D_k}\right) log(v_k) + \left(\frac{D_i-D_k}{D_{k+1}-D_k}\right) log(v_{k+1})$ $+ \left(\frac{(D_{k+1}-D_i)^2(D_i-D_k)}{(D_{k+1}-D_k)^3}\right) \alpha + \left(\frac{(D_{k+1}-D_i)(D_i-D_k)^2}{(D_{k+1}-D_k)^3}\right) \beta$ Smooth, continuous O/N rates between knots. Global dependence and complicated to implement.

Table 6.3: Summary table of some of the discussed forms of curve interpolation.

6.3.2 Log-linear DF interpolation

We show in this section that log-linear DF interpolation produces constant O/N rates obtained from resultant DFs.

Suppose for $m_k \leq m_i < m_{k+1}$, where k indexes a knot point with the respective DF, v_k, then under this interpolation style it is true that,

$$log(v_i) = log(v_k) + \frac{D_i - D_k}{D_{k+1} - D_k}\left(log(v_{k+1}) - log(v_k)\right).$$

Additionally the DF for one day after m_i is,

$$log(v_{i(+1)}) = log(v_k) + \frac{1 + D_i - D_k}{D_{k+1} - D_k}\left(log(v_{k+1}) - log(v_k)\right).$$

The O/N forward rate obtained through $v_i, v_{i(+1)}$ is,

$$r_i^{O/N} = \frac{1}{d_i}\left(\frac{v_i}{v_{i(+1)}} - 1\right),$$

which with the substitution of the exponential of the above logarithms gives,

$$r_i^{O/N} = \frac{1}{d_i}\left(\left(\frac{v_k}{v_{k+1}}\right)^{\frac{1}{D_{k+1}-D_k}} - 1\right),$$

so for any m_i between $[m_k..m_{k+1})$ the O/N rate is always the same, dependent only upon k, $k+1$.

6.3.3 Log-cubic DF interpolation

We show here firstly that the above interpolation style gives rise to quadratic CC O/N rates obtained from resultant DFs.

Under this interpolation style it is true that,

$$log(v_i) = \alpha + \beta D_i + \gamma D_i^2 + \epsilon D_i^3, \quad \text{for constants} \quad \alpha, \beta, \gamma, \epsilon .$$

Additional to this, the DF for one day after m_i is,

$$log(v_{i(+1)}) = \alpha + \beta(D_i + 1) + \gamma(D_i + 1)^2 + \epsilon(D_i + 1)^3 .$$

Then the CC O/N rate on date, m_i, is,

$$\bar{r}_i^{O/N} = \frac{1}{d_i} log\left(\frac{v_i}{v_{i(+1)}}\right) = \frac{1}{d_i}\left((\beta + \gamma + \epsilon) + (2\gamma + 3\epsilon)D_i + (3\epsilon)D_i^2\right) ,$$

which is quadratic in D_i. Given $r_i^{O/N} \approx \bar{r}_i^{O/N}$, we conclude that the O/N rate on date m_i is approximately quadratic.

Secondly, we show that the instantaneous CC forward rates before and after knot, m_k are equal, from which we infer the smooth nature of O/N rates about m_k. Because the construction is necessarily a cubic spline the derivative of each piecewise polynomial about m_k is equal, therefore,

$$\bar{r}_{k(-\Delta)}^{\Delta} = \frac{log(v_{k(-\Delta)}) - log(v_k)}{\lambda\Delta} = \frac{log(v_k) - log(v_{k(+\Delta)})}{\lambda\Delta} = \bar{r}_k^{\Delta}, \quad \text{as} \quad \Delta \to 0 .$$

Multi-Currency Curve Modelling

In section 5.2 it is shown that in order to price derivatives accurately, according to their CSAs, multi-currency curve models are required. XCSs are also one of the basic IR products that require multi-currency curve models to explicitly price them, so in this chapter we present all of the information regarding the creation of these kinds of models. Explicitly we look at;

- what forward FX rates are and what influences them,
- what XCSs really are and their relation with FX rates and collateral,
- an explicit explanation of the difference between MTM XCSs and non-MTM XCSs,
- some of the considerations of multi-currency models such as structure and curve cataloguing.

Multi-currency curve modelling is complicated in its theoretical basis. There are potentially different ways to go about explaining it but none seem to me to be especially illustrative or explicatory. Collateral and the effect of different CSAs is an important aspect of the theory but I think this represents the least clear way of explaining the concepts behind multi-currency curve pricing.

Instead, we focus on items that one might have seen before and build from there. Firstly we will discuss forward FX rates. Forward FX rates are inextricably linked to XCSs due to the no arbitrage principle. We will also show that multi-currency curve modelling, when done accurately, results in a complete set of forecast and discount curves in all currencies which price all of the IR derivatives in the market such that there is no arbitrage available anywhere, regardless of which products might be traded or under whatever CSA terms might be proposed (excluding CSA optionality as discussed in section 5.2.6).

As a historical aside, this was not always the case. As we know, mathematical models frequently start life in their simplest forms and endeavour to become more comprehensive. In the early days of IRD markets it was common for institutions to have one form of a single currency curve model for each currency and another form of multi-currency curve model, for specific currencies. These separate models were not consistent with each other. In fact, the specific term 'financial bias' or 'fin-bias', still lingers in risk management spheres today. This will be mentioned again in coming sections but this term was coined to generically describe by how much the single currency model was altered to arrive at a multi-currency model which accurately priced XCSs; therefore alluding to the separation and difference between the models. In those early days this 'fin-bias' was small and the differences tolerable from a point of view of asset and liability management, but the financial crisis bought about large changes to XCS prices. After that it became imperative to marry these models in terms of consistency.

7.1   Forward FX rates

Interest rate parity and XCSs

The classical description of forward FX rates, that which might be found online or in Wikipedia for example, is as follows.

Where two currencies have distinct interest rates, the forward FX rate will be dependent upon the immediate FX rate and those interest rates such that a parity is reached and the 'no arbitrage principle' is adhered to.

What this means is that if one currency has a higher rate of interest than another, then each day the FX rate will adjust slightly so that the 'buying' power of each currency is maintained. You can't get rich by exchanging your currency to the one with the highest interest rate and expect to be able to exchange it back to your domestic currency at the same exchange rate after accruing vast quantities of interest. Indeed, the equation for determining the forward FX rate, f_i, from the initial FX rate, f_{i-1}, under the classical approach is:

$$f_i = \frac{1 + d_i r_i}{1 + d_i^* r_i^*} f_{i-1} \, ,$$

where $d_i^* r_i^*$ is the domestic DCF and rate and $d_i r_i$ is the foreign DCF and rate.

The above formula for forward FX rates can also be presented via DFs rather than rates. As a concept I personally think it much easier to explain and characterise in terms of the interest rates in each currency, but for practical calculations the DF approach is easier to apply. In this approach, the ratio of discount factors in each currency generated from their RFR curve provides the forward FX rate dependent just on the immediate FX rate, F_0:

$$f_i = \frac{v_i^*}{v_{i-1}^*} \frac{v_{i-1}}{v_i} f_{i-1} = \frac{v_i^*}{v_i} F_0 \, .$$

(Note that the immediate FX rate settles T+0, whereas the typical FX rate that is always visible on screens, say, is the spot FX rate which settles T+2. The two rates are also linked by the above formula)

Example 7.1.
The EURUSD immediate FX rate is 1.20. An investor has $1.2mm to deposit and considers in which currency he should deposit his funds. The EUR RFR rate is 5% and USD RFR rate is 1%. He calculates the one day forward FX rate which equates both possible options:

$$f_1 = \frac{1 + \frac{1}{360}1\%}{1 + \frac{1}{360}5\%}1.20 = 1.19987 \ .$$

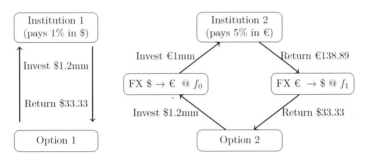

Figure 7.1: Classical argument of covered interest rate parity adhering to no arbitrage principle, demonstrating example 7.1.

Unfortunately this classical approach is not one hundred percent accurate, albeit it is an excellent starting point. There is a slight amendment that needs to be considered in this context. Suppose that rather than enact either of the options in figure 7.1 a sophisticated party engineers a third option utilising XCSs, where not only does he acquire the daily return of $33.33 but also gets an extra €27.78. See figure 7.2.

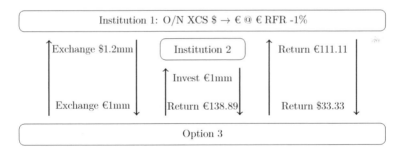

Figure 7.2: An overlay of a XCS creates an arbitrage.

The result is that to calculate forward FX rates and to truly adhere to the no arbitrage principle the interest rates and DFs inferred from the XCS market have to be used, so that instead:

$$f_i = \frac{1 + d_i r_i}{1 + d_i^*(r_i^* + z_i^*)}f_{i-1} = \frac{w_i^*}{v_i}F_0 \ . \tag{7.1}$$

notice the inclusion here of the term w_i^*, which is the DF in EUR adjusted for the XCS basis spread.

Example 7.2.
The EURUSD immediate FX rate is 1.20. The same investor has $1.2mm to deposit and considers again how to deposit his funds, this time with knowledge of the XCS market. The

USD OIS rate is 1%, EUR OIS rate is 5%, and the O/N EUR/USD OIS XCS rate is -100bps. He recalculates the one day forward FX rate:

$$f_1 = \frac{1 + \frac{1}{360}1\%}{1 + \frac{1}{360}(5\% - 1\%)}1.20 = 1.19990 \ .$$

FX swaps

The above figures and examples were crafted as demonstrations to lead to the reader into thinking about forward FX rates in combination with interest rates. In practice, for such short tenors, XCSs do not really trade. It is much more common to trade FX swaps, which represent a spot FX transaction and forward FX transaction in opposing directions. This is a liquid and established market in its own right. These FX swaps then define the forward FX rates directly in their market quotes, which are a spread of points between the initial exchange rate and the forward exchange rate. In turn these then imply DFs from which one can derive short dated XCS prices (see this chapter's appendix for relevant formulae).

The reason that XCSs are so important to the forward FX market is that they represent the only *long* term product in which one can exchange a notional currency and secure an agreed amount of interest on each leg for the term. So, *their* rates or prices are the ones which determine the comparative levels of interest payments and so determine the forward FX rates of these *longer* tenors.

As one might expect there are many factors that influence FX rates, spot or forward. Interest rates are a big factor but so too are inflation expectations or forecast central bank actions. Supply and demand dynamics from traditional flows and collateral requirements also drive the XCS prices. A good understanding of these aspects can give any rates trader a perspective of markets seen from the bigger picture, so to speak. We highlight some of these in more detail in section 8.2.2.

7.2   Cross-currency swaps (XCSs)

I appreciate that XCSs are often considered as reasonably difficult products to fathom. In some ways that is true; their mathematical formulation looks pretty horrible at first glance, they probably have the most aspects involved in their pricing, and also they are the central component in one of the more complex types of model, the multi-currency curve model. I acutely remember being in the position of not understanding XCSs at all but remember an explanation given to me many years ago which I found most helpful. Hopefully I can transcribe it over the next page or two, if their concept still seems alien to the reader at this point.

Start by considering a simple floating rate loan in a single currency. Say that one party *loans* €100 to another for 10Y and receives quarterly € ESTR interest for the length of the loan and at the end receives back €100. What is the PV of this loan? Well, of course, it depends on which discount curve to use to discount the cashflows, but say we use the same € ESTR curve to discount them (which is what institutions traditionally used to do), then the PV of that loan will be *exactly* €0, which is +€100 from future cashflows and -€100 from the immediate outflow of the loan payment.

At the same time imagine that the same party has *been loaned* $120 by that other party for 10Y, and is expected to pay quarterly $ SOFR interest and at the end repay the full $120. What is the PV of this loan? Well by the same reasoning, and discounting at $ SOFR, it must be $0.

Look back to chapter 3 and you will see that this is exactly the same structure as a non-MTM XCS, except in this case we haven't made any suggestion of a bp spread to either leg. Why? Well, in fact because under our discounting methodology the value of the transaction is precisely zero; the EUR loan is valued at zero and the USD loan is valued at zero. Any inclusion of a spread would surely create some PnL. But, XCSs usually trade with a spread (as a result of market supply and demand dynamics) so how is this compensated for? The answer, as has been alluded to in this chapter already, is using fin-bias. This means that one of the discount curves, usually the non-USD discount curve, is manually adjusted so that even with the inclusion of a bp spread the two legs (or loans in this case) would each have zero PV, and thus the mid-market XCS prices to zero.

This manual adjustment, the fin-bias, is calibrated so that it reprices the interbank XCS prices and then the PV of every other XCS in the portfolio, that have not been executed at mid-market of course, can be calculated using this specific curve. See figure 7.3.

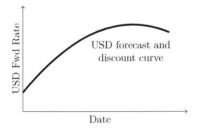 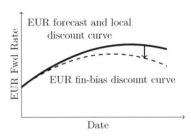

Figure 7.3: Classical multi-currency curve model. Non-USD discount curve is adjusted to satisfy the prices of XCSs.

Between 2007 and 2022, this became a more involved model. In that case a different forecast curve (IBOR) and discount curve (OIS) was required in each single currency but the discount curve still had to be evaluated to ensure the XCSs were repriced. It did so using the same fin-bias approach.

An important inclusion was really how these curves were (and are) catalogued in modern curvesets, so that the process creates a completely consistent set of discount curves that provide a means to price any CSA in use. We can show this for the **basic interbank EUR/USD XCS which has a benchmark CSA of USD cash remunerated at OIS** (note that we are referencing the obsolete IBOR indexes here);

(i) in USD there is the 3M $ LIBOR forecast curve and benchmark discount curve equal to $ OIS,

(ii) in EUR there is the 3M € EURIBOR forecast curve and benchmark discount curve, again equal to € OIS,

(iii) the € OIS curve is adjusted to create another discount curve that satisfies the XCS prices, the same as the fin-bias process before. This curve is precisely the EUR:USD-CSA discount curve, i.e. the curve to discount EUR cashflows based on a USD cash CSA.

With the transition from IBOR, RFRs now simultaneously provide both the local currency forecasting and the local currency discounting curves so this is, essentially, a reversion back to the traditional ways of pricing. We can redraw the above charts where the curves re-align yet we maintain the labelling.

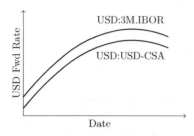 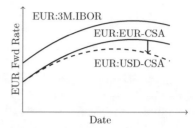

Figure 7.4: Modern multi-currency curve model. Non-USD discount curve is adjusted to satisfy the prices of XCSs, and termed the USD-CSA discount curve in that currency.

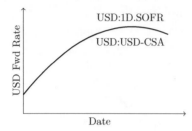 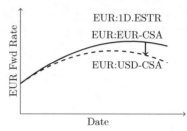

Figure 7.5: Modern multi-currency curve model, where forecast and discount curves align due to RFRs.

7.3   XCSs and collateral

Section 5.2 introduced collateral, CSAs, and the concept of discounting cashflows. Much of that chapter simply assumed the existence of discount curves for various CSAs, and it is now clear that multi-currency curve modelling is how they are created. We mentioned above the technique of cataloguing, which is a system for naming all the types of curves that are used. This is important because where multiple currencies are concerned the number of available curves spirals upwards. The cataloguing system proposed here is simple but effective;

(i) the 3-letter marker before the ':' defines the currency to which that curve is **only** applicable, that is in which currency cashflows can be discounted, or rates can be forecast,

(ii) after the colon is the descriptor, a '.' denotes a curve used for forecasting rates (which might be DF based or forecast rate based) and a '-' denotes some discounting curve (which is necessarily DF based).

Figure 7.6 provides an illustration of how a cataloguing system might work and also in which stage, via various models, each of the curves can be constructed. It perhaps looks more daunting than it actually is. It can be summed up simply as; the single currency curve models feed into the multi-currency model, which incorporates XCSs and FX swaps, and produces (finbias) adjusted discounted curves and forward FX rates. Every other curve is then constructed with a simple mathematical process from this result.

If we look at the mathematical process it is an application of the no arbitrage principle demanding that **the forward FX rates are the same regardless of under which CSA the XCSs are traded.** XCSs trade with a benchmark CSA based upon the USD-RFR, SOFR, usually. This is why we have always adjusted the non-USD discount curve in the finbias process, but if a XCS was traded, say with a EUR-RFR CSA this would not be expected

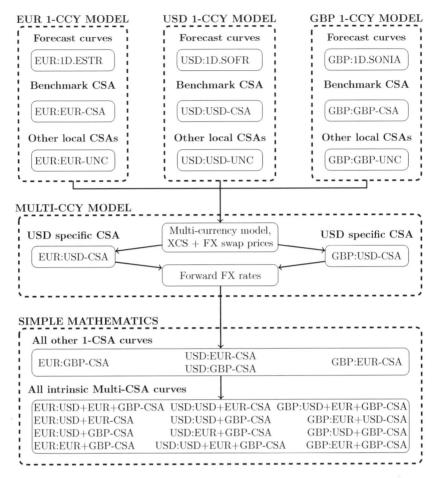

Figure 7.6: A modern multi-currency curve model configuration and cataloguing example.

to change the prediction of forward FX rates. If we write the formula for forward FX rates using DFs from earlier, but with more transparency according to our cataloguing system, this means that:

$$(\text{EURUSD})f_i = \frac{(\text{EUR:USD-CSA})w_i^*}{(\text{USD:USD-CSA})v_i} F_0 = \frac{(\text{EUR:EUR-CSA})v_i^*}{(\text{USD:EUR-CSA})w_i} F_0 \ .$$

Example 7.3.
A multi-currency curve model has used XCS prices and determined the EUR:USD-CSA curve, that is the USD-CSA discount curve for EUR cashflows. A trader requires the USD:EUR-CSA discount curve (w_i) so he can price a USD cashflow collateralised at EUR RFR. The immediate EURUSD FX rate, $F_0 = 1.20$. His calculation for three arbitrary dates is shown in table 7.1.

Figure 7.6 shows how three benchmark CSA curves, each in their respective currencies, give rise to a total of twenty one curves, seven in each of the three currencies. The need for cataloguing is quite clear. This is especially true in the context of thousands of IRDs whose individual CSAs will require a mapping to assign one of these as the 'true' discount curve to value that trade. With the push to clearing a large amount of standardisation is taking place but specific ISDA agreements with specific CSAss still exist.

	from 1-Ccy		from Multi-Ccy		Implicit
Date	v_i	v_i^*	w_i^*	f_i	w_i
$i = 1$	0.990	0.985	0.986	$1.1952 \left(\frac{0.986}{0.99} F_0 \right)$	$0.989 \left(\frac{0.99}{0.986} v_1^* \right)$
$i = 2$	0.975	0.962	0.961	$1.1828 \left(\frac{0.961}{0.975} F_0 \right)$	$0.976 \left(\frac{0.975}{0.961} v_2^* \right)$
$i = 3$	0.951	0.941	0.937	$1.1823 \left(\frac{0.937}{0.951} F_0 \right)$	$0.955 \left(\frac{0.951}{0.937} v_3^* \right)$

Table 7.1: Example calculation of cross CSA DFs.

7.4   MTM and non-MTM XCSs

What is the difference between MTM and non-MTM XCSs? The structural difference is that non-MTM XCSs have the same notional exchange at the start and at the end of the XCS, regardless of the fact of that the FX rates are normally different at the start and at the end of the swap. MTM XCSs have an interim notional exchange so that the outstanding notional on one leg, normally the USD leg, is adjusted each period to take account of evolving FX rates.

MTM XCSs are the benchmark interbank trade because they permit much more stable PVs throughout the life of the trade. In a world where collateral management and accurate derivative valuation is necessary, trading derivatives which are not forecast to represent large assets or liabilities, midway through their lives, is much preferred over those that do[1]. Firstly, MTM XCSs help to mitigate the *forecast* PV of the derivative at any point throughout its life, that is in the case that all forecast rates and forecast forward FX rates are published as initially predicted out the outset. Secondly, because the MTM component takes place as a notional exchange at the end of each period it is also reactionary to a changing FX market. This helps to dynamically mitigate the effect of the PV change of the derivative even when there might be a sizeable shift in FX rates, because the notional exchange will be adjusted according to the prevailing levels. Non-MTM XCS do not offer either of these properties and their PVs can easily become very large, particularly compared to the level of risk they actually possess which ultimately makes them capital intensive products and highly inefficient.

Although from the point of view of corporates, who usually trade these in relation to issued debt in foreign currencies they are the preferred product since they can apply **cashflow hedge accounting** to their underlying issued bond under IFRS 9 accounting rules. This mitigates the PV effect of the individual XCS, when all of their foreign currency assets are considered together as part of an accounting package.

Example 7.4.
Alpha Corp, whose domestic accounting currency is EUR, issues 5Y foreign debt to the amount of £90mm fixed at 2%, when the immediate EURGBP FX rate is 0.9000.

Alpha Corp also receives a GBP/EUR fixed (2%)/float non-MTM XCS in £90mm with an initial exchange rate of 0.9000, which fully nets its GBP cashflows.

The EUR weakens relative to GBP and the FX rate falls to 0.8000. The accounting would report:

1. *A MTM loss of €12.5mm (£10mm) on the foreign issued debt instrument,*

2. *A MTM gain of €12.5mm (£10mm) on the XCS (assuming no basis market movement).*

In this case the GBP cashflows all net out and the advantage to the corporate is that the PV of the XCS is sensitive to the full movement of the FX rates. As of 2022 few XCSs of this nature

---

[1]section 5.3 and chapter 17 detail why in terms of credit exposure and regulatory capital respectively.

are cleared which does mean that Alpha Corp (and its counterparty) have the unpleasant aspect of dealing with potentially large CVA risks and collateral management issues.

Example 7.5.
In 2017, a trader has the following information available to him from his multi-currency curve model:

Date	USD:3M.IBOR r_i	USD:USD-CSA v_i	EUR:3M.IBOR r_i^*	EUR:USD-CSA w_i^*	EURUSD f_i
0D	0.25%	1.00000	3.00%	1.00000	1.2000
3M	0.33%	0.99960	3.02%	0.99294	1.1920
6M	0.43%	0.99910	3.05%	0.98578	1.1840
9M	0.57%	0.99820	3.08%	0.97824	1.1760
12M	n/a	0.99710	n/a	0.97134	1.1690

He analyses[2] the cashflows of a €1mm EUR/USD 1Y MTM XCS priced at -1.4bps:

Date	Description	Cashflow ($)	DF	PV($) of CF
0D	Initial	-1,200,000	1.00000	-1,200,000
3M	IBOR Float + MTM exchange	8,750	0.99960	8,747
6M	IBOR Float + MTM exchange	8,983	0.99910	8,975
9M	IBOR Float + MTM exchange	9,273	0.99820	9,256
12M	IBOR Float + Final	1,177,676	0.99710	1,174,261

Date	Description	Cashflow (€)	DF	PV($) of CF
0D	Initial	1,000,000	1.00000	1,200,000
3M	IBOR Float	-7,465	0.99294	-8,895
6M	IBOR Float	-7,515	0.98578	-8,890
9M	IBOR Float	-7,590	0.97824	-8,910
12M	IBOR Float + Final	-1,007,665	0.97134	-1,174,542

Similarly, he analyses the cashflows of a €1mm EUR/USD (IBOR) 1Y non-MTM XCS priced at -1.3bps:

Date	Description	Cashflow ($)	DF	PV($) of CF
0D	Initial	-1,200,000	1.00000	-1,200,000
3M	IBOR Float	750	0.99960	750
6M	IBOR Float	990	0.99910	989
9M	IBOR Float	1,290	0.99820	1,288
12M	IBOR Float + Final	1,201,710	0.99710	1,198,225

Date	Description	Cashflow (€)	DF	PV($) of CF
0D	Initial	1,000,000	1.0000	1,200,000
3M	IBOR Float	-7,468	0.99294	-8,898
6M	IBOR Float	-7,518	0.98578	-8,893
9M	IBOR Float	-7,593	0.97824	-8,913
12M	IBOR Float + Final	-1,007,668	0.97134	-1,174,545

The trader forecasts (by summing remaining cashflows) the PV of the derivative at each respective date throughout its life in table 7.2:

---

[2]quarterly DCFs are set to 0.25 in all periods. Small inconsistencies with previous formulae are due to rounding

Date	PV($) of MTM XCS	PV($) of non-MTM XCS
0D	2	3
3M	150	8,151
6M	64	16,055
9M	-282	23,680
12M	0	0

Table 7.2: Outstanding asset value of each example IRD at various points throughout its life.

The example is included to visually demonstrate how non-MTM XCSs can build up large PVs. This example does not show the case where the FX rates move unexpectedly, which would create genuine PV. It, in fact, only shows the case in which all rates evolve as initially forecast, but hopefully makes it apparent that the overall size of the expected PV at various points in the life of the XCS is mitigated with the inclusion of MTM notional exchanges. In this example the effect is so pronounced because the USD 3M rates are so much lower than the EUR 3M rates, which creates two effects; an imbalance in floating interest payments each period, and forward FX rates which deviate substantially from the immediate FX rate.

7.5   Curve structure

Having outlined the basic theory of multi-currency curves it is left to make the necessary choices about the structure of the model, which are similar to the single currency curve model considerations. This requires the choice of;

(i) the **calibrating market input XCS, or FX swap, instrument data**,

(ii) the specific method and **style of interpolation** used, and choices of nodes and knots,

(iii) a chosen **implementation method** to interpolate XCSs, forward FX rates, the biased DF curve, or the bias adjustments applicable to the DF curve.

7.6 Appendix

Here we discuss various cross currency and forward FX pricing formulae. We base our formulae on the domestic currency being non-USD, in which the nominal, N, is stated, and the foreign currency being USD. The XCS spread is attached to the domestic currency. All derivatives here are collateralised in the foreign currency (USD).

It is sufficient to consider, in the following sections, a EURUSD FX rate (f_i), and for the swaps a notional, N, expressed in EUR, where the PV is in the foreign (i.e. USD) currency. Asterisked variables refer to the domestic, i.e. EUR, leg.

7.6.1 Interest rate parity restated

$$f_i = \frac{1 + d_i r_i}{1 + d_i^*(r_i^* + z_i^*)} f_{i-1} = \frac{w_i^*}{v_i} F_0$$

where F_0 is the exchange rate measured for immediate settlement, i.e. aligning with v_0, w_0^* both equal to 1.0, and the rates, r_i, r_i^*, are the appropriate RFRs compounded over the period and z_i^* is the appropriate single period, fwd, XCS basis spread added to the domestic currency.

7.6.2 Forward FX rate equivalence

The forward FX rate is a source of truth and adheres to the no arbitrage principle. Therefore,

$$(\text{EURUSD})f_i = \frac{(\text{EUR:USD-CSA})w_i^*}{(\text{USD:USD-CSA})v_i} F_0 = \frac{(\text{EUR:EUR-CSA})v_i^*}{(\text{USD:EUR-CSA})w_i} F_0 \; .$$

7.6.3 FX swap pricing

The PV of a general FX swap, where z_i^{fx} is the agreed FX swap points price, is:

$$PV(\$) = \underbrace{f_{i-1}Nv_{i-1} - F_0Nw_{i-1}^*}_{\text{initial exchange}} \underbrace{-(f_{i-1} + z_i^{fx})Nv_i + F_0Nw_i^*}_{\text{forward exchange}}$$

If the initial exchange has already settled then the PV is equivalent to that of an FX forward and includes only the rightmost terms.

7.6.4   MTM XCS pricing

The PV of a general MTM XCS from the point of view of the payer of the spread is:

$$PV(\$) = + NF_0 w_0^* \qquad \text{(receive initial domestic notional)}$$

$$- NF_0 \sum_{i=1}^{T_1} (r_i^* + Z^*) d_i^* w_i^* \quad \text{(pay domestic floating)}$$

$$- NF_0 w_{T_1}^* \qquad \text{(pay final domestic notional)}$$

$$- Nf_0 v_0 \qquad \text{(pay initial dollar notional)}$$

$$+ N \sum_{j=1}^{T_2} (f_{j-1} - f_j) \, v_j \quad \text{(exchange MTM dollar notional)}$$

$$+ N \sum_{j=1}^{T_2} f_{j-1} r_j d_j v_j \quad \text{(receive dollar floating)}$$

$$+ N f_{T_2} v_{T_2} \qquad \text{(receive final dollar notional)} \,.$$

If we now make the following assumptions:

i) the MTM XCS is priced at mid-market and therefore has a PV of zero,

ii) the immediate DFs, v_0, w_0^* both equal 1.0 as above,

iii) the swap schedule starts immediately so that F_0 can be taken to be equal to f_0 without a spot settled adjustment,

iv) the schedules align so that T_1 equals T_2, and the number of periods are equivalent,

then the above reduces, if we also use the interest rate parity equation from above, to,

$$F_0 \left(\sum_{i=1}^{T} \left(1 + (r_i^* + Z^*) d_i^*\right) w_i^* + w_T^* \right) = \sum_{i=1}^{T} f_{i-1} \left(1 + r_i d_i\right) v_i + f_T v_T$$

If the further assumption, v), is made such that the foreign rates and DFs are derived from the same curve, e.g. the RFR curve, and in the case of USD the SOFR rate, then the above can be further reduced to,

$$\sum_{i=1}^{T} (1 + (r_i^* + Z^*) d_i^*) w_i^* = \sum_{i=1}^{T} w_{i-1}^*$$

7.6.5   Mid-market XCS spread

The above formula, upon including the above first four assumptions, can be rearranged to yield the mid-market basis spread, Z^*,

$$Z^* = \frac{\sum\limits_{i=1}^{T} \left(f_{i-1} \left(1 + r_i d_i\right) v_i - F_0 \left(1 + r_i^* d_i^*\right) w_i^*\right)}{F_0 \sum\limits_{i=1}^{T} d_i^* w_i^*} \,.$$

If assumption v) is also included we have further,

$$Z^* = \frac{\sum_{i=1}^{T} w_{i-1}^* - \sum_{i=1}^{T} (1 + r_i^* d_i^*) w_i^*}{\sum_{i=1}^{T} d_i^* w_i^*}$$

We highlight this formula shows no direct dependence to the foreign leg, which is also the currency of collateral (provided w_i are known).

7.6.6 Bootstrapping the DFs, w_i^*

The DF at date, m_i, of a non-USD currency with a USD cash only CSA, can be bootstrapped with knowledge of fwd XCS basis or fwd FX swap prices.

From FX swaps

Applying assumptions i), ii), iii) to the FX swap pricing formula yields,

$$F_0 w_i^* = (f_{i-1} + z_i^{fx})v_i \implies w_i^* = \left(\frac{w_{i-1}^*}{v_{i-1}} + \frac{z_i^{fx}}{F_0}\right)v_i = \left(1 + \frac{z_i^{fx}}{f_{i-1}}\right)\frac{v_i}{v_{i-1}}w_{i-1}^*$$

When the swap points, z_i^{fx}, are zero it is plain to see that $\frac{w_i^*}{w_{i-1}^*} = \frac{v_i}{v_{i-1}}$ which is a re-expression of interest rate parity.

From XCSs

Applying the same assumptions i), ii), iii) to the pricing formula for a single period XCS (which has no MTM flows by definition) and rearranging yields,

$$w_i^* = \frac{1 + r_i d_i}{1 + (r_i^* + z_i^*)d_i^*}\frac{v_i}{v_{i-1}}\,w_{i-1}^* \;.$$

Interdependence

All of the above formulae clearly show cyclic dependence of XCS basis, DFs under the influence of a non-domestic CSA and forward FX rates:

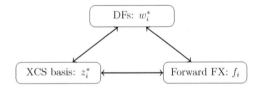

Term Structure of Interest Rate Curves

The previous, and upcoming, chapters discuss the technicalities of building curvesets. It is shown how to incorporate all of the market prices of tradable products to build consistent and reliable models. But what is not discussed, at all, is *why* some of those prices are what they are. Financial markets, of course, have a supply and demand dynamic meaning prices can be low or high and have great variability, but there are some fundamental, economic reasons for the levels of specific prices relative to each other.

Much of this chapter is theoretical in nature, even subjectively speculative. But, it aims to present logical and coherent arguments supporting (or contradicting) real market price action. As with some other chapters of this book the material is included as basic foundation but hopefully encourages the reader to form their own opinions and have their own insights on the nature of the shape and structure of the curveset, in any given, nuanced currency.

8.1 Transmission mechanism

An economy is sought to be controlled by its central bank, so let's begin there. A central bank's mandate is to protect the confidence and credibility in the currency it oversees and encourage stable and prosperous financial conditions. All the major central banks of the world aim to communicate their assessments of conditions, and their target objectives, in public forums and through official statements. They seek to achieve their targets by means of policies, systems and market operations, which are applicable to recognised domestic banking institutions. In turn it is hoped that these central bank actions will filter through to have an impact on the wider domestic economy. This process of filtering through to impact the economy is known as the **transmission mechanism**.

There are a number of ways in which a central bank attempts to influence the interest rates of its economy, and the availability of credit within an economy. Different central banks operate different systems and policies, based on their subjective opinion about which provide the optimal transmission mechanism. However, the overarching principles are broadly the same across central banks. It is usually just the technical details that differ. We begin with a basic example of the most frequently used central bank tool, the deposit rate.

8.1.1   The deposit rate

This is the per annum rate of interest that a central bank will pay to recognised banking institutions who deposit cash on account, with that central bank, on an overnight basis. This type of asset, being a cash deposit with a central bank, is the definition of a risk free asset; if a central bank defaulted it would be tantamount to the collapse of the entire currency, thus not really worth contemplating. The rate of interest that a central bank pays on this deposit is then, in the simplest terms the risk-free rate, which we denote R_f.

The deposit rate is the basic rate from which other short term interest rates are derived. As a simple example consider a banking institution which can deposit cash at the central bank or can lend money on an unsecured basis to another banking institution. Obviously lending to another banking institution is more risky than depositing with the central bank. Being more risky, the rate of interest that the original bank should demand as compensation for the increased risk is higher than the rate offered by the central bank. This, so called interbank unsecured lending, is the first direct example of the transmission mechanism in action. Theoretically, if we suggest that p is the uniform probability of a particular counterparty defaulting within a given year then the original banking institution would charge a lending rate, R_p, subject to the no arbitrage argument:

$$R_f = -LGD.p + (1-p)R_p, \quad \implies \quad R_p = \frac{R_f + LGD.p}{1-p} \approx R_f + p(LGD + R_f) \,,$$

$$\text{so} \quad R_p \approx R_f + p, \quad \text{for} \quad LGD = 100\% \quad \text{and} \quad |R_f|, p \ll 1 \,.$$

This approximation is useful because the number of basis points of R_p above R_f serves to represent credit risk and indicates the number of average financial institutions per 10,000 that are expected to fail annually. For example if R_p is 5bps above R_f then 5 per 10,000 is the expected default rate. Of course this is just a simple approximation but it gives a sensible and fundamental place to base opinions.

In practical trading it is likely that there will be other factors that are influential. The LGD value was an assumed value and also there will be an opportunistic element embedded into the value of rate, R_p. What is meant by this is that if a bank can, with certainty, deposit funds with the central bank then it wouldn't be sensible to lend at precisely the no-arbitrage price to another institution; a small increase in value for facilitating the service to the borrowing bank would be extracted, otherwise depositing with the central bank is easily arranged at no loss. Indeed if the unsecured lending asset is considered in a weaker sense for regulatory capital purposes[1], then this also might demand higher pricing. So, in all, this would likely push R_p above the price assumed simply from the average annual default rate.

$$R_p = R_f + \text{Credit Adjustment}(p) + \text{Opportunity Cost} + \text{Balance Sheet Cost} \,.$$

---

[1] see chapter 17

The influence on RFR and OIS rates

RFR and OIS fixings are directly calculated from interbank lending (with differing methodologies in different currencies) so the previous section is completely relevant. In other words, it sets the scene for where daily RFR or OIS fixings would be expected to be published relative to central bank deposit rates. In this section we will discuss the EUR and GBP OIS rate fixings, EONIA and SONIA, respectively. These two currencies have been chosen to highlight in this section, because they provide an interesting example where theory matches practice, and also where the theory is distorted by a technical detail to reflect supply and demand dynamics in the market. Note that SONIA has been reformed in recent years which has not distinctly affected its calculation but made it more robust by expanding the data collection set: the below analysis directly references the old SONIA calculation, pre-reform. ESTR has effectively replaced EONIA, which is a similar form of reform improving the reliability of the calculation.

We begin with the EONIA fixing. In the EUR area there are a large number of financial institutions, almost all of whom are expected to be able to access the European Central Bank (ECB)'s facilities directly or via their own national central bank (NCB). This means that lending rates between any of these institutions are effectively floored by the ECB. No bank would rather lend to another than deposit directly with the ECB at the same rate. So in these cases the rates at which lending transactions take place is roughly the same as R_p from above.

In the case of the EONIA, the fixing itself is calculated by the ECB based on data that is submitted from a chosen number of large panel banks. These panel banks provide the notional and rate at which they have *lent* unsecured overnight EUR cash to other interbank counterparties. These transactions are averaged to form the EONIA fixing rate. The result of this is that the EONIA fixing on a daily basis prints a few bps above the ECB's deposit rate, as expected given the theoretical argument above (note only deposits can be made to the ECB). This is broadly illustrated in figure 8.1.

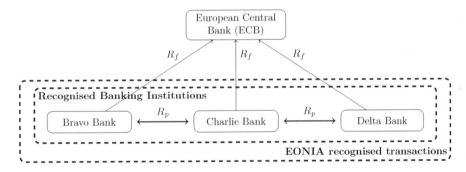

Figure 8.1: The EONIA fixing and institutions with access to ECB facilities.

In GBP, however, SONIA rates frequently fix below the Bank of England's base (deposit) rate. The above theory still stands, but where SONIA fixes is due to a quirk in the technical details. In order to use the Bank of England's facilities, or deposit funds directly with the Bank of England, an institution must be recognised. This means having made an application, been approved and had the necessary administration completed by the Bank of England. For one reason or another, it is anticipated that a number of institutions who wish to deposit GBP are unrecognised. *Unrecognised* institutions must then instead lend money to *recognised* banking institutions, who can then deposit directly with the central bank. This creates a supply of unsecured funding for those recognised banks typically of excellent credit standing. The reaction by those banks is to offer a rate below base rate, so that when the money is passed on to the Bank of England, that recognised bank has accrued an amount, or fee, for facilitating the service. This is, as we mentioned before, an opportunistic element to pricing, but in this scenario acts a cost to the lender.

This supply dynamic can increase or decrease. When there is a lot of liquidity in the banking system (for example created by quantitative easing (QE)) the supply of money is increased and therefore the SONIA fixing would be expected to fall as recognised banks react opportunistically to increased deposit demand from unrecognised institutions. When overall liquidity is less the effect will, too, be reduced, and SONIA should tend to be more like EONIA and the theoretical price. In the last few years SONIA has traded between a few bps above and a few bps below the base rate.

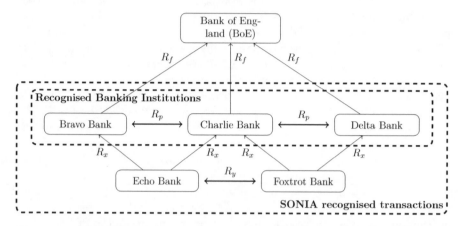

Figure 8.2: The SONIA fixing and institutions with access to BoE facilities.

In figure 8.2, when there is a lot of liquidity in the system it is unlikely that much trading between recognised institutions at R_p will occur, since any demand they have for cash will likely be supplied by the unrecognised institutions at the superior R_x rates. The SONIA fixing will then be influenced by these other prevailing lending rates, and not by R_p.

An interesting discussion paper that we do not cite as evidence for any of these effects but as a point of interest discussing some of the mechanics of these and other central banks can be found in the bibliography, [22].

8.1.2   Standing facilities

The financial crisis of '07 an '08 brought about reactions to the OIS market that created excessively high overnight unsecured lending rates, with it sometimes rising by 25-100bps. The number of defaulting institutions did also rise in this period considerably and thus this is broadly consistent with the theory. However, in times of panic and uncertainty it is not typical of a market to come to a warranted mathematical derivation of a pricing mechanic. Personally, I believe it is more likely for this to be a coincidence that prices settled at some of the levels they did, and that numbers of defaulting banks was an effect of tighter liquidity conditions, not the other way around.

Central banks, of course, were unhappy about the nature of these developments at the time. Huge variability in a most basic, unsecured overnight lending market reflected very badly on the currency. It weakened its credibility and threatened its existence by suggesting a flawed banking system, with many banks at potential risk of collapse. As a result, many central banks around the world now have, not only, a deposit system in place, akin to that above, but also a standing facility. This is a kind of back stop so to say. If OIS rates or RFRs begin to vary significantly these central banks have facilities in place where they will act as secured lender (or additional deposit taker in some respects) of last resort. The rates they specify are usually in a specific range, or 'corridor', around the specified deposit rate.

The purpose of these standing facilities is to provide stability, credibility and some security to the wider banking sector. Rarely are they utilised, but they are referenced in banking institutions' liquidity plans that are submitted to regulators. These plans outline a bank's ability to deal with stressed market conditions[2].

Furthermore, in anticipation of stress on the financial system, central banks extend **swap lines** between themselves. This means that a central bank is able to offer its domestic banking institutions other currencies than the one that it presides over. Its ability to do this is due to agreements that the central banks of the world have between themselves to exchange currencies and permit a liquid global financial system.

8.2 Term structure

8.2.1 What drives the shape of yield curves in a single currency?

In this section we focus on the more general term structure, particularly of tenors longer than the first year or two. Much has been written in literature attempting to model and understand the term structure of IRs, either with empirical studies or analytical assertions (good examples are [23] [24] [25] [26] [27] [28] [29]). The quantity of work demonstrates a large number of suggested influences and effects, and hints at a lack of consensus.

For the reader's benefit, though, we can list a number of qualitative factors that are core drivers of the curve. Albeit these factors contribute in different, unknown measures. Personally, I think a good introduction can be seen in [23], which surmises many of the aspects explained here by adopting a very basic premise. The factors we will touch upon briefly are the following:

(i) Central bank rate expectations

(ii) Volatility and distribution

(iii) Volatility and gamma

(iv) Risk aversion

(v) Supply and demand

Central bank rate expectations

Naturally, the transmission mechanism that impacts short dated rates is expected to persist in a similar manner in the future. Meaning that if central bank rates are expected to be higher in five year's time then other interest rates would be expected to be higher at that time also. Uncertainty about future central bank rates increases the further one looks to the future, meaning this effect becomes less of a direct influence on the shape of the yield curve and more of an observable factor from the state of the IR market itself. This distinction becomes even more blurred when (the following) additional factors are considered at the same time. But, central bank rates are always a foundation of interest rates in general and it is wise, at least, to keep them in mind.

---

[2]see chapter 17 regarding liquidity regulations

Often central banks' mandates are centred about maintaining stable prices - targeting specific levels of medium term inflation. Since central bank policy changes target impacting inflation then inflation forecasts and market prices of future inflation are also important variables to monitor when judging the macro structure of the yield curve.

Volatility and distribution

Imagine central bank rates are currently 3% and that the most likely outcome for future central bank rates is for them to be 3% perpetually. These, we take to be the modal values of a probability distribution of possible rates. Also suppose that market interest rates are priced equivalently to the central bank rates for simplicity (without any basis). Now, the mid-market rates will not be the same as the mode of those central bank expectations - instead they will settle on the prices that give the expected values, i.e. the means of those distributions.

We are then confronted with the question of what distribution to assume for the path of central bank rates. If a normal distribution is applied then the mode is equal to the mean, and there is no distinction. But frequently markets price a bias towards sharp rises in interest rates, and a bias against negative rates in general. To date there has never been a fall into deeply negative territory, albeit some rates have gone marginally negative. But there have been many examples of exaggerated interest rate hikes to high levels. This lends weight to the argument of applying a log-normal distribution to the path of interest rates. This distribution can often be inferred from the prices of certain swaptions also.

Using a log-normal distribution creates the effect of determining a higher mean value than the assumed modal value. The size of the disparity depends upon the volatility of the fwd rate. Figure 8.3 qualitatively demonstrates this concept, and creates a basic curve structure simply from this initial assumption.

Volatility and gamma

IRSs exhibit gamma[3] (and bonds exhibit convexity), and have associated expected PnL values dependent upon the assumed volatility of the rates. That is, the gamma on an IRS has some inherent value[4]. If we consider all things to be equal on two consecutive fwd IRSs, except their gammas and their respective volatilities, then to equate the two under the no arbitrage principle requires an upfront adjustment. This adjustment is, again, qualitatively shown in figure 8.3. The figure plots a theorised resultant fwd and par IR curve from the basic premise of 3% central bank rate modal expectations with volatility distribution and gamma impacts.

Risk aversion

In other literature, often that which is specific to bonds, risk aversion is often cited as a reason why longer yields are higher than shorter yields. Known as the term premium, longer bond holders are typically exposed to more delta risk than shorter bond holders of the same principal value. Applying a utility function other than a linear (risk neutral) one, such as the isoelastic utility function, allows this theory some mathematical merit. Since IRDs are leverage instruments, without a necessary capital injection and therefore *not* real assets as a store of capital, it is more difficult to convincingly apply this logic to the IRS curve. However, bonds and IRDs are intimately linked and therefore this effect should be present in one to some degree if present in the other. The connection may be explained by the term structure of the swap spread curve.

---

[3]see chapters 21 and 22
[4]see section 22.9.1

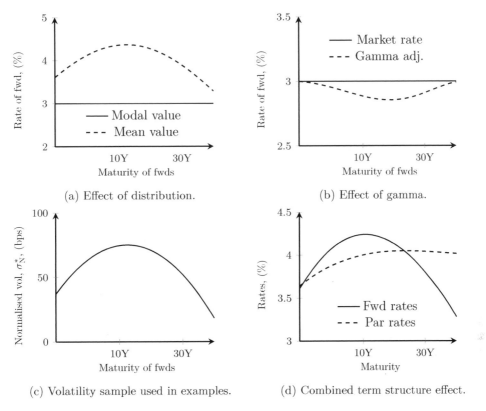

(a) Effect of distribution.

(b) Effect of gamma.

(c) Volatility sample used in examples.

(d) Combined term structure effect.

Figure 8.3: Qualitatively outlining the effect of volatility on the structure of a standardised yield curve, due to gamma and probability distribution choice.

The difficulty in modelling this effect is in deciding on observations to characterise the utility function parameters and how to isolate effects on the term structure due solely to risk aversion, although general consensus would assert a particularly risk averse environment would be characterised by steeper curves and vice versa.

Supply and demand

It must be anticipated that some tenors will, at times and through cycles, be either in greater supply or greater demand, dependent upon the activity of all of the different types of IRD and broader fixed income users. Meaning their rates will be determined to a degree by this factor alone and not explained through any natural rationalisation.

One example of such a driver is pension fund regulation. When pension funds are required to account for their liabilities in specific ways, such as the ultimate forward rate (UFR) in Europe, this creates specific hedging requirements which can dominate local markets.

The difficulty in completely characterising the term structure of the yield curve is the isolation of any of these component factors, and it is hard to assign any meaningful numbers to their individual impacts. The best takeaway from this section is to recognise what the impact of higher and lower volatilities are, and the impact of increased or decreased risk aversion. This will be helpful in making qualitative assessments of yield curve moves in light of all relevant data.

8.2.2　What drives the shape and nature of the cross-currency basis?

Section 7.2 introduces XCSs from the point of view of RFR based loans in each currency. It asserts that in a stylised world there would be no basis - it would all be zero. That's correct, but supply and demand exist and they impact the XCS basis to a large degree. We will outline two of the major supply and demand factors here; issuer and investor preference, and collateral management. These permit the reader a qualitative feel for the dynamics of these markets.

Issuer and investor preference

Liquid spot FX markets allow an issuer or investor to exchange funds from one currency to another with ease, but this creates an exposure to FX risk on an ongoing basis. XCSs permit the same upfront exchange but also commit to a future exchange thereby removing the FX risk component. This allows issuers and investors to tap into foreign markets without the concern of FX risk, widening the scope of their pool of investors or assets respectively.

Let's create a hypothetical environment to demonstrate how these factors interact. Suppose that EUR rates were at 1% and USD rates were at 3%. Additionally suppose that the domestic credit spreads of two identical[5] issuing corporations are 40bps for the EUR domesticated one and 80bps for the USD domesticated one. Suppose also that the EUR/USD XCS par basis declines each year by 8bps. See figure 8.4.

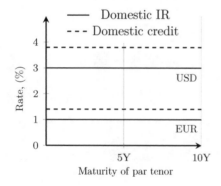 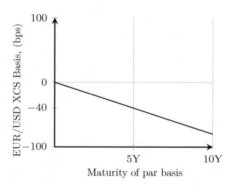

Figure 8.4: Hypothetical scenario of IRs, credit rates and XCS rates in EUR and USD.

Now let's consider this market from the perspective of the issuers, i.e. the supply of bond assets. The break-even maturity in this scenario is 5Y at which point the corporations are indifferent to geographic issuance. Table 8.1 outlines the preference otherwise. When foreign issuance is preferred this would require the USD domesticated corporation to receive the XCS basis and the EUR domesticated corporation to pay the XCS basis.

Corporation	<5Y maturity	>5Y maturity
USD domesticated	Foreign	Domestic
EUR domesticated	Domestic	Foreign

Table 8.1: Issuer preference in relation to the hypothetical credit spreads and XCS basis levels.

---

[5]identical in the sense of ratings, business activity, and balance sheet composition, etc.

Alternatively we can consider the same mechanics from the perspective of the investors, i.e. the demand of bond assets. In this case a USD domesticated investor would have to pay the XCS basis to buy a foreign issue and a EUR domesticated investor would have to receive the XCS basis to, similarly, buy a foreign issue. Table 8.2 outlines their preference.

Investor	<5Y maturity	>5Y maturity
USD domesticated	Domestic	Foreign
EUR domesticated	Foreign	Domestic

Table 8.2: Investor preference in relation to the hypothetical credit spreads and XCS basis levels.

Figure 8.5 graphically illustrates why each issuer or investor prefers either type. The domestic rates versus the swapped foreign rates are shown for each currency. The issuers seek the lowest possible rates, whilst the investors seek the highest possible rates. The asymmetry in this hypothetical scenario creates a supply and demand imbalance, and exerts pressure on all three factors; USD credit spreads, EUR credit spreads, and the XCS basis. The pressure exerted by either party works in the same direction. It is shown in figure 8.6.

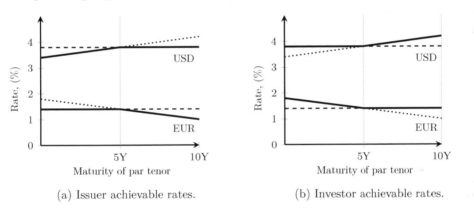

(a) Issuer achievable rates.   (b) Investor achievable rates.

Figure 8.5: Attainable yields of issuers and investors comparing domestic with swapped foreign issuance.

Collateral management

The collateral that needs to be posted on IRD liabilities is specified by the CSA agreement made between two counterparties. To demonstrate how this effect can impact capital markets we again establish a hypothetical scenario.

Suppose two counterparties transact an IRD where the CSA agreed between them with respect to this derivative is USD cash only. This is quite common because USD is a benchmark, so called 'high quality', currency which either party can rely on to insure the value of their derivative asset. At a point in the future, after market prices have fluctuated, one party will possess the liability side while the other will possess the asset side of the IRD (in fact this need not be specific to IRDs but can be any financial transaction which needs collateralising). The liability holding party, whomever it is, will then be required to source and post USD to the asset holder. It may be that that party has USD available from other derivatives, or other

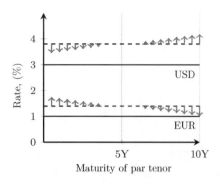
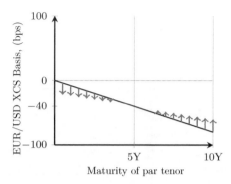

Figure 8.6: Showing the pressure exerted on market prices due to supply and demand imbalances of the hypothetical scenario.

business. But that will not necessarily be the case. If USD are not readily available for that counterparty then USD will have to be sourced, either through the spot FX market, FX swap market or the XCS market.

The demand this creates for benchmark currencies, particularly USD, is quite high in times of stress. This effect is asymmetric in a respect because regardless of who has transacted the derivative one party will eventually have to source USD if those are the bilateral terms of the CSA. When markets become volatile and liabilities and assets are expected to increase then so too is the need for this type collateral, and this is often reflected in short dated XCS prices.

8.3   Appendix

8.3.1   Term structure and volatility

Log-distribution and means and modes

Under a log-normal distribution, $X \sim \ln N(\mu, \sigma)$, the modal value is given by $e^{\mu - \sigma^2}$ and the mean value is given by $e^{\mu + \frac{1}{2}\sigma^2}$. Thus the mean is related to the mode, explicitly with respect to log volatility, by the equation,

$$\text{Mean} = \text{Mode} \times e^{\frac{3}{2}\sigma^2} .$$

Gamma and no arbitrage

Consider an xY1Y and an $(x+1)$Y1Y pair of fwd IRSs, paying the first and receiving the second in \$10,000 present value of a basis point (pv01). For simplicity of the model, further assume their rates to be perfectly correlated normal random variables with an expected market move equal to zero. The gamma of each IRS is estimated using the simple formula from section 22.10.1, so that the expected PnL of the portfolio is;

$$E[P] \approx -x(\sigma_N^{x\text{Y1Y}})^2 + (x+1)(\sigma_N^{(x+1)\text{Y1Y}})^2 .$$

When this value is positive it represents an upfront amount which the longer IRS should be adjusted, or biased, in order to adhere to the no arbitrage principle under the assumptions we have adopted. Expressed in bps this creates a particular shape of the yield curve dictated by the volatilities. Varying the assumptions alters the adjustments, or bias, but the general shape and concept remains intact.

Delta and Basis Risk

One of the most important concepts in trading is that of risk. There are many different types of risk but this chapter details the one relevant to the movement of financial markets: **market risk**. It explains;

- what market risk is and the difference between delta and basis risks, in single currencies only,
- the difference between the analytic and numeric risk approach,
- when and how to calculate analytic risk and estimate it,
- what a risk model is and how to calculate numeric risk,
- how to design a risk model and the properties of such,
- pitfalls of risk models and effects such as risk bleed,
- some of the terminology and conventions of market risk,
- the typical look of a derivatives portfolio's market risk.

9.1 Defining market risk

Market risk is the essence of entering into any IRD contract. It permits monetary exposure to the movement, or changes, in financial markets. *Risk* is typically an all encompassing term used to collectively refer to any type of exposure, such as credit risk, market risk, reputational risk, etc. Two specific types of market risk, *delta risk* and *basis risk*, are defined in the context of the interest rate market as being the amount of money an IRD will gain (or lose) if the interest rate market were to change by a single bp. These terms are synonymous with the other frequently used terms *delta pv01* and *basis pv01*.

Delta risk is the term used to describe PnL changes to a portfolio when the **overall level of the IR market changes by one bp** (the greek name here is also synonymous with the same *delta* risk that is prevalent in the context of options). This means that all types of interest rate, be it the RFR curve, or any specific CSA curve, or central bank rate are expected to change together. Of course with the existence of a curveset this means that each curve in the set must move in tandem, and so that the basis between each curve is preserved. Figure 9.1 (a) shows this in practice; two curves, one designated the outright curve and the other designated the basis curve, both increase in parallel[1].

Basis risk is that which describes PnL changes to a portfolio when **curves move relative to each other by one bp and the overall level of the IR market remains constant**. Figure 9.1 (b) shows how the curve that has been dubbed the outright curve, representative of the overall level of rates, does not move, but another curve moves relative to it. Practically speaking, basis risk was much more of a concern prior to the transition from IBOR. IBOR curves relative to the OIS curves (which functioned as the the discount curve for cashflows) gave rise to sizeable effects. Since the transition from IBOR and the RFR curve commonly acting as both the forecast curve and discount curve simultaneously this risk has predominantly disappeared.

Semantically speaking we can still refer to forecasting risks and discounting risks as separate risks. The equations are still calculable and valid. However, the basis spreads, z_i and s_i, that are referred to below become useful only in a specific context that we will explain. They are required in chapter 22, for gamma and cross-gamma calculations.

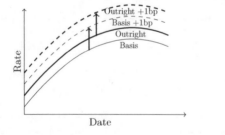
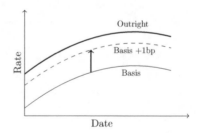

(a) **Delta** IR market move; outright and basis curves move in tandem.

(b) **Basis** IR market move; only the basis curve moves relatively.

Figure 9.1: Market movements described by delta and basis risk.

The above descriptions of delta and basis risk are simplified because they have treated each curve as if its entirety, across every date, moves by the same amount. Nonetheless this is still a commonly used way to measure market risk. However, it is, of course, rare that a curve will change by the same amount across every date. Normally, on a given day, some parts of the curve will move more than others. Therefore to fully explain market risk, curvesets should be segregated, and the aforementioned footnote gives one sensible way to do this, although many are possible[2].

Delta and basis risks are sometimes referred to as *first order* or *linear* risks. These risks represent the first derivative of the PV of an IRD with respect to the movement of IR curves, afterwards scaled to a single bp. If a curveset is segregated in the suggested way according to

---

[1]see introductory notation for further description of curveset segregation

[2]see also chapter 10 for alternatively inferred curveset segregations

notation in this book then the total delta and total basis (and total specific discounting basis) can be expressed as the sum of all of the individually measured components of the respective risk type:

$$\text{Total delta risk is,} \quad \frac{DP}{D\mathbf{r}} = \frac{\partial P}{\partial r_1} + \ldots + \frac{\partial P}{\partial r_n} = \nabla_{\mathbf{r}} P \cdot \boldsymbol{\delta} \,,$$

$$\text{Total basis risk is,} \quad \frac{DP}{D\mathbf{z}} = \frac{\partial P}{\partial z_1} + \ldots + \frac{\partial P}{\partial z_n} = \nabla_{\mathbf{z}} P \cdot \boldsymbol{\delta} \,,$$

$$\text{Total discounting basis risk is,} \quad \frac{DP}{D\mathbf{s}} = \frac{\partial P}{\partial s_1} + \ldots + \frac{\partial P}{\partial s_n} = \nabla_{\mathbf{s}} P \cdot \boldsymbol{\delta} \,.$$

By means of our defined segregation it is also true mathematically that,

$$\frac{DP}{D\mathbf{r}} = \frac{DP}{D\mathbf{z}} + \frac{DP}{D\mathbf{s}} = (\nabla_{\mathbf{z}} P + \nabla_{\mathbf{s}} P) \cdot \boldsymbol{\delta}$$

Example 9.1.
A trader has paid fixed on a 10Y IRS. Interest rates rise by 1bp, across the entire curve, and the PV of the trade increases by $25,000, therefore the delta risk of the trade was:

$$\frac{DP}{D\mathbf{r}} = \$25,000 \ p/bp \,.$$

Market risks are used to estimate the PnL of an IRD or portfolio of IRDs based on given market movements, by multiplying the respective risk by the parallel bp change in market rates, Δr:

$$\Delta P \approx \frac{DP}{D\mathbf{r}} \Delta r \,,$$

Example 9.2.
*Another trader has paid fixed on a 5Y IRS with a live, numeric delta risk of £10,000 p/bp. The market rate of the 5Y IRS falls by 3.5bps and the loss in PnL is **estimated** to be £35,000.*

9.2 Calculating delta or basis risk

In the above example the reader might notice the careful inclusion of the terms *live* and *numeric* in the description of the delta. This is because the risk of IRD contracts can change as the market moves[3], so to have a live, i.e up to date, representation of the risk can be important.

In this section we will discuss different ways to calculate market risks. The use of the word numeric was chosen because that describes one particular method for estimating delta or basis risks. Another well known method is called analytic risk, which we begin with.

9.2.1 Analytic risk

The approach taken by analytic risk measurement is to calculate risk derived from the mathematical formulation of an IRD contract. The most common form of doing this is to measure the rate of change of PV against a standardised change in the mid-market fixed rate, R^{mid}, scaled to a single bp: $-\frac{\partial P}{\partial R} (\times 0.0001(1bp))$. For example using the appropriate formula from section 3.5, then for a standard IRS, having paid fixed, the analytic delta is:

$$\frac{\partial P}{\partial R} = N \sum_{i=1}^{T_1} d_i v_i \,.$$

---

[3]this effect is known as 'gamma' or 'convexity', with each IR product exhibiting differently. See chapter 21

A keen observer will recognise that this approach is actually subtly different from the description of risk given in the previous section. This is because in the previous section risk was defined in terms of the IR market moving and this having an effect on the PV of static derivative contracts. This analytic risk approach, however, actually supposes that IR market rates remain static and the analytical derivative is taken with respect to changing the fixed rate on the derivative contract itself.

Analytic risk, then, is a weaker measure of risk than the alternative numeric risk method since it does not measure risk in the true sense of market rates actually moving. It has further drawbacks that the PV of the contract, if, for example, it is ITM or OTM, is not taken into account and also that it gives only a single number (and does not show risk to different segments of the curve).

But, analytic risk also has its advantages; it is quick and easy to calculate and it gives a reasonably reliable measure of risk for mid-market trades where the PV is close to zero, i.e.,

$$\frac{\partial P}{\partial R} \approx \frac{DP}{D\mathbf{r}}$$

The fact it yields only a single number representing the total risk can also be helpful at times. In practical trading too there are occasions when analytic risk is the only tool that can be used. As an example suppose a trader knows the mid-market rate of an IRS and wishes to show an amount of margin to a price-taker which creates a specific amount of PnL. In this case the amount of margin can be precisely and exactly calculated using the analytic delta of the trade.

Often these formulae comprise only data on notional size, DCFs and DFs. Since the DFs are a key component of these formulae this means that CSAs play an integral part in assessing this quantity of risk.

Example 9.3.
The mid-market rate of the 5Y IRS is 3.00%. The analytic delta of a $100mm 5Y is $45,000. Receiving fixed, in this notional, at 3.01%, 3.02%, or 3.10% will result in exactly $45,000, $90,000 or $450,000 PnL respectively.

Estimating risk

Very frequently trades are executed and agreed in short spans of time, either voice brokered or on electronic screens. It is favourable to have an estimate of the amount of delta or basis risk that one traded to permit fast execution of hedges at similar market rates. Brokers make use of analytic delta calculations all the time, even to define notional quantities in certain trade combinations[4]. Table 9.1 is useful for making a broad assessment of the risk of IRSs and XCSs. It is derived through the use of analytic delta formulae and an assumed flat yield curve.

Expanding analytic risk

Although the method shown above is the standard when discussing analytic risk this is not to say that it can't be done differently. Indeed, taking the derivatives of the mathematical formulation of the PV of trades with respect to market rates, r_i, rather than the fixed rate, R, gives a more accurate assessment of risk in the truest sense of its definition. Furthermore second derivatives can then be calculated to yield estimations of gamma and cross-gamma. Chapter 22 explores this.

---

[4]see section 16.2.1

Tenor	0%	1%	2%	3%	4%	5%
1Y	10,000	9,900	9,800	9,700	9,600	9,500
2Y	20,000	19,700	19,400	19,100	18,900	18,600
3Y	30,000	29,400	28,800	28,300	27,800	27,200
4Y	40,000	39,000	38,000	37,000	36,000	35,500
5Y	50,000	48,500	47,000	46,000	44,500	43,500
6Y	60,000	58,000	56,000	54,000	52,500	51,000
7Y	70,000	67,000	64,500	62,500	60,000	58,000
8Y	80,000	76,500	73,000	70,000	67,500	64,500
9Y	90,000	85,500	81,500	78,000	74,500	71,000
10Y	100,000	94,500	90,000	85,500	81,000	77,000
12Y	120,000	112,500	105,500	99,500	94,000	88,500
15Y	150,000	138,500	128,500	119,500	111,000	104,000
20Y	200,000	180,500	163,500	149,000	136,000	124,500
25Y	250,000	220,000	195,000	174,000	156,000	141,000
30Y	300,000	258,000	224,000	196,000	173,000	153,500
40Y	400,000	328,000	273,500	231,000	198,000	171,500

Table 9.1: Estimated delta (or basis) risk (pv01) of a **100mm nominal** swap with market rates at specified values (will vary dependent upon the shape of the term structure of the curve).

9.2.2 Numeric (or automatic) risk

Analytic delta has its uses, but numeric risk makes possible advanced risk management for IRD portfolios. Let us consider the philosophic question: *what is the purpose of accurately representing a portfolio's risk?* The crux of this answer lies in **hedging** - trying, with the addition of easily executable, interbank trades, to minimise the daily PnL volatility of a portfolio of an assortment of arbitrary IRDs. The answer might also be **speculation** - trying to target a specific amount of PnL dependent upon a given market movement scenario. Either way, a robust and structured framework needs to be created to produce accurate information.

Numeric risk is given its name because, with this technique, the risk of any derivative contract is calculated numerically and algorithmically. It can be done through an iterative approach, with automated processes calculating the original PV of the IRD, then building a new implied curveset for a simulated environment with specific market rates one bp higher, then repricing that IRD with those simulated curves and DFs. The difference between the original and simulated PVs is reported as the risk for that specific scenario. With modern techniques this can also be implemented using automatic differentiation techniques, but for legacy reasons we maintain the name *numeric*. The linear sum of all IRD numeric risks within a portfolio gives the entire portfolio numeric risk.

In this way, numeric risk, unlike analytic risk, assumes that the fixed rates, or fixed spreads, are indeed fixed per IRD and it is the market level of rates which are subject to change. This means the figures reported are market risks in the truest sense of their definition. Additionally this approach allows more scope and can provide more data because there exists a potential array of delta or basis risks dependent upon which market rates were simulated to change, or indeed what scenarios the risks are chosen to be measured against.

Example 9.4.
A trading portfolio is risked under three scenarios; where the 5Y IRS rate is increased, the 10Y IRS rate is increased and the 30Y IRS rate is increased, each by one bp. The respective PnLs

are recorded as +2,000, -3,000 and +6,000. This produces the numeric delta risk array:

$$\mathbf{S} = \begin{matrix}(5Y)\\(10Y)\\(30Y)\end{matrix}\begin{bmatrix} 2,000\\ -3,000\\ 6,000 \end{bmatrix},$$

where the ordering of elements here is by tenor. Suppose the real market movements, on any given day, of the 5Y, 10Y, and 30Y rates are +3, +2, +1 bps and represented by column array, $\mathbf{\Delta r}$, then the PnL estimate is given by simply multiplying the two and summing (vector dot product):

$$\Delta P \approx \mathbf{S} \cdot \mathbf{\Delta r} = 6,000, \quad \text{for,} \quad \mathbf{\Delta r} = \begin{bmatrix} +3.0\\ +2.0\\ +1.0 \end{bmatrix} \text{ bps .}$$

9.3   Numeric risk in detail

The above sections serve as a general overview and introduction to the concept of market risk and its calculation. This section's goal is to make clear all aspects of numeric risk, such as when it does and does *not* work, and how it should and should *not* be applied.

9.3.1   Processes

Numeric risk requires a specific set of processes and information available:

(i) **a risk model** must be developed to construct a specific risk curveset with the input instruments representing the scenarios against which risk will be measured,

(ii) **the real pricing curveset** must be available to provide accurate prices to the instruments present and included in the risk model,

(iii) either **a cycling algorithm** must exist to iterate through each instrument or scenario, generating simulated bumped curvesets, or **a coding library with automatic differentiation** must exist, to ultimately return risk data.

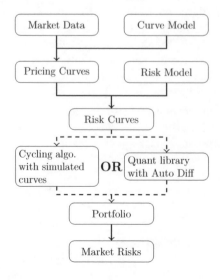

It is well worth noting that the simulated curves are often called 'bumped' curves, because they are traditionally created by bumping the input price of each instrument in the risk model by one bp and then generating a simulated curveset. This is done repeatedly, for each instrument in the risk model, and therefore, depending on the risk model, can generate a large number of simulated curvesets and by implication an even greater number of simulated curves. Automatic approaches are explained in chapter 11.

9.3.2 Design of a risk model

The reader might legitimately query the purpose of a risk model and the choice not simply to replicate the curve model and bump each instrument of it. We tackle this query directly in this section. We begin by highlighting the purpose and properties of each model to indicate their inherent differences in table 9.2. Hopefully the table presents a clear distinction to the reader and alludes to the requirement of a risk model. It suffices to say that frequently a number of risk models might be designed to present a number of ways of considering risk.

Curve model	Risk model(s)
Exists to produce an accurate curveset for pricing, calibrated to market data.	Exists to produce perspicuous delta and basis risks.
Can be particularly complicated with large numbers of instruments, intricate design, and use of non-tradable products.	Exists to produce reliable delta and basis risks, in the sense that PnL estimates are reasonably accurate.
Has no need for structure, other than that inferred from a risk consideration.	Prefers to have a desired structure and limited number of instruments to facilitate understanding of risks.

Table 9.2: Purpose and features of models.

Preferably, it would be best to have a curve model, suitably complex to give high accuracy of pricing, and a risk model, suitably simple enough to be easily understood and indicate simple market hedges, whilst simultaneously providing a **reliable**[5] PnL estimate, and whose hedges are perfectly effective.

Alas, this is not to be; as the models diverge in terms of complexity the reliability decreases. Heuristically this is also a sensible conclusion. If a simple curve was able to describe the PnL evolution of any portfolio as accurately as a complex one, and by inference accurately price any IR product, there would be no benefit of the existence of the complex curve in the first place - it would simply constitute superfluous construction parameters.

Since unreliability of PnL estimates is a factor dependent upon the distinction between a curve model and a risk model, this is precisely the reason that when constructing a curve model a consideration has to be made with regard to risk. A trade off has to made that weighs the respective importance of each item. Of course, this is also a subjective assessment which again highlights the nature of trading as a craft rather than a science.

Figure 9.2 is poor in the sense that it might subconsciously create the impression that complexity and reliability are somehow linearly proportional. They are both, of course, abstract

---

[5]always in this context reliable means consistently accurate.

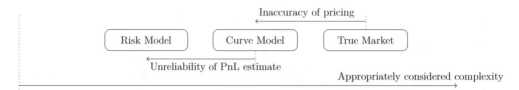

Figure 9.2: Models weighing unreliability against complexity.

concepts with an undefined scale. It may very well be the case that increasing the complexity of a risk model has no impact on its reliability until a certain threshold is passed. It may well be that increasing complexity of a risk model, but in a distinctly different manner to the curve model, decreases its reliability. There will be examples, we can be sure, of any of these or similar scenarios, but the idea stands as a rule of thumb. Analogously, a very complex curve model will not necessarily reflect true market prices unless it has managed to capture the 'right kind of complexity' which is probably impossible to gauge at all times.

As a guide to the types of factors that can introduce unreliability, by comparing risk models with curve model construction, table 9.3 aims to steer the design considerations for a risk model. If we choose to consider some of these items in more detail, the easiest to demonstrate is the effect of interpolation style. We look to provide a demonstration of the unreliability that is introduced when interpolation styles are changed in example 9.5.

Model consideration	Details
Curves in set:	All curve model curves should be replicated, to permit risking of every type of trade.
Foundation:	Not replicating the curve model foundations will introduce unreliability.
Input instruments:	Deviating from curve model inputs in terms of misaligning dates will introduce unreliability because interpolation will change. Simplifying the model by using less inputs will also increase unreliability. Selecting instruments around liquid products as basis for hedges is good practice.
Node/Knot placement:	Not replicating the curve model nodes/knots may introduce unreliability.
Interpolation style:	Not replicating the curve model interpolation styles will introduce unreliability.

Table 9.3: Risk model considerations, in reference to a pricing curve model, to limit PnL unreliability.

Example 9.5.
A trader has a curve model and a risk model using log-cubic and log-linear DF interpolation respectively. For the input instruments 1Y, 2Y, 3Y, 4Y, figure 9.3 below indicates the prices of intermediate IRSs under each model for two separate closing dates. The trader pays fixed on a 100mm 2.5Y IRS, at the rate determined by the pricing curves, and his risk model generates

the following delta risk:

$$\mathbf{S} = \begin{matrix} (1Y) \\ (2Y) \\ (3Y) \\ (4Y) \end{matrix} \begin{bmatrix} 0 \\ 12,000 \\ 12,000 \\ 0 \end{bmatrix}.$$

The trader hedges the IRS by receiving fixed on 2Y and 3Y IRSs in the appropriate notional so that the total delta risk of the portfolio, $\mathbf{S} = \mathbf{0}$.

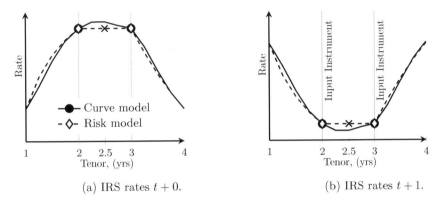

(a) IRS rates $t + 0$.   (b) IRS rates $t + 1$.

Figure 9.3: Chart for example 9.5.

After a day, the IR market has moved. However, the 2Y and 3Y rates are still the same price as each other, even though they both have fallen relative to the rest of the curve. The risk model still maintains that the delta risk of the portfolio, $\mathbf{S} = \mathbf{0}$. The risk model also records the total PnL change of the portfolio as zero because the 2.5Y rate has moved equally as much as the 2Y and 3Y rates under the structure of this model.

*However, **the official PnL change of the portfolio is a loss.** Under the curve model the 2.5Y rate which was originally higher than the 2Y and 3Y rates is now lower than the 2Y and 3Y rates due to the relative movement of the pricing curve under the different interpolation, so the trader has lost more money on his trade than he has gained back from the hedge trades.*

*The trader concludes his risk model is too different to his curve model, indicated suboptimal hedges and ultimately is **too unreliable**.*

We also give an example of misaligned input instruments to demonstrate how they give rise to unreliability of risk and PnL.

Example 9.6.
A trader has a curve model and a risk model both using log-linear DF interpolation. Some of the input instruments to the curve model are 1Y, 2Y, 3Y, 4Y, and the risk model has 1.5Y, 2.5Y, 3.5Y. Figure 9.4 indicates the prices of intermediate IRSs under each model for two separate closing dates. The trader pays fixed on a 100mm 2Y IRS, at the rate determined by the pricing curves, and his risk model generates the following delta risk of the trade:

$$\mathbf{S} = \begin{matrix} (1.5Y) \\ (2.5Y) \\ (3.5Y) \end{matrix} \begin{bmatrix} 9,000 \\ 9,000 \\ 0 \end{bmatrix}.$$

The trader hedges the IRS by receiving fixed on 1.5Y and 2.5Y IRSs in the appropriate notional so that the total delta risk of the portfolio, $\mathbf{S} = \mathbf{0}$.

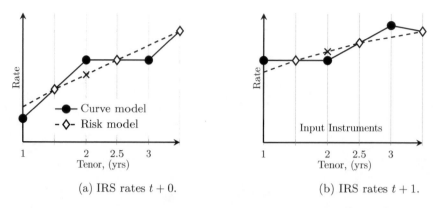

(a) IRS rates $t + 0$.   (b) IRS rates $t + 1$.

Figure 9.4: Chart for example 9.6.

After a day, the IR market has moved. The 1Y and 3Y IRS rates have moved higher but the 2Y rate remains the same. The risk model still maintains that the delta risk of the portfolio, **S** $= \mathbf{0}$. *The risk model also records the total PnL change of the portfolio as zero because, under the risk model, the 2Y rate has moved equally as much as the average of the 1.5Y and 2.5Y rate moves.*

However, **the official PnL change of the portfolio is, again, a loss.** *Under the curve model the 2Y rate is unchanged but the trader has lost money on his hedge trades since those rates have both moved higher.*

The trader concludes his risk model is too different to his curve model, indicated suboptimal hedges and ultimately is **too unreliable**.

Our final example demonstrates the use of layered curvesets to produce simpler risk models reliable in certain cases.

Example 9.7.
A trader has a curve model which uses 5Y, 7Y and 10Y instruments to build the first, or preliminary, layer of a curveset. It then builds a second layer by adjusting the 6Y, 8Y, and 9Y interpolated points by specified, skewed, values. The interpolation method used derives approximately linearly interpolated par IRS rates.

The trader pays fixed on 100mm 8.5Y IRS. His risk models, one designed for the preliminary curve build (1) and the second designed for the additional layer (2) show the numeric delta risk:

$$\mathbf{S_1} = \begin{matrix} (5Y) \\ (7Y) \\ (10Y) \end{matrix} \begin{bmatrix} 0 \\ 35,000 \\ 35,000 \end{bmatrix}, \qquad \mathbf{S_2} = \begin{matrix} (5Y) \\ (6Y) \\ (7Y) \\ (8Y) \\ (9Y) \\ (10Y) \end{matrix} \begin{bmatrix} 0 \\ 0 \\ 0 \\ 35,000 \\ 35,000 \\ 0 \end{bmatrix}.$$

The IR market again experiences a daily movement. The 5Y and 10Y IRS rates have moved higher but the 7Y rate remains the same. Additionally the skew adjustments that affect the 6Y, 8Y and 9Y point have also remained the same from one day to the next. Since the skews have remained the same the market movements of each instrument are the same across any of the models. So in this case hedging against either **S₁** *or* **S₂** *makes no difference. Either hedge would be satisfactory and result in no PnL loss.*

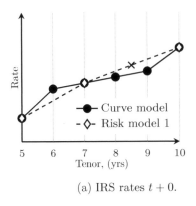

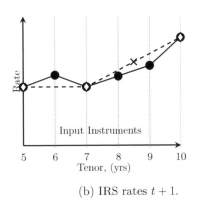

(a) IRS rates $t + 0$.   (b) IRS rates $t + 1$.

Figure 9.5: Chart for example 9.7.

Example 9.7 is included to demonstrate how curvesets with well designed layers can lead to less complex risk models that are reliable, *when* higher layers (second, third, etc.) have no daily movement. This does not mean they are entirely without unreliability, though. A non-linear interpolation style can result in the highest layer's interpolation being impacted by just some larger movements of the first layer. Although in my experience this has never been significant, instead the unreliability of the first layer model is overwhelmingly due to movements of the skews in the higher layers, on those days when they do actually move.

Why is this layering technique useful? It provides another way of reducing the number of dimensions from which to consider risk, but remain theoretically reliable. A risk supervisor might only be interested in the $\mathbf{S_1}$ risk, whilst an individual trader might make use of both risk models. The supervisor will rarely be presented with the scenario that market movements, taken in the context of the risks he sees, do not explain the PnL (within a tolerance understood from a design perspective).

In contrast, other *simplified* risk models that attempt to reduce the dimensionality of risk without being fully coherent with these principles (their simplification achieved with other means) typically produce much more unreliable risk. Indeed what makes those inferior simplified models worse is that they often suffer from unreliability from the unfavourable perspective of being *unexplainably* unreliable.

The content of this book focuses on conveying sound principles to ensure risk reliability, including explained unreliability. From our perspective unexplained unreliability can be fully eliminated or marginalised and indicates erroneous or poorly implemented risk models if it is frequently encountered.

9.3.3   Properties of risk models

In this section we digress from the design of a risk model and its reliability, and instead focus on the properties of risk models and the different types of results one expects to obtain under different models.

Up to this point we have suggested that when bumping curves with a cycling algorithm (and not using automatic differentiation), the variation is made in terms of a single bp. Although this is the true concept, in practice the size of the bump is usually much smaller, and then the resulting PnL change of an analysed portfolio (and therefore risk) is scaled by an equivalent multiplier to better approximate a single bp bump. This is often done for two reasons;

(i) reduce the impact of gamma (or convexity) and therefore eliminate the asymmetric bias of whether input instruments are bumped upwards or downwards to ascertain a more accurate reflection of pure delta or basis risk[6],

(ii) reduce strange phenomena and odd curve shapes when a single bp actually represents quite a large bump relative to surrounding instruments.

In the following example we give details and illustrations of how a single bump tends to affect the shapes of curves built using the risk model, and will, afterwards, use this information to draw conclusions as to the appropriateness and usefulness of adopting certain models.

Example 9.8.
This example illustrates the reaction of various types of risk model (and curve model) to the action of bumping a single input instrument. In each risk model the input instruments are the same; 1Y, 2Y, ..., 9Y IRSs. We assume that the curve is flat leading to par IRSs that are all 2%. In each model we bump the 5Y rate by 0.1bps and examine the reaction of the fwd curve and of the par IRS rates.

Log-linear DF *interpolation is the simplest curve model to describe. This is because the reaction in this case is* **local**. *The only fwd rates that show a reaction in this build, and what is also a general result, are those between the surrounding knots about the specifically bumped instrument (see figure 9.6). Also observable is that the impact to the O/N fwd curve is a consistent amount between the relevant knots.*

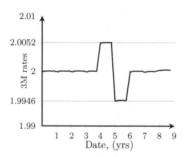 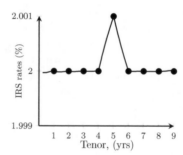

Figure 9.6: Log-linear DF interpolated case study.

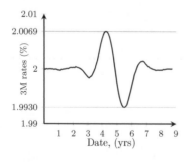 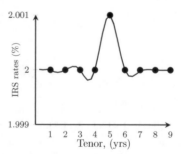

Figure 9.7: Log-cubic DF interpolated case study.

Log-cubic DF *interpolation shows global dependence. All fwd rates can potentially experience a change based on any bump, but the effect is dampened the further from the specific bumped*

---

[6]see this chapter's appendix for a mathematical description

instrument (see figure 9.7). This also impacts all the intermediate tenor IRS rates between knots, as opposed to log-linear interpolation. The O/N fwd rates impact is a continuous function unlike the log-linear case where the impacts are discontinuous at knot points.

Example 9.8 serves to highlight differences across risk models in terms of how they function. Choosing an interpolation style suffers from a large amount of subjectivity. Other interpolation styles exist, other than those here, and are used to try to marry local dependence, or at least limited global dependence, with justifiably smooth and functioning curves. This is because global dependence is more difficult to risk manage but often provides smoother curve shapes, so the best compromise is preferred. Chapter 12 introduces mixed interpolation styles with discussion about the specific choices made and optimal means of implementation.

9.3.4   Risking a trade or a portfolio

Having discussed the design of risk models and the properties of such, dependent upon input instrument bumps, the next step is to demonstrate actual risk strips of a trade or a portfolio of trades.

The first point to make about risk strips of this nature is that **if the specific trade which is to be risked is the same as any of the calibrating input instruments to the risk model then that instrument alone will show risk**, regardless of any of the considerations of interpolation style or foundation (for curves that are not overspecified). It is the case that only this instrument will show risk because it is only under the specific scenario where this instrument is bumped will there be any PnL change. In the scenarios where other input instruments to the risk model are bumped the instrument equivalent to the trade is held constant and therefore no PnL can be generated. This is relevant to point ii) made in section 11.4 and more thoroughly examined in section 11.5.4.

If a trade is not an input instrument, and indeed it falls between some of the input instruments then the cycling algorithm must iterate through and bump each input instrument to determine the effect that each bump has on the PnL of the underlying trade. If automatic differentiation is used these calculations will be given automatically. This is where the interpolation style, choice of input instruments and foundation of the risk model has the biggest impact. The example below illustrates this.

Example 9.9.
*A trader pays €300mm 4.25Y IRS, and calculates that it has an analytic delta of €122,115 pv01. He also obtains the **numeric delta** of the trade using the two risk models discussed in example 9.8, presented in the same order, and a third with linear par zero rate interpolation:*

$$
\mathbf{S} = \begin{array}{l}(1Y)\\(2Y)\\(3Y)\\(4Y)\\(5Y)\\(6Y)\\(7Y)\\(8Y)\\(9Y)\end{array}
\begin{bmatrix} 0 \\ 0 \\ 0 \\ 86,663 \\ 35,453 \\ 0 \\ 0 \\ 0 \\ 0 \end{bmatrix} ,
\begin{bmatrix} -231 \\ 1,848 \\ -10,478 \\ 101,598 \\ 38,234 \\ -11,642 \\ 3,635 \\ -1,047 \\ 197 \end{bmatrix} ,
\begin{bmatrix} -6 \\ -10 \\ -16 \\ 92,015 \\ 30,132 \\ 0 \\ 0 \\ 0 \\ 0 \end{bmatrix}
$$

$$122,115 \qquad 122,115 \qquad 122,115$$

He accepts the three models as viable, but his particular curve model uses log-cubic DF interpolation, so to minimise unreliability of PnL estimates he adopts the log-cubic DF interpolated risk model.

The trader decides to hedge the trade by receiving €90,000 pv01 of 4Y IRS and €32,000 pv01 of 5Y IRS, leaving himself some residual risk. Using his log-cubic DF risk model the delta risk of his portfolio of the trade and the two hedges is stated, as is his PnL estimate for the day's market movements, $\Delta \mathbf{r}$:

$$
\mathbf{S} =
\begin{array}{c}
(1Y) \\
(2Y) \\
(3Y) \\
(4Y) \\
(5Y) \\
(6Y) \\
(7Y) \\
(8Y) \\
(9Y)
\end{array}
\begin{bmatrix}
-231 \\
1,848 \\
-10,478 \\
11,598 \\
6,234 \\
-11,642 \\
3,635 \\
-1,047 \\
197
\end{bmatrix}
, \quad
\Delta \mathbf{r} =
\begin{bmatrix}
+1.1 \\
+1.2 \\
+1.4 \\
+1.7 \\
+1.6 \\
+1.7 \\
+1.4 \\
+1.3 \\
+1.3
\end{bmatrix}
, \quad
\Delta P \approx \mathbf{S} \cdot \Delta \mathbf{r} = €1,179 \; .
$$

115

His official PnL is determined as €1,178, so the unreliability here is only €1. Had he adopted any of the other models the unreliability would have increased to €1,328 and €784, respectively.

The above example is designed to illustrate the difference in risk seen on a trade under different models. In practice a trader will be accustomed to using only models from a similar class (e.g. log-cubic interpolators) in regular trading, although alternative models might be infrequently consulted for specific comparisons[7].

Up to this point we have also taken for granted the mathematical property of **linearity of risk**, and have used it in previous examples without referencing it. Here we quote it officially; the market risk of a trade or portfolio plus the market risk of another trade or portfolio is equivalent to the market risk of the aggregate trades or portfolios:

$$
\mathbf{S}(A_1) + \ldots + \mathbf{S}(A_k) = \mathbf{S}(A_1 + \ldots + A_k) \; .
$$

In the chapter regarding VaR we will see that the same property is not true for VaR.

Terminology, direction and quoting convention

Very often arrays of market risk are referred to as **risk strips**, often because they are presented vertically and usually only as a single column representing delta risks. Basis risks are often considered separately and referred to, without change, *as* basis risks, but terminology varies as does presentation.

A specific element of a risk strip is frequently called a **bucket**, e.g. the 7Y bucket or the 8Y bucket. A trade that has a lot of bucket risk would be one whose total delta might be small but has a number of large buckets with opposing signs to each other. In chapters 14, 16 and 19 we propose methods by which one can assess and compare the overall riskiness of portfolios with varying degrees of bucket risk.

Recognising the direction of trades from a given risk strip is clearly of utmost importance, especially when considering executing hedges. The direction adopted for the examples thus far and which is continued throughout the book is stated in the introductory notation section. Each trader or institution establishes their own preference for delta and basis direction, it suffices only to say that the reader should never take the direction for granted and always ensure that it is fully understood before taking any action.

---

[7]see chapters 10 and 16 for ways in which multiple risk models are used

9.3.5   Risk bleed

Risk bleed, or risk evolution for want of a better term, describes the effect of an evolving risk strip as time passes and the relative tenors of trades change with respect to the input instruments of a risk model. For example a 4Y IRS executed today shows up as risk to only the 4Y input instrument. In six months time, however, that same 4Y IRS will only be a 3.5Y IRS and the risk will then appear, under log-linear DF risk model, as c.50% in each of the 3Y and 4Y input instruments of the constantly rolling risk model. The term 'bleed' generates the appropriate connotations as this is an inconvenient property for risk models to possess. If one executed a trade and hedged it at inception under the risks ascertained by a risk model it is not optimal to have to continually re-hedge the portfolio with each passing day, as the model changes its formulation of the risks. Below we look in more detail how this effect is generated and what can be done to mitigate it.

We begin by considering only log-linear DF interpolated risk models, because we have seen their dependence is local and much better for example purposes.

Example 9.10.
A trader pays an 11.5Y IRS and hedges it according to his log-linear DF risk model with 25% 10Y and 75% 12Y. Figure 9.8 illustrates the portfolio's trades and risk and states the portfolio's numeric risk.

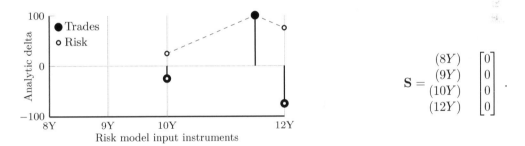

$$\mathbf{S} = \begin{matrix} (8Y) \\ (9Y) \\ (10Y) \\ (12Y) \end{matrix} \begin{bmatrix} 0 \\ 0 \\ 0 \\ 0 \end{bmatrix}.$$

Figure 9.8: The original portfolio's trades and risk in example 9.10.

The portfolio remains untouched for one and a half years. At this point the risk is reassessed using the original risk model. The result is depicted in figure 9.9[8]. The portfolio needs to be re-hedged, having steadily built up a position over the passage of time.

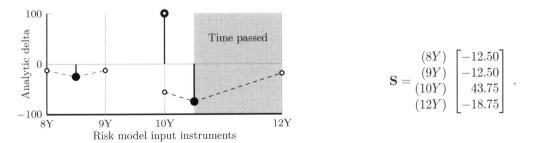

$$\mathbf{S} = \begin{matrix} (8Y) \\ (9Y) \\ (10Y) \\ (12Y) \end{matrix} \begin{bmatrix} -12.50 \\ -12.50 \\ 43.75 \\ -18.75 \end{bmatrix}.$$

Figure 9.9: The effect of risk bleed of the portfolio in example 9.10.

---

[8]note that to avoid complicating the example the effect of risk reduction of par swaps as time passes and resets occur has been ignored, in fact the original analytic risk is falsely kept constant

Performing the same kind of analysis as in the example for log-cubic DF interpolated risk models or other models with global dependence yields a similar result. Of course it happens to be a little more non-linear and dependent upon precisely the structure of the model[9], the included elements and their spacing etc.. The effect of risk bleed present in these other models does not always occur at the same rate and in the same magnitude as log-linear, but in the absence of other information this provides a practical and workable estimate.

Why is risk bleed an important consideration?

Analogous to reset risk, risk bleed is an effect that will not show up in VaR and represents risk that will arise in the future. A portfolio without any risk bleed is clearly more favourable to one with it, all other things being equal. It is also difficult to characterise this effect so an overall subjective assessment typically needs to be made. Personally, I would venture that this effect is only important if it is noticed by a trader managing a portfolio. Given the small changes that might occur on a daily basis due to this effect it might remain undetected or rise to a significant enough size that its effect becomes noticeable. Where it does become noticeable it might have been favourable to pre-empt the condition rather than have to react to the condition.

How to mitigate risk bleed?

The cause of risk bleed is having large traded positions with dates falling between input instruments, which are hedged *by* input instruments. There are generally two ways of mitigating the effect of risk bleed;

(i) design risk models where the effect of risk bleed is minimised, and,

(ii) eliminate traded positions which give rise to the effect of risk bleed.

Both of these solutions are possible, except other considerations may take precedence.

In order to design risk models where the effect of risk bleed is minimised it is important to space the input instruments of a curve and risk model appropriately. Wider gaps will produce slower, and therefore lesser, risk bleed, as each day represents a smaller fraction of a period for wider gaps compared to narrower gaps. It is a happy coincidence that wider gaps might permit more possibility of accumulating a more broadly offsetting collection of trades in between the input instruments, rather than a small gap which might accumulate trades in a similar direction for one reason or another. Since risk bleed is often a minor concern it may not be practical to alter curve and risk models to minimise this effect. Indeed their design might need to be kept for more pressing pricing or other risk management reasons.

Eliminating traded positions that gives rise to risk bleed is obviously the best way but is difficult. Firstly, it requires the positions to be identified. This means that a more detailed risk model must be designed to examine the spacing between the input instruments on the benchmark risk model. Secondly, once these positions have been identified new hedges must be executed, either through the interbank market or with a counterparty who has offsetting positions. Executing in the interbank market might be very difficult as the positions are likely to be illiquid, but it may be possible to find offsetting positions within the same institution as it is likely the risk models used in the same institution are also the same.

Anecdotally I have previously inherited portfolios from departing traders which had, rather foolishly, traded extremely large trades without a concern for the ongoing management of risk bleed. In order to hedge them properly using interbank trades, and to eliminate the effect, I had to wait until the right time during the year where the par interbank tenors aligned with

---

[9]see section 12.5.2

the respective dates on the specific trades under analysis. Then I could transact the hedges which took place over a period of a few weeks, due to the size of transactions that needed to occur.

Example 9.11.
A trader is reviewing his curve model and risk model. Some of the input instruments to the existing models are 10Y, 11Y, ... , 19Y, 20Y and then 25Y, but he finds the risk bleed about the 19Y, 20Y and 25Y buckets difficult to assess and understand. He acknowledges that it is very rare for trades other than 10Y, 12Y, 15Y 20Y and 25Y to occur in the interbank market, but still wishes to command a little more control of his curve outside of just those tenors. The trader makes the decision to remodel and test using the following, better spaced, input instruments; 10Y, 11Y, 12Y, 13Y, 14Y, 15Y, 17Y, 20Y, 25Y.

Example 9.12.
A trader believes he has a good curve model and benchmark risk model, $\mathbf{S_b}$. Some of the input instruments to his models are 8Y, 9Y, 10Y and 12Y. He perceives some risk bleed and creates a more detailed risk model, $\mathbf{S_d}$, with an additional 11Y instrument to understand why. The numeric risks returned are:

$$\mathbf{S_b} = \begin{matrix} (8Y) \\ (9Y) \\ (10Y) \\ (12Y) \end{matrix} \begin{bmatrix} 0 \\ 0 \\ 0 \\ 0 \end{bmatrix} , \quad \mathbf{S_d} = \begin{matrix} (8Y) \\ (9Y) \\ (10Y) \\ (11Y) \\ (12Y) \end{matrix} \begin{bmatrix} 0 \\ 0 \\ -50 \\ 100 \\ -50 \end{bmatrix} .$$

The trader attempts to reduce his exposure to 11Y vs 10Y and 12Y, and therefore reduce risk bleed under his benchmark risk model.

Example 9.12 provides a rare example of where it is useful to utilise a risk model that is more complex than the curve model. In terms of reliability of PnL estimates it will be no better than the benchmark PnL estimate if that is already completely reliable, but it does provide more information about the structure of the portfolio.

9.4 Practical market risks

We have alluded to the grid structure and delta and basis separation of market risks in this chapter. Of course, numeric risk is flexible enough that one can design risk models however one might like. Personally, I prefer risk models that have some consistency across currencies in order to provide better comparisons.. I believe items that are more aesthetic are better fathomed, and ultimately produce better trading results. This particular structure allows for easier development of other tools, for example in chapter 16.

This section serves to give a practical example of how the benchmark market risk of a real IR derivative portfolio might look.

Example 9.13.
A trader's USD and EUR IR derivatives portfolio's market risk is shown in figure 9.10, numerically generated from his designed risk model. Note that '1f' stands for first future and represents an IMM date.

Additionally the figure shows how the trader can expand items so he can isolate individual elements. In particular his system separates new trades from existing trades and also compares today's open risk to yesterday's closing risk to determine the risk bleed. He also has a column to show risk generated from gamma. This information is shown for the example 6Y, 7Y and 8Y buckets.

Input instruments		USD RFR Delta		EUR RFR Delta	
Start	Tenor	$\frac{\partial P}{\partial r}$	$\frac{\partial P}{\partial s}$	$\frac{\partial P}{\partial r}$	$\frac{\partial P}{\partial s}$
t+2	3M	11	1	-14	-5
1f	3M	-5	1	9	-2
2f	3M	3	1	8	-2
3f	3M	5	1	47	-2
4f	3M	-11	1	-15	-2
5f	3M	6	1	41	1
6f	3M	14	2	16	1
7f	3M	-21	2	-20	1
8f	3M	7	2	41	1
9f	3M	9	3	14	-1
10f	3M	11	3	-34	-1
11f	3M	0	3	31	-2
12f	3M	-3	3	-13	-2
t+2	4Y	-56	0	77	4
t+2	5Y	110	5	-24	5
t+2	6Y	-38	6	-119	6
t+2	7Y	-27	7	133	0
t+2	8Y	98	0	-428	0
t+2	9Y	210	-3	-38	0
t+2	10Y	-403	-4	-113	-4
t+2	12Y	-24	-5	-96	-5
t+2	15Y	1,003	-6	-553	-6
t+2	20Y	-834	-8	1,180	-8
t+2	25Y	12	0	913	12
t+2	30Y	776	0	-1,606	13
t+2	40Y	-1,867	0	1,254	14
t+2	50Y	956	10	-559	15
Total		**-58**	**26**	**132**	**31**

Input instruments		USD RFR Delta		(all risk expressed in $000s)			
		$\frac{\partial P}{\partial r}$					
		$\Longrightarrow$	New	Gamma	Open		
Start	Tenor				$\Longrightarrow$	Close (t-1)	Bleed
..	..	..	..	..	..	..	..
t+2	6Y	**-38**	56	0	-94	-92	-2
t+2	7Y	**-27**	0	0	-27	-31	4
t+2	8Y	**98**	-56	0	154	156	-2
..	..	..	..	..	..	..	..

Figure 9.10: A practical example of a portfolio's benchmark risks.

9.5 Appendix

9.5.1 Approximating risks with numerical processes

Let us correctly assume that IRSs experience gamma and cross-gamma, and therefore the PnL, calculated in terms of the market movements, $\Delta\mathbf{r}$, is approximated to second order as follows,

$$\Delta P \approx \mathbf{S^T}\Delta\mathbf{r} + \frac{1}{2}\Delta\mathbf{r^T}\mathbf{G}\Delta\mathbf{r}$$

This is, in fact, a very accurate approximation, where $\mathbf{S}$ are the delta risks and $\mathbf{G}$ is the cross-gamma grid. Furthermore suppose that only a single element of $\Delta\mathbf{r}$ is non-zero such that, say $\Delta r_i = \epsilon \ll 1$. Thus the above reduces to,

$$\Delta P(\epsilon) \approx S_i\epsilon + \frac{1}{2}\epsilon^2 G_{ii}$$

The value of $\Delta P(\epsilon)$ is numerically assessed by comparing the before and after PV of the portfolio or individual IRD, and then the delta risk, S_i, is approximated as,

$$S_i \approx \frac{\Delta P(\epsilon)}{\epsilon} - \frac{1}{2}\epsilon G_{ii}$$

When ϵ is taken to be small enough (but not sufficiently small that machine precision and truncation errors can affect the numerical result) the rightmost term involving the gamma component is simply ignored yielding the result. This is a forward difference approximation.

Alternatively a central difference approximation can be made where a positive market movement, $\Delta r_i = \epsilon$, and a negative market movement, $\Delta r_i = -\epsilon$, are separately evaluated in terms of their impacts to the portfolio or IRD, and we can observe that in this case the gamma component cancels,

$$\Delta P(\epsilon) - \Delta P(-\epsilon) \approx S_i\epsilon + \frac{1}{2}\epsilon^2 G_{ii} + S_i\epsilon - \frac{1}{2}\epsilon^2 G_{i,i} = 2S_i\epsilon$$

$$\implies S_i \approx \frac{\Delta P(\epsilon) - \Delta P(-\epsilon)}{2\epsilon}$$

Whilst mathematically more accurate this central difference method gains little in practice and requires twice as much computation so is often avoided.

Of course the process needs to be repeated for all i in order to evaluate all risk elements in $\mathbf{S}$.

Risk Models

The previous chapter introduced numeric risk and explained many of its properties and how the results can be influenced based on the design of an individual risk model. This chapter departs from those considerations and focuses instead on the practical aspect of utilising multiple risk models simultaneously. Particularly this chapter outlines;

- why one would choose to use more than one risk model,

- some efficient numerical approaches to extracting risk from multiple models,

- what Jacobian transformations are and how they are used to transform risk from one model to another,

- what lossless Jacobian transformations are and their implications,

- the difference between risk models using fwd instruments and par instruments,

- some examples of creating Jacobians between fwd and par based models,

- the use of Jacobians in estimating market movements by transforming one model's market movements to another,

- the use of Jacobians for estimating covariance matrices and cross-gamma grids for other models than the one used for their primary calculation.

10.1   Using multiple risk models

The purpose of using multiple risk models is for information assimilation. Risk managing a derivatives portfolio is a complex task and using multiple risk models helps to break information down into manageable chunks and act appropriately. One might have a large number of models worth considering even if some of those are only referred to once a day, week or even month. One should also develop models for use on a minute to minute basis which will steer the dominant share of any trader's decision making process.

As an example, a reasonable choice of different risk models to utilise are;

(i) a simple, broadly reliable, grid based fwd instrument model,

(ii) a simple, broadly reliable, grid based par instrument model,

(iii) a complex, extremely reliable, fwd instrument model, useful for evaluating losses not apparent in the other simpler models,

(iv) an alternative, individually designed model, broadly reliable, for considering risks from different basis or delta perspectives.

Along with risk models there are other tools that can be utilised, but we reserve those for other chapters[1]. The distinction we make between fwd and par risk models in this chapter is important but first we need a little theory to put multiple models in context.

10.2   Risking with multiple models

Seeking to risk a portfolio from multiple risk models obviously requires more steps and greater numerical processing than risking a single model. There are two ways of going about doing this; a brute force method of replicating the same numerical processes for additional models (see figure 10.1), and a semi analytical approach which develops a way of transforming the first set of obtained risks (see figure 10.2).

Although this section serves to introduce theory and demonstrate numerical efficiency that institutions can benefit greatly from, risk transformation is an important concept that should not be overlooked by any trader irrespective of its initially perceived usefulness. Risk transformations give a tactically rapid means for a trader to develop alternative views of his risk 'on-the-fly' and I, myself, have used these techniques hundreds of times.

The numerical efficiency from adopting a transformation based approach is that each trade in the portfolio does not have to be risked a second time, and for large portfolios with thousands of trades this saving can mount up, even if using state-of-the-art automatic differentiation libraries.

10.3   Jacobian transformations for risk

The overall mathematical process for transforming one risk model to another is a reasonably straight forward process. In fact it is a simple application of the chain rule for differentiation. Let us suggest we have two risk models, $\mathbf{S_A}$ and $\mathbf{S_B}$, and that the first risk model has been

---

[1]see chapters 14 and 16 on VAR and trader models respectively

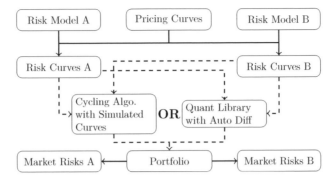

Figure 10.1: Illustrating the approach of identical numerical processes for each model.

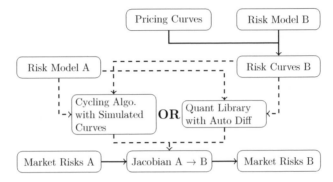

Figure 10.2: Illustrating the approach using Jacobian matrix transformations. Notice the portfolio is only analysed once to derive market risks A, as in figure 10.1.

processed and the risk sensitivities are available;

$$
\mathbf{S_A} = \begin{bmatrix} S_A^1 \\ S_A^2 \\ \vdots \\ S_A^{n-1} \\ S_A^n \end{bmatrix} = \begin{bmatrix} \frac{\partial P}{\partial r_{A,1}} \\ \frac{\partial P}{\partial r_{A,2}} \\ \vdots \\ \frac{\partial P}{\partial r_{A,n-1}} \\ \frac{\partial P}{\partial r_{A,n}} \end{bmatrix} .
$$

The second risk model can be analytically determined from the first, where each S_B^{*i} is:

$$
S_B^{*i} = \frac{\partial P}{\partial r_{B:i}}^* = \frac{\partial P}{\partial r_{A,1}} \frac{\partial r_{A,1}}{\partial r_{B,i}} + \ldots + \frac{\partial P}{\partial r_{A,n}} \frac{\partial r_{A,n}}{\partial r_{B,i}} ,
$$

and which leads to the matrix system describing **Jacobian risk transformations**[2]:

$$
\mathbf{S_B^*} = \mathbf{J_{A \to B} S_A}, \quad \text{for} \quad \mathbf{J_{A \to B}} = [J_{ij}], \quad \text{where} \quad J_{ij} = \frac{\partial r_{A,j}}{\partial r_{B,i}} .
$$

Readers uninterested in the mathematical aspect need pay no attention to the formulae. Indeed, how one practically acquires the Jacobian matrix is **to risk every input instrument**

---

[2]note that the definition of Jacobian matrices can differ between authors in their transpose. The version is chosen here since I believe it is more intuitive and resultant formulae are simplified in terms of column vectors

in model A (the columns) using the allowable market instrument movements in model B (the rows), with a standardised pv01 of 1 and insert the results as each column entry, note how in example 10.1 the sum of each column is 1 (although, if determined numerically, more accurate values might not be precisely 1).

Example 10.1.
A short-end trader has a risk model (A) with 1Y, 2Y and 3Y par IRSs. He wishes to view his risk against a fwd IRSs model (B) instead but hasn't the numerical resources to examine his entire portfolio. He constructs the Jacobian:

$$\mathbf{J_{A\to B}} = \begin{matrix} (0Y1Y) \\ (1Y1Y) \\ (2Y1Y) \end{matrix} \begin{bmatrix} 1 & 0.513 & 0.346 \\ 0 & 0.487 & 0.329 \\ 0 & 0 & 0.325 \end{bmatrix} \quad \begin{matrix} (1Y) \ (2Y) \ (3Y) \end{matrix}$$

Looking specifically at the elements; J_{11} is 1 because the 1Y instrument is the same in model A as model B so there is a direct relationship. J_{22}, with value 0.487, is due to the result of the movement of the 2Y IRS rate, of model A, when the 1Y1Y IRS rate, of model B, is increased by one bp. Similarly J_{32} is zero because the 2Y rate is not at all impacted by any movement in the 2Y1Y rate[3].

Using his current risk model, $\mathbf{S_A}$, the trader obtains his sought risk view, $\mathbf{S_B^*}$, through the transformation:

$$\mathbf{S_A} = \begin{matrix} (1Y) \\ (2Y) \\ (3Y) \end{matrix} \begin{bmatrix} -820 \\ -1,100 \\ 4,000 \end{bmatrix}, \qquad \mathbf{S_B^*} = \mathbf{J_{A\to B}} \mathbf{S_A} = \begin{matrix} (0Y1Y) \\ (1Y1Y) \\ (2Y1Y) \end{matrix} \begin{bmatrix} 0 \\ 780 \\ 1,300 \end{bmatrix} .$$

Lossless transformations

We can draw an analogy to applying Jacobian transformations to that of video or image compression. If an image is compressed, say a bitmap (.bmp) to a jpeg (.jpeg), then it will lose some information in order to take up less storage space, and the image will lose some clarity. If it is compressed again, say from the jpeg to a gif (.gif), then there will be further degradation and departure from the original image. In particular the quality of the final gif will be lower than had the original image been compressed into gif format directly, even though the amount of saved storage space might be the same.

The same is generally true for applying Jacobian transformations. Let's say for model A the risk is derived directly from the portfolio, and in order to acquire the risk against model C, the risk from A is first transformed to B and then transformed to C. The risk obtained for model C in this way is likely to be less reliable for PnL estimates. Had the risk been obtained directly from the portfolio, or indeed through a single transformation from model A, it would be more reliable and more accurate.

The concept of **lossless transformations** is useful for determining amounts of reliability of risk models. Under a lossless transformation a risk model could be transformed and that transformation reversed without introducing error:

$$\mathbf{S_A^{**}} = \mathbf{J_{B\to A}} \mathbf{S_B^*} = \mathbf{J_{B\to A}} \mathbf{J_{A\to B}} \mathbf{S_A} = \mathbf{S_A} .$$

This necessarily requires that the reverse transformation, $\mathbf{J_{B\to A}}$, is equal to the inverse matrix, $\mathbf{J_{A\to B}^{-1}}$, of the original transformation, $\mathbf{J_{A\to B}}$. Example 10.1 was in fact an example of a lossless

---

[3]a more detailed explanation of how these figures can be derived is shown later in example 10.4

transformation.

For a transformation that is not-lossless these matrices will not be the same and some unreliability of PnL estimates can creep in[4]. What provides a pertinent example of a not-lossless transformation is the **curve model** and the **risk model** described in chapter 9. Imagining for a second that the curve model and all of its complexities are denoted by and subsumed to be risk model A, and the specific risk model chosen in that chapter we respectively term model B. We know that the risk model is not completely reliable, even though it has been designed to be as good as possible, and thus:

$$\mathbf{S_A^{**}} = \mathbf{J_{B \to A}} \mathbf{S_B^*} = \mathbf{J_{B \to A}} \mathbf{J_{A \to B}} \mathbf{S_A} \neq \mathbf{S_A}, \quad \text{and} \quad \mathbf{J_{B \to A}} \neq \mathbf{J_{A \to B}^{-1}} \, .$$

In words, if our curve risk model (A) is transformed to the simpler risk model (B), then applying the reverse transformation from the risk model (B) to the curve model (A) does not retrieve the original complex risks of the curve model (A). It can't, since information was lost in the first simplification transformation.

Example 10.2.
A trader has two linearly interpolated par swap (quite similar to log-linear DF) risk models, A and B, with the input instruments 2Y,3Y,4Y,5Y and 2Y,2.75Y,4.25Y,5Y respectively. He pays 100 pv01 3.25Y IRS and examines his numerically determined risks, and also his risks determined for each model through a Jacobian transformation from the other (see figure 10.3).

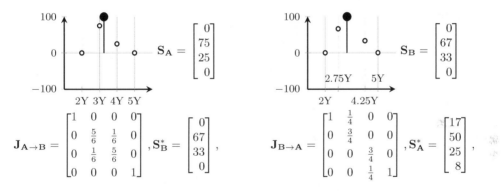

Figure 10.3: Example of a not-lossless Jacobian transformation.

The trader observes that $\mathbf{S_B}$ and $\mathbf{S_B^*}$ are the same, which means for this particular 3.25Y trade the Jacobian transformation from A to B was accurate. He also observes the transformation from B to A is quite poor.

The trader recognises that considering other trades, 2.5Y or 4.5Y for example, would not necessarily show that the Jacobian transformation from A to B would be equally accurate. It is clearly a not-lossless transformation since the Jacobian matrices are not matrix inverses of each other.

Up to this point the examples have all been presented with the risk models involved in transformations having the same number of instruments. This creates square transformation matrices and implies the possible existence of an inverse matrix. Of course that need not be the case; one model might have only slightly less or considerably less instruments than another model. In fact, this is often encouraged and very useful. Indeed, simpler models will tend to

---

[4]see the final section of this chapter for more information on how to improve consistency of estimates

always have less instruments. In these cases the Jacobian transformation matrix won't have a direct inverse[5] and the transformation will certainly be not-lossless.

Being lossless is a nice to have property because the reliability across PnL estimates is consistent. A lossless transformation suggests that two risk models are of equal complexity, but it is not always practical or useful to be restricted to lossless transformations. A good deal of time was spent in chapter 9 discussing, albeit in another manner, why a risk model will not be lossless in respect to a curve model. We also discussed methods of mitigating against this loss so as to minimise unreliability. By understanding the associations between risk models, one can appreciate the nuances of specific models and derive confidence in their ability to estimate PnL. The next part of this chapter's focus is on not-lossless transformations. It tries to formalise some theory, identifying information that will promote the recognition of sources of error when PnLs are not fully explained or understood.

We summarise Jacobian transformations to give some guidelines as to their use;

(i) the most practical use is to transform determined risk sensitivities from a complex risk model to a simpler risk model, which represents a not-lossless transformation,

(ii) simpler risk models exist that introduce minimal unreliability if they are well designed, relative to the complex model they transform from,

(iii) transformations between very different models (in terms of knot points, interpolation styles, etc.) will be particularly not-lossless and are not advised,

(iv) a simpler risk model risk should never be transformed to a more complex one because the lost information cannot be recreated,

(v) avoid performing successive transformations unless the transformations are known to be lossless,

(vi) finally one should recognise that a risk model often represents a simpler model than a pricing curve model and is thus a not-lossless transformation from that curve model, which gives rise to unreliability of PnL estimates discussed in chapter 9.

10.4   Par and forward (fwd) based models

The distinction between fwd and par instrument based models is probably the most commonly used and quoted distinction across risk models and it is important to understand. It also demonstrates the property of leverage, which is very important for pricing, and which we come on to later. To reiterate the quoting convention, an 'xYzY' swap is one that starts in 'x' years time with a tenor of 'z' years. A 'zY' swap is otherwise a par swap with a tenor of 'z' years and thus it is implicit that it is really a '0YzY' swap.

Interbank markets trade in par swaps. Of course one can generally transact any number of different trades, fwd or par, but this does not mean that they are liquid. One of the reasons that par swaps are the default choice is due to interconnectivity of markets. Bonds and loans are always transacted on a par basis thus this provides a direct comparison to those other liquid products. Analysis is often preferred on a fwd basis, however, because the forward rate curve is much more sensitive to small movements in par rates. Example 10.3 makes use of analytic delta and the linearity of swaps' pricing to produce good estimates of market movements of corresponding fwd rates. The reliance is on the pricing identity,

$$R_{i+j}A_{i+j} \equiv R_i A_i + R_j A_j \, ,$$

---

[5]the Moore-Penrose pseudo-inverse is a generalisation which is useful in the context of Jacobian matrices for least squares regression applied to risk

where R is a fixed rate, A is an analytic delta and, where $(i + j)$ is an instrument made from the combination of i and j. For example a 10Y IRS is the combination of a 5Y and 5Y5Y pair of IRSs or a 4Y and 4Y6Y pair[6].

Example 10.3.
The 10Y rate has fallen on the day by 4.1bps to 1.46%, but the 20Y rate has risen by +1.4bps to 1.88%. How much has the 10Y10Y rate moved by?

Swap	Analytic delta, A_k	Rate move (bps)
0Y10Y	9.27	-4.1
10Y10Y	7.38	$+8.3 \left(+1.4 \times \frac{16.65}{7.38} - 4.1 \times \frac{9.27}{7.38} \right)$
0Y20Y	16.65	+1.4

The 5Y rate remains unchanged on the day at 1.4928%, but the 10Y rate has risen by +1bp to 2.0933%. How much has the 5Y5Y rate moved by?

Swap	Analytic delta, A_k	Rate move (bps)
0Y5Y	4.8415	0.00
5Y5Y	4.3790	$+2.11 \left(+1.0 \times \frac{9.2205}{4.3790} - 0 \times \frac{4.8415}{4.3790} \right)$
0Y10Y	9.2205	+1.00

Table 10.1 gives an overview of the benefits of each model type. The highlighted point about distinct sections of the curve, illustrated by Figure 10.4, is quite important for many concepts. In the case that a 2Y swap rate, for example, moves higher but the 3Y rate is unchanged, implies that the 2Y1Y fwd rate must move to compensate since 2Y comprises a sizeable part of the 3Y. This again highlights leverage.

Par	Fwd
Shows risk in standard market traded instruments.	Shows risk for distinct sections of the curve, allowing analysis of the economic environment to be applied directly.
Useful to make an assessment of the cost of market liquidation of all positions.	Useful to consider the sizes of relative value (RV) trades.
Useful for applying heuristic intuition to market instruments' correlations, particularly with interconnected markets.	Removes the effect of leverage from par risk to obtain scaleable quantities.

Table 10.1: Uses of each risk model type.

Constructing lossless transformations between par and fwd instruments

One of the most frequent uses of a Jacobian transformation is to quickly and tactically convert a set of risks given in one format to another. In order to estimate (to first order) the Jacobian transformation we can use analytic delta, ensure the matrix is square, and ensure

---

[6]this assumes the date schedules completely align and match with roll dates, etc.

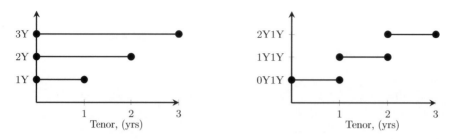

Figure 10.4: Distinction between par and fwd rates.

the instruments are aligned in terms of dates. This allows for a lossless transformation. Otherwise numerical methods are often used for precise results, particularly if there are a lot of instruments which don't necessarily align, or to add discounting basis risks as well.

Example 10.4.
To construct a par to fwd Jacobian transformation, with only the tenor and analytic delta information available on the par swaps, first derive the fwd swap analytic deltas and then construct the Jacobian with appropriate ratios.

Par	A.Delta	Fwd	A.Delta
1Y	**0.988**	0Y1Y	0.988
2Y	**1.956**	1Y1Y	0.968 $(1.956 - 0.988)$
5Y	**4.747**	2Y3Y	2.791 $(4.747 - 1.956)$
10Y	**9.043**	5Y5Y	4.296 $(9.043 - 4.747)$

$$
\mathbf{J}_{\text{par}\to\text{fwd}} =
\begin{array}{c}
(0Y1Y) \\
(1Y1Y) \\
(2Y3Y) \\
(5Y5Y)
\end{array}
\begin{bmatrix}
1.00 & 0.51(\frac{0.988}{1.956}) & 0.21(\frac{0.988}{4.747}) & 0.11(\frac{0.988}{9.043}) \\
0 & 0.49(\frac{0.968}{1.956}) & 0.20(\frac{0.968}{4.747}) & 0.11(\frac{0.968}{9.043}) \\
0 & 0 & 0.59(\frac{2.791}{4.747}) & 0.31(\frac{2.791}{9.043}) \\
0 & 0 & 0 & 0.47(\frac{4.296}{9.043})
\end{bmatrix},
$$

with column headers $(1Y)$ $(2Y)$ $(5Y)$ $(10Y)$.

The fwd risk is obtained by matrix multiplication:

$$
\mathbf{S}^*_{\text{fwd}} = \mathbf{J}_{\text{par}\to\text{fwd}}\mathbf{S}_{\text{par}} .
$$

Example 10.5.
To construct a fwd to par transformation, one can invert the above matrix or take a similar approach as before.

Fwd	A.Delta	Par	A.Delta
0Y1Y	**0.988**	1Y	0.988
1Y1Y	**0.968**	2Y	1.956 $(0.988 + 0.968)$
2Y3Y	**2.791**	5Y	4.747 $(1.956 + 2.791)$
5Y5Y	**4.296**	10Y	9.043 $(4.747 + 4.296)$

$$
\mathbf{J}_{\text{fwd}\to\text{par}} = \begin{array}{c} \\ (1Y) \\ (2Y) \\ (5Y) \\ (10Y) \end{array} \begin{array}{c} (0Y1Y) \quad\quad (1Y1Y) \quad\quad\quad (2Y3Y) \quad\quad\quad (5Y5Y) \\ \begin{bmatrix} 1.00 & -1.02(\frac{-0.988}{0.968}) & 0 & 0 \\ 0 & 2.02(\frac{1.956}{0.968}) & -0.70(\frac{-1.956}{2.791}) & 0 \\ 0 & 0 & 1.70(\frac{4.747}{2.791}) & -1.10(\frac{-4.747}{4.296}) \\ 0 & 0 & 0 & 2.10(\frac{9.043}{4.296}) \end{bmatrix} \end{array},
$$

The par risk is obtained by matrix multiplication:

$$\mathbf{S}^*_{\text{par}} = \mathbf{J}_{\text{fwd}\to\text{par}}\mathbf{S}_{\text{fwd}} .$$

The fwd to par transformation is useful for observing the amount of **leverage** a fwd instrument is exposed to by the par instruments. The greater the tenor of the par instrument and the shorter the tenor of the fwd the more leverage it has. The sub-matrix below containing a few long tenor par swaps is an example where these chosen fwds have broadly 10× times leverage.

$$
\begin{array}{c} (30Y) \\ (35Y) \\ (40Y) \end{array} \begin{array}{c} (30Y5Y) \quad (35Y5Y) \\ \begin{bmatrix} -8.62 & 0 \\ 9.62 & -10.60 \\ 0 & 11.60 \end{bmatrix} \end{array}
$$

10.5 Other uses of Jacobian transformations

The primary use of Jacobian transformations is transforming risk of one model into another. There are secondary uses of Jacobian transformations that we describe here. Showing how Jacobians apply to different aspects of swaps demonstrates the interconnectedness of all of the chapters. More flexible and useful trading systems can be constructed with the understanding of transformations.

10.5.1 PnL estimates and market movements

Chapter 9 outlines the basic linear PnL estimate given delta risks and market movements,

$$\Delta P \approx \mathbf{S} \cdot \mathbf{\Delta r} .$$

If the risk model used for this estimate replicates the curve model, say $\mathbf{S}_{\text{curve}}$, then for a portfolio with negligible amounts of gamma or cross-gamma this estimate will be extremely reliable, so that,

$$\Delta P \simeq \mathbf{S}_{\text{curve}} \cdot \mathbf{\Delta r}_{\text{curve}} .$$

Often in trading, PnL estimates are referred to as 'explains' because their function is to explain where PnL is due and which curve movements give rise to what PnL. The error in any PnL estimate is termed the 'unexplained'. Reliable risk models will have minimal unexplained, particularly if those estimates are expanded to incorporate gamma and cross-gamma too. If a trader notices an amount of unexplained on a regular basis this is a clear indication that the risk model is not well designed and can lead to systematic losses (or gains) being accrued. Well designed risk models can produce PnL estimates that are almost as reliable as the curve model, so that mathematically speaking,

$$\Delta P \simeq \mathbf{S}_{\text{curve}} \cdot \mathbf{\Delta r}_{\text{curve}} \simeq \mathbf{S}_{\text{A}} \cdot \mathbf{\Delta r}_{\text{A}} .$$

In the few cases where these estimates might diverge, an experienced trader might be able to recognise why. Particularly with knowledge of the differences between the risk model and curve model, the trader might well be able to speculate about specific nuanced curve movements that have given rise to unusual PnL. This is often a really useful trick.

This chapter has discussed using Jacobian transformations to transform the calculated risk sensitivities of one risk model into another. With respect to PnL estimates we will now discuss using this technique to obtain the market movements of one model with knowledge of the market movements of another. One might legitimately ask why the physical market movements, Δr_B, of the second risk model could not be used? Well, of course they can be used but it might not always be so easy to directly calculate them. Secondly there is a subtle, but strong, argument that shows **using transformed risk with real market movements will not necessarily give a PnL estimate that is consistent with the first risk model - instead it is better to use transformed market movements**. Additionally, there are two ways one might do this; either the reverse transformation can be used or the inverse transformation is used to derive market movements, so that,

$$\Delta r_B^* := \left(J_{B \to A}\right)^T \Delta r_A \quad \text{or} \quad \Delta r_B^* := \left(J_{A \to B}^{-1}\right)^T \Delta r_A \ .$$

For a lossless transformation these two methods are exactly the same. If the transformation is not-lossless then they will each give different results. If the transformation is not a square matrix and does not have an inverse then the more general Moore-Penrose pseudoinverse, $J_{A \to B}^+$, can be used instead. Of course this then raises the question which is **better** to use?

Market movements are often used to generate PnL explains and thus the choice of how to calculate market movements with Jacobian transformations should be made with reliability and practicality in mind for this purpose. My personal opinion is that using the (pseudo)inverse is better than using the reverse transformation for two reasons; firstly the reverse transformation might not be readily available but calculating a (pseudo)inverse from a given transformation is always possible, and secondly PnL estimates derived this way are usually more consistent with the underlying model.

Consistency with the underlying risk model is important, particularly if that first model is very reliable and that reliability is sought to be maintained. For a lossless transformation, or even for a not-lossless transformation with an inverse, then the PnL estimates are guaranteed to be the same, if inverses are used, since,

$$\Delta P \simeq S_B^* \cdot \Delta r_B^* = S_A^T J_{A \to B}^T \left(J_{A \to B}^{-1}\right)^T \Delta r_A = S_A \cdot \Delta r_A \ .$$

If the reverse transformation is used instead to generate market movements then these estimates for the not-lossless transformations will be, in fact, different. This can be problematic because it can lead to greater unexplained PnL.

For a not-lossless transformation that is not square and therefore does not have a direct inverse then the PnL estimates will usually also be different. They can be the same but it is unlikely and coincidental. Using the pseudoinverse produces estimates that are more similar on average but that does *not* mean that they will *always* be more similar than using the reverse transformation. It actually depends upon the structure and sizes of the various risk buckets.

As we have highlighted in this chapter not-lossless transformations are most commonly found when a complex risk model is transformed to a simpler one. This means that there is some expectation that information about risk is lost in the process. Of course this means that a PnL estimate is not expected to be as good as the original more complex model either. Using the pseudoinverse is an attempt to compensate for this lack of information to provide a more consistent PnL estimate, in line with the underlying model's but it does not always succeed. Indeed, it is mathematically impossible that this is the case.

Example 10.6.
A trader has a risk model, A, with log-linear DF interpolation and with the 1Y, 2Y, 3Y and 4Y points. He also has a second risk model, B, with the same interpolation but with only the 1Y and 4Y points. The Jacobian transformation matrices and the pseudoinverse are,

$$
\mathbf{J_{A \to B}} = \begin{array}{c} \\ (1Y) \\ (4Y) \end{array} \overset{\begin{array}{cccc} (1Y) & (2Y) & (3Y) & (4Y) \end{array}}{\begin{bmatrix} 1 & 0.33 & 0.11 & 0 \\ 0 & 0.67 & 0.89 & 1 \end{bmatrix}} ,
$$

$$
\mathbf{J_{B \to A}} = \begin{array}{c} (1Y) \\ (2Y) \\ (3Y) \\ (4Y) \end{array} \overset{\begin{array}{cc} (1Y) & (4Y) \end{array}}{\begin{bmatrix} 1 & 0 \\ 0 & 0 \\ 0 & 0 \\ 0 & 1 \end{bmatrix}} , \qquad
\mathbf{J^+_{A \to B}} = \begin{array}{c} (1Y) \\ (2Y) \\ (3Y) \\ (4Y) \end{array} \overset{\begin{array}{cc} (1Y) & (4Y) \end{array}}{\begin{bmatrix} 0.93 & -0.13 \\ 0.22 & 0.27 \\ -0.02 & 0.40 \\ -0.13 & 0.47 \end{bmatrix}} .
$$

His numerical risk strip, $\mathbf{S_A}$, is known as well as the market movements for the 1Y, 2Y, 3Y and 4Y points, $\mathbf{\Delta r_A}$. The trader can estimate his PnL using model A and also calculate his transformed risks in model B,

$$
\Delta P \simeq \mathbf{S_A} \cdot \mathbf{\Delta r_A} = \begin{bmatrix} 5 \\ 7 \\ 8 \\ 4 \end{bmatrix} \cdot \begin{bmatrix} +2.0 \\ +2.0 \\ +2.2 \\ +3.0 \end{bmatrix} = 53.6, \qquad \mathbf{S^*_B} = \mathbf{J_{A \to B}} \mathbf{S_A} = \begin{bmatrix} 8.2 \\ 15.8 \end{bmatrix} .
$$

For model B the trader can either use the reverse transformation($\leftarrow$) to calculate transformed market movements or the pseudoinverse($+$). The resulting PnL estimate is shown in both cases,

$$
\mathbf{\Delta r^{*\leftarrow}_B} = \begin{bmatrix} +2.0 \\ +3.0 \end{bmatrix} , \quad \text{and} \quad \Delta P \approx \mathbf{S^*_B} \cdot \mathbf{\Delta r^{*\leftarrow}_B} = 63.8 ,
$$

$$
\mathbf{\Delta r^{*+}_B} = \begin{bmatrix} +1.9 \\ +2.6 \end{bmatrix} , \quad \text{and} \quad \Delta P \approx \mathbf{S^*_B} \cdot \mathbf{\Delta r^{*+}_B} = 56.7 .
$$

In this example the trader's PnL estimate from model B is more consistent with that of model A when the pseudoinverse is used to calculate the market movements. This means that the market movements of the 1Y and 4Y points are not necessarily the actual market movements but are adjusted to reflect the fact that information about the 2Y and 3Y points is omitted.

In fact, when all of the risk buckets of model A are the same then the pseudoinverse method will produce a consistent estimate, but the more the buckets deviate from each other then this ability is lost. The same cannot be said for the reverse transformation method, it is always a bit hit and miss regardless of the buckets.

A point worth pondering over in this section regarding Jacobian transformations regards the difference between consistent PnL estimates and accurate transformations of risks and market movements. The details above explain how to generate market movements that, **only** when combined with transformed risks, produce consistent PnL estimates with the underlying model from which they are derived. This does not mean to say that the individually transformed risks and transformed market movements are accurate, in fact they can both be inaccurate but when determined in the right manner (i.e. using inverses) means their inaccuracies offset to give a consistent PnL estimate. Mathematically then, one should be aware from the above that it is generally true that, $\mathbf{S_B^*} \neq \mathbf{S_B}$ and $\mathbf{\Delta r_B^*} \neq \mathbf{\Delta r_B}$. But combining the inequality in both equations produces a consistent PnL estimate with model A.

Furthermore if two risk models are known to be as reliable as each other and that the transformed risk and market movements produce an equal PnL estimate, one can infer that the transformed risks are accurate **if** the transformed market movements are as well.

$$\text{If} \quad \mathbf{S_A} \cdot \mathbf{\Delta r_A} \simeq \mathbf{S_B} \cdot \mathbf{\Delta r_B} \quad \text{and} \quad \mathbf{S_A} \cdot \mathbf{\Delta r_A} = \mathbf{S_B^*} \cdot \mathbf{\Delta r_B^*} ,$$

$$\text{then for} \quad \mathbf{\Delta r_B} \simeq \mathbf{\Delta r_B^*} \Longleftrightarrow \mathbf{S_B} \simeq \mathbf{S_B^*} .$$

This is actually a useful property since it is often easy to check if two risk models give as reliable PnL estimates as each other. If they do, and the transformed market movements are the same as the real market movements, then it follows that the risk transformations are accurate too, and one should have full confidence in them (which would otherwise be difficult to check without doing the numerical calculation we hoped to avoid in the first place).

10.5.2 Covariance matrices

Covariance matrices are useful in the context of principal component analysis (PCA), VaR and calculating implied volatility of fwd rates. Each is discussed in relevant chapters. It is conceivable, and frequent, that a trader will have obtained a covariance matrix for a set of market instruments attributable to one particular risk model, say risk model A, and might want the equivalent covariance matrix for another set of instruments, say from risk model B.

In this instance we can use the Jacobian transformation to derive the second covariance matrix given the details of the first. With the knowledge of the first covariance matrix the formula that should be used to obtain the desired new matrix is[7],

$$\mathbf{Q}(\mathbf{\Delta r_B^*}) = \left(\mathbf{J_{A \to B}^+}\right)^{\mathbf{T}} \mathbf{Q}(\mathbf{\Delta r_A}) \mathbf{J_{A \to B}^+} .$$

10.5.3 Cross-gamma grids

Cross-gamma is discussed in detail in chapters 21 and 22. The purpose of a cross-gamma grid is to determine risk changes of a portfolio that have occurred solely as the result of market movements. Under model A, for some given market movements, the changes in risk can be written,

$$\mathbf{\Delta S_A} = \mathbf{G_A} \mathbf{\Delta r_A} .$$

If the transformation,

$$\mathbf{G_B^*} = \mathbf{J_{A \to B}} \mathbf{G_A} \mathbf{J_{A \to B}^T} ,$$

is used to calculate the the cross-gamma grid expressed under the relevant B model, then the risk changes of model B can be assessed in a similar way using,

$$\mathbf{\Delta S_B^*} = \mathbf{G_B^*} \mathbf{\Delta r_B^*} .$$

---

[7]the derivation and further comment about the accuracy of this formula is given in the appendix

10.6 Summary of transformation formulae

To conclude the chapter we summarise all of the preceding sections.

For instruments of a given risk model, A, where the numeric risk, $\mathbf{S_A}$, is known along with the market movements, $\mathbf{\Delta r_A}$, the covariance matrix of instruments, $\mathbf{Q(\Delta r_A)}$, and the cross-gamma risk grid of a trade or portfolio, $\mathbf{G_A}$, then table 10.2 lists all of the relevant transformation formulae. $\mathbf{J_{A \to B}}$ is the Jacobian transformation from model A to model B, obtained by risking every instrument in model A with the allowable market instrument movements in model B.

Transformation Type	Notation	Transformation formulae
Risk	$\mathbf{S_B^*}$	$= \mathbf{J_{A \to B} S_A}$
Market movements	$\mathbf{\Delta r_B^*}$	$= \left(\mathbf{J_{A \to B}^+}\right)^{\mathbf{T}} \mathbf{\Delta r_A}$ or $\mathbf{J_{B \to A}^T \Delta r_A}$
Covariance matrix	$\mathbf{Q(\Delta r_B^*)}$	$= \left(\mathbf{J_{A \to B}^+}\right)^{\mathbf{T}} \mathbf{Q(\Delta r_A) J_{A \to B}^+}$
Cross-gamma grid	$\mathbf{G_B^*}$	$= \mathbf{J_{A \to B} G_A J_{A \to B}^T}$
PnL estimate	ΔP	Invariant under certain conditions
VaR multiplier	c	Invariant under certain conditions

Table 10.2: Jacobian transformation formulae.

10.7 Appendix

10.7.1 Jacobian transformations of market movements

If we assume that;

(i) risk model A is reliably good and thus, $\Delta P \simeq \mathbf{S_A} \cdot \mathbf{\Delta r_A}$,

(ii) risk model A and risk model B have a lossless or a minimally not-lossless transformation between them then, $\mathbf{S_A} \cdot \mathbf{\Delta r_A} \simeq \mathbf{S_B} \cdot \mathbf{\Delta r_B}$,

Then by (i),

$$\Delta P \simeq \mathbf{S_A} \cdot \mathbf{\Delta r_A} = \mathbf{S_A}^{\mathbf{T}} \mathbf{\Delta r_A} = \mathbf{S_A}^{\mathbf{T}} \mathbf{J_{A \to B}^T} \left(\mathbf{J_{A \to B}^{-1}}\right)^{\mathbf{T}} \mathbf{\Delta r_A} = \mathbf{S_B}^{*\mathbf{T}} \mathbf{\Delta r_B^*} = \mathbf{S_B^*} \cdot \mathbf{\Delta r_B^*} \,,$$

and by (ii),

$$\mathbf{S_B^*} \cdot \mathbf{\Delta r_B^*} \simeq \mathbf{S_B} \cdot \mathbf{\Delta r_B} \simeq \Delta P \,,$$

thus we infer that where $\mathbf{S_B^*} \simeq \mathbf{S_B}$, i.e. where the risk obtained by transformation is close to the numerically obtained risk under model B, then $\mathbf{\Delta r_B^*} = \left(\mathbf{J_{A \to B}^{-1}}\right)^{\mathbf{T}} \mathbf{\Delta r_A}$ is a reliably good estimate for the real market movements, $\mathbf{\Delta r_B}$. Conversely, we could state that where $\mathbf{\Delta r_B^*} \simeq \mathbf{\Delta r_B}$ then it will also be true that $\mathbf{S_B^*} \simeq \mathbf{S_B}$.

10.7.2 Jacobian transformations of covariance matrices

Suppose a covariance matrix of market movements of risk model A has been obtained,

$$\mathbf{Q(\Delta r_A)} = Cov(\mathbf{\Delta r_A}, \mathbf{\Delta r_A}) \,.$$

Now we obtain the market movements of model B in a way as discussed in the text, so either[8],

$$\Delta \mathbf{r}_{\mathbf{B}}^* = \left(\mathbf{J}_{\mathbf{B}\to\mathbf{A}}\right)^{\mathbf{T}} \Delta \mathbf{r}_{\mathbf{A}} \quad \text{or} \quad \Delta \mathbf{r}_{\mathbf{B}}^* = \left(\mathbf{J}_{\mathbf{A}\to\mathbf{B}}^+\right)^{\mathbf{T}} \Delta \mathbf{r}_{\mathbf{A}} .$$

It is important to make the choice, above, based on the context. For example we show below that for consistent CoVaR multipliers of square transformations then the inverse is the most appropriate method. Adopting this choice then the transformed covariance matrix follows as,

$$Cov(\Delta \mathbf{r}_{\mathbf{B}}^*, \Delta \mathbf{r}_{\mathbf{B}}^*) = Cov\left(\left(\mathbf{J}_{\mathbf{A}\to\mathbf{B}}^{-1}\right)^{\mathbf{T}} \Delta \mathbf{r}_{\mathbf{A}}, \left(\mathbf{J}_{\mathbf{A}\to\mathbf{B}}^{-1}\right)^{\mathbf{T}} \Delta \mathbf{r}_{\mathbf{A}}\right) ,$$

$$\implies \quad \mathbf{Q}(\Delta \mathbf{r}_{\mathbf{B}}^*) = \left(\mathbf{J}_{\mathbf{A}\to\mathbf{B}}^{-1}\right)^{\mathbf{T}} \mathbf{Q}(\Delta \mathbf{r}_{\mathbf{A}})\mathbf{J}_{\mathbf{A}\to\mathbf{B}}^{-1} .$$

Chapter 14 on VaR introduces the CoVaR multiplier, c, but we can illustrate briefly here that by transforming the covariance matrix in this way then it provides a consistent measure of risk. Intuitively this is sensible, since if VaR is a risk metric of a portfolio of trades then two arbitrary, but equally reliable, risk models should not give rise to different values of the same risk metric .

$$c = \sqrt{(\mathbf{S}_{\mathbf{B}}^*)^{\mathbf{T}} \mathbf{Q}(\Delta \mathbf{r}_{\mathbf{B}}^*)\mathbf{S}_{\mathbf{B}}^*} ,$$
$$= \sqrt{\mathbf{S}_{\mathbf{A}}^{\mathbf{T}}\mathbf{J}_{\mathbf{A}\to\mathbf{B}}^{\mathbf{T}} \left(\mathbf{J}_{\mathbf{A}\to\mathbf{B}}^{-1}\right)^{\mathbf{T}} \mathbf{Q}(\Delta \mathbf{r}_{\mathbf{A}})\mathbf{J}_{\mathbf{A}\to\mathbf{B}}^{-1}\mathbf{J}_{\mathbf{A}\to\mathbf{B}}\mathbf{S}_{\mathbf{A}}} ,$$
$$= \sqrt{\mathbf{S}_{\mathbf{A}}^{\mathbf{T}}\mathbf{Q}(\Delta \mathbf{r}_{\mathbf{A}})\mathbf{S}_{\mathbf{A}}} .$$

Note that there is the concern that covariance matrices are often constructed from historical samples, but that the Jacobian transformation is not constant throughout the period. The transformation is, in general, dependent upon the level of prevailing interest rates. By using this transformation it is implicit that the historical levels of the transformed model have all been implied with the current Jacobian transformation and this is inconsistent with the transformation for that historical data point. Thus, this transformation, unlike the others which have no interaction with historical data and only transform current data, should be considered as an approximation.

---

[8]where '+' indicates the pseudoinverse which reduces to the usual matrix inverse for square transformations

Quant Library and Automatic Differentiation

To reinforce many of this book's concepts, a valuable exercise is to build a modern code library from scratch. In particular, we want to show that these concepts and techniques are, perhaps contrary to popular belief, relatively simple and readily implemented. Obviously though, quant libraries are often large codebases that have been extended and carefully optimised over many years so ours will be fairly limited by comparison. Saying that, even implemented in Python, our curve solver will iterate to reprice 30 market instruments often in less than 50ms, and it is hoped that it will still be sufficient to use as a sandbox testing environment, and for exploration of further topics in later chapters. This chapter aims to;

- build a basic quant library with typical Swap, Curve, and Schedule objects,

- implement a curve solving algorithm to construct a curve from known market prices,

- explain automatic differentiation through the concept of dual numbers and extend our library to utilise it,

- explain some of the considerations for extracting delta risk from our library, then implement it and give examples.

The cited code repository inline gives commit references so that the specific code editions can be seen in isolation to the entire project which is obviously constructed and referenced throughout the book.

11.1   Core library objects

We will build our library in Python. This is a poor choice really, since our library would benefit greatly, performance wise, by being coded in a lower level language like C. However, for tutelage purposes Python is an excellent language since its code is very readable, even for non-programmers, and much less verbose than those other alternatives.

Since we don't want to fill the book with reams of code we will make many simplifying assumptions, which are discussed inline. Furthermore, this code is not designed to be efficient computationally, rather it is designed to be efficient pedagogically.

11.1.1   Curve

The first thing we will build is a `Curve` object. As discussed in earlier chapters our curve will be an object which is parametrised by a series of DFs defined at specific node dates. For any date not specifically defined we will calculate the DF through an interpolation scheme also defined as a hyper-parameter. To our `Curve` class we will add a representation method for console printing and a get item method for returning the DF for an arbitrary date.

```python
from datetime import datetime, timedelta
from math import log, exp, ceil


def interpolate(x, x_1, y_1, x_2, y_2, method):
    """
    Interpolate a coordinate with given x value between two known coordinates
    """
    if method == "linear":
        op = lambda x: x
    elif method == "log_linear":
        op, y_1, y_2 = exp, log(y_1), log(y_2)
    return op(y_1 + (y_2 - y_1) * (x - x_1) / (x_2 - x_1))


class Curve:

    def __init__(self, nodes: dict, interpolation: str):
        self.nodes = nodes.copy()
        self.node_dates = list(self.nodes.keys())
        self.interpolation = interpolation

    def __repr__(self):
        output = ""
        for k, v in self.nodes.items():
            output += f"{k.strftime('%Y-%b-%d')}: {v:.6f}\n"
        return output

    def __getitem__(self, date: datetime):
        for i, node_date_1 in enumerate(self.node_dates[1:]):
            if date <= node_date_1 or i == len(self.node_dates) - 2:
                node_date_0 = self.node_dates[i]
                return interpolate(
                    date,
```

```
35                     node_date_0, self.nodes[node_date_0],
36                     node_date_1, self.nodes[node_date_1],
37                     self.interpolation
38                 )
```

Having defined the Curve [21, #5f9c3c] we give an example of its use below.

```
1  >>> curve = Curve(interpolation="log_linear", nodes={
2          datetime(2022, 1, 1): 1.00,
3          datetime(2022, 4, 1): 0.9975,
4          datetime(2022, 7, 1): 0.9945,
5      })
6  >>> print(curve)
7  2022-Jan-01: 1.000000
8  2022-Apr-01: 0.997500
9  2022-Jul-01: 0.994500
```

Let's calculate the log-linearly interpolated DFs for a couple of arbitrary dates.

```
1  >>> curve[datetime(2022, 3, 15)]
2  0.9979717429663241
3  >>> curve[datetime(2022, 4, 1)]
4  0.9975000000000115
```

Notice how, in the second case, the DF of 1st-Apr-22 is not returned as exactly the known parameter supplied to the curve. This is due to numerical precision around $1e^{-13}$ (and, probably, a lack of efficiently written code).

11.1.2 Schedule

With our Curve object created we will now build a Schedule object. This will be responsible for generating the dates that are associated with the accrual, forecasting and payment dates of a leg of an IRD. For simplification purposes, we assume the following:

- accrual, forecasting and payment dates always exactly align,

- the DCF is based on an actual/365fixed convention,

- holiday calendars are completely ignored, or rather, we propose no holidays,

- schedules are generated from the front creating back stubs for any fractional periods.

```
1  def add_months(start: datetime, months: int) -> datetime:
2      """add a given number of months to an input date with a modified month end rule"""
3      year_roll = int((start.month + months - 1) / 12)
4      month = (start.month + months) % 12
5      month = 12 if month == 0 else month
6      try:
7          end = datetime(start.year + year_roll, month, start.day)
8      except ValueError:  # day is out of range for month
9          return add_months(datetime(start.year, start.month, start.day-1), months)
10     else:
11         return end
12
13
14 class Schedule:
15
16     def __init__(self, start: datetime, tenor: int, period: int):
17         self.start = start
18         self.end = add_months(start, tenor)
19         self.tenor = tenor
20         self.period = period
21         self.dcf_conv = timedelta(days=365)
22         self.n_periods = ceil(tenor / period)
23
24     def __repr__(self):
25         output = "period start | period end | period DCF\n"
26         for period in self.data:
```

```
27        output += f"{period[0].strftime('%Y-%b-%d')} | " \
28                  f"{period[1].strftime('%Y-%b-%d')} | {period[2]:3f}\n"
29    return output
30
31    @property
32    def data(self):
33        schedule = []
34        period_start = self.start
35        for i in range(self.n_periods - 1):
36            period_end = add_months(period_start, self.period)
37            schedule.append(
38                [period_start, period_end, (period_end - period_start) / self.dcf_conv]
39            )
40            period_start = period_end
41        schedule.append(
42            [period_start, self.end, (self.end - period_start) / self.dcf_conv]
43        )
44        return schedule
```

In this implementation we have used a loop to successively generate the required schedule dates in a list data structure. Below we give an example of the use of the new `Schedule` object [21, #86a545] .

```
1 >>> schedule = Schedule(datetime(2022, 1, 1), tenor=11, period=3)
2 >>> print(schedule)
3 period start | period end | period DCF
4 2022-Jan-01 | 2022-Apr-01 | 0.246575
5 2022-Apr-01 | 2022-Jul-01 | 0.249315
6 2022-Jul-01 | 2022-Oct-01 | 0.252055
7 2022-Oct-01 | 2022-Dec-01 | 0.167123
```

11.1.3   Swap

Now that we have `Curve` and `Schedule` objects we will add a `Swap` object. To our `Swap` we will add functions to return the PV (given an executed fixed rate), the analytic delta and a mid market fixed rate of the swap based on the formula we have seen previously,

$$R = \frac{v_0 - v_n}{A_{fixed}} \quad \text{where} \quad A_{fixed} = \sum_{j=1}^{m} d_j v_j$$

```
1  class Swap:
2
3      def __init__(self, start: datetime, tenor:int, period_fix:int, period_float:int):
4          self.start = start
5          self.end = add_months(start, tenor)
6          self.schedule_fix = Schedule(start, tenor, period_fix)
7          self.schedule_float = Schedule(start, tenor, period_float)
8
9      def __repr__(self):
10         return f"<Swap: {self.start.strftime('%Y-%m-%d')} -> " \
11                 f"{self.end.strftime('%Y-%m-%d')}>"
12
13     def analytic_delta(self, curve: Curve, leg: str = "fix", notional: float = 1e4):
14         delta = 0
15         for period in getattr(self, f"schedule_{leg}").data:
16             delta += curve[period[1]] * period[2]
17         return delta * notional / 10000
18
19     def rate(self, curve: Curve):
20         rate = (curve[self.start] - curve[self.end]) / self.analytic_delta(curve)
21         return rate * 100
22
23     def npv(self, curve: Curve, fixed_rate: float, notional: float = 1e6):
24         npv = (self.rate(curve) - fixed_rate) * self.analytic_delta(curve)
25         return npv * notional / 100
```

An example of using our new object [21, #75356d] is below.

```
1 >>> swap = Swap(datetime(2022, 2, 14), tenor=4, period_fix=12, period_float=1)
2 >>> print(swap, swap.schedule_fix, swap.schedule_float)
3 <Swap: 2022-02-14 -> 2022-06-14>
4 period start | period end | period DCF
5 2022-Feb-14 | 2022-Jun-14 | 0.328767
6 period start | period end | period DCF
7 2022-Feb-14 | 2022-Mar-14 | 0.076712
8 2022-Mar-14 | 2022-Apr-14 | 0.084932
9 2022-Apr-14 | 2022-May-14 | 0.082192
10 2022-May-14 | 2022-Jun-14 | 0.084932
11 >>> swap.rate(curve)
12 1.1362747413101932
13 >>> swap.analytic_delta(curve, notional=1e9)
14 32714.29326303417
15 >>> swap.npv(curve, fixed_rate=1.15, notional=1e9)
16 -44901.21378893437
```

We have now created some core objects which define curves and price simple IRD instruments. The next item of relevancy is that of risk, or sensitivity. How do these values that we can calculate change with respect to changing input parameters? To deal with this we have to start thinking about derivatives. It is reasonably simple to code a loop that can vary the discount factors and determine the changes to rates with respect to these. This is known as numerical differentiation. However, as we will see in the next section this comes with disadvantages, so we will consider an alternate approach.

11.2   Automatic differentiation and dual numbers

Before we explore automatic differentiation and dual numbers we'll review calculating derivatives and explore the methods we have available to us. See figure 11.1.

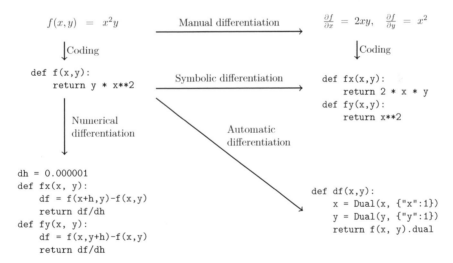

Figure 11.1: Possible differentiation techniques for a given function.

Manual

The advantage of manual differentiation is that it is exact, and, usually, ingenuity while calculating leads to efficient programs and greater insight into the problem. The disadvantage is that it is only valid on tractable closed form solutions which can greatly limit its scope. It is also much slower for dynamic problems and can be susceptible to human error!

Symbolic

Symbolic differentiation is similar to manual differentiation in that it is also exact, albeit much faster to operate. It suffers the same disadvantage of being applicable to only closed form problems, and although has a greater scope through its programmatic nature experiences limits when memory issues arise from expression swell. It also requires the use of a configured symbolic differentiation code library.

Numerical

Numerical differentiation has the advantage of being applicable in many cases including iterative processes. It is often relatively easy to code, albeit is harder to code efficiently. It also suffers the disadvantage of round-off and numerical truncation errors and is often quite expensive computationally, even when optimally coded.

Automatic

Automatic differentiation yields exact results. It can be implemented efficiently so it is not computationally expensive but it relies on effectively changing the source code of the arithmetic in a coding language, and writing functions that are valid within that new framework. New challenges can arise as a result of trying to fit existing methods into the framework.

Next we will describe how to implement automatic differentiation with the use of Dual numbers (there are other approaches using computational graphs but we do not cover those here). Dual numbers provide an alternative arithmetic, similar to complex numbers, whose imaginary, i, squared is defined to be negative one. Here we define them as per [30],

$$\{z_1 = x_1 + \beta_1 \epsilon_x \quad : x_1, \beta_1 \in \mathbf{R}, \quad \epsilon_x^2 = 0, \ \epsilon_x \neq 0\}$$

Furthermore, we can define some of the key arithmetic operations of dual numbers,

$$
\begin{aligned}
\text{Negation:} \quad & -z_1 = -x_1 - \beta_1 \epsilon_x \\
\text{Equality:} \quad & z_1 = z_2 \implies x_1 = x_2, \ \beta_1 = \beta_2 \\
\text{Addition:} \quad & z_1 + z_2 = x_1 + x_2 + (\beta_1 + \beta_2)\epsilon_x \\
\text{Subtraction:} \quad & z_1 - z_2 = x_1 - x_2 + (\beta_1 - \beta_2)\epsilon_x \\
\text{Multiplication:} \quad & z_1 * z_2 = x_1 x_2 + (\beta_1 x_2 + \beta_2 x_1)\epsilon_x \\
\text{Conjugate:} \quad & \bar{z}_1 = x_1 - \beta_1 \epsilon_x \\
\text{Division:} \quad & \frac{z_1}{z_2} = \frac{z_1}{z_2}\frac{\bar{z}_2}{\bar{z}_2} = \frac{x_1 x_2 + (\beta_1 x_2 - \beta_2 x_1)\epsilon_x}{x_2^2} \\
\text{Exponential:} \quad & e^{z_1} = e^{x_1}(1 + \beta_1 \epsilon_x) \\
\text{Logarithm:} \quad & \ln z_1 = \ln x_1 + \frac{\beta_1}{x_1}\epsilon_x \\
\text{Power:} \quad & z_1^n = x_1^n + nx_1(n-1)\beta_1 \epsilon_x
\end{aligned}
$$

This list can be extended to trigonometric and hyperbolic functions (as per the citation above) but we will not need those here.

If we now want to evaluate some function, say $f(x) = x^3 e^x$, we can define our dual number, $z = x + 1\epsilon_x$, and calculate,

$$f(z) = z^3 e^z = (x + \epsilon_x)^3 e^x (1 + \epsilon_x) = x^3 e^x + (x^3 e^x + 3x^2 e^x)\epsilon_x \ .$$

The function value is given by the *real* component and the derivative with respect to x is given by the coefficient of the dual component, ϵ_x.

When this is extended to multiple variables we can use what is referred to as tagging. Here we define the product of any tagged variables, $\epsilon_x \epsilon_y = 0$, so that if we want to evaluate our original function,

$$f(x,y) = x^2 y, \quad \Longrightarrow \quad f(x + 1\epsilon_x, y + 1\epsilon_y) = (x^2 + 2x\epsilon_x)(y + \epsilon_y) = x^2 + 2xy\epsilon_x + x^2\epsilon_y$$

Again, the function value is given by the *real* component and the partial derivative with respect to x is the coefficient of the ϵ_x dual component and the partial derivative with respect to y is the coefficient of the ϵ_y dual component. We will see this example again after implementing our code below.

11.2.1 Dual

We will now look to implement the theory above by coding our `Dual` type which is essentially an extension of the `float` number type, however the basic arithmetic has been overwritten in a manner that is referred to, in computer science, as operator overloading.

```python
class Dual:

    def __init__(self, real, dual=None):
        """
        A dual number is denoted in the form:
            z = x + be, such that e**2 = 0 and e != 0

        real: real number
        dual: dict (key=name_index and value=value)
        """
        self.real = real
        self.dual = {} if dual is None else dual.copy()

    def __str__(self):
        output = f"   f = {self.real:.8f}\n"
        for k, v in self.dual.items():
            output += f"df/d{k} = {v:.6f}\n"
        return output

    def __repr__(self):
        output = f"{self.real}"
        for key in self.dual.keys():
            output += f"{self.dual[key]:+.3f}e_{key}"
        return output

    def __neg__(self):
        """-z = -x - b_0e_0 - b_1e_1"""
        dual = {}
        for key in self.dual:
            dual[key] = -self.dual[key]
        return Dual(-self.real, dual)

    def __eq__(self, argument):
        """equality iff real and dual components the same"""
        if not isinstance(argument, Dual):
            return False
        return False if self.real != argument.real else self.dual == argument.dual

    def conjugate(self):
        dual = {}
        for key in self.dual:
            dual[key] = -self.dual[key]
        return Dual(self.real, dual)

    def __ne__(self, argument):
        """inequality iff not equal"""
        return not (self.__eq__(argument))
```

```
49      def __add__(self, argument):
50          """z_1 + z_2 = (x_1 + x_2) + (b_1_0 + b_2_0)e_0 + (b_1_1 + b_2_1)e_1"""
51          if isinstance(argument, Dual):
52              real = self.real + argument.real
53              dual = self.dual.copy()
54              for key in argument.dual:
55                  val = 0 if key not in dual else dual[key]
56                  dual[key] = val + argument.dual[key]
57              return Dual(real, dual)
58          else:
59              return Dual(self.real + argument, self.dual)
60
61      __radd__ = __add__
62
63      def __sub__(self, argument):
64          """z_1 - z_2 = (x_1 - x_2) + (b_1_0 - b_2_0)e_0 + (b_1_1 - b_2_1)e_1"""
65          if isinstance(argument, Dual):
66              real = self.real - argument.real
67              dual = self.dual.copy()
68              for key in argument.dual:
69                  val = 0 if key not in dual else dual[key]
70                  dual[key] = val - argument.dual[key]
71              return Dual(real, dual)
72          else:
73              return Dual(self.real - argument, self.dual)
74
75      def __rsub__(self, argument):
76          """z_2 - z_1 = -(z_1 - z_2)"""
77          return -(self - argument)
78
79      def __mul__(self, argument):
80          """z_1 * z_2 = x_1 * x_2 + (x_1 * b_2_0 + x_2 * b_1_0)e_0"""
81          if isinstance(argument, Dual):
82              real = self.real * argument.real
83              dual = {}
84              for key in self.dual:
85                  dual[key] = self.dual[key] * argument.real
86              for key in argument.dual:
87                  val = 0 if key not in dual else dual[key]
88                  dual[key] = val + argument.dual[key] * self.real
89              return Dual(real, dual)
90          else:
91              dual = {}
92              for key in self.dual:
93                  dual[key] = self.dual[key] * argument
94              return Dual(self.real * argument, dual)
95
96      __rmul__ = __mul__
97
98      def __truediv__(self, argument):
99          """z_1 / z_2 = (z_1 * ^z_2) / (z_2 * ^z_2)"""
100         if isinstance(argument, Dual):
101             numerator = self * argument.conjugate()
102             return numerator / argument.real**2
103         else:
104             dual = {}
105             for key in self.dual:
106                 dual[key] = self.dual[key] / argument
107             return Dual(self.real / argument, dual)
108
109     def __rtruediv__(self, argument):
110         """x / z = (x * ^z) / (z * ^z)"""
111         numerator = Dual(argument, {})
112         return numerator / self
113
114     def __pow__(self, power):
115         """z**n = x**n + n x**(n-1)(b_0e_0 + b_1e_1)"""
116         dual = {}
117         for key in self.dual:
118             dual[key] = power * self.dual[key] * (self.real ** (power - 1))
119         return Dual(self.real ** power, dual)
120
121     def __exp__(self):
122         """exp(z) = exp(x) + exp(x) * (b_0e_0 + b_1e_1)"""
```

```
123        real = exp(self.real)
124        dual = {}
125        for key in self.dual:
126            dual[key] = real * self.dual[key]
127        return Dual(real, dual)
128
129    def __log__(self):
130        """log(z) = log(x) + 1/x * (b_0e_0 + b_1e_1)"""
131        real = log(self.real)
132        dual = {}
133        for key in self.dual:
134            dual[key] = self.dual[key] / self.real
135        return Dual(real, dual)
```

After implementation [21, #f51e82] we have the ability to perform the operations we defined above programmatically.

```
1  >>> def f(x, y):
2  ...     return x**2 * y
3  >>> f(x=2.5, y=3.5)
4  21.875
5  >>> f(x=Dual(2.5, {"x": 1}), y=Dual(3.5, {"y": 1}))
6  21.875+17.500e_x+6.250e_y
7  >>> print(f(x=Dual(2.5, {"x": 1}), y=Dual(3.5, {"y": 1})))
8      f = 21.87500000
9  df/dx = 17.500000
10 df/dy = 6.250000
```

Notice that in the above code we have defined a python function as usual, and then used regular float arguments to determine the output of that function. When we supply, instead, Dual arguments to the function it returns a Dual output which contains our derivative information. One can verify that these are the exact partial derivatives of the function with respect to each variable evaluated at the point (2.5, 3.5). This is the power of the Dual implementation since the derivatives are essentially given to us, almost for free, when we evaluate our regularly defined functions in terms of elementary operations such as addition, subtraction, etc. that we have overloaded.

Adapting the existing codebase

We have discussed writing functions that adapt our codebase to work with our Dual type. This can be one of the largest challenges in adopting dual numbers. We now need to make sure that the code we wrote above for our Curve, Schedule and Swap objects can handle Dual. Fortunately almost everything works since all functions are composed of these simple arithmetic operations. However, the exp and log functions are imported from the math module and those are ignorant of our new data type. It is easy to overload these functions. First we **remove** the following,

```
1  from math import exp, log, ceil
```

and **replace** it with new functions that we already added to our Dual class.

```
1  import math
2  from math import ceil
3
4  def exp(x):
5      if isinstance(x, Dual):
6          return x.__exp__()
7      return math.exp(x)
8
9
10 def log(x):
11     if isinstance(x, Dual):
12         return x.__log__()
13     return math.log(x)
```

Previous example with automatic differentiation

With the changes in place [21, #9e3e00] we are now able to replicate the previous example of using our quant library. This time we define our curve using the same discount factors but defined with tagged `Dual` data types.

```
 1  >>> dual_curve = Curve(interpolation="log_linear", nodes={
 2          datetime(2022, 1, 1): Dual(1.0000, {"v0": 1}),
 3          datetime(2022, 4, 1): Dual(0.9975, {"v1": 1}),
 4          datetime(2022, 7, 1): Dual(0.9945, {"v2": 1})
 5      })
 6  >>> print(swap.rate(dual_curve))
 7        f = 1.13627474
 8  df/dv0 = 156.043726
 9  df/dv1 = 92.455740
10  df/dv2 = -249.641353
11  >>> print(swap.analytic_delta(dual_curve, notional=1e9))
12        f = 32714.29326303
13  df/dv1 = 6126.778325
14  df/dv2 = 26749.956646
15  >>> print(swap.npv(dual_curve, fixed_rate=1.15, notional=1e9))
16        f = -44901.21378893
17  df/dv0 = 510486020.141361
18  df/dv1 = 302454009.146232
19  df/dv2 = -816720759.656647
```

One can see that the output of these functions now contains information about their rate of change with respect to the DF node points controlling the curve. The derivative values look a little nonsensical but that is because the rate of change is referenced versus a change of unit 1 in the DF, which is practically too large a change. In the next section we give an example of scaling this rate of change for a specific purpose.

Zero rate sensitivity

Sensitivity to DFs is a valid calculation, which will be very useful in subsequent sections, but in practical trading it is not usually something that is monitored. Generally, we want sensitivity to changes in rates, i.e. to tradeable market instruments. This becomes a little more complicated and that is what those subsequent sections will tackle.

However, in this section we will make use of the property that CC zero rates are entirely dependent upon their terminal DF, and therefore there is one to one correspondence with the node point DF on our `Curve`. Mathematically we have that,

$$v_i = e^{-D_i Z_i}, \quad \implies \quad \frac{\partial v_i}{\partial Z_i} = \frac{dv_i}{dZ_i} = -D_i v_i$$

So if we would like to calculate derivatives with respect to CC zero rates, Z_i, we can scale the partial derivatives with respect to v_i that we can already automatically calculate.

$$\frac{\partial f}{\partial Z_i} = \sum_j \frac{\partial f}{\partial v_j} \frac{\partial v_j}{\partial Z_i} = \frac{\partial f}{\partial v_i} \frac{dv_i}{dZ_i} = -D_i v_i \frac{\partial f}{\partial v_i}$$

If we redefine our `Dual` numbers parametrising the curve we can specifically code these scalars by further using the notion of tagging. Below we also introduce a bp scalar to ensure that Z_1 and Z_2 are interpreted as moving by only one bp:

```
 1  >>> conv, bp_scale = timedelta(days=365), 1e-4
 2  >>> dates = [datetime(2022, 1, 1), datetime(2022, 4, 1), datetime(2022, 7, 1)]
 3  >>> v = [1, 0.9975, 0.9945]
 4  >>> curve_dual2 = Curve(interpolation="log_linear", nodes={
 5          dates[0]: Dual(v[0], {"v0": 1}),
 6          dates[1]: Dual(v[1], {"v1": 1, "Z1": -v[1]*bp_scale*(dates[1]-dates[0])/conv}),
 7          dates[2]: Dual(v[2], {"v2": 1, "Z2": -v[2]*bp_scale*(dates[2]-dates[0])/conv})
```

```
 8        })
 9  >>> print(swap.rate(curve_dual2))
10        f =  1.13627474
11  df/dv0 =  156.043726
12  df/dv1 =  92.455740
13  df/dZ1 =  -0.002274
14  df/dv2 =  -249.641353
15  df/dZ2 =  0.012311
16  >>> print(swap.npv(curve_dual2, fixed_rate=1.15, notional=1e9))
17        f =  -44901.21378893
18  df/dv0 =  510486020.141361
19  df/dv1 =  302454009.146232
20  df/dZ1 =  -7439.125644
21  df/dv2 =  -816720759.656647
22  df/dZ2 =  40277.647099
```

The above output now includes the correct sensitivity to CC zero rates and shows the typical risk representation of a forwarding starting swap, risked with par rates. The rate has leveraged sensitivity of 123% to the 6m rate and -23% sensitivity to the 3m rate, which we determine by observing the value of $\frac{\partial f}{\partial Z_2}$ and $\frac{\partial f}{\partial Z_1}$ have values of 1.23bps and -0.23bps respectively.

11.3 Curve Solver

So far our library is functional but it is completely dependent upon the known DF parameters we supply to our Curve. This is not practical since DFs are not observable, tradable instruments. Instead, one tends to observe par swap rates and the task becomes one of calibrating a DF Curve, such that it then **reprices** those observed rates.

The purpose of a curve solver is to use extraneous information, such as market quoted swap rates, and internally derive the DFs it needs. This is exactly what we will build here. When one decides to build a curve solving engine there are a number of choices that must be made with respect to the process.

11.3.1 Analytic or numeric process

With the correct formulation of the problem it is possible to analytically derive the sequence of DFs at determined node dates that will create a curve which reprices those given swap rates. This process is generally referred to as **bootstrapping**. This is a perfectly valid approach and, with the formulae contained in the book for product description, one should be able to design a bootstrap procedure in simple cases. The disadvantage with this analytic approach is that it is not particularly flexible, and in certain cases (such as multi-curve frameworks) may be very complicated, or even impossible, to derive. It may be impossible if rates are interdependent so therefore values cannot be solved in sequence, which is a requirement of the bootstrap process.

A numerical approach, on the other hand, is one which uses an iterative algorithm to solve an optimisation problem to determine a curve based on given constraints. This is more flexible since it typically allows for varying more parameters, or hyper parameters, without adapting the core process. For example trying to create a curve which is overspecified (the number of swap rates is greater than the number of DF nodes) is possible. It will also always be possible to make this approach work.

We will use a numerical process and show how it can be adapted for use with our dual numbers definition.

11.3.2 Objective functions

We must find a suitable function to minimise, which in the field of optimisation is referred to as an objective function. In our case we will choose to minimise the Euclidean distance (or method of least squares) between the swap rates derived from our solved curve and the known swap rates that serve as parameters to the curve. This is specified mathematically as,

$$\min_{\mathbf{v}} f(\mathbf{v}, \mathbf{S}) = \min_{\mathbf{v}} ||\mathbf{r} - \mathbf{S}||_2 = \min_{\mathbf{v}} (\mathbf{r} - \mathbf{S})^{\mathbf{T}}(\mathbf{r} - \mathbf{S}), \quad \text{for} \quad \mathbf{r} = \mathbf{r}(\mathbf{v}) \tag{11.1}$$

where $\mathbf{v} = $ *discount factors to solve for (excluding the initial value, $v_0 \equiv 1.00$)*

$\mathbf{S} = $ *known swap rates (this notation differs to previous chapters)*

$\mathbf{r} = $ *corresponding swap rates derived from the solved curve*

and $\nabla_{\mathbf{v}} f = 2\mathbf{J}(\mathbf{r} - \mathbf{S}) = $ *gradient of f with respect to $\mathbf{v}$*

$$\mathbf{J} = \nabla_{\mathbf{v}} \mathbf{r}^{\mathbf{T}} = \textit{Jacobian of } \mathbf{r} \textit{ with respect to } \mathbf{v}\text{:} \ \ [\mathbf{J}]_{ij} = \frac{\partial r_j}{\partial v_i}$$

This is a non-linear optimisation problem and does not have a closed form solution. This is why we must use iterative procedures. The following observations can also be made:

i) $\nabla_{\mathbf{v}} f$ and $\mathbf{J}$ are derivatives with respect to the DFs, $\mathbf{v}$, which can be automatically extracted from our codebase with `Dual` number implementation,

ii) obviously, the length of vectors $\mathbf{r}$ and $\mathbf{S}$, defined as m, must be the same as they contain the same instruments,

iii) if the length of $\mathbf{v}$, defined as $n + 1$, is one greater than $\mathbf{S}$ (since $v_0 \equiv 1$), i.e. if $n = m$, and the node points are suitably chosen based on the maturities of the instruments in $\mathbf{S}$, then the curve is **completely specified** and the minimum f achievable is zero,

iv) if the length of $\mathbf{v}$ is less than in iii), i.e if $n < m$, the curve is **overspecified**. This means that the achievable minimum of f will likely be greater than zero, although this may still serve a purpose,

v) if the length of $\mathbf{v}$ is greater than in iii), i.e. if $n > m$, the curve is **underspecified**. This means that there is not enough information to fully calibrate the DFs and it may lead to spurious behaviour, as in section 12.6. Other techniques may have to be employed to control the parameters - this is often is termed **regularisation**. Usually regularisation approaches such as **ridge regression** or **lasso regression** may be used,

vi) **weighted least squares** is a common extension to this function where a weight vector, $\mathbf{w}$, assigns a weight to each rate and the formulation of the problem becomes,

$$\min_{\mathbf{v}} (\mathbf{r} - \mathbf{S})^{\mathbf{T}} \mathbf{diag}(\mathbf{w})(\mathbf{r} - \mathbf{S})$$

The code written in this chapter is augmented in section 12.5 to use weights as a regularisation technique.

11.3.3   Optimisation algorithms

In general optimisation the steps of any algorithm proceed as follows:

1. Specify some initial guess of the solution, $\mathbf{v_0}$, yielding objective function value $f(\mathbf{v_0})$.

2. For $i = 0, 1, ...$

    (a) If $\mathbf{v_i}$ is considered optimal, and $f(\mathbf{v_i})$ considered minimal, then stop.

    (b) Otherwise, determine a search direction, $\mathbf{p_i}$,

(c) Determine a step size, α_i, along that search direction, that leads to an improved estimate of the solution: $\mathbf{v_{i+1}} = \mathbf{v_i} + \alpha_i \mathbf{p_i}$, such that $f(\mathbf{v_{i+1}}) < f(\mathbf{v_i})$.

The determination of the search direction and the step size are essentially dependent upon the choice of optimisation algorithm. Different algorithms may have advantages in terms of computational efficiency or likelihood of convergence to a solution, but may have the disadvantages of complex calculation. We will consider three algorithms below.

11.3.4 Gradient descent method

In this section, we state the gradient descent algorithm's update rule as follows[1],

$$\mathbf{v_{i+1}} = \mathbf{v_i} - \alpha_i \nabla_\mathbf{v} f|_{\mathbf{v_i}} \tag{11.2}$$

$$\text{and} \quad \alpha_i = \frac{\mathbf{y_i^T}(\mathbf{r_i} - \mathbf{S})}{\mathbf{y_i^T y_i}}, \quad \text{for} \quad \mathbf{y_i} = \mathbf{J_i^T} \nabla_\mathbf{v} f|_{\mathbf{v_i}}$$

The gradient descent algorithm is usually the first given in a pedagogical context. The search direction is in the direction of negative gradient so this is an instinctive and sensible place to start. The step size is chosen via an analytically solved secondary optimisation problem, given the direction is known. The advantage of this method is that it is a numerically stable algorithm, and its equations are tractable if one wishes to perform any mathematical analysis. However it is very slow, and often requires many iterations to converge, particularly as it becomes closer to target. The following algorithms are superior in practice.

11.3.5 Gauss-Newton method

The Gauss-Newton algorithm is designed specifically for least squares problems. Using this method we essentially solve a secondary optimisation problem, akin to the above's step size problem, but solve the step size and search direction simultaneously as a single vector. The update rule is as follows[2],

$$\mathbf{v_{i+1}} = \mathbf{v_i} + \boldsymbol{\delta_i} \tag{11.3}$$

$$\text{where} \quad \mathbf{J_i J_i^T} \boldsymbol{\delta_i} = -\frac{1}{2} \nabla_\mathbf{v} f|_{\mathbf{v_i}}$$

This method is sometimes not numerically stable, particularly if the initial point is far from the solution. However, upon success, the rate of convergence is much faster. Since our problem often has knowledge of a reasonably good initial guess (usually a known curve exists that is reasonably close to the final solution) this is usually the best algorithm to choose. It will often converge after single or low double digit numbers of iterations.

11.3.6 Levenberg-Marquardt method

This is a blend of the above two methods to simultaneously extract the properties of numerical stability with good rate of convergence. A damping parameter, λ, is used to control the blend of the two algorithms. This parameter is set to be large initially, where the iterate is typically far from the solution and possibly unstable under Gauss-Newton yet amenable to gradient descent. As the solution progresses the damping parameter is systematically reduced to allow Gauss-Newton to take over where it is much more likely to be stable, and to avoid the poor

---

[1]see appendix section 11.5.1 for further information on the gradient descent method
[2]see appendix section 11.5.2 for further information on the Gauss-Newton algorithm

convergence properties of gradient descent as it approaches the solution. The update method is,

$$\mathbf{v_{i+1}} = \mathbf{v_i} + \boldsymbol{\delta_i} \tag{11.4}$$

$$\text{where} \quad (\mathbf{J_i}\mathbf{J_i^T} + \lambda\mathbf{I})\boldsymbol{\delta_i} = -\frac{1}{2}\nabla_{\mathbf{v}}f|_{\mathbf{v_i}}$$

In our implementation we choose to set $\lambda = 1000$ initially and half it or double it in each iteration depending upon the relative success or failure of the previous iteration. This method is only really recommended over Gauss-Newton where the initial guess is not particularly good.

Implementation

For our implementation we will create a SolvedCurve object which inherits the properties of the Curve object we have already created, and we will add the following items:

  i) additional variables at initialisation such as the length of vectors, and variables to solve, etc,

 ii) a calculate_metrics method which calculates function values and extracts automatic derivatives using our Dual numbers,

iii) an update_step method which updates the DFs to the next iteration based on the chosen algorithm,

 iv) an iterate method which is the wrapper to coordinate all the items inside a loop,

```
1  import numpy as np
2
3  class SolvedCurve(Curve):
4      def __init__(self, nodes: dict, interpolation: str, swaps: list, obj_rates: list,
5                   algorithm: str = "levenberg_marquardt"):
6          super().__init__(nodes=nodes, interpolation=interpolation)
7          self.swaps, self.obj_rates, self.algo = swaps, obj_rates, algorithm
8          self.n, self.m = len(self.nodes.keys()) - 1, len(self.swaps)
9          self.s = np.array([self.obj_rates]).transpose()
10         self.lam = 1000
11
12     def calculate_metrics(self):
13         self.r = np.array([[swap.rate(self) for swap in self.swaps]]).transpose()
14         self.v = np.array([[v for v in list(self.nodes.values())[1:]]]).transpose()
15         x = self.r - self.s
16         self.f = np.matmul(x.transpose(), x)[0][0]
17         self.grad_v_f = np.array(
18             [[self.f.dual.get(f"v{i+1}") for i in range(self.n)]]
19         ).transpose()
20         self.J = np.array([
21             [rate.dual.get(f"v{j+1}", 0) for rate in self.r[:, 0]]
22             for j in range(self.n)
23         ])
24
25     def update_step_gradient_descent(self):
26         y = np.matmul(self.J.transpose(), self.grad_v_f)
27         alpha = np.matmul(y.transpose(), self.r - self.s) / np.matmul(y.transpose(), y)
28         alpha = alpha[0][0].real
29         v_1 = self.v - self.grad_v_f * alpha
30         return v_1
31
32     def update_step_gauss_newton(self):
33         A = np.matmul(self.J, self.J.transpose())
34         b = -0.5 * self.grad_v_f
35         delta = np.linalg.solve(A, b)
36         v_1 = self.v + delta
37         return v_1
38
39     def update_step_levenberg_marquardt(self):
```

```
40    self.lam *= 2 if self.f_prev < self.f.real else 0.5
41    A = np.matmul(self.J, self.J.transpose()) + self.lam * np.eye(self.J.shape[0])
42    b = -0.5 * self.grad_v_f
43    delta = np.linalg.solve(A, b)
44    v_1 = self.v + delta
45    return v_1
46
47  def iterate(self, max_i=2000, tol=1e-10):
48    ret, self.f_prev, self.f_list = None, 1e10, []
49    for i in range(max_i):
50        self.calculate_metrics()
51        self.f_list.append(self.f.real)
52        if self.f.real < self.f_prev and (self.f_prev - self.f.real) < tol:
53            ret = f"tolerance reached ({self.algo}) after {i} iterations"
54            break
55        v_1 = getattr(self, f"update_step_{self.algo}")()
56        for i, (k, v) in enumerate(self.nodes.items()):
57            if i == 0:
58                continue
59            self.nodes[k] = v_1[i - 1, 0]
60        self.f_prev = self.f.real
61    self.lam = 1000
62    return f"max iters ({self.algo}), f: {self.f.real}" if ret is None else ret
```

See example 11.1, where the `SolvedCurve` is used.

11.4   Risk

Earlier in this chapter we discussed being able to directly extract the risk, or sensitivity, of a `Swap` to the DFs parametrising our `Curve` automatically. From a practical point of view this is not useful since you cannot reconcile tradable market hedges relative to DF sensitivities. However, using a simple mathematical trick and knowledge of the properties of CC zero coupon rates and `Dual` numbers, we were able to manipulate those DF sensitivities to those against par zero coupon rates. This is more useful but far from ideal.

What we would really like to do is obtain the sensitivities of a `Swap` (or a portfolio of `Swaps` which is their linear sum) with respect to the known market rates that parametrise our `SolvedCurve`. In other words, varying those known rate parameters will affect the solved DFs and therefore the specific `Swap` rate, and PV of that swap.

Suppose that a `SolvedCurve` has been iterated and optimally solved so that $\nabla_{\mathbf{v}} f$ evaluates to precisely the zero vector (a condition of optimality). The mathematical formulation for how the PV of a `Swap` varies with respect to changes in the known market rates, $\mathbf{S}$, i.e. the risk sensitivities to the instruments in $\mathbf{S}$, is stated as,

$$\nabla_{\mathbf{S}} P(\mathbf{v}(\mathbf{S}))$$

By application of the chain rule we have that,

$$\nabla_{\mathbf{S}} P(\mathbf{v}) = \underbrace{\nabla_{\mathbf{S}} \mathbf{v}^{\mathbf{T}}}_{\text{tbd}} \underbrace{\nabla_{\mathbf{v}} P(\mathbf{v})}_{\text{automatic}}$$

where $\nabla_{\mathbf{S}} \mathbf{v}^{\mathbf{T}} = \mathbf{K} = $ *Jacobian of* $\mathbf{v}$ *with respect to* $\mathbf{S}$ *such that,* $[\mathbf{K}]_{ij} = \dfrac{\partial v_j}{\partial S_i}$

As indicated by the under braces the second half of the right hand side is automatic. We have already produced these values in section 11.2.1. Our problem is with calculating the Jacobian, $\mathbf{K}$, which depends upon an iterative process. However three potential solutions are available:

  i) the appendix section 11.5.3 illustrates how one can reformulate and extract this Jacobian automatically if our `Dual` number implementation was to be extended to calculate second order derivatives,

ii) alternatively, the assumption that risk to the explicit instruments in **S** should only be expressed to those exact points and all other buckets should be zero, leads to a craftable linear system that is directly solvable for **K** (see appendix section 11.5.4),

iii) thirdly, we can calculate this Jacobian numerically through finite difference methods and measuring the change in **v** for small changes in **S**.

We will choose to demonstrate the third method below. Although this is likely the least efficient method it is simple to code, robust and serves as an example of numerical differentiation. Since this Jacobian is a property of the `SolvedCurve` it can be calculated just once and then stored for negligible memory. Any subsequent risk calculation for an arbitrary, and dynamic, `Swap` is efficient since it involves only a matrix multiplication of a stored matrix and automatically generated derivatives.

Below we implement the forward finite difference method. A central difference method is more accurate but requires twice as much calculation and a little extra code. We add the following to our existing `SolvedCurve` class, as demonstrated in [21, #caa549].

```
1  class SolvedCurve(Curve):
2      ...
3
4      @property
5      def grad_s_v(self):
6          if getattr(self, "grad_s_v_", None) is None:
7              self.grad_s_v_numeric()
8          return self.grad_s_v_
9
10     def grad_s_v_numeric(self):
11         grad_s_v = np.zeros(shape=(self.m, self.n))
12         ds = 1e-3
13         s_cv_fwd = SolvedCurve(
14             nodes=self.nodes, interpolation=self.interpolation,
15             swaps=self.swaps, obj_rates=self.obj_rates, algorithm="gauss_newton",
16         )
17         for s in range(self.m):
18             s_cv_fwd.nodes, s_cv_fwd.s = self.nodes, self.s.copy()
19             s_cv_fwd.s[s, 0] += ds
20             s_cv_fwd.iterate()
21             dvds_fwd = np.array([v.real for v in (s_cv_fwd.v[:, 0] - self.v[:, 0])/ds])
22             grad_s_v[s, :] = dvds_fwd
23         self.grad_s_v_ = grad_s_v
```

The above loop begins by creating a copy, `s_cv_fwd`, of the underlying `SolvedCurve`. For each swap in the set of those which parametrise the curve it varies each by a factor of 0.1bps, inside a loop, and manually extracts the changes to each DF node with respect to the original curve, and stores these values inside a matrix.

To calculate the risk on a swap according to the formula above we add the following to our `Swap` object.

```
1  class Swap:
2      ...
3
4      def risk(self, curve: SolvedCurve, fixed_rate: float, notional: float = 1e6):
5          grad_v_P = np.array([
6              [self.npv(curve, fixed_rate, notional).dual.get(f"v{i+1}", 0)
7               for i in range(curve.n)]
8          ]).transpose()
9          grad_s_P = np.matmul(curve.grad_s_v, grad_v_P)
10         return grad_s_P / 100
```

Example 11.1.

As an example we will replicate all the calculations from examples 10.4 and 10.5, which we calculated analytically, using our new library. Refer back to those sections if necessary. The first thing we need to do is define our nodes, swaps and create a SolvedCurve. The swap rates we use here are chosen to yield the analytic deltas that were used in the previous examples.

```
 1  >>> nodes = {
 2          datetime(2022, 1, 1): Dual(1, {"v0": 1}),
 3          datetime(2023, 1, 1): Dual(1, {"v1": 1}),
 4          datetime(2024, 1, 1): Dual(1, {"v2": 1}),
 5          datetime(2027, 1, 1): Dual(1, {"v3": 1}),
 6          datetime(2032, 1, 1): Dual(1, {"v4": 1}),
 7      }
 8  >>> par_swaps = {
 9          Swap(datetime(2022, 1, 1), 12*1, 12, 12): 1.210,
10          Swap(datetime(2022, 1, 1), 12*2, 12, 12): 1.635,
11          Swap(datetime(2022, 1, 1), 12*5, 12, 12): 1.885,
12          Swap(datetime(2022, 1, 1), 12*10, 12, 12): 1.930,
13      }
14  >>> s_cv = SolvedCurve(
15          nodes=nodes, swaps=list(par_swaps.keys()),
16          obj_rates=list(par_swaps.values()), interpolation="log_linear",
17          algorithm="levenberg_marquardt"
18      )
19  >>> print(s_cv.iterate())
20  tolerance reached (levenberg_marquardt) after 9 iterations
```

Now the curve is solved, if we check the mid rates for these Swaps we will find that they match the given input rates as expected. Before we build the par to fwd Jacobians we can risk a single mid-market 5Y5Y IRS in 100mm notional to demonstrate the use of the library.

```
1  >>> swap = Swap(datetime(2027, 1, 1), 12*5, 12, 12)   # 5Y5Y
2  >>> swap.risk(s_cv, fixed_rate=swap.rate(s_cv).real, notional=100e6)
3  [[-5],        # 1Y
4   [-19],       # 2Y
5   [-47447],    # 5Y
6   [90594]]     # 10Y
```

Then the next thing to do is to build our fwd Swaps and then risk them relative to the par instruments parametrising our SolvedCurve. Below we also set the fwd Swaps to have a mid market rate consistent with our SolvedCurve.

```
1  >>> fwd_swaps = {
2          Swap(datetime(2022, 1, 1), 12*1, 12, 12): 1,
3          Swap(datetime(2023, 1, 1), 12*1, 12, 12): 1,
4          Swap(datetime(2024, 1, 1), 12*3, 12, 12): 1,
5          Swap(datetime(2027, 1, 1), 12*5, 12, 12): 1,
6      }
7  >>> for swap in fwd_swaps.keys():
8          fwd_swaps[swap] = swap.rate(s_cv).real
```

Finally we risk those instruments we just created, scaling the columns to sum to one to directly compare with the examples.

```
 1  >>> risk = {}
 2  >>> for swap, rate in fwd_swaps.items():
 3          risk.update({swap.end: swap.risk(s_cv, fixed_rate=rate)[:, 0]})
 4  >>> df = pandas.DataFrame(risk)
 5  >>> df / df.sum()
 6          1y      1y1y    2y3y    5y5y
 7  1y      1.000   -1.021  -0.001  0.000
 8  2y      0.000   2.021   -0.699  -0.000
 9  5y      0.000   0.000   1.699   -1.104
10  10y     0.000   0.000   0.000   2.105
```

This compares directly with example 10.5. We can repeat the same process building a SolvedCurve with fwd Swaps and then risking par Swaps.

```
1  >>> s_cv = SolvedCurve(
2          nodes=nodes, swaps=list(fwd_swaps.keys()),
3          obj_rates=list(fwd_swaps.values()), interpolation="log_linear",
4          algorithm="levenberg_marquardt"
5      )
6  >>> print(s_cv.iterate())
7  tolerance reached (levenberg_marquardt) after 8 iterations
8  >>> risk = {}
9  >>> for swap, rate in par_swaps.items():
```

```
10          risk.update({swap.end: swap.risk(s_cv, fixed_rate=rate)[:, 0]})
11 >>> df = pandas.DataFrame(risk)
12 >>> df / df.sum()
13          1y      2y      5y      10y
14 1y      1.000   0.506   0.209   0.110
15 1y1y    0.000   0.494   0.203   0.107
16 2y3y    0.000   0.000   0.588   0.308
17 5y5y    0.000   0.000   0.000   0.476
```

This compares directly with example 10.4.

11.5 Appendix

11.5.1 Gradient descent method

Here we include more details of the gradient descent method's update rule. By its nature the gradient descent algorithm's search direction is that of negative gradient evaluated at the current iterate and therefore has the following update rule,

$$\mathbf{v_{i+1}} = \mathbf{v_i} - \alpha_i \nabla_{\mathbf{v}} f|_{\mathbf{v_i}} = \mathbf{v_i} - 2\alpha_i \mathbf{J_i} \mathbf{W}(\mathbf{r_i} - \mathbf{S}) \tag{11.5}$$

Note that we included a weights matrix here in the objective function, $\mathbf{W} = \mathrm{diag}(\mathbf{w})$, which is otherwise the identity and can be ignored. The step size is an important part of the iteration overall and should not be overlooked. In order to determine the step size, α_i, we will approximate the updated derived rates vector to first order,

$$\begin{aligned} \mathbf{r_{i+1}} \approx \mathbf{\tilde{r}_{i+1}} &= \mathbf{r_i} + \mathbf{J_i^T}(\mathbf{v_{i+1}} - \mathbf{v_i}) \\ &= \mathbf{r_i} - 2\alpha_i \mathbf{J_i^T} \mathbf{W} \mathbf{J_i}(\mathbf{r_i} - \mathbf{S}) \end{aligned} \tag{11.6}$$

Depending upon the interpolation style of the curve the rates may well be non-linear functions of the discount factors. Therefore this linear assumption, which is expected to be sufficiently accurate for the relatively small changes near optimality, helps to simplify the calculations.

To then determine the value of the step size, α_i, we implement a secondary optimisation routine that seeks to minimise the approximated objective function under this iterate with respect to the step size,

$$\min_{\alpha_i} f(\mathbf{\tilde{r}_{i+1}}) = \min_{\alpha_i} (\mathbf{r_i} - 2\alpha_i \mathbf{J_i^T} \mathbf{W} \mathbf{J_i}(\mathbf{r_i} - \mathbf{S}) - \mathbf{S})^{\mathbf{T}} (\mathbf{r_i} - 2\alpha_i \mathbf{J_i^T} \mathbf{W} \mathbf{J_i}(\mathbf{r_i} - \mathbf{S}) - \mathbf{S}) \tag{11.7}$$

We assume that this secondary optimisation problem can be solved analytically, by taking the derivative with respect to α_i, equating it to zero as a necessary condition of optimality and yielding the result,

$$\frac{\partial f(\mathbf{\tilde{r}_{i+1}})}{\partial \alpha_i} = 4 \left(\mathbf{J_i^T} \mathbf{W} \mathbf{J_i}(\mathbf{r_i} - \mathbf{S}) \right)^{\mathbf{T}} \left(\mathbf{r_i} - \mathbf{S} - 2\alpha_i \mathbf{J_i^T} \mathbf{W} \mathbf{J_i}(\mathbf{r_i} - \mathbf{S}) \right) = 0$$

$$\implies \quad \alpha_i^* = \frac{\mathbf{y^T}(\mathbf{r_i} - \mathbf{S})}{\mathbf{y^T y}}, \quad \text{for} \quad \mathbf{y} = \mathbf{J_i^T} \nabla_{\mathbf{v}} f|_{\mathbf{v_i}} = 2\mathbf{J_i^T} \mathbf{W} \mathbf{J_i}(\mathbf{r_i} - \mathbf{S}) \tag{11.8}$$

11.5.2 Gauss-Newton method

The Gauss-Newton method is an algorithm designed specifically for least squares problems. Using this method we essentially solve a secondary optimisation problem, akin to equation 11.7, but solve the step size and search direction simultaneously as a single vector. This method begins by assuming an increment,

$$\mathbf{v_{i+1}} = \mathbf{v_i} + \boldsymbol{\delta_i} \tag{11.9}$$

and the linear approximation shown in equation 11.6 also holds so that,

$$\mathbf{r_{i+1}} \approx \mathbf{\tilde{r}_{i+1}} = \mathbf{r_i} + \mathbf{J_i^T} \boldsymbol{\delta_i}$$

We then solve the secondary optimisation problem for $\boldsymbol{\delta_i}$,

$$\min_{\boldsymbol{\delta_i}} f(\mathbf{v_{i+1}}) = (\mathbf{r_i} - \mathbf{S})^{\mathbf{T}} \mathbf{W}(\mathbf{r_i} - \mathbf{S}) + 2(\mathbf{r_i} - \mathbf{S})^{\mathbf{T}} \mathbf{W} \mathbf{J_i^T} \boldsymbol{\delta_i} + \boldsymbol{\delta_i^T} \mathbf{J_i} \mathbf{W} \mathbf{J_i^T} \boldsymbol{\delta_i} \tag{11.10}$$

Since this is an unconstrained quadratic form in $\boldsymbol{\delta_i}$ we can take the derivative with respect to $\boldsymbol{\delta_i}$ and equate it to zero as a necessary condition of optimality yielding the linear system,

$$\mathbf{J_i W J_i^T \delta_i} = -\mathbf{J_i W}(\mathbf{r_i} - \mathbf{S}) = -\frac{1}{2}\nabla_\mathbf{v} f|_\mathbf{v_i} \qquad (11.11)$$

11.5.3 Fixed point iteration

As an example suppose we want to find the minimum of a function of x with fixed parameter, s, say,

$$\min_x f(x,s) = \min_x \frac{1}{4}x^4 - \frac{1}{2}sx^2$$

This is a non-linear optimisation problem which can, in this case, be solved analytically using classical calculus techniques. The solution is $x^* = \pm\sqrt{s}$, and, knowing this, we can analytically calculate that $\frac{dx^*}{ds} = \pm\frac{1}{2\sqrt{s}}$.

However, if instead we applied some iterative algorithm to numerically determine the solution this would lead to the update formula,

$$x_{i+1} = g(x_i, s) = x_i - \alpha\frac{\partial f}{\partial x}|_{x_i} \quad \text{(if } g \text{ was to implement gradient descent, say)}$$

At the minimum, x^*, this equation yields a fixed point,

$$x^* = g(x^*, s) = x^* - \alpha\frac{\partial f}{\partial x}|_{x^*}$$

We can use this to determine the sensitivity of x^* to the parameter, s,

$$\frac{dx^*}{ds} = \frac{dg}{ds} = \frac{\partial g}{\partial x^*}\frac{dx^*}{ds} + \frac{\partial g}{\partial s} = \left(1 - \alpha\frac{\partial^2 f}{\partial x \partial x}\bigg|_{x^*}\right)\frac{dx^*}{ds} - \alpha\frac{\partial f}{\partial x \partial s}\bigg|_{x^*}$$

$$\implies \quad \frac{dx^*}{ds} = \frac{-\frac{\partial^2 f}{\partial x \partial s}}{\frac{\partial^2 f}{\partial x \partial x}}\bigg|_{x^*}$$

Observe two things; firstly the right hand side is independent of α which is to be expected since the choice of iterative procedure should not impact sensitivity (the converged solution should be identical regardless of the converging algorithm); secondly that the right hand side of this equation is the function value, f, with second order sensitivity to x and s. If our Dual number implementation was capable of producing higher order derivatives, then these would be automatically available. As it is, we can just substitute the exact derivatives calculated manually in our example to yield the expected value,

$$\frac{dx^*}{ds} = \frac{\pm\sqrt{s}}{3s - s} = \pm\frac{1}{2\sqrt{s}}$$

An equivalent, multidimensional version of this argument would lead to the following equation applicable to the main text,

$$\nabla_\mathbf{s}\mathbf{v}^{*\mathbf{T}} = -\left[(\nabla_\mathbf{s}\nabla_\mathbf{v}^\mathbf{T} f)(\nabla_\mathbf{v}\nabla_\mathbf{v}^\mathbf{T} f)^{-1}\right]|_{\mathbf{v}^*}, \quad [\nabla_\mathbf{s}\nabla_\mathbf{v}^\mathbf{T} f]_{ij} = \frac{\partial f}{\partial s_i \partial v_j}, \quad [\nabla_\mathbf{v}\nabla_\mathbf{v}^\mathbf{T} f]_{ij} = \frac{\partial f}{\partial v_i \partial v_j}$$

For further reading on convergence and other mathematical properties consider [31].

11.5.4 Risk of calibrating instruments

Apply the *weak* assumption that the curve solver objective function, $f(\mathbf{v}^*, \mathbf{S})$, is always zero at solution, for completely specified or underspecified curves. Also apply the *strong* assumption that if one calibrating instrument is varied, the solved values for alternative instruments are unchanged, for overspecified curves.

Let the column vector, $\mathbf{P}$, be such that the k'th row is the PV of a trade which is the k'th calibrating instrument of our curve solver, and whose initial fixed rate is set identically to its input, S_k.

Our assumptions imply that if we vary one or more calibrating instruments that are **not** the calibrating instrument associated with the specific row in, $\mathbf{P}$, the mid-market of that that instrument based on an updated (reiterated) curve does not change and therefore experiences no risk. Thus we have,

$$\nabla_{\mathbf{S}} \mathbf{P}^{\mathbf{T}} = \mathbf{diag}(\boldsymbol{\beta})$$

where the values, β_j, are the risk values dependent upon the notional applied to each trade, P_j. If we can *find* suitable notional amounts for each trade then we can engineer, $\beta_j = 1$ for all j, such that, $\nabla_{\mathbf{S}} \mathbf{P}^{\mathbf{T}} = \mathbf{I}$, which leads to,

$$\underset{m \times m}{\nabla_{\mathbf{S}} \mathbf{P}^{\mathbf{T}}} = \underset{m \times n}{\nabla_{\mathbf{S}} \mathbf{v}^{\mathbf{T}}} \underset{n \times m}{\nabla_{\mathbf{v}} \mathbf{P}^{\mathbf{T}}} = \underset{m \times m}{\mathbf{I}} \qquad \implies \qquad \nabla_{\mathbf{S}} \mathbf{v}^{\mathbf{T}} = \begin{cases} (\nabla_{\mathbf{v}} \mathbf{P}^{\mathbf{T}})^{-1} & n = m \\ (\nabla_{\mathbf{v}} \mathbf{P}^{\mathbf{T}})^{+} & n \neq m \end{cases}$$

Since, $\nabla_{\mathbf{v}} \mathbf{P}^{\mathbf{T}}$, is automatic the only thing preventing us from efficiently calculating, $\nabla_{\mathbf{S}} \mathbf{v}^{\mathbf{T}}$, is how to choose the notionals for each trade in rows of, $\mathbf{P}$. It suffices that, in each case, we can use the *analytic delta* (scaled to 1bp), setting it to unity,

$$1 \times \frac{1}{10000} = N \sum_{i=1}^{T_1} d_i v_i$$

Proof: consider two parametrising sets, $\mathbf{S_1}$ and $\mathbf{S_2}$, where the rates are identical except in one element, say, $S_{2,j} = S_{1,j} + \delta s$. Associated with these are the relevant solved curves, $\mathbf{v_1^*}$ and $\mathbf{v_2^*}$. For any IRS calibrating instrument, k, we have that:

$$\frac{P_{1,k}}{N_k} = S_{1,k} \sum_{i=1}^{T_{1,k}} d_i v_i(\mathbf{v_1^*}) - \sum_{j=1}^{T_{2,k}} r_j(\mathbf{v_1^*}) d_j v_j(\mathbf{v_1^*}), \qquad \frac{P_{2,k}}{N_k} = S_{2,k} \sum_{i=1}^{T_{1,k}} d_i v_i(\mathbf{v_2^*}) - \sum_{j=1}^{T_{2,k}} r_j(\mathbf{v_2^*}) d_j v_j(\mathbf{v_2^*})$$

where, for all $k \neq j$, **under the assumptions specified above** $P_{1,k} = P_{2,k}$, and in the case of completely specified or underspecified curves $P_{1,k} \doteq P_{2,k} = 0$. Now evaluate $P_{1,j}(\mathbf{v_2^*})$:

$$\begin{aligned} P_{1,j}(\mathbf{v_2^*}) &= N_j \left(S_{1,j} \sum_{i=1}^{T_{1,j}} d_i v_i(\mathbf{v_2^*}) - \sum_{j=1}^{T_{2,j}} r_j(\mathbf{v_2^*}) d_j v_j(\mathbf{v_2^*}) \right) \\ &= N_j \left((S_{2,j} - \delta s) \sum_{i=1}^{T_{1,j}} d_i v_i(\mathbf{v_2^*}) - \sum_{j=1}^{T_{2,j}} r_j(\mathbf{v_2^*}) d_j v_j(\mathbf{v_2^*}) \right) = N_j \left(P_{2,j} - \delta s \sum_{i=1}^{T_{1,j}} d_i v_i(\mathbf{v_2^*}) \right) \end{aligned}$$

Thus, if $\lim_{\delta s \to 0} P_{2,j} = P_{1,j}$,

$$\frac{\partial P_{1,j}}{\partial s} = \lim_{\delta s \to 0} \frac{P_{1,j}(\mathbf{v_2^*}) - P_{1,j}}{\delta s} = \lim_{\delta s \to 0} -N_j \sum_{i=1}^{T_{1,j}} d_i v_i(\mathbf{v_2^*}) = -N_j \sum_{i=1}^{T_{1,j}} d_i v_i(\mathbf{v_1^*})$$

Advanced Curve Building

12.1 Log-cubic spline interpolation

The implementation of our `Curve` currently only includsd two interpolation styles for DFs; *linear* and *log-linear*. This is because those methods are easy to code since their dependence is local, i.e. the interpolated DF depends only on the two surrounding nodes. However, log-cubic spline is a useful and frequently used interpolation method so we must cover it. It will form a part of our `AdvancedCurve` implementation.

Cubic splines come in a variety of forms and ways to calculate them. This chapter's appendix outlines the method of B-splines, which is by far my favourite due to its useful form and properties, and how to parametrise them. A reader should, at this point, read this first as a completely isolated section on spline construction in general. For cubic interpolation fourth order B-splines are required[1], and to determine the logarithm of the DF on an arbitrary date, x, we will use the spline function,

$$\$_{4,\mathbf{t}}(x) = \sum_{i=1}^{n} \alpha_i B_{i,4,\mathbf{t}}(x)$$

where α_i are the coefficients controlling our spline over the **chosen knot sequence**, $\mathbf{t}$, and must be calculated by our curve solver.

---

[1] this corresponds to $k = 4$ in relevant appendix sections

In order to implement cubic spline interpolation we will create a new `AdvancedCurve` class which inherits the `SolvedCurve` object and all of the methods we have already coded for iterative solving. We need to include new methods to calibrate the spline, which is dependent upon the instructed knot sequence, **t**. We will allow mixed interpolation in our `AdvancedCurve` so that if the requested date is prior to the first given spline knot then we fall back to the original interpolation methods, e.g. *log-linear*.

Also our cubic spline is specifically coded to be a **natural** spline with second derivatives taking the value zero at the endpoints (this could, of course, be amended if necessary by altering the spline collocation matrix). The DF nodes serve as the **datasites** which calibrate the spline. The spline has been coded to implement `Dual` numbers in its own methods which is necessary for the `SolvedCurve` iteration methods to function correctly when calculating derivatives automatically.

```
class AdvancedCurve(SolvedCurve):
    def __init__(self, nodes: dict, interpolation: str, swaps: list, obj_rates: list,
                 t: list, algorithm: str = "gauss_newton"):
        super().__init__(nodes, interpolation, swaps, obj_rates, algorithm)
        self.t = t
        self.bs = BSpline(4, t)

    def __getitem__(self, date: datetime):
        if date <= self.t[0]:
            return super().__getitem__(date)
        else:
            return self.bs.ppev_single(date).__exp__()

    def solve_bspline(self):
        tau = [k for k in self.nodes.keys() if k >= self.t[0]]
        y = [v.__log__() for k, v in self.nodes.items() if k >= self.t[0]]

        tau.insert(0, self.t[0])     # add second derivative endpoints
        tau.append(self.t[-1])
        y.insert(0, 0)
        y.append(0)

        self.bs.bsplsolve(np.array(tau), np.array(y), 2, 2)
```

During the iterative solving process the B-spline must be updated before we calculate the metrics. So we must add the following method overload,

```
    def calculate_metrics(self):
        self.solve_bspline()
        super().calculate_metrics()
```

12.2   Mixed interpolation

The above implementation [21, #dfe280] was enough to allow a cubic spline interpolation from a given starting point, which is the first knot point in the **t** sequence. As long as sensible knot placement is used, akin to the appendix description, this automatically creates a mixed interpolation where the first part of the curve uses *log-linear* by default or *linear* if specified. It is of course possible to do a full cubic spline, if the **t** sequence encompasses the whole domain.

Example 12.1.
Here we create a very simple 3Y curve, calibrated by 3 swaps. The DF nodes are placed at 1Y gaps. For the `AdvancedCurve`, the log-cubic spline initiates after the first year.

```
>>> nodes = {
        datetime(2022, 1, 1): Dual(1.00, {"v0": 1}),
        datetime(2023, 1, 1): Dual(1.00, {"v1": 1}),
        datetime(2024, 1, 1): Dual(1.00, {"v2": 1}),
        datetime(2025, 1, 1): Dual(1.00, {"v3": 1}),
    }
```

```
 7 >>> swaps = {
 8        Swap(datetime(2022, 1, 1), 12*1, 3, 3): 1.0,
 9        Swap(datetime(2022, 1, 1), 12*2, 3, 3): 1.5,
10        Swap(datetime(2022, 1, 1), 12*3, 3, 3): 2.0,
11     }
12 >>> s_cv = SolvedCurve(
13        nodes=nodes_dual, interpolation="log_linear",
14        swaps=list(swaps.keys()), obj_rates=list(swaps.values()),
15        algorithm="levenberg_marquardt"
16     )
17 >>> t_left, t_right = datetime(2023, 1, 1), datetime(2025, 1, 1)
18 >>> t = [
19        t_left, t_left, t_left, t_left,
20        datetime(2024, 1, 1),
21        t_right, t_right, t_right, t_right,
22     ]
23 >>> adv_cv = AdvancedCurve(
24        nodes=nodes_dual, interpolation="log_linear",
25        swaps=list(swaps.keys()), obj_rates=list(swaps.values()),
26        t=t, algorithm="levenberg_marquardt"
27     )
28 >>> s_cv.iterate()
29 tolerance reached (levenberg_marquardt) after 7 iterations
30 >>> adv_cv.iterate()
31 tolerance reached (levenberg_marquardt) after 7 iterations
```

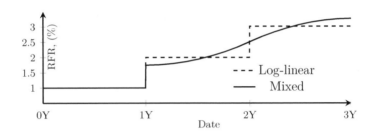

Figure 12.1: Overnight forward RFR rates

12.3 Layered curvesets

The numerical solvers we have constructed so far solve for all calibrating instrument inputs simultaneously. Experience has shown that this is suboptimal for some instruments that are less observable or possibly dependent upon the curve shape itself. A layered curveset is one that solves and constructs parts of the curve in at least two stages, often producing temporary, intermediate curvesets.

Consider a curve which has been optimally solved to yield DF nodes, $\mathbf{v}^*$, and was parametrised so that the objective function obtained its minimum value of zero,

$$\mathbf{v}^* = \mathrm{argmin}_{\mathbf{v}} f(\mathbf{v}, \mathbf{S}) = \mathrm{argmin}_{\mathbf{v}} ||\mathbf{r}(\mathbf{v}) - \mathbf{S}||_2 \quad \text{s.t.} \quad f(\mathbf{v}^*, \mathbf{S}) = 0$$

Suppose that one then calculates new, additional rates, $\mathbf{r}_2(\mathbf{v}^*)$, and sets these as additional fixed parameters in a second, expanded optimisation,

$$\mathbf{v}_2^* = \mathrm{argmin}_{\mathbf{v}} f(\mathbf{v}, \mathbf{S}, \mathbf{S}_2) = \mathrm{argmin}_{\mathbf{v}} ||[\mathbf{r} : \mathbf{r}_2] - [\mathbf{S} : \mathbf{S}_2]||_2 \quad \text{s.t.} \quad f(\mathbf{v}_2^*, \mathbf{S}, \mathbf{S}_2) = 0$$

This only shows that $\mathbf{v}_2^*$ must be identical to $\mathbf{v}^*$, plus its interpolated points for any additionally inserted nodes. So, the insertion of calibrated instruments that are derived from the original curve itself do not introduce any variation in the second curve from the first.

This property allows us to expand the flexibility of our input system. Instead of providing specific rates which must be solved, we can provide, **for some chosen rates**, a skewed price adjustment from that which is interpolated in the first curve layer.

Example 12.2.
We solve a curveset which, in the first layer has 1Y, 2Y, 3Y, 5Y, 7Y, and 10Y instruments. In the second layer it adjusts the price of the 4Y, 6Y, 8Y and 9Y instruments by the skews contained in the table below.

Input Instrument	First Layer Rate	Second Layer Skew
1Y	1.00%	
2Y	1.40%	
3Y	1.64%	
4Y		0.1bp
5Y	1.84%	
6Y		0.1bp
7Y	1.90%	
8Y		0.2bp
9Y		0.25bp
10Y	1.97%	

There is the advantage here that the **skew perturbations** from a smooth curve in these lesser observable instruments are often maintained at particular quantities, even as the other, more observable, instrument prices vary. The perturbations tends to be quite stable parameters, shifting as a result of supply-demand dynamics and of wider curve shape changes, which are often slow to materialise. However, their existence still permits complete control of the curve. We have not reduced our parameter space by implementing this change. Essentially we have converted ten volatile inputs in the non-layered curveset and converted them into six volatile inputs and four stable ones.

This has risk benefits as well. A risk model can be readily created without the above skew inputs, i.e. a risk model crafted from only the first layer. Unless the skews were changed on a given day, it would be the case that the risk model with only the non-skewed instruments would be almost as reliable (subject to negligible interpolation misalignments) as one that *did* include those skew inputs[2]. The reason for this is that the first layer risk model replicates the first layer curveset of the two layer curveset. This first layer contains a lot of the inherent information used by the final, second layer curveset. If the skew is unaltered on a given day then the final, open and close curves on that given day are related to the first layer, open and close curves in the same way, so that *all* market movements are effectively captured by those first layer curves.

This type of design favours quantitative analysts and risk supervisors who seek to reduce the dimensionality of curvesets into few parameters (the first stage construction) and traders who desire more control to skew the output (second and latter stage constructions).

---

[2]example 9.7 demonstrates this in the section on risk models

12.4 Turns

Turns represent *out of character* market rates for specific dates, created by some fundamental, economic artefact. For example, the well know **year-end turn** is an effect that impacts rates which have term periods that include midnight on 31st December. Suppose the effect has been to impact the rate upwards. One might speculate the reason being that financial institutions are typically less inclined to lend money over the 31st December. On this particular date they prefer to withhold their cash so that their year end financial balance sheet can report a larger cash asset, rather than a loan asset, and this has the effect of creating a premium in the rate. On the other hand, suppose a market dominated by deposits instead of lending. At a year end financial institutions without access to central bank deposit facilities may have additional cash on hand (for similar reason as above) and need to lend it to banks *with* those facilities, who therefore choose to borrow money with a negative premium instead. If one looks at, for example, historical data on the SONIA publication during 2021, it is apparent that a negative premium of about 0.25-1bps impacts the date immediately before a quarter end, i.e. on 31st Mar, 30th Jun, 30 Sep and 31st Dec.

Turns have much less significance for RFR curves than their predecessor, the IBOR curves, since the impact is restricted to a single day's or a few days' fixings. When the impact previously affected 1M, 3M, or 6M fixings the risk exposure was often much more pronounced and the mathematically implied turn impact when considered over a single day was much larger than what the current RFR curves seem to experience.

Never-the-less we will explore the methods to implement turns here for completeness. In order to support turns we need to expand our `Schedule` and `Swap` classes from sections 11.1.2 and 11.1.3 respectively, to accept tenor periods in days rather than months. This is a minimal code block change as follows [21, #bf1f92],

```
1  def add_days(start: datetime, days: int) -> datetime:
2      return start + timedelta(days=days)
3
4  class Schedule:
5      def __init__(self, start: datetime, tenor: int,
6          period: int, days: bool=False
7      ):
8          self.add_op = add_days if days else add_months
9          self.end = self.add_op(start, tenor)
10         ...
11
12     @property
13     def data(self):
14         ...
15         for i in range(self.n_periods - 1):
16             period_end = self.add_op(period_start, self.period)
17         ...
18
19 class Swap:
20     def __init__(self, start: datetime, tenor: int, period_fix: int,
21         period_float: int, days: bool=False
22     ):
23         self.add_op = add_days if days else add_months
24         self.end = self.add_op(start, tenor)
25         self.schedule_fix = Schedule(start, tenor, period_fix, days=days)
26         self.schedule_float = Schedule(start, tenor, period_float, days=days)
27         ...
```

Since turns are defined as relative jumps, i.e. one particular rate should be greater than or equal to another rate by a specific amount, we need to extend our library to include `SwapSpread` objects. These simply combine two swaps and return a spread rate.

```
1  class SwapSpread:
2      def __init__(self, swap1: Swap, swap2: Swap):
3          self.swap1 = swap1
```

```
4            self.swap2 = swap2
5
6        def rate(self, curve: Curve):
7            return self.swap2.rate(curve) - self.swap1.rate(curve)
```

Now to actually implement the turns, expanding example 12.1. Note, the way we implement these into our solver **cannot** be applied to the cubic spline interpolation method, only the local interpolators. This is due to the nature of the splines requiring degrees of continuity, and this creates unavoidably large oscillations otherwise.

Example 12.3.

We add an exaggerated negative 25bps turn to the 2022 year end and 2023 half year end. Since a node already exists at 1st Jan-23 the 2022 turn needs only one additional parametrisation. Since the 2023 half year end turn is in between periods we must create two additional nodes and two additional instruments. The plots shows sharp spikes lower for the 1D rates applicable on 31st Dec 2022 and 30 June 2023 as expected.

```
1  >>> nodes = {
2      datetime(2022, 1, 1): Dual(1.00, {"v0": 1}),
3      datetime(2022, 12, 31): Dual(1.00, {"v1": 1}),
4      datetime(2023, 1, 1): Dual(1.00, {"v2": 1}),
5      datetime(2023, 6, 30): Dual(1.00, {"v3": 1}),
6      datetime(2023, 7, 1): Dual(1.00, {"v4": 1}),
7      datetime(2024, 1, 1): Dual(1.00, {"v5": 1}),
8      datetime(2025, 1, 1): Dual(1.00, {"v6": 1}),
9  }
10 >>> swaps = {
11     Swap(datetime(2022, 1, 1), 12*1, 3, 3): 1.0,
12     Swap(datetime(2022, 1, 1), 12*2, 3, 3): 1.5,
13     Swap(datetime(2022, 1, 1), 12*3, 3, 3): 2.0,
14     SwapSpread(
15         Swap(datetime(2022, 12, 30), 1, 1, 1, days=True),
16         Swap(datetime(2022, 12, 31), 1, 1, 1, days=True)
17     ): -0.25,
18     SwapSpread(
19         Swap(datetime(2023, 6, 29), 1, 1, 1, days=True),
20         Swap(datetime(2023, 6, 30), 1, 1, 1, days=True)
21     ): -0.25,
22     SwapSpread(
23         Swap(datetime(2023, 6, 30), 1, 1, 1, days=True),
24         Swap(datetime(2023, 7, 1), 1, 1, 1, days=True)
25     ): 0.25,
26 }
27 >>> s_cv = SolvedCurve(
28     nodes=nodes_dual, interpolation="log_linear",
29     swaps=list(swaps.keys()), obj_rates=list(swaps.values()),
30     algorithm="levenberg_marquardt"
31 )
32 >>> s_cv.iterate()
33 tolerance reached (levenberg_marquardt) after 7 iterations
```

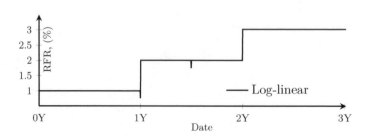

12.5 Nodes, knots and instrument selection

In light of adopting mixed interpolation it is worth revisiting the purpose of nodes, knots and instruments. Recall that,

- **Instruments** are required to calibrate the curve to market observable prices,

- **Nodes** are required to allow the iterative solver to vary DFs such that the resultant curve reprices the input instruments to minimise the objective function,

- **Knots** are only required to define the piecewise polynomial spline space for the log-cubic spline interpolators and affect the shape of the curve dependent upon their placement.

12.5.1 Monetary policy meeting dates and log-linear interpolation

The transmission mechanism[3] was a primary focus for central banks in the design of RFRs. It therefore stands to reason that their value closely aligns with central bank policy rates. Log-linear interpolation is therefore ideal for use in modelling curves since it preserves overnight rates until nodes dates where those rates discontinuously jump to another value, much like central bank policy rates.

The choice of node dates for log-linear interpolators should then align with those dates where new central bank policy rates become effective. Very often these dates are known only for about one year, with some prospective dates for the following year, and then most likely crude estimates for the third year and subsequently. At the same time market observable instruments become sparser after about three years. This is the reason that mixed interpolation methods were introduced to provide the specificity at the short end where there is greater certainty and, at the medium to longer term, some consistent form of averaging that calibrates to market instruments.

IMM RFR futures are liquid in the established RFR markets, such as SONIA and SOFR. These instruments are very strongly recommended for inclusion in a curve since they are electronic so can update the curve in real-time. There may also be quite a liquid short dated RFR market which can be worthwhile incorporating into the first six months or so. But after that decision, the question then becomes how many IMM swaps to use? Usually this is a question of liquidity. 8 might be applicable for small currencies, but certainly 12 or more can be incorporated into the most liquid currencies. More than 12 might be considered overkill though - adding complexity without gaining much from it. Either 6, 7, 10, 11, or 14 are the worst choices for the number of IMM contracts to use. The reason these numbers are suboptimal is related to the 'roll' (when the front contract expires and the i'th contract takes the place of the $i-1$'th contract), and the effect it has on risk changes in terms of leverage. Firstly, note that we will recommend that instruments that dictate the section of the curve after the furthest IMM contract will be par instruments: typically 2Y, 3Y, 4Y or 5Y depending on how many IMM contracts have been chosen. For example, suppose that 10 contracts have been chosen, then the maximum tenor distance these can collectively extend to is 2.75Y (which occurs immediately after the expiry of an imminent contract), falling to a minimum of 2.5Y (just before the expiry of an imminent contract). Due to the effect of leverage[4] this creates a large strain on risk models to show 2.75Y0.25Y rate risk. It is not good for that reason alone, but is worsened with the expiry of one contract and introduction of a new contract. After the roll, risk models then have to incorporate a new instrument, when the leverage is largest, and the change in risk from

---

[3]see section 8.1 on the transmission mechanism of IRs
[4]see section 10.4 explaining fwds and pars

one day to the next yields unwieldy and unintuitive positions that traders need to decide how to consider.

Using 8 or 12 futures is better suited because it minimises the leverage effect, and always maintains an ultimate tenor length that extends just passed a par tenor. E.g. 8 contracts always collectively extends beyond 2Y and 12 contracts always extends beyond 3Y. Using 7 or 11 contracts would create the problem of having to *add-in* or *take-out* par instruments at certain times (to avoid underspecified or overspecified curves), which is also completely undesirable for risk models used on a continuous basis.

12.5.2   Par tenors and log-cubic spline interpolation

If par tenors are then recommended after the IMM period, we again question how many par tenor rates to include? Quantitative analysts would argue for few. They would argue their analytic interest rate models replicate real world data with only a few parameters. Traders would argue for a lot, since it gives them more control of the curveset and permits them to more accurately price (and risk) any trade in the interbank market, reacting to supply and demand anomalies. Both viewpoints are actually valid and we highlight the previous section on layered curvesets as a good solution.

The interbank IRS market has a strong tendency to trade in par IRSs, and *not* IMM IRSs (which start, end and roll on IMM dates). However, it is frequent for hedge funds to trade IMM IRSs (for ease of risk management purposes) and this does create a tendency for the density of IMM IRSs to be larger than those for other arbitrary dates. But, the general IR market is far larger than the hedge fund speculator type of trading. Bonds, for example, will always have arbitrary start dates, dependent upon when they issue, and traditional par maturities, and these dictate a large share of the market. This is particularly true for real money and asset manager investor user groups. There is no reason that other hedging or trading activity should be centralised about IMM dates. Given the current structure of the interbank market and the cross-comparison of products it is likely that par IRSs will remain dominant over IMM IRSs, as has been the case for the last 30 years. **Thus it is more sensible to use the directly observable par instruments as inputs to the curveset, and for traditional risk models.**

Since par tenors tend to be sparse, log-linear interpolation is not a sensible option here. **Instead we recommend log-cubic spline interpolation and must carefully consider our node dates and knot sequence.** Some basic properties under our currently implemented `AdvancedCurve`;

i) the knot sequence of length, $n + 4$, with only repeated end knots, defines, $n - 3$, intervals, and enforces continuity of the first derivative, second derivative and value of the spline function by definition, at interior breakpoints,

ii) that same knot sequence requires, $n - 2$, nodes as datasites to solve the spline collocation matrix system, of which at least one node must be contained within each interval, which satisfies the Schoenberg and Whitney theorem [32].

Example 12.4.
*Suppose a **knot sequence** of [3Y, 3Y, 3Y 3Y, 4Y, 5Y, 6Y, 6Y, 6Y, 6Y], constructed from par tenor maturity dates, of length, $6 + 4 = 10$. This defines, $6 - 3 = 3$, intervals which are: [3Y, 4Y], [4Y, 5Y], [5Y, 6Y]. We require a total of, $6 - 2 = 4$, nodes contained within these intervals, and at least one node in each interval which act as datasites.*

It is practical to set the first knot as the final node in the log-linear part of the curve. This alleviates most problems related to dimensionality. In example 12.4 this would mean there would likely be a node at the 3Y date relevant to the first, log-linear part of the curve. The other nodes would then have some flexibility of placement.

In the log-cubic spline section of the curve the positioning of nodes, within valid ranges, is not nearly as important as in the log-linear section. What is more important is the positioning of knots. Let us consider two very common scenarios;

i) **knots are placed at the maturity of par tenor instruments** and therefore roll by one day on a daily basis (akin to example 12.4), and nodes are likely to follow suit,

ii) **knots are placed at strategic points such as IMM dates** which do not change on a daily basis but, only, at key IMM roll dates during the year. Nodes may follow suit or align with par maturity dates, it doesn't necessarily matter.

It turns out that the first of these scenarios has an inherent disadvantage. Changing the knot points of a piecewise polynomial function makes difficult to predict changes to that function even when the datasites are consistent. For our curve build process this means that even if par tenor rates evolve through time exactly as initially expected our curve will suffer rates changes from the variation we are introducing through the changes in our piecewise polynomial function. On the other hand, the second approach produces an identically stable curve build throughout time if rates were to evolve exactly as predicted. The unique solution of the spline collocation matrix system (see section 12.9.2) ensures that the spline coefficients, α, are identical even where node datasites are at different points but consistently calculated from the same underlying spline function.

Example 12.5 performs an experiment to show how some sample forward rates change through time solely on the dependence of shifting knot points, even when the curve is expected to evolve exactly as forecast on the initial base date.

Example 12.5.
Suppose for an initial base date of 1st Jan 2022 we have;

i) ten yearly par tenor IRSs with mid-market rates intended to calibrate the curves,

ii) an initial node and then nodes on IMM dates following the maturity of each tenor IRS,

iii) knot dates for the log-cubic spline aligning with the IMM dates.

*After solving this curve to reprice the ten input IRS instruments, we price all yearly tenor swaps starting on each of the 73 dates between 1st Jan 2022 and 14th March 2022, which we will use, in our experiment to create a series of curves simulating the evolution of time **without** the variation of market movements, i.e. we assume market rates evolve exactly as expected from our prediction on 1st Jan 2022.*

For each of these curves we change the node and knot positioning to align as follows;

i) an initial node on construction date (i.e. each of the 73 interim dates) and then on dates of the maturity of each tenor IRS measured from the construction date,

ii) knot dates for the log-cubic spline aligning with the tenor maturity dates in i).

For five different test IRSs, 6M tenors starting on 15 Apr '26, 15 Aug '27, 15 Feb '28, 15 Jun '29 and 15 July'30, we analyse the change in rates from the initial rate calculated from the base curve. We observe the results and plot their changes.

This chart shows us that, even though the par tenor rates, as inputs to our constructed curves on interim dates, are exactly as were forecast, the curves that we construct price these arbitrary forward swaps differently. This is as a result of the shape of the spline changing as

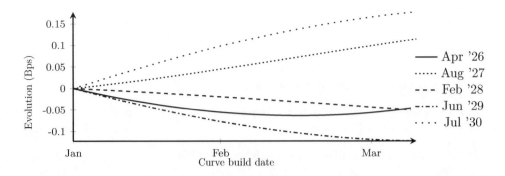

the knot points vary. Some of the spread changes between two rates, in the chart, amount to a quarter of a basis point which should really be considered significant in the context of risk management and systematic PnL.

*The equivalent chart for the approach of using consistent IMM knot placement shows **no variation** in these, or any other, swap rates, since the resultant spline is always the same.*

So what can go wrong if we adopt strategic knot dates on IMM dates? Well every three months we have to roll the curves, i.e. add a new twelfth IMM contract as the front one expires. However, this is, in fact, also true for whatever knot sequence we adopt, so there is no relative disadvantage to adopting static IMM knots over par tenor knots here. Never-the-less we can also perform an experiment to observe what happens to the rates when we roll, see example 12.6.

Example 12.6.
Suppose our initial curve is constructed on 14th Mar 2022 with par tenor mid-market rates and our strategic knot and node dates are aligned with March IMM dates (the entire curve is set to be a spline in this example). As a comparison we shift the knot and node dates to June IMM dates and plot the differences in the curve, using the same par tenor swaps as calibrating instruments.

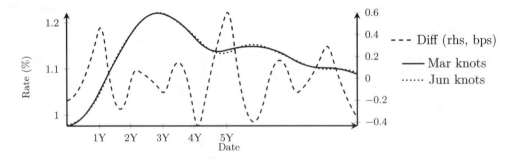

12.6   A practical curveset

To finalise this chapter we will build a real curveset and incorporate all the features of this chapter. We will find that a real curveset still offers other challenges that we will also solve in this section.

Table 12.1 describes the instruments and nodes we will capture in the first stage. The initial date of our curve will be 1st Jan 2022, to align with previous examples, the rates used are taken from the first quarter of 2022, with some literary licence. Information from the Bank of England's website lists official monetary policy meeting dates (which have an immediate effect on monetary policy), which we incorporate.

Node dates		Market Instruments	
Initial date	01-Jan-22	Current policy period	01-Jan-22 → 03-Feb-22
MPC meetings	03-Feb-22	Part Dec'21 Future	01-Jan-22 → 16-Mar-22
	17-Mar-22	12 IMM Futures	16-Mar-22 → 15-Jun-22
			15-Jun-22 → 16-Sep-22
	⋮		
	15-Dec-22		⋮
Provisional MPC meetings	02-Feb-23		18-Dec-24 → 19-Mar-25
	23-Mar-23	Par IRS	01-Jan-22 → 5Y
	⋮		01-Jan-22 → 7Y
			01-Jan-22 → 10Y
	14-Dec-23		01-Jan-22 → 15Y
Estimated MPC meetings	08-Feb-24		01-Jan-22 → 20Y
	21-Mar-24		01-Jan-22 → 30Y
			01-Jan-22 → 40Y
	⋮		01-Jan-22 → 50Y
	12-Dec-24		
Strategic IMM dates	19-Mar-25		
	17-Mar-27		
	21-Mar-29		
	⋮		
	15-Mar-62		
	16-Mar-72		

Table 12.1: Information regarding our SONIA curve build

This initial curve is well underspecified. It is expected that the solver will be able to reprice the instruments exactly but unlikely to be able to keep the curve contained without large oscillation, because it lacks regularisation. Indeed, upon constructing this curve with a *log-linear* interpolator this is exactly what happens (see figure 12.2). Thus we need to insert some constraints somehow to our objective function. Our iterative solving algorithms (Gauss-Newton and Levenberg-Marquardt) have been implemented for unconstrained least squares regression, so if we were to change that paradigm they would no longer be applicable and we would have to redesign and recode another solving algorithm. To reuse our existing codebase we must design regularising constraints that fit into the current framework.

The goal is to reduce oscillations which, at a fundamental level, means reducing curvature as much as possible. Curvature is a second derivative property, and second derivatives measure the change in first derivative. On our log-linear curve we know that the rates will jump discontinuously after node dates. We can proxy a first derivative by measuring the difference in overnight rates immediately following a node, for example,

```
>>> mpc_1 = Swap(datetime(2022, 2, 3), 1, 1, 1, days=True)
>>> mpc_2 = Swap(datetime(2022, 3, 17), 1, 1, 1, days=True)
>>> SwapSpread(mpc_1, mpc_2)
```

It is possible to take a SwapSpread of two SwapSpreads and thereby proxy a second derivative.

```
>>> mpc_3 = Swap(datetime(2022, 5, 5), 1, 1, 1, days=True)
>>> SwapSpread(SwapSpread(mpc_1, mpc_2), SwapSpread(mpc_2, mpc_3))
```

It is these instruments that we would like to target to equal zero for each successive period until the 20-Mar-25 meeting. Targeting zero is akin to minimising curvature.

Of course these instruments that we intend to create and insert into our objective rates are just guiding constraints - we do not need, or expect, them to solve exactly to zero. On the other hand our market prices should reprice exactly. This is the first instance where we have some instruments which should be targeted much more heavily than others within our solver, and therefore we have created a need to implement **weights** into the solver. Fortunately the amendments to the calculations of the SolvedCurve are reasonably simple. The below code changes [21, #888601] show just the calculations needed for this (and appendix sections 11.5.1 and 11.5.2 contain further info).

```python
class SolvedCurve(Curve):
    def __init__(self, nodes: dict, interpolation: str, swaps: list, obj_rates: list,
                 algorithm: str = "gauss_newton", w: list=None):
        ...
        self.W = None if w is None else np.diag(w)

    def calculate_metrics(self):
        ...
        Wx = x if self.W is None else np.matmul(self.W, x)
        self.f = np.matmul(x.transpose(), Wx)[0][0]
        ...

    def update_step_gauss_newton(self):
        J_T = self.J.transpose()
        A = np.matmul(self.J, J_T if self.W is None else np.matmul(self.W, J_T))
        ...

    def update_step_levenberg_marquardt(self):
        ...
        J_T = self.J.transpose()
        WJ_T = J_T if self.W is None else np.matmul(self.W, J_T)
        A = np.matmul(self.J, WJ_T) + self.lam * np.eye(self.J.shape[0])
        ...
```

Note we must also add w to the initialisation of the AdvancedCurve as a subclass, which is shown in the code repository.

We are now in a position to build a better curve.

```python
>>> nodes = {
        datetime(2022, 1, 1): 1.0,
        datetime(2022, 2, 3): 1.0,
        ...
        datetime(2072, 3, 15): 1.0
    }
>>> dual_nodes = {k: Dual(v, {f"v{i}": 1}) for i, (k,v) in enumerate(nodes.items())}
>>> swaps = {
        Swap(datetime(2022, 1, 1), 34, 34, 34 days=True): 0.695,
        Swap(datetime(2022, 1, 1), 75, 75, 75, days=True): 0.95,
        Swap(datetime(2022, 3, 16), 93, 93, 93, days=True): 1.40,
        ...
        Swap(datetime(2024, 12, 18), 91, 91, 91, days=True): 1.40,
        Swap(datetime(2022, 1, 1), 12*5, 12, 12): 2.195,
        ...
        Swap(datetime(2022, 1, 1), 12*50, 12, 12): 2.09,
    }
>>> mpc_1 = Swap(datetime(2022, 2, 3), 1, 1, 1, days=True)
    ...
>>> mpc_25 = Swap(datetime(2025, 3, 20), 1, 1, 1, days=True)
>>> curvature_conds = {
        SwapSpread(SwapSpread(mpc_1, mpc_2), SwapSpread(mpc_2, mpc_3)): 0,
        ...
        SwapSpread(SwapSpread(mpc_23, mpc_24), SwapSpread(mpc_24, mpc_25)): 0,
    }
>>> instruments = {**swaps, **curvature_conds}
>>> weights = [1]*len(swaps) + [0.0001]*len(curvature_conds)
>>> s_cv = SolvedCurve(
        nodes=nodes_dual, interpolation="log_linear",
        swaps=list(instruments.keys()), obj_rates=list(instruments.values()),
        algorithm="levenberg_marquardt", w=weights
    )
```

```
32 >>> s_cv.iterate()
33 tolerance reached (levenberg_marquardt) after 13 iterations, func: 1.530e-06
```

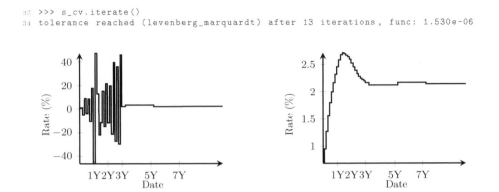

(a) without curvature constraints   (b) with curvature constraints

Figure 12.2: Overnight forward rates from constructed curves

Having created a valid log-linear curve we now look to **add turns**. We will add eight quarterly end turns, using the **turns method using** `SwapSpreads` from the previous section. None of the nodes currently align with turn dates so we **must add two nodes for each turn**. We also note that these do not overlap with the curvature constraints so the additional turns create no further complications.

```
 1 >>> nodes = {
 2         ...
 3         datetime(2022, 3, 31): 1.0,  # turn1
 4         datetime(2022, 4, 1): 1.0,   # turn1
 5         ...
 6     }
 7 >>> dual_nodes = {k: Dual(v, {f"v{i}": 1}) for i, (k,v) in enumerate(nodes.items())}
 8 >>> turns = {
 9         SwapSpread(
10             Swap(datetime(2022, 3, 30), 1, 1, 1, days=True),
11             Swap(datetime(2022, 3, 31), 1, 1, 1, days=True),
12         ): -0.03,  # turn1
13         SwapSpread(
14             Swap(datetime(2022, 3, 31), 1, 1, 1, days=True),
15             Swap(datetime(2022, 4, 1), 1, 1, 1, days=True),
16         ): 0.03,   # turn1
17         ...
18     }
19 >>> instruments = {**swaps, **turns, **curvature_conds}
20 >>> weights = [1]*len(swaps) + [1]*len(turns) + [0.0001]*len(curvature_conds)
21 >>> s_cv_turns = SolvedCurve(
22         nodes=nodes_dual, interpolation="log_linear",
23         swaps=list(instruments.keys()), obj_rates=list(instruments.values()),
24         algorithm="levenberg_marquardt", w=weights
25     )
26 >>> s_cv_turns.iterate()
27 tolerance reached (levenberg_marquardt) after 13 iterations, func: 1.527e-06
```

With the log-linear curve constructed with appropriate node points, turns and curvature constraints we can **implement the log-cubic spline interpolator for longer tenors**. This is as simple as defining the relevant knot sequence, **t**, which we discussed above, where we have adopted strategic IMM dates.

```
 1 >>> t_left, t_right =  datetime(2025, 3, 19), datetime(2072, 3, 15)
 2 >>> t_layer_1 = [
 3         t_left, t_left, t_left, t_left,
 4         datetime(2027, 3, 15),
 5         datetime(2029, 3, 15),
 6         ...
 7         datetime(2062, 3, 15),
 8         t_right, t_right, t_right, t_right,
```

```
 9        ]
10 >>> adv_cv_1 = AdvancedCurve(
11         nodes=nodes_dual, interpolation="log_linear",
12         swaps=list(instruments.keys()), obj_rates=list(instruments.values()),
13         t=t_layer_1, algorithm="levenberg_marquardt", w=weights,
14     )
15 >>> adv_cv_1.iterate()
16 tolerance reached (levenberg_marquardt) after 14 iterations, func: 1.555e-06
```

In the final step we will add a second layer to the curve which skews the 4Y, 6Y, 8Y, 9Y, 12Y, 25Y, 35Y and 45Y tenors. In order to do this we need to **add the relevant market instruments,** and also **add new nodes** and **add new knots**.

```
 1 >>> skews_layer_2 = {
 2         Swap(datetime(2022, 1, 1), 12*4, 12, 12): -0.0015,   # 4Y
 3         ...
 4         Swap(datetime(2022, 1, 1), 12*45, 12, 12): 0,   # 45Y
 5     }
 6 >>> swaps_layer_2 = {
 7         swap: swap.rate(adv_cv_1).real + skew for (swap, skew) in skews_layer_2.items()
 8     }
 9 >>> t_layer_2 = [
10         t_left, t_left, t_left, t_left,
11         datetime(2026, 3, 15),   # 4Y
12         datetime(2027, 3, 15),   # 5Y
13         ...
14         datetime(2067, 3, 15),   # 45y
15         t_right, t_right, t_right, t_right
16     ]
17 >>> nodes = {...}  # contains extra nodes
18 >>> nodes_dual_2 = {k: Dual(v, {f"v{i}": 1}) for i, (k,v) in enumerate(nodes.items())}
19 >>> instruments_2 = {**swaps, **swaps_layer_2, **turns, **curvature_conds}
20 >>> weights_2 = [1]*(len(swaps) + len(swaps_layer_2) + len(turns)) + [0.0001]*len(
        curvature_conds)
21 >>> adv_cv_2 = AdvancedCurve(
22     nodes=nodes_dual_2, interpolation="log_linear",
23     swaps=list(instruments_2.keys()), obj_rates=list(instruments_2.values()),
24     t=t_layer_2, algorithm="levenberg_marquardt", w=weights_2
25 )
26 >>> adv_cv_2.iterate()
27 tolerance reached (levenberg_marquardt) after 13 iterations, func: 1.600e-06
```

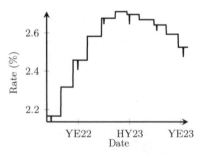

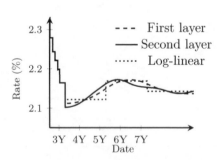

(a) Quarterly turns at -3bp, half-year and year end turns at -5bps implemented correctly.

(b) Advanced curve constructions showing the log-cubic spline overlay, for the first and second layer implementations.

Figure 12.3: Overnight forward rates from constructed curves

12.7   Performance enhancements

With the major parts of this curve library constructed we can spare a moment for some performance considerations. It has already been commented that Python is a poor choice and a lower level language such as C would certainly improve performance. However, we can also observe that solving the log-linear curve in our practical curve example is approximately 4 times faster. We can readily implement [21, #6211d8] the `iterate` method to first solve the log-linear curve and use the same node solution to then make the final few log-cubic iterations. This reduces the the calculation time of an AdvancedCurve to 50%.

```
class AdvancedCurve(SolvedCurve):
    def __init__(...)
        ...
        self.not_iterated = True

    def iterate(self):
        if self.not_iterated:
            w = None if self.W is None else np.diagonal(self.W)
            base_solve = SolvedCurve(
                self.nodes, self.interpolation, self.swaps,
                self.obj_rates, algorithm=self.algo, w=w
            )
            print("basic solve: ", base_solve.iterate())
            self.nodes = base_solve.nodes
            self.not_iterated, self.algo = False, "gauss_newton"
        return super().iterate()
```

12.8 Risk

In order to ensure our `risk` method still works we need to overload the `grad_s_v_` method to include knot sequence, **t**, and ensure that it also recreates an AdvancedCurve in the numerical derivatives calculation [21, #5fd565].

```
class AdvancedCurve(SolvedCurve):
    ...

    @property
    def grad_s_v(self):
        if getattr(self, "grad_s_v_", None) is None:
            self.grad_s_v_numeric(t=self.t)
        return self.grad_s_v_
```

Risk is programmed to be calculated against any input instrument, including curvature constraints. Therefore care must be taken when interpreting risk. For example curvature constraints will always be maintained at zero (although they may not always solve to price at zero due to their low weighting in the objective function), and they are not market instruments, so their risk can be disregarded. Turns, on the other hand are market effects and may move. But the turns we have added were implemented as two `SwapSpread` instruments, which have equal and opposite values, e.g. -5bps and +5bps. Therefore for the risk of a turn to be assessed we should subtract risk instrument values in each pair.

Example 12.7.
Consider the Swap starting 31-Mar-2022 for a 1-day tenor. This is precisely the instrument that is impacted by the first quarter end turn. When we calculate risk against this swap in a notional of 10bn, which has an analytic delta of approximately £2740/bp, we get:

The amount of risk allocated to the Mar 22 IMM is close to the analytical delta, whilst the surrounding risks are due to the shape of the curve being dependent upon the movement of other instruments via our curvature constraints. The risks are not completely localised because of this global shape dependence. The turn risks should be differenced. Subtracting turn1_right from turn1_left gives a monetary impact would be £2703.6/bp. The other turn risks have approximately the same value and the same sign meaning their effective risks are much smaller in comparison, as we would expect.

Instrument	Risk Value
Current MPC	-0.1
Expired IMM	396.9
Mar 22 IMM	2755.0
Jun 22 IMM	-566.6
Sep 22 IMM	187.2
Dec 22 IMM	-67.1
Mar 23 IMM	24.5
Jun 23 IMM	-7.7
...	...

Instrument	Risk Value
turn1_left	1681.8
turn1_right	-1021.8
turn2_left	216.4
turn2_right	210.3
turn3_left	-70.4
turn3_right	-68.34
...	...
curvature1	-427.4
curvature2	406
curvature3	-16.4
...	...

Figure 12.4: Risk array separated by IRS instruments and turn and curvature instruments.

12.9 Appendix

12.9.1 B-splines

The authoritative resource for splines is the excellent [33]. The following pages are dedicated to summarising that material and extracting key parts for our purpose. B-splines are a truly ingenious invention in my opinion with many useful and practical applications. The immediate theory is kept as succinct as possible and necessary for the latter parts. The code repository [21, #c9250b] and [21, #9dc6a8] contains a spline implementation and example notebook respectively.

The space of polynomial functions, $\Pi_{<k}$

The set of all polynomial functions of order k with real coefficients forms a vector space. For example the monomial basis, $\{1, x, x^2, ..., x^{k-1}\}$, spans the space, which is denoted in literature by $\Pi_{<k}$. The dimension of such a space is k.

The space of piecewise polynomial functions, $\Pi_{<k,\boldsymbol{\xi}}$

Next, consider a domain, $[a..b]$, and suggest a partition,

$$\{\xi_1, \xi_2, ..., \xi_{l+1}\} \quad \text{such that} \quad a = \xi_1 < \xi_2 < ... < \xi_{l+1} = b \quad \text{and} \quad [a..b] = \bigcup_{i=1}^{l} [\xi_i..\xi_{i+1}]$$

For each subdomain, $[\xi_i..\xi_{i+1}]$, denote by $f_i(x)$ any polynomial function of order, k, and highlight:

$$f_i(x) = \begin{cases} f_i(x) & : x \in [\xi_i..\xi_{i+1}] \\ 0 & : x \notin [\xi_i..\xi_{i+1}] \end{cases}$$

For $f(x)$ to be continuous, $f_i(\xi_{i+1}) = f_{i+1}(\xi_{i+1}) \ \forall i \in [1, l-1]$. The space of all piecewise polynomial functions of order, k, with break sequence, $\boldsymbol{\xi}$, also forms a vector space with dimension, $kl - (l-1)$. Such a space is denoted, $\Pi_{<k,\boldsymbol{\xi}}$.

The space of piecewise polynomial functions with imposed continuity, $\Pi_{<k,\boldsymbol{\xi},\boldsymbol{\nu}}$

Other than continuity of function value, $\Pi_{<k,\boldsymbol{\xi}}$ said nothing about the continuity of the derivatives of $f(x)$, from the left and right, at the interior breakpoints of $\boldsymbol{\xi}$. Such constraints form subspaces and each derivative constraint imposed reduces the dimension by one. It is customary to denote by $\boldsymbol{\nu}$ the integer-vector of length, $(l-1)$, which indicates the number of continuity conditions imposed on f at each interior breakpoint (prioritising function value and lowest derivatives first). This space is denoted by $\Pi_{<k,\boldsymbol{\xi},\boldsymbol{\nu}}$, and has dimension, $n = kl - \sum_{i=1}^{l-1} v_i$.

Construction of a knot sequence, t

It suffices that the combination of information provided by the order, k, of the piecewise polynomial, $\boldsymbol{\xi}$ and $\boldsymbol{\nu}$ can be encoded into a single sequence, called the knot sequence denoted by t. The length of such a sequence is $n+k$ and the construction here is identical to that description which forms part of the Curry and Schoenberg theorem, and the steps are as follows;

i) let the first k knots equal ξ_1, or a,

ii) each interior breakpoint, ξ_i, has a number of knots equal to, $k - v_{i-1}$,

iii) the final k knots equal ξ_{l+1}, or b.

The **basic interval** in this definition is referred to as, $I_{k,\mathbf{t}} = [t_k..t_{n+1}] = [a..b]$.

B-splines

Having established a procedure for constructing a general knot sequence, $\mathbf{t}$, which outlines the piecewise polynomial space we are in a position to explain basis-splines, or B-splines. We will first define them, and then through, examples, explain their purpose and usefulness. The **basic B-splines** are of order one with a step function profile:

$$B_{i,1,\mathbf{t}}(x) = \begin{cases} 1, & t_i \leq x < t_{i+1} \\ 0, & \text{otherwise} \end{cases}$$

Via a **recurrence relation** we can construct splines of higher order,

$$B_{i,k,\mathbf{t}}(x) = \frac{x - t_i}{t_{i+k-1} - t_i} B_{i,k-1}(x) + \frac{t_{i+k} - x}{t_{i+k} - t_{i+1}} B_{i+1,k-1}(x)$$

Care must be taken with these definitions when coding in order to avoid division by zero errors. The mantra *anything times zero is zero* works in these cases, as does simply avoiding the part of calculation when the denominator is zero. Care must also be taken for **endpoint support**. Although left point support is accounted for in the definition, the rightmost basic B-spline must also be made to be left continuous such that, $B_{n+k-1,1,\mathbf{t}}(t_{n+k}) = 1$. When coding for derivatives of B-splines we must also extend this definition to each successive rightmost basic B-spline.

Below we include the Python function, bsplev_single, to evaluate a single x value on a specified B-spline for given k and $\mathbf{t}$ (note that python uses an initial '0' index whilst the above derivation is based on an initial '1' index).

```
def bsplev_single(x, i, k, t, org_k=None):
    ## Endpoint support
    org_k = org_k or k   # original_k adds right point support for derivative recursion
    if x == t[0] and i == 0:
        return 1
    elif x == t[-1] and i >= len(t) - org_k - 1:
        return 1

    ## Recursion
    if k == 1:
        if t[i] <= x < t[i+1]:
            return 1
        return 0
    else:
        left, right = 0, 0
        if t[i] != t[i+k-1]:
            left = (x - t[i]) / (t[i+k-1] - t[i]) * bsplev_single(x, i, k-1, t)
        if t[i+1] != t[i+k]:
            right = (t[i+k] - x) / (t[i+k] - t[i+1]) * bsplev_single(x, i+1, k-1, t)
        return left + right
```

Example 12.8.

Suppose the knot sequence, $\mathbf{t} = [1, 1, 1, 1, 2, 2, 2, 3, 4, 4, 4, 4]$, which encodes a 4'th order piecewise polynomial spline space with breakpoints, $\boldsymbol{\xi} = [1, 2, 3, 4]$ with 8 dimensions. The corresponding 8 B-splines are plotted for x in figure 12.5.

Note that continuity of the 1st and 2nd derivatives are not encoded into the piecewise polynomial at $x = 2$, and the shape of the B-splines demonstrates these discontinuities. At $x = 3$ derivative continuity is encoded.

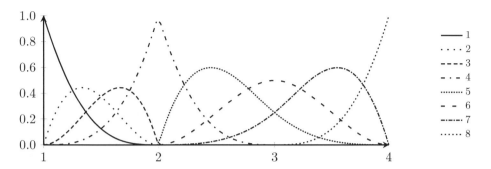

Figure 12.5: 8 B-splines of order 4 associated with given example knot sequence.

Properties of B-splines

The following properties are observable in the above example.

Support and positivity [33, p91]

$$B_{i,k,\mathbf{t}}(x) \begin{cases} > 0, & : t_i < x < t_{i+k} \\ = 0, & : x < t_i \text{ and } x > t_{i+k} \end{cases}$$

Positivity and local, partition of unity [33, p96]

$$\sum_i B_{i,k,\mathbf{t}}(x) = 1, \quad x \in [a..b]$$

Derivatives [33]

$$\frac{dB_{i,1,\mathbf{t}}}{dx} = 0, \quad \frac{dB_{i,k,\mathbf{t}}}{dx} = (k-1)\left(\frac{B_{i,k-1,\mathbf{t}}(x)}{t_{i+k-1} - t_i} - \frac{B_{i+1,k-1,\mathbf{t}}(x)}{t_{i+k} - t_{i+1}}\right)$$

The below function, `bspldnev_single`, evaluates the n'th derivative of a specified B-spline for a single x value,

```
def bspldnev_single(x, i, k, t, n, org_k=None):
    if n == 0:
        return bsplev_single(x, i, k, t)
    elif k == 1 or n >= k:
        return 0

    org_k = org_k or k
    r, div1, div2 = 0, t[i+k-1] - t[i], t[i+k] - t[i+1]

    if n == 1:
        if div1 != 0:
            r += bsplev_single(x, i, k-1, t, org_k) / div1
        if div2 != 0:
            r -= bsplev_single(x, i+1, k-1, t, org_k) / div2
        r *= k - 1
    else:
        if div1 != 0:
            r += bspldnev_single(x, i, k-1, t, n-1, org_k) / div1
        if div2 != 0:
            r -= bspldnev_single(x, i+1, k-1, t, n-1, org_k) / div2
        r *= k - 1
    return r
```

Example 12.9.
The first derivatives of the previous B-splines are shown demonstrating, importantly, the end-point support on the right side.

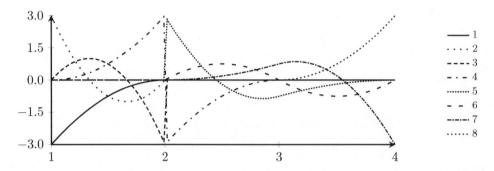

Figure 12.6: First derivative of 8 B-splines of order 4 associated with given example knot sequence.

12.9.2   Spline space

The preceding section was all introduced to yield **the key result** here. We define a spline space of order, k, and knot sequence, $\mathbf{t}$, as any linear combination of B-splines of order, k, generated from $\mathbf{t}$:

$$\$_{k,\mathbf{t}} := \left\{ \sum_{i=1}^{n} \alpha_i B_{i,k,\mathbf{t}}(x) \; : \alpha_i \text{ real} \right\}$$

The Curry and Schoenberg theorem asserts that $\$_{k,\mathbf{t}} = \mathbf{\Pi}_{<k,\boldsymbol{\xi},\boldsymbol{\nu}}$ on $I_{k,\mathbf{t}}$, which means that our linear combination of these B-splines is enough to cover every possible piecewise polynomial with our choice of breakpoints and imposed continuity conditions.

Interpolation

In practice this means that we have either some underlying function, say $g(x)$, that we wish to approximate with our spline space, or we have some known datasites we wish to use to instruct our spline space. Suppose that we have a set of n distinct datasites for which we know the function value,

$$\{(\tau_1, g(\tau_1)), (\tau_2, g(\tau_2)), ..., (\tau_n, g(\tau_n))\}$$

Then we seek a spline which agrees with g at these datasites so we have the following linear system, where the number of B-splines equals the number of datasites,

$$\sum_{i=1}^{n} \alpha_i B_{i,k,\mathbf{t}}(\tau_j) = g(\tau_j) \quad \forall j \quad \Longrightarrow \quad \mathbf{B}_{k,\mathbf{t}}(\boldsymbol{\tau})\boldsymbol{\alpha} = g(\boldsymbol{\tau})$$

where $[\mathbf{B}_{k,\mathbf{t}}(\boldsymbol{\tau})]_{j,i} = B_{i,k,\mathbf{t}}(\tau_j)$ is termed the **spline collocation matrix**. The relatively straightforward condition that, if $\boldsymbol{\tau}$ is strictly increasing, the spline collocation matrix is invertible and the system uniquely solvable iff $t_i < \tau_i < t_{i+k}$, allowing $t_1 \leq \tau_1$ and $\tau_n \leq t_{n+k}$. Essentially this means we need some physical information about our curve in the relevant sections of the spline that we wish to calibrate, otherwise the solution is unfeasible. This result is attributed as the Schoenberg and Whitney theorem [32].

A common adjustment to this linear system is often to take the first or second derivatives at the endpoints, e.g. setting $\tau_1 = t_1 = a$ and $\tau_n = t_{n+k} = b$ and calculating, as the top and bottoms rows in the spline collocation matrix, the derivatives or second derivatives of the B-splines, and equating their combinations to either $g'(a), g''(a)$, and $g'(b), g''(b)$ respectively or zero. When second derivatives are set to zero for an order 4 spline this creates what is termed a **natural cubic spline**.

B-spline class

With the complete theory laid out above, and the `bsplev_single` and `bsplndev_single` methods already described above we can describe the creation of a `BSpline` class object which will construct a spline interpolation for our given knot sequence, and allow us to calculate values from it,

i) `bsplev` and `bspldnev` are the vectorised versions of the above, so they can calculate an array of x values simultaneously,

ii) `bsplmatrix` constructs the spline collocation matrix for the given datasites, τ, and chosen function or derivative values on the top and bottom rows,

iii) `bsplsolve` calculates the spline coefficients α,

iv) `ppev_single` calculate the piecewise polynomial spline value for single x value.

```
class BSpline:
    def __init__(self, k, t):
        self.t, self.k, self.n = t, k, len(t) - k

    def bsplev(self, x, i, otypes=["float64"]):
        func = np.vectorize(bsplev_single, excluded=["k", "t"], otypes=otypes)
        return func(x, i=i, k=self.k, t=self.t)

    def bspldnev(self, x, i, n, otypes=["float64"]):
        func = np.vectorize(bsplndev_single, excluded=["k", "t"], otypes=otypes)
        return func(x, i=i, k=self.k, t=self.t, n=n)

    def bsplmatrix(self, tau, left_n=0, right_n=0):
        B_ji = np.zeros(shape=(len(tau), self.n))
        for i in range(self.n):
            B_ji[0, i] = bsplndev_single(tau[0], i, self.k, self.t, left_n)
            B_ji[1:-1, i] = self.bsplev(tau[1:-1], i=i)
            B_ji[-1, i] = bsplndev_single(tau[-1], i, self.k, self.t, right_n)
        return B_ji

    def bsplsolve(self, tau, y, left_n, right_n):
        B_ji = self.bsplmatrix(tau, left_n, right_n)
        alpha = solve(B_ji, y[:, np.newaxis])
        self.alpha = alpha[:, 0]

    def ppev_single(self, x):
        sum = 0
        for i, alpha_ in enumerate(self.alpha):
            sum += alpha_ * bsplev_single(x, i, self.k, self.t)
        return sum
```

Note that the `solve` method used here is our own linear system solver, implemented via the Doolittle algorithm, capable of handling `Dual` numbers to preserve our automatic differentiation [21, #3b7842]. Otherwise we could have just used `numpy.linalg.solve` or `scipy.linalg.solve`.

To utilise the `BSpline` class (of order 4) in our `AdvancedCurve`, **t** must define at least two intervals, $[\xi_1, \xi_2]$ and $[\xi_2, \xi_3]$. This creates $n = 5$ dimensions, with two accounted for by the natural spline derivative constraints and therefore we must have three DF nodes contained within. Each additional interval will require a further DF node.

Multi-Currency Risk

Building a multi-currency curveset by combining multiple single currency curvesets required the addition of at most a couple new instrument types; XCSs and FX swaps. Since FX swap pricing can be formulated in terms of XCSs, this too simplifies multi-currency risk since the only new risk that will be introduced is the cross-currency basis spread risk. However, there are complexities of another sort. This chapter will outline;

- what the basic element of multi-currency risk is, including FX risk considerations,

- the impact of different CSAs to multi-currency risks,

- a number of examples to highlight how multi-currency risk reacts to different trades,

- an overview of how multi-currency risks can be affected by optionality of CSAs.

The examples in this chapter utilise the direction convention that has been adopted elsewhere in the book, and stated in the introductory notation. Specifically, where a EUR/USD or GBP/USD XCS has the spread attached to the domestic currency, i.e. the EUR leg or GBP leg respectively in this case, then we state that if the direction is to pay the spread then this shows positive risk in the respective bucket(s) of the risk strip.

13.1 Cross-currency basis risk

Since XCSs are priced according to a spread on one of the legs (usually the non-USD leg), cross-currency basis risk is the sensitivity of PnL relative to that spread increasing or decreasing by one bp.

Since multi-currency risk involves multiple currencies there is a further question of which currency to express risk in. A single currency trader, e.g. a EUR trader, will exclusively use the local currency, i.e. EUR, to view risks, but it may be beneficial for a multi-currency trader to view risks against a currency local to the product, or against a standardised currency, USD. For the rest of the chapter it is easier to view risk against a standardised currency, so every risk number will be expressed in USD equivalent. This also avoids the confusion of having FX rates move considerably after this book has been published and therefore be non-intuitive to a future reader.

Example 13.1.
A trader has executed the following mid-market trades;

(i)   received fixed on $50k pv01 of a USD SOFR 10Y IRS,

(ii) paid the basis in $25k pv01 of a 10Y EUR/USD XCS ,

(iii) paid fixed on $40k pv01 of a EUR ESTR 10Y IRS.

His risk view shows the following risks:

($ per bp)	IRS	XCS	IRS
Tenor	USD RFR	EUR/USD	EUR RFR
10Y	-50,000	25,000	40,000

13.2   FX risk

As well as cross-currency basis risk, trading multi-currency portfolios incurs FX risk. This is because the portfolio will adopt a standardised currency, usually USD, to record the PnL over time. This means that everything becomes relative to that USD benchmark, and fluctuations in FX rates will naturally impact the PnL of the portfolio that is stated in USD.

For example suppose a portfolio had £5mm in cash and a PV of future GBP cashflows of -£1mm, then the portfolio would be exposed to a net £4mm GBPUSD FX rate. The spot FX risk here is determined by aggregating the sum of the cash position and the PV of future cashflows in the relevant currency.

Even traders who do not trade multi-currency portfolios can be exposed to FX risk in a similar way. If their reporting currency is different to the traded currency, say JPY traders who report PnL in USD, then they will be exposed to the spot FX market and will look to hedge PnL back into USD to fix the amount.

FX risk can be expressed in different ways but the simplest, and most common in my experience, is to quote a domestic notional exposure, whether it is in fact a physical currency exposure or a virtual one created through trading derivatives. For example, in a portfolio one might have €10mm EURUSD exposure, meaning if the FX rate moves from say 1.20 to 1.21 this represents a gain of $100,000.

Just to be clear, the FX exposure in an IRD portfolio is very different to the actual cash balance of that portfolio in any given currency. The reader is referred to the section on cash balances in chapter 5 if this statement is not immediately obvious.

13.3   Non-standard CSAs

Outside the remit of trading XCSs with explicit cross-currency risks, it is also possible to acquire these risks in other ways. A trade executed with a non-standard CSA in another currency, for example a EUR IRS with a USD cash only CSA, will also create cross-currency basis risk. To understand why one must first realise that the EUR:USD-CSA discount curve, that is needed in this example, is dependent upon XCS prices (see section 7.3).

Discount curves affect the PV of trades in two ways; firstly they amplify or dampen the cashflows by scaling up or scaling down the PV component of the trade respectively, and secondly they affect the mid-market level of the trade affecting its PV in turn. If we consider the first of these items in the first instance, then example 13.2 shows the influence of discounting risk with respect to a particular CSA.

Example 13.2.

*A trader has received €100mm EUR ESTR 10Y IRS which now has a PV of €5mm and a discounting basis amount of €2,500 pv01. This trade has a **EUR cash only CSA** and the trader's risk view shows the following (EURUSD FX at 1.2):*

($ per bp)	EUR Delta		XCS	USD Delta	
Tenor	$\frac{\partial P}{\partial r}$	$\frac{\partial P}{\partial s}$	EUR/USD	$\frac{\partial P}{\partial r}$	$\frac{\partial P}{\partial s}$
10Y	-99,000	+3,000	0	0	0

*Suppose instead the trader has received exactly the same trade with a **USD cash only CSA** then the trader's risk view shows the following:*

($ per bp)	EUR Delta		XCS	USD Delta	
Tenor	$\frac{\partial P}{\partial r}$	$\frac{\partial P}{\partial s}$	EUR/USD	$\frac{\partial P}{\partial r}$	$\frac{\partial P}{\partial s}$
10Y	-99,000	0	-3,000	0	+3,000

This discounting basis component of risk has changed from explicit dependency to the EUR OIS curve to dependency to the USD OIS curve via the XCS market. Empirically the structure of the risk change reflects the mechanics. To hedge, the trader could use the USD collateral to enter into a paid EUR/USD XCS and this converts the collateral to EUR.

The total EUR delta risk is approximately the same, -$99k, in each case, from which one can infer that over the 10Y life of the trade that the two collateral types are approximately of equal cheapness, i.e. the 10Y XCS basis is around zero. If one currency were cheaper than the other the total delta risk of that case would be discounted more heavily, and thus have smaller magnitude.

Whilst the EUR forecasting risk can be hedged with a cleared EUR IRS, the discounting risk with USD CSA will experience cross-gamma. As the PV of the trade changes with movements to EUR IRs the exposure to XCSs will either increase or decrease dependent upon those PV changes.

The second item about how the mid-market level of trades is affected by the CSA is more subtle. For flat yield curve term structures there is no noticeable effect, since all netted future cashflows are often zero or minimal. However, when the yield curve(s) has a steep slope term structure this effect is more pronounced because any mid-market price obtained by using any discount curve must take into account the distribution of positive and negative cashflows that are forecast to occur over the life of the trade. This will impact the cash balance profile of the trade and the CSA determines the rate at which these cash balances accrue or pay interest. Different discount curves will, of course, give different results. In turn this means that numerical risk might show some slightly unexpected results for cross-currency risks due to the PV of trades becoming sensitive to unintuitive movements in yield curves or basis spreads.

Example 13.2 is succinct because it seeks to highlight how discounting risk can be transferred to other risk types when different CSAs are present, but the effect of altering the mid-market level of trades is environment dependent and so difficult to characterise in simple examples. A trader is encouraged to experiment with numerical risk considering mid-market, ITM and OTM trades to get a feel for how all of these risks interoperate when different single currency CSAs are used.

13.4   Multi-CSAs

If a CSA contains more than one currency this can also give rise to multi-currency risk, and the optionality that was discussed in chapter 5 adds to the complexity. The immediate, or intrinsic, risk that a trader is exposed to is always to the CTD currency. Measuring the optionality of risk and deciding how it should be categorised or even hedged, if at all possible, is difficult. Practical traders will always look to acknowledge the immediate and intrinsic risk first before looking to analyse the more complicated case of incorporating any idea of optionality.

Example 13.3.
*The trader has received exactly the same trade as in example 13.2, except **the CSA is now EUR+USD cash only.** Currently EUR is CTD in the first 5Y but after that USD becomes the CTD. This is reflected in the trader's risk view, which shows the following immediate and intrinsic risks:*

($ per bp)	EUR Delta		XCS	USD Delta	
Tenor	$\frac{\partial P}{\partial r}$	$\frac{\partial P}{\partial s}$	EUR/USD	$\frac{\partial P}{\partial r}$	$\frac{\partial P}{\partial s}$
5Y	0	+1,600	+1,500	0	-1,500
10Y	-98,900	0	-3,000	0	+3,000

The discounting risk now totals slightly less than $3,000 pv01 and has been distributed across the first 5Y against the EUR OIS curve and in the 5Y5Y section against the USD OIS curve via the XCS market.

The amount of total EUR delta risk is slightly less that the previous -$99k. This is because the combination of EUR+USD collateral is cheaper overall than either the USD or EUR in isolation. This means the overall risk is discounted more heavily by higher rates. Incidentally the PV of the trade will also be less than €5mm.

If, in example 13.3, there was very little to distinguish the CTD between EUR and USD it would not be appropriate to segment the risks in such a distinct way, and this is precisely the consideration that optionality seeks to address. Indeed at the 5Y point where the CTD switches from EUR to USD it will represent a tenor where the two currencies are approximately of equal cheapness before USD edges ahead. And again, making this distinction to be at precisely a single point without acknowledging the potential of variation might be misleading.

Ultimately, the PV of the derivative would be dependent upon the choice of which currency to actually post as collateral throughout the life of the trade, and then the immediate PV could be hedged by executing the right set of trades for that currency choice. There would be no point, for example, hedging any EUR/USD XCS basis risk or OIS/USD 3M risk if one has committed to posting EUR cash collateral at the outset for the life of the trade. Committing to such a decision is of course not the best possible course of action (in this case it is not even expected to be the CTD). But even committing to the post the expected CTD currency limits one's ability to respond to a changing CTD currency and therefore removes the ability to profit from the market move. From an asset holder's perspective committing to any kind of hedge is also made difficult because it is the collateral poster's choice which currency to post and therefore dependent upon their decision. Viewing risk in this way hopefully clarifies that of optionality in chapter 5, putting the advantage of the poster of collateral in perspective and its affect on the value of optionality of multi-CSAs.

Because of optionality, theoretically correct attribution of risks must include references to volatility as this is a key component in the valuation of those options. This is an active area of fixed income research and one of the more quantitative endeavours. The consideration for advanced risk management of the optionality effect of multi-currency risks is outside of the scope of this book, in light of limited published progress.

13.5 Risk management

All of the techniques that are discussed in this book for single currency delta and basis risk management are all applicable to intrinsic style multi-currency basis risks. This list includes those topics such as interpolation, risk models, standard and customised transformations, bleed, VaR and PCA. With the number of currencies and number of potential risk buckets involved in a multi-currency portfolio, having a CoVaR based *simplified portfolio representation* as an initial guide might be even more useful than in the single currency case. Techniques for reset risk as well are directly associable to multi-currency portfolios (including multi-currency correlation extensions).

Building and implementing all of these techniques might require an investment of a good deal of time and effort. But, having managed a multi-currency IRD portfolio, I can attest to the usefulness and improved level of understanding and control they offer overall.

Value at Risk

This chapter introduces two commonly used measures of risk. These are VaR and expected shortfall (ES). We also show techniques to monitor, understand and influence these measures of an IRD portfolio's risk. Specifically it outlines;

- what VaR is and what ES is,
- different calculation methods for these risk measures,
- aspects relating to covariance matrices for use with the CoVaR model of calculating VaR,
- how to calculate VaR with a CoVaR model approach,
- how a trader can incorporate VaR into their risk management,
- calculations for single and multiple instrument VaR minimising trades,
- one method of allocating VaR to specific trading positions,
- how managers can consider VaR and assess risk limits.

14.1   Portfolio construction

Our code implemented in chapters 11 and 12 was specifically built around curves and simple object creation. We avoided adding code in those chapters that detracted from its pedagogical nature. For this chapter we will need a `Portfolio` object which is a collection of trades. We need to be able to return the risk and PV of that portfolio in this chapter and subsequent chapters, so we make some modifications to our code.

Firstly we allow `Swap` objects to have their notional and fixed rates set at creation [21, #6dbc14], which will also allow us to create a collection of pre-defined objects in our `Portfolio`. Secondly we need to add the container object and its local methods [21, #b59834]:

```
 1  class Portfolio:
 2      def __init__(self, objects: list = []):
 3          self.objects = objects
 4
 5      def risk(self, curve: SolvedCurve):
 6          risk = self.objects[0].risk(curve)
 7          for obj in self.objects[1:]:
 8              risk += obj.risk(curve)
 9          return risk
10
11      def npv(self, curve: SolvedCurve):
12          npv = self.objects[0].npv(curve)
13          for obj in self.objects[1:]:
14              npv += obj.npv(curve)
15          return npv
```

14.2   Value at risk (VaR)

VaR is a term often used by risk managers. It is one of the most widely used metrics and is probably universally understood by all types of risk manager thanks to its straightforward concept. In its basic form, VaR seeks to ascribe a **single number, or metric,** to a set of trading positions to describe their overall level of risk. Much has been written about VaR in financial literature, due its nature as a statistical model to represent risk. A VaR metric assesses a trade, a portfolio of trades, or a collection of portfolios, and indicates the level of loss, which is only expected to be exceeded a specific percentage of the time.

As a matter of course, then, a **time horizon** and a **percentage confidence interval** are required to interpret the metric. As an example, using a one-day time horizon and 95% c.i., a VaR of £0.4mm would indicate that 5% of the time a portfolio could expect to lose more than £0.4mm over a one-day period. To put this into context consider the question posed in the example.

Example 14.1.
A manager analyses the numeric risk of two portfolios under his supervision. He queries which is running the most risk in terms of likely PnL values due to dynamic market movements, and what is the collective amount of risk.

	Alpha's risk	Bravo's risk	Collective
2Y	-180	-50	-230
5Y	-10	-10	-20
10Y	180	-50	130
30Y	25	-25	0

There are different ways in which VaR can be calculated. Here we discuss the popular methods, and revert later to provide an answer to this question posed in example 14.1.

14.3 Historical VaR simulation model

One of the ways in which VaR can be modelled is to perform backward analysis. The trade or portfolio of trades are subjected to the relevant daily changes that have taken place over a historical period, say the last two years, and the PnL is noted. In a two year simulation this would produce approximately 500 b.d.s worth of potential valuation changes, and the 25th worst may be used to report the 5% VaR or the 5th worst to report the 1% VaR, for example.

For any kind of regulatory reporting, it is usually required to analyse based on a historical period with a sufficient amount of data points. Stressed periods, such as those of the financial crisis of '07 and '08, can be used to report 'stressed VaRs'. When running historical analysis for VaR or ES calculation, it is well worth sparing a thought for the economic conditions that were present in the specific historical period and whether it is an accurate reflection of future expectations.

Historical VaR is a **non-parametric** method of calculation because no modelling parameters are used, nor are needed, in its construction (besides the chosen historical period, which is really a hyper-parameter of the model).

14.4 Monte Carlo VaR simulation model

Instead of historical simulation, it is also possible to randomly predict the movement of markets over the specified time horizon. This would be done by simulating random walks (a series of guesses of market movements), and by running enough of these tests derive lots of possible valuation changes under the assumed model parameters. Then it would be possible to report the relevant VaR or ES, according to a chosen c.i.. This can be quite difficult because many parameters of the economic state of the market must be input as model variables, for example, the volatilities of every instrument, their correlations, the distribution of how each instrument moves to account for tail risk, etc.. These models are often intricately designed and complex.

Monte Carlo is often used when the assumed distributions and correlations are difficult, or impossible, to calculate with closed form equations, or when the instruments are sufficiently non-linear that even with a tractable distribution of market movements it is difficult, or impossible, to analytically calculate confidence intervals of PV. Therefore this provides a numerical solution.

Monte Carlo simulation, therefore, is a **parametric, numerical** method of calculation because many parameters are required. Many hyper-parameters are also required, such as the assumed statistical distributions of the simulated market movements, and the dynamics of their time series.

14.5 Variance-covariance (CoVaR) model

CoVaR is a method of calculating VaR assuming that market movements follow a multivariate normal distribution, with assumed covariance matrix, and the PnL of the of portfolio is assumed to be a first order approximation of risks multiplied by market movements[1].

The first step is to derive, what we call here, the CoVaR multiplier, c. The CoVaR multiplier reflects a single s.d. of the PnL over the specified time period, which we usually take to be one

---

[1] see appendix section 14.9.1

day. To obtain the VaR metric relevant to the chosen c.i., the 5% or 1% for example, one can use the CoVaR multiplier scaled by an appropriate factor for the chosen c.i.[2].

The previous methods are the most frequently used by group managers, risk analytics teams, and for regulatory reporting. But, for individual traders this CoVaR model is superior because its nature permits much greater scope of analytic methods to provide useful information relating to how VaR can be increased or reduced. The same information could, probably, be gleaned with the other numerical methods but may well be cumbersome and a numerically inefficient process: I have never attempted it for this reason. CoVaR techniques are easier to apply, practical, and exemplified in this chapter.

CoVaR is a **parametric, analytic** method of calculation.

Each model described above and also this CoVaR model utilises historical data in some fashion; historical simulation uses the previous movement of market instruments to directly infer possible valuation changes; Monte Carlo simulation iterates through random scenarios but, of course, the parameters used to define how to generate the scenarios are based on expectations of how markets can behave and a large factor into this consideration is historical data; CoVaR uses a covariance matrix, whose construction is based on historical data. Provided the assumptions across each model are broadly similar in these respects the results will be broadly the same as well, meaning each model will report similar VaR metrics (although not exactly the same).

This CoVaR model is a linear measure of risk, meaning the derivation given here does not incorporate the gamma and cross-gamma of IRSs as other chapters quantify[3]. This does not mean it is inconsistent with those chapters but as a risk management tool it should be acknowledged. The CoVaR model is best used on short time scales where market movements are limited and the impact of gamma is small. In this way the techniques can be utilised without the worry of accumulating errors. For longer time scales, such as in constructing trade strategies or portfolios with inherent cross-gamma then further considerations are made, which we demonstrate in those additional chapters.

14.5.1   Construction of covariance matrices

The CoVaR method requires the construction of a covariance matrix[4] to determine volatilities and correlations of each and every market instrument, or risk bucket, in scope. Estimating covariance matrices (with an accurate forecasting ability) is a detailed and difficult problem. It also features frequently in academic literature with wide applications outside of finance. The ideas behind covariance matrix estimation are also key concepts in swaption pricing (chapter 20), and the accuracy of covariance matrices can determine the difference between a trade strategy being considered worthwhile or not (chapter 23).

To put this in context we begin with some basics of time series analysis. The key question in the context of this section is, **given a set of market rates, what is the likely range of possible new rates after the passage of a set amount of time** (which we can subdivide into a number of single periods of time)? For example say the 5Y rate is 1%, and the 10Y rate is 1.5% what is the likely distribution of possible values after one period, or two periods, or three?

---

[2]see section 1.3.2 which details c.i.s
[3]note the derivation in the appendix section 14.9.1 uses a first order PnL estimate
[4]see section 1.3.5 for an introduction of covariance matrices

To model a multivariate time series in its basic form we use a simplified vector autoregression (VAR)[5]. For those unfamiliar with this term it means that **the rates after a single period are equal to the previous rates, $\mathbf{r}_{t-1}$, plus a fixed trend, $\boldsymbol{\mu}$, plus an 'error' term, $\boldsymbol{\epsilon}_t$, which is the random market movement of that period,**

$$\mathbf{r}_t = \mathbf{r}_{t-1} + \boldsymbol{\mu} + \boldsymbol{\epsilon}_t , \quad \text{for vectors} \quad \mathbf{r}_t = [r_{1,t}, ..., r_{N,t}]^T . \; \boldsymbol{\epsilon}_t = [\epsilon_{1,t}, ..., \epsilon_{N,t}]^T .$$

This model assumes the expected value of any random movement, in any period, is zero, $E[\boldsymbol{\epsilon}_j] = \mathbf{0}$. It also assumes the random market movements, $\boldsymbol{\epsilon}_j$, have no autocorrelation, meaning the market movements of one period are not connected to any past or future period. But it does assume the market movements of different instruments, in the same period, are correlated. In our case we will suppose the random market movements follow a multivariate normal distribution, $\boldsymbol{\epsilon}_j \sim N(\mathbf{0}, \boldsymbol{\Sigma})$.

The question for our model is then how best to estimate the trend and covariance parameters. If we expect the future to be similar to the sampled period then we can assume the mean market movements and covariance matrix of the sampled market movements as the maximum likelihood estimators for these parameters[6].

Advanced estimation techniques might take other information into account such as volatility implied by the swaption market, implied correlation from available information on more exotic swaptions, or machine learning techniques for pattern recognition in standard or shifting volatility regimes. One might also choose to assume no trend parameter.

It is *not* a sensible idea to estimate a covariance matrix using *absolute price levels*. Doing so is inconsistent with swaption theory and introduces systematic bias to the earliest data points in the sample[7].

We will progress the chapter by means of an on going example in which we have chosen to use a small set of instruments, namely we choose 2y, 5y, 10y, 30y IRSs in a single currency. We seek to build a covariance matrix. In practice we point out that;

(i) the number of instruments will be much greater than in this example, i.e. hundreds if not thousands of risk instruments might be considered, building a large covariance matrix,

(ii) the number of historically sampled data points, or other construction methodology, must be large enough, or robust enough, to produce statistically significant results. Heuristically, one might adequately accept the maxim of one hundred data points per instrument, or at least as many data points per instrument as there are instruments,

(iii) the market conditions present over a sampled time period ought to be similar to one's expectation of future market conditions. This way the statistics will produce results akin to one's anticipation of those future markets, or at least minimise forecast error,

(iv) the instruments do not have to be of the same type. In this example we have used IRSs of a single currency but they could equivalently be different currencies or different types of instrument, e.g. basis swaps, bonds or stocks. This is one reason the number of risk buckets can become large, as more and more correlations are introduced. But in this case the units of each instrument might be better served if standardised across the whole set,

(v) the covariance matrix's time horizon must be aligned with that of the VaR model. In this example a single period is one day meaning the CoVaR output will be a one-day VaR metric.

---

[5] detailed mathematical treatment of time series analysis and maximum likelihood estimators can be found in [34]

[6] since we are assuming the special case of a multivariate normal distribution, the unbiased estimator is in fact $\frac{N-1}{N} \times$ equation 1.1. For large enough samples this makes little difference

[7] see appendix section 14.9.6

	2y	5y	10y	30y	2yΔ	5yΔ	10yΔ	30yΔ
Day 10	1.199	1.663	1.928	2.201	-2.9	-3.3	-1.7	-1.6
Day 9	1.228	1.696	1.945	2.217	+1.8	+3.1	+1.1	-1.1
Day 8	1.210	1.665	1.934	2.228	-0.5	-1.5	+0.4	-1.1
Day 7	1.215	1.680	1.930	2.239	+1.2	+0.3	-0.4	+1.3
Day 6	1.203	1.677	1.934	2.226	+4.4	+2.0	+0.3	-0.9
Day 5	1.159	1.657	1.931	2.235	-1.6	-1.6	-2.7	-0.7
Day 4	1.175	1.673	1.958	2.242	-1.3	-0.3	-1.4	+0.6
Day 3	1.188	1.676	1.972	2.236	+3.0	+2.3	+4.0	+1.6
Day 2	1.159	1.653	1.932	2.220	+5.9	+5.3	+3.2	+2.0
Day 1	1.100	1.600	1.900	2.200	-	-	-	-

Table 14.1: Simulated market rates (%) and daily market movements (bps) for each instrument.

Our forecast covariance matrix, $\mathbf{Q}(\mathbf{\Delta}) = [q_{jk}(\mathbf{\Delta})]$, is calculated from the daily market movements and is stated in equation 14.1. This calculation uses the unbiased estimator according to equation 1.1, however with the specific assumption of multivariate normality this should be varied according to the former footnote.

$$\mathbf{Q}(\mathbf{\Delta}) = \begin{bmatrix} 8.7 & 7.4 & 5.1 & 2.2 \\ 7.4 & 7.3 & 4.7 & 2.2 \\ 5.1 & 4.7 & 4.9 & 1.8 \\ 2.2 & 2.2 & 1.8 & 1.9 \end{bmatrix} \qquad (14.1)$$

14.5.2   Covariance matrix smoothing

From time to time it might be noticeable, when using a lot of instruments, that the covariance matrix (or correlation matrix), constructed through historical sampling, is a bit noisy. There might be unexpected, outlying correlations, for example created by spurious and one-off market movements of individual instruments, or even errors in the dataset. Covariance smoothing is the term adopted for techniques to try and adjust the matrix to remove this noise. There are a few theorised methods. A practical and simple method is described in section 15.4.1 incorporated into the chapter on PCA. An example of further reading is article [35].

Covariance smoothing has advantages because it means that for rolling covariance matrices (where the number of historical data points remains static but updates with newly available information) the variation will be reduced. If CoVaR techniques were used to measure market-making margin, which we see in part in section 19.4.3, then removing noise helps to produce optically consistent margin from trade to trade. It will also help when rolling from day to day, but this might be minimised in another way, though, by taking a large number of historical data points where the introduction of a new point and exclusion of an old point has a small effect.

There is a disadvantage with the method outlined in this book for covariance smoothing, which is likely true for other methods also. This is that it involves reducing information in the matrix and some of the variance. This usually gives rise to lower CoVaR multipliers than would otherwise be determined for a portfolio of large but oscillatory bucket risk, due to higher than usual correlations of very similar instruments. There is the potential consideration of a CoVaR add-on value for the additional risk of forecasting too high correlations. But we only make reference to this consideration and no further comment.

14.5.3 CoVar multiplier and VaR calculation

Armed with the forecast covariance matrix we also require the risk of each instrument to calculate VaR with the CoVaR technique. Since we have adopted par instruments we extend the on going example by letting:

$$\mathbf{S_{par}} = \begin{matrix} (2Y) \\ (5Y) \\ (10Y) \\ (30Y) \end{matrix} \begin{bmatrix} -10,000 \\ 2,500 \\ 10,000 \\ -4,000 \end{bmatrix} .$$

Equation 14.2 outlines the calculation for CoVaR multiplier, c, representing a single standard deviation of PnL under a specified distribution.

$$c = \sqrt{\mathbf{S_{par}^T Q S_{par}}} , \quad \text{or equivalently (using Einstein summation convention),}$$

$$c = \sqrt{q_{jk}S_{par}^j S_{par}^k} = \sqrt{q_{11}S^1 S^1 + q_{12}S^1 S^2 + \ldots + q_{43}S^4 S^3 + q_{44}S^4 S^4} . \tag{14.2}$$

Therefore for our example,

$$c = \sqrt{\begin{bmatrix} -10,000 & 2,500 & 10,000 & -4,000 \end{bmatrix} \begin{bmatrix} 8.7 & 7.4 & 5.1 & 2.2 \\ 7.4 & 7.3 & 4.7 & 2.2 \\ 5.1 & 4.7 & 4.9 & 1.8 \\ 2.2 & 2.2 & 1.8 & 1.9 \end{bmatrix} \begin{bmatrix} -10,000 \\ 2,500 \\ 10,000 \\ -4,000 \end{bmatrix}} ,$$

$$c = 16,174 .$$

As already mentioned the calculated CoVaR multiplier is the portfolio measure that can be used to determine the level of loss a portfolio is expected to exceed with specific c.i.s. If we naturally assume a normal distribution of valuation changes, with the mean of those changes being zero, then 16% of the time the portfolio would be expected to lose more than c in a one day period.

We can calculate to 95% and 99% c.i.s for VaR, respectively, as:

$$VaR_{5\%} = \Phi^{-1}(0.95)c = 1.644 \times c = 26,590$$

$$VaR_{1\%} = \Phi^{-1}(0.99)c = 2.326 \times c = 37,620$$

This can be added into our code library using a Covar class mixin [21, #642801]

```
1  import numpy as np
2  from scipy.stats import norm
3
4  class Covar_:
5
6      def covar(self, curve, Q, alpha: float=None):
7          S = self.risk(curve=curve)
8          c = np.sqrt(np.matmul(S.T, np.matmul(Q, S)))[0, 0]
9          if alpha is not None:
10             return norm.ppf(1-alpha) * c
11         return c
```

Swap and Portfolio are set to inherit this calculation:

```
1  class Swap(Covar_):
2      ...
3
4  class Portfolio(Covar_):
5      ...
```

Provided we have created a `Curve` we can use the new implementation to risk a portfolio of swaps and to replicate the calculations above.

```
 1  >>> swaps = [
 2      Swap(datetime(2022,1,1), 12*2,  12, 12, fixed_rate=1.20, notional=-50.9e6),
 3      Swap(datetime(2022,1,1), 12*5,  12, 12, fixed_rate=1.66, notional=5.23e6),
 4      Swap(datetime(2022,1,1), 12*10, 12, 12, fixed_rate=1.93, notional=11.0e6),
 5      Swap(datetime(2022,1,1), 12*30, 12, 12, fixed_rate=2.20, notional=-1.81e6),
 6  ]
 7  >>> portfolio = Portfolio(objects=swaps)
 8  >>> portfolio.risk(curve)
 9  [[-10000],
10   [2502],
11   [10006],
12   [-3999]]
13  >>> market_data = DataFrame({
14      "2Y":  [1.199, 1.228, 1.210, 1.215, 1.203, 1.159, 1.175, 1.188, 1.159, 1.100],
15      "5Y":  [1.663, 1.696, 1.665, 1.680, 1.677, 1.657, 1.673, 1.676, 1.653, 1.600],
16      "10Y": [1.928, 1.945, 1.934, 1.93, 1.934, 1.931, 1.958, 1.972, 1.932, 1.900],
17      "30Y": [2.201, 2.217, 2.228, 2.239, 2.226, 2.235, 2.242, 2.236, 2.22, 2.200],
18  })
19  >>> market_movements = market_data.diff(-1) * 100
20  >>> Q = market_movements.cov()
21  >>> portfolio.covar(curve, Q)
22  16171.64
23  >>> portfolio.covar(curve, Q, alpha=0.01)
24  37620.86
```

Example 14.2.
The question posed by the risk manager in example 14.2 can now be answered using the same covariance matrix established in this section. The calculated CoVaR multipliers are added to the table:

	Alpha's risk	Bravo's risk	Collective
2Y	-180	-50	-230
5Y	-10	-10	-20
10Y	180	-50	130
30Y	25	-25	0
$c =$	336	291	529

The manager acknowledges that both portfolios have similar levels of risk albeit Alpha has slightly more and a different type of risk. Alpha has a spread position and Bravo has an outright position. Collectively their risks somewhat offset each other but not to a large degree.

14.6   Using CoVaR in practice

For an individual trader the sole knowledge of one's VaR is helpful but not of extensive use. It can become much more useful if a trader gets an intuitive feel for how each successive trade he might do will increase it or decrease it. Clearly its purpose is to provide an assessment of potential loss and it can also allow direct comparison of the riskiness of one's portfolio against another portfolio, or against the same portfolio at some previous point in time. Making these comparisons is an important way to gain points of reference against levels of risk a trader is comfortable running and not comfortable running.

Due to its analytic nature the CoVaR method permits certain calculations useful in practice. In particular it can dynamically calculate suggestive trades which will **minimise VaR**. Occasionally this might be obvious to the trader and provide no new information but will frequently give more insight.

Below we explain how to calculate VaR minimising trades. The most commonly used application of this technique is probably the single instrument VaR minimisation, given its ease of display, but we also present multiple instrument VaR minimisation which also has practical uses. The functions in the following sections are included in the code repository[21, #c76061].

14.6.1 Single instrument VaR minimisation

The appendix outlines the derivation of this method but here we focus on the practical application and just outline the required steps. Single instrument VaR minimising calculations produce trades that **only suggest new risk in a single instrument at a time, and the risk position in all the other instruments should remain constant to minimise VaR**.

First calculate the column vector quantity below. This requires the matrix multiplication of the covariance matrix and the current risk strip:

$$c\frac{\partial c}{\partial \mathbf{S}} = \mathbf{QS} \ .$$

Then to calculate the specific quantity of risk to execute in the single i'th instrument that will minimise VaR take the i'th element of the above column vector and divide it by the appropriate diagonal element of the covariance matrix, $-q_{ii}$:

$$S^{i:\text{trade}} = -\frac{1}{q_{ii}} c\frac{\partial c}{\partial S^i},$$

This can also be represented as the vector equation (note that this is independent of α since VaR scaling does not impact these results),

$$\mathbf{S}^{\text{trade}} = -\mathbf{diag}(\mathbf{diagonal}(\mathbf{Q}))^{-1}\mathbf{QS} \ .$$

For our specific on going example:

$$\mathbf{S}^{\text{trade}} = - \begin{bmatrix} \frac{1}{8.7} & 0 & 0 & 0 \\ 0 & \frac{1}{7.3} & 0 & 0 \\ 0 & 0 & \frac{1}{4.9} & 0 \\ 0 & 0 & 0 & \frac{1}{1.9} \end{bmatrix} \begin{bmatrix} 8.7 & 7.4 & 5.1 & 2.2 \\ 7.4 & 7.3 & 4.7 & 2.2 \\ 5.1 & 4.7 & 4.9 & 1.8 \\ 2.2 & 2.2 & 1.8 & 1.9 \end{bmatrix} \begin{bmatrix} -10,000 \\ 2,500 \\ 10,000 \\ -4,000 \end{bmatrix} = \begin{matrix} (2Y) \\ (5Y) \\ (10Y) \\ (30Y) \end{matrix} \begin{bmatrix} 2,948 \\ 2,304 \\ -475 \\ 3,373 \end{bmatrix}$$

A minor method addition to our `Covar_` class will also be able to make these calculations (subject to rounding):

```
def covar_smt(self, curve, Q):
    """single instrument minimising trade"""
    S = self.risk(curve=curve)
    Q_inv = np.diag(-1 / np.diagonal(Q))
    return np.matmul(Q_inv, np.matmul(Q, S))

>>> portfolio.covar_smt(curve, Q)
[[2942],
 [2297],
 [-484],
 [3362]]
```

With a simple extension one can also easily calculate the overall risk position in a single instrument that actually minimises the VaR with respect to all the other individual positions remaining the same by evaluating:

$$\mathbf{S}^{\text{min}} = \mathbf{S} + \mathbf{S}^{\text{trade}} = \begin{matrix} (2Y) \\ (5Y) \\ (10Y) \\ (30Y) \end{matrix} \begin{bmatrix} -7,052 \\ 4,804 \\ 9,525 \\ -627 \end{bmatrix} \ .$$

Although the above calculations give trading and minimising values for each of the instruments 2Y, 5Y, 10Y and 30Y **only one** of them would be traded to minimise VaR with respect to that instrument. All the other three instruments should remain constant under this assumption. This system of calculation only represents a convenient way of displaying the values for each single instrument VaR minimising trade simultaneously, in vector notation. For example, where the 30Y minimising trade is to pay 3,373 pv01 this cannot be done in conjunction with any of the other minimising trades such as pay 2Y in 2,948 pv01, because if this were to be done then minimal VaR values would not be attained and in fact the VaR might actually increase from its original value[8].

With the knowledge of four possible minimising trades which should be traded to achieve the best reduction in VaR? It is very useful to see side by side what is the VaR minimising trade and by how much it will reduce the VaR. This gives a steer on which instrument should be traded if VaR reduction is the goal at any point in time. The way the reduction in VaR must be calculated is to compare the minimised VaR for each instrument with the original VaR:

$$\Delta c^i = c^{i:\min} - c \ .$$

The appendix outlines a method which is useful in Excel for determining this quantity with some matrix multiplication, otherwise the process is a little laborious if each instrument is considered in turn. We also state the Python code that is added to our code repository [21, #c76061], which uses vector broadcasting to calculate all values simultaneously.

```
def covar_smt_impact(self, curve, Q):
    S, c = self.risk(curve=curve), self.covar(curve, Q)
    S_trade = self.covar_smt(curve, Q)
    S_min = S + np.diag(S_trade[:, 0])   # tensor
    c_impact = np.sqrt(np.matmul(S_min.T, np.matmul(Q, S_min))) - c
    return np.diagonal(c_impact)[:, np.newaxis]

>>> portfolio.covar_smt_impact(curve, Q)
[[-2513],
 [-1240],
 [-36],
 [-664]]
```

With the calculations completed the results are shown in table 14.2. The greatest reduction any singular trade can achieve is about 15% if say approximately 3,000 pv01 of 2Y IRS was paid. This is not a high proportional reduction suggesting the portfolio's risk is dominated by RV trades, or combinations of buckets. This can also be inferred from the fact that the minimising trade in 10Y would be to receive 475 pv01 but in other tenors the VaR minimising trade is obtained by paying fixed. If outright market risk was a dominant factor the VaR minimising trade would likely be the same direction across all tenors. Further ways to utilise single instrument VaR minimisation, in conjunction with benchmark trade combinations, are explored in chapter 16 on customised risk management and models. The following section also gives a complimentary assessment from a second perspective.

---

[8]Section 16.4.2 describes a technique for interpreting the single instrument VaR minimising information and systematically trading multiple instruments simultaneously to reduce VaR to an even greater extent

	S	**S**^{trade}	Δc^i	$|\frac{\Delta c^i}{c}|$
2Y	-10,000	2,948	-2,524	15.6%
5Y	2,500	2,304	-1,247	7.7%
10Y	10,000	-475	-34	0.2%
30Y	-4,000	3,373	-688	4.1%
$c =$	16,174			

Table 14.2: Single instrument VaR minimisation, showing the trade to be executed and the reduction in VaR it can achieve.

14.6.2 Allocation of VaR

Allocation of anything; cost of capital, VaR, initial margin requirements, or funding costs of bonds at an aggregate level is a difficult task. Often one without a uniquely associated solution. Allocation in general is discussed in more depth in section 17.2.6 with respect to allocated RWA values and costs of capital, but it is useful for a trader to spare a thought for other areas in which individual components can be allocated a proportion of an overall value or metric to put this in context.

In this section we present the concept of allocation of VaR to each individual risk bucket. This is not something that I have used extensively in my trading career, although partly this is due to my relatively recent discovery of it. It is an interesting concept, however, that fits well into the narrative and provides a good example of allocation in general, aiding the reader's all round comprehension.

If we adopt the Aumann-Shapley method[9] of allocation then each risk bucket's allocation of VaR can be directly calculated as,

$$\mathbf{c}_{\text{alloc}} = \frac{1}{c}\mathbf{diag}(\mathbf{S})\mathbf{QS} , \quad \text{for} \quad \mathbf{diag}(\mathbf{S}) = \begin{bmatrix} S_1 & & \mathbf{0} \\ & \ddots & \\ \mathbf{0} & & S_n \end{bmatrix} .$$

Extending this to our ongoing example, the CoVaR multiplier's, c, value of 16,174, is allocated to each risk bucket in the proportions:

$$\mathbf{c}_{\text{alloc}} = \begin{matrix} (2Y) \\ (5Y) \\ (10Y) \\ (30Y) \end{matrix} \begin{bmatrix} 15,787 \\ -2,602 \\ 1,437 \\ 1,552 \end{bmatrix}$$
$$\mathbf{16,174}$$

```
 1 def covar_alloc(self, curve, Q):
 2     S, c = self.risk(curve=curve), self.covar(curve, Q)
 3     S_diag = np.diag(S[:, 0])
 4     return 1 / c * np.matmul(S_diag, np.matmul(Q, S))
 5
 6 >>> portfolio.covar_alloc(s_cv, Q)
 7 [[15756],
 8  [-2597],
 9  [1466],
10  [1547]]
```

So what value does this add to the process of risk management? This indicates that the 2Y bucket is currently the main contributor to the CoVaR multiplier (under this allocation

---

[9]for a derivation see section 17.6.1

procedure). VaR minimisation also hints at this conclusion by suggesting trading 2Y can achieve the best reduction. Importantly this allocation also attributes a negative value to 5Y suggesting it works to offset the impact by other buckets, so it would be unwise (in the context of risk minimisation) to reduce the 5Y bucket. This also compares with the VaR minimisation results.

To highlight the consistency across these different perspectives mathematically, a bucket which takes the value $S^{\text{i:min}}$ and minimises VaR with respect to that bucket will have an allocated contribution to VaR of zero. These two processes work to compliment each other in their approach and provide information from two almost opposing perspectives. Combined I think they provide a very instructional basis for risk management of large and complicated portfolios.

14.6.3   Multiple instrument VaR minimisation

Previous sections show the method of minimising VaR along with the concept of trading only one of all the possible instruments in the risk model. There are a few reasons why this is a useful approach. Firstly, a trader will find it easier to contemplate executing only a single instrument. It is often difficult in markets to orchestrate the execution of multiple instruments in the interbank market, let alone be precisely the right instruments in precisely the right quantities. Secondly, a single instrument hedge often produces a VaR reduction that is only marginally inferior to executing multiple trades so the increased complexity of analysis is, heuristically, not worth the effort. Thirdly, an experienced trader can often recognise his portfolio and acknowledge which suggested single instrument VaR minimising trades are likely to be independent from each other and therefore can leverage his use of the technique with practice, in effect guessing what his multiple instrument VaR reduction trades are just from the information available about single instruments. For this purpose allocation of VaR might also come into own.

Multiple instrument VaR minimisation does exist, however, and generalises the previous approach. It supposes a certain number of instruments can be traded simultaneously and calculates the tradable amounts of risk in each one to minimise the VaR. It will always create at least as good a VaR reduction than any single trade in isolation, but the procedure is more cumbersome to calculate in a spreadsheet and particularly difficult to display. Consider the above example where the instruments are 2Y, 5Y, 10Y and 30Y. Clearly there are only four single instrument VaR minimising trades, each assigning a specific trade to either of 2Y, 5Y, 10Y or 30Y. But, there are six dual instrument VaR minimising trades, where each would have to specify two simultaneous trades. These would be 2Y & 5Y, 2Y & 10Y, 2Y & 30Y, 5Y & 10Y, 5Y & 30Y, and 10Y & 30Y. So not only are there more combinations but displaying the data is harder because one would have to show the risk for each instrument in each combination. Of course this naturally becomes much harder when there are many, many more instruments in the risk model.

Multiple instrument VaR minimisation can be used for other purposes, such as simplified portfolio representation, demonstrated in section 16.4.3, or trade directionality hedging in section 23.1.2.

Procedure

Below we describe how to obtain the VaR minimising trades across multiple instruments[10].

---

[10]see the appendix for a mathematical derivation

Step one: for a risk model, with risk $\mathbf{S}$, that has N instruments, obtain a covariance matrix, $\mathbf{Q}$ of dimension $N \times N$, for those instruments. This is done in the same manner and with the same considerations as for single instrument VaR minimisation.

Step two: from those N instruments choose a subset of M instruments, those being the ones that the multiple instrument VaR minimisation is to be measured against. From risk strip, $\mathbf{S}$, extract only the entries corresponding to the M instruments to form the smaller risk strip, $\hat{\mathbf{S}}$.

Step three: from the matrix $\mathbf{Q}$ extract the relevant M rows to create the sub-matrix, $\hat{\mathbf{Q}}$ of dimension $M \times N$. Additionally extract the relevant M columns from $\hat{\mathbf{Q}}$ to create the sub-matrix $\hat{\hat{\mathbf{Q}}}$ of dimension $M \times M$.

Step four: calculate the specific quantity of risk to execute in the chosen M instruments that will minimise VaR by performing the following matrix calculation:

$$\hat{\mathbf{S}}^{\text{trade}} = -\hat{\hat{\mathbf{Q}}}^{-1}\hat{\mathbf{Q}}\mathbf{S} ,$$

so that,

$$\hat{\mathbf{S}}^{\text{min}} = \hat{\mathbf{S}} + \hat{\mathbf{S}}^{\text{trade}} .$$

Step five: calculate the reduction in VaR by comparing the new minimised VaR with the original.

To complete this section by extending the on going example, suppose we choose 2Y & 10Y to be the dual instruments against which we minimise VaR. Note that this seems a sensible choice because not only do these represent the largest individual risk buckets in the example but that also 2Y is the most volatile instrument and 10Y is midway between the remaining three so it is effectively a structured choice. Following the above procedure we have:

$$\mathbf{Q} = \begin{bmatrix} 8.7 & 7.4 & 5.1 & 2.2 \\ 7.4 & 7.3 & 4.7 & 2.2 \\ 5.1 & 4.7 & 4.9 & 1.8 \\ 2.2 & 2.2 & 1.8 & 1.9 \end{bmatrix}, \quad \hat{\mathbf{Q}} = \begin{bmatrix} 8.7 & 7.4 & 5.1 & 2.2 \\ 5.1 & 4.7 & 4.9 & 1.8 \end{bmatrix}, \quad \hat{\hat{\mathbf{Q}}} = \begin{bmatrix} 8.7 & 5.1 \\ 5.1 & 4.9 \end{bmatrix},$$

$$\hat{\mathbf{S}}^{\text{trade}} = \begin{matrix}(2Y) \\ (10Y)\end{matrix} \begin{bmatrix} 8,564 \\ -9,469 \end{bmatrix} .$$

```
def covar_mmt(self, curve, Q, instruments):
    """multi-instrument minimising trade"""
    S = self.risk(curve=curve)
    S_hat, Q_hat = S[instruments, :], Q[instruments, :]
    Q_hat_hat = Q[np.ix_(instruments, instruments)]
    S_trade_hat = np.linalg.solve(Q_hat_hat, -np.matmul(Q_hat, S))
    S_trade = np.zeros_like(S)
    for ix, val in zip(instruments, S_trade_hat[:, 0]):
        S_trade[ix, 0] = val
    return S_trade

def covar_mmt_impact(self, curve, Q, instruments):
    S, c = self.risk(curve=curve), self.covar(curve, Q)
    S_min = S + self.covar_mmt(curve, Q, instruments)
    return np.sqrt(np.matmul(S_min.T, np.matmul(Q, S_min)))[0, 0] - c

>>> portfolio.covar_mmt(curve, Q, [0,2])
[[8562],
 [0],
 [-9475],
 [0]]
```

Further calculations would show that dual instrument VaR minimising trade would reduce VaR by just over 70%, indicating that this is the dominant risk position in the portfolio. One might say that this was obvious from the start and in the case of only have having four instruments in the risk model the risk reducing trades might always be obvious. CoVaR techniques are designed to display fundamentally useful information to a trader where the number of instruments is quite large, say one or two hundred. In this edition, since we have migrated away from Excel to Python we can quite easily loop through the various combinations and display the results quite nicely:

```
>>> combinations = [(0,1), (0,2), (0,3), (1,2), (1,3), (2,3)]
>>> df_mmt = DataFrame(index=["2Y", "5Y", "10Y", "30Y", "impact"])
>>> for combo in combinations:
        df_mmt.loc[["2Y", "5Y", "10Y", "30Y"], f"{combo}"] =\
            portfolio.covar_mmt(s_cv, Q, list(combo))[:, 0]
        df_mmt.loc["impact", f"{combo}"] =\
            portfolio.covar_mmt_impact(s_cv, Q, list(combo))
>>> print(df_mmt)
```

	(0,1)	(0,2)	(0,3)	(1,2)	(1,3)	(2,3)
2Y	7,042	8,562	2,975	0	0	0
5Y	-4,812	0	0	6,979	1,983	0
10Y	0	-9,476	0	-7,234	0	-2,574
30Y	0	0	-130	0	1,064	5,800
impact	-3,410	-11,600	-2,514	-4,892	-1,286	-1,369

Table 14.3: Multi instrument VaR minimisation, showing the dual-instrument-trades to be executed and the reduction in VaR multiplier they achieve.

With experience a successful trader can quickly assimilate all of the information to understand his risks and their interactions with each other. Knowledge of the mathematical processes behind the derivation of these techniques is not necessary (other than to build a spreadsheet or code library) but the understanding of their concepts and how they fit it to an individual trader's risk management process is, I would say, the key to success. Note that this multi-instrument VaR minimising technique is also used in a different capacity in sections 16.4.3 and 23.1.2.

14.7   Properties of VaR

Strictly speaking VaR is *not* a coherent risk measure because it fails in one respect; it is *not* subadditive, meaning two portfolios can be combined and the resulting VaR of the combined portfolio might be larger than the individual VaRs. This is unintuitive and not typically exemplified by linear IRD portfolios. The bibliography lists a well cited article[36] that analyses how rarely the subadditivity condition is actually broken and the extreme conditions needed for such cases to matter.

Therefore we adopt the view that VaR is subadditive for practical applications. In particular, CoVaR is technically subadditive, due to its mathematical method of construction and assumption that market movements are modelled as correlated normal random variables. This is expanded in the appendix.

VaR is well used as a measure of risk by managers and risk controllers within financial institutions. It is used less, now, by regulators, who have adopted instead ES, since ES can be shown to be a truly coherent risk measure. But regulators aside, an accurately modelled portfolio's VaR is useful because it allows for comparison of the risk of various portfolios in a standardised way, and allows a means of placing controls to limit losses.

Managers and risk controllers have to assess multiple portfolios everyday so they cannot become bogged down by detail, and thus a single metric is very useful to draw conclusions, and highlight items of investigation. It also permits a very easy way to set rules and limits for individual traders which are difficult to circumvent, besides building large risk positions that are not captured by VaR models such as reset risk. Breaches in VaR limits are very easily monitored and can be quickly addressed.

We mentioned that VaR is effectively subadditive, while CoVaR is definitively subadditive. The nature of subadditivity qualitatively describes risk reduction of diversified portfolios, where instruments and portfolios tend to be correlated. Mathematically this is simply stated, for any portfolios, A_i:

$$c_\Sigma(A_1 + A_2 + \ldots + A_N) \leq c_1(A_1) + c_2(A_2) + \ldots + c_N(A_N)$$

where $(A_1 + A_2 + \ldots + A_N)$ denotes the single portfolio attained through the aggregation of all of the constituent portfolios. What this means is that a manager can assess the diversification of two or more portfolios by comparing their individual VaRs with the VaR of the aggregate. If the aggregate VaR is the sum of the individual portfolios' VaRs then they are all effectively running the same risks or uncorrelated risks, but if the aggregate VaR is much less than that then the portfolios are diversified. It may even be the case that one portfolio is running the opposite risks to another.

14.8 Expected shortfall (ES)

We relegated ES to the end of the chapter because it is not (practically) useful for IRD portfolios. But, it is included in the book because BASEL, and the regulators, prefer it to VaR, so a reader should be made aware of it, and its acronym!

The argument for ES over VaR is applicable and valid for assets that can suffer tail risk losses such as complete capital write down on default. This makes it a good measure for a bank's total assets. But our focus is (linear) IRDs and the previous section discussed why VaR is well suited. ES is a fully coherent risk measure in a mathematical sense, but its more difficult calculation makes it unwieldy and this forces many hindrances. This is why we do not consider it in greater detail in the book.

Another name for ES is conditional-VaR or CVaR. This is in reference to its calculation methodology. ES is defined as the expected loss conditional on the event that the loss exceeds a specific c.i.. For example the $ES_{2.5\%}$ is the expected loss given the loss exceeds the $VaR_{2.5\%}$ figure.

Example 14.3.
A portfolio is measured for its $VaR_{1\%}$ and $ES_{2.5\%}$, using historical simulation method. 400 previous days are sampled and the worst 10 losses are listed in reverse order as,

10	-9,000	$\leftarrow VaR_{2.5\%}$.
9	10,000	
8	-11,000	
7	-12,000	
6	-19,000	
5	-25,000	
4	-30,000	$\leftarrow VaR_{1\%}$.
3	-40,000	
2	-95,000	
1	-170,000	
Total	-421,000	$\leftarrow ES_{2.5\%}$ is -42,100 ($\frac{1}{10}$th total).

It is plain to see that if the 3 worst losses were much larger, i.e. if the tail risk becomes extremely 'fat' (and the distribution has higher values of kurtosis), then the ES would be much larger, without either the 1% or 2.5% VaRs being affected.

As an excellent rule of thumb, if a normal distribution of losses is assumed (which is a reasonable assumption for linear IRDs) then the $VaR_{1\%}$ and $ES_{2.5\%}$ are very close to the same value[11], and can be used in place of each other.

---

[11]the appendix outlines this calculation

14.9 Appendix

14.9.1 The CoVaR approach, mathematically

The CoVaR model uses fundamental assumptions of **normal random variables** to achieve its result. Let the PnL of a portfolio, ΔP be assumed to be equal to,

$$\Delta P = S^1 X_1 + \ldots + S^n X_n ,$$

for X_i the random variable representing the market movement corresponding to risk bucket S^i. If the X_i's are **assumed to be normally distributed** with a multivariate normal distribution with covariance matrix, $\mathbf{Q}$, then the PCA transformation of section 15.5.1 can transform the variables so that each is an identical and independently distributed (i.i.d.) standard normal random variable. Then,

$$\Delta P = \widetilde{S}^1 \sqrt{\lambda_1} Z_1 + \ldots + \widetilde{S}^n \sqrt{\lambda_n} Z_n ,$$

By the properties of sums of normal random variables,

$$\Delta P \sim N\left(0, (\widetilde{S}^1)^2 \lambda_1 + \ldots + (\widetilde{S}^n)^2 \lambda_n \right) .$$

The α % VaR is determined as,

$$VaR_{\alpha\%}(\Delta P) = x\sqrt{(\widetilde{S}^1)^2 \lambda_1 + \ldots + (\widetilde{S}^n)^2 \lambda_n} = xc , \quad \text{where} \quad \Phi(-x) = \alpha .$$

Φ is the cumulative standard normal distribution function. For a given c.i., α, x is a constant which leads to the remaining term being called the **CoVaR multiplier**, c. Expressed in terms of the original variables this yields equation 14.2.

14.9.2 CoVaR is subadditive

VaR is, in general, *not subadditive*, but the assumptions of normality for the CoVaR model mean that *it* is subadditive.

Given two portfolios P_1 and P_2, with CoVaR multipliers, c_1 and c_2, measured with CoVaR techniques, then under the assumptions of the previous section, we have,

$$\Delta P_1 \sim N\left(0, c_1^2\right) , \quad \Delta P_2 \sim N\left(0, c_2^2\right) .$$

P_1 and P_2 are not necessarily independent. In fact they are more likely to be correlated, with assumed correlation, ρ. By the properties of sums of normal random variables,

$$\Delta P_1 + \Delta P_2 \sim N\left(0, c_1^2 + c_2^2 + 2\rho c_1 c_2\right) .$$

Additionally,

$$c_1^2 + c_2^2 + 2\rho c_1 c_2 \leq c_1^2 + c_2^2 + 2 c_1 c_2 = (c_1 + c_2)^2 , \quad \text{for} \quad -1 \leq \rho \leq 1 .$$

So that finally,

$$\sqrt{c_1^2 + c_2^2 + 2\rho c_1 c_2} \leq c_1 + c_2 \quad \implies \quad VaR_{\alpha\%}(\Delta P_1 + \Delta P_2) \leq VaR_{\alpha\%}(\Delta P_1) + VaR_{\alpha\%}(P_2) .$$

14.9.3   Deriving single instrument VaR minimisation trades

Given $c = \sqrt{\mathbf{S^T Q S}}$, for each risk instrument, S^i in $\mathbf{S}$ we have that:

$$\frac{\partial c}{\partial \mathbf{S}} = \frac{\mathbf{QS}}{c}, \quad \text{or equivalently,}$$

$$\frac{\partial c}{\partial S^i} = \frac{1}{2}\frac{(q_{ij}S^j + q_{ji}S^j)}{c} = \frac{(q_{i1}S^1 + q_{i2}S^2 + \ldots + q_{iN}S^N)}{c}.$$

To find the optimal, VaR minimising, risk position, $S^{i:\min}$, for the singular i'th instrument set this derivative equal to zero for the appropriate i'th equation:

$$0 = \frac{(q_{i1}S^1 + \ldots + q_{ii}S^{i:\min} + \ldots + q_{iN}S^N)}{c}, \quad \text{or equivalently,}$$

$$S^{i:\min} = S^i - \frac{(q_{i1}S^1 + \ldots + q_{ii}S^i + \ldots + q_{iN}S^N)}{q_{ii}} = S^i - \frac{c}{q_{ii}}\frac{\partial c}{\partial S^i}. \tag{14.3}$$

The position, $S^{i:\text{trade}}$, that needs to be physically traded to attain the minimising position is then simply:

$$S^{i:\text{trade}} = S^{i:\min} - S^i = -\frac{c}{q_{ii}}\frac{\partial c}{\partial S^i}.$$

To calculate the VaR reduction, Δc^i, from a single instrument minimising trade construct a temporary vector, $\mathbf{T}$, with all elements set to zero except the i'th where it is equal to $S^{i:\text{trade}}$. Then the minimum VaR with respect to this instrument is:

$$c^{i:\min} = \sqrt{(\mathbf{S+T})^{\mathbf{T}}\mathbf{Q}(\mathbf{S+T})} = \sqrt{\mathbf{S^T Q S} + 2\mathbf{S^T Q T} + \mathbf{T^T Q T}}, \quad \text{or,}$$

$$c^{i:\min} = \sqrt{q_{jk}S^j S^k + 2q_{ji}S^j T^i + q_{ii}T^i T^i} = \sqrt{c^2 + 2q_{ji}S^j T^i + q_{ii}T^i T^i}.$$

$$\Delta c^i = c^{i:\min} - c.$$

The above formula allows the calculation of $c^{i:\min}$ with multiplication of known scalar quantities and a single row by column matrix multiplication which is more easily implemented in Excel. The code shown in the text uses vector broadcasting in Python to calculate all values simultaneously.

14.9.4   Deriving multiple instrument VaR minimisation trades

Given c as above, and the definition of $\hat{\ }$ operator defined in chapter 14:

$$\frac{\partial c}{\partial \hat{\mathbf{S}}} = \frac{\hat{\mathbf{Q}}\mathbf{S}}{c}.$$

To find the optimal, VaR minimising, risk position, $\hat{\mathbf{S}}^{\min}$, for a chosen subset of M instruments set this derivative equal to zero for those relevant M instruments and then we can write:

$$\hat{\mathbf{Q}}\mathbf{S}^{\min} = \hat{\mathbf{Q}}\mathbf{S} - \hat{\hat{\mathbf{Q}}}\hat{\mathbf{S}} + \hat{\hat{\mathbf{Q}}}\hat{\mathbf{S}}^{\min} = \mathbf{0},$$

and hence rearranged to:

$$\hat{\mathbf{S}}^{\min} = \hat{\hat{\mathbf{Q}}}^{-1}(\hat{\hat{\mathbf{Q}}}\hat{\mathbf{S}} - \hat{\mathbf{Q}}\mathbf{S}),$$

and if expressed in terms of tradable risk:

$$\hat{\mathbf{S}}^{\text{trade}} = \hat{\mathbf{S}}^{\min} - \hat{\mathbf{S}} = -\hat{\hat{\mathbf{Q}}}^{-1}\hat{\mathbf{Q}}\mathbf{S}.$$

14.9.5 Comparing ES with VaR

Under the assumption of the normal distribution, i.e. adopting a CoVaR mentality, we can equate the $ES_{2.5\%}$ with that of the $VaR_{1\%}$. We highlight this relationship because BASEL and other regulators often cite the $ES_{2.5\%}$ as their preferred metric, and given the nature of linear IRDs it is often easier to equate this to the $VaR_{1\%}$, especially if CoVaR approaches have been adopted elsewhere. Below we make the comparison for $X \sim N(0,1)$.

The $VaR_{1\%}$ is numerically calculated, using for example Excel's NORMINV(99%,0,1) function, to be 2.326.

The $ES_{2.5\%}$, on the other hand, is modelled as,

$$ES_{2.5\%} = \frac{1}{2.5\%} \int_{\alpha}^{\infty} x f(x) dx , \quad \text{for,} \quad \alpha = VaR_{2.5\%} = 1.960, \quad f(x) = \frac{1}{\sqrt{2\pi}} e^{-\frac{1}{2}x^2} ,$$

$$= \frac{40}{\sqrt{2\pi}} \left[-e^{-\frac{1}{2}x^2} \right]_{\alpha}^{\infty} = \frac{40}{\sqrt{2\pi}} e^{-\frac{1}{2}1.960^2} = 2.338 .$$

14.9.6 Estimating covariance matrices using prices

If we assume that a financial asset price, such as the rate on an IRS, has a change that is a Wiener process then the future price of that asset is equivalent to the initial value plus the sum of the independent periodic changes (for equities or otherwise one should use a log version of this):

$$S_t = S_0 + \sum \Delta S_i \quad \text{for} \quad \Delta S_i = S_i - S_{i-1} \quad \text{is a Wiener process}$$

We can also assert a similar formula for a second asset T_t. Now if we evaluate the covariance of the **absolute prices** (rather than the changes) then we have:

$$Cov(S,T) = \frac{1}{n} \sum_{t=1}^{n} (S_t - E[S])(T_t - E[T])$$

Recognise that, under the assumed Wiener process, $E[S] = S_0$ and similarly for T then this reduces to:

$$Cov(S,T) = \frac{1}{n} \sum_{t=1}^{n} \left(\sum_{i=1}^{t} \Delta S_i \sum_{i=1}^{t} \Delta T_i \right)$$

This shows the covariance result is heavily dominated by the initial periodic changes rather than any of the latter, which is not valid under the assumed pricing process, and incompatible with option pricing theory. On the other hand, if the **covariance of the periodic changes** were to be examined we would have,

$$Cov(\Delta S, \Delta T) = \frac{1}{n} \sum_{t=1}^{n} \Delta S_t \Delta T_t$$

which treats all period changes with equal weight, and is the **only appropriate choice**.

Principal Component Analysis

In summary, PCA is a statistical technique that seeks to find patterns in datasets and present them, ordered by their degree of impact. Theoretically, this should sound as if it would be useful for direct risk management because the relative movement of different tenor swap rates could be captured, patterns observed, and then taken advantage of. In fact, in practice I have personally found PCA to be of limited use in this regard, and not for lack of trying. On the other hand it has been very useful for other trading related tasks and since I have used it in the odd instance for some risk management it should definitely be included in this book to allow the reader the chance to develop and draw their own conclusions.

This chapter will introduce and develop the following;

- what the overall concept of PCA is and how to calculate principal components (PCs),

- what are the characteristics of PCA usage such as dominance and residuals,

- how to combine PCA with risk management and the associated drawbacks to the approach,

- how PCA is comparable to and outperformed by CoVaR,

- the way in which PCA can be utilised usefully to generate random walks, and perform dimensionality reduction for tasks such as correlation smoothing.

15.1   General application

As mentioned PCA is a way to discover patterns in datasets. What it does is to look at all the data collectively, with all of the associated correlations between variables and tries to group them in various ways to better describe the whole. There are two stages involved in PCA;

(i) **centralising** the data, so that it is standardised about zero (and the variance is standardised if appropriate),

(ii) **transforming** the data, so that patterns are observed and the PCs can be shown.

Probably, this is best visualised with a simple example.

Example 15.1.
The below graphs plots some data on the length of c.40 infants given their different ages. The graph on the left is the raw data, and the graph on the right has been centralised. Centralising is a very simple process involving subtracting the mean of 11.05 from the months data and the mean of 70.63 from the length data, so that the origin becomes fixed at the centre.

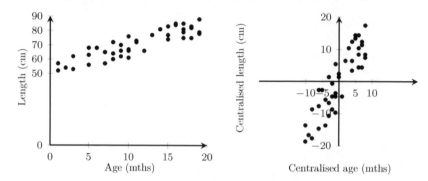

The next stage is to transform the data. This involves rotating the axes of the chart about the origin so that the error from the new x-axis is minimised, shown diagrammatically below.

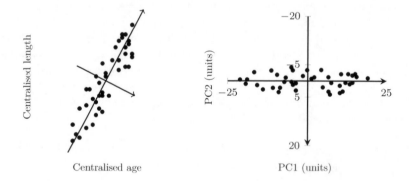

PC1 is the dominant component and this describes the overall trend that every half a month an infant's length increases by about one centimetre. PC2 is a non dominant component which provides the degree of freedom for infants to have individuality. In this case the number of PC2 units from zero determines an infant's specific individuality, that is how far removed from the average it is being long or short for its age.

The above example is of course rather basic in the sense it has only two variables or two dimensions. Utilising PCA with swap rates extends the data to many more variables depending on how many instruments one believes it is useful to include. There are many ways of conceptualising PCA. The example here was used to demonstrate the concept of minimising orthogonal error by rotating the axes. PCA is well documented online and a simply search will reveal other concepts such as fitting the best ellipse or ellipsoid across the data and the concept of transforming the data to produce a completely uncorrelated covariance matrix[1]. Practically though, the steps involved to calculate PCs are outlined below.

Step one: centralise each data variable, $\mathbf{g_i}$, by subtracting the mean, $\mathbf{g_i^c} = \mathbf{g_i} - \bar{g}_i$.

Step two: calculate the covariance matrix, $\mathbf{Q} = Cov(\mathbf{G^c})$, between each of the n centralised data variables.

Step three: calculate the n eigenvalues[2], λ_i, of matrix $\mathbf{Q}$ and sort them so the first is highest and last is smallest.

Step four: calculate the eigenvectors of $\mathbf{Q}$ corresponding to each λ_i, which represent the ordered PCs and create the $n \times n$ matrix $\mathbf{E}$ by combining the sorted eigenvectors as columns.

Step five: calculate the centralised PC multipliers, $\mathbf{H^c}$, of $\mathbf{G^c}$, for each given day by matrix multiplication: $\mathbf{H^c} = \mathbf{G^c E}$.

Example 15.2.
A trader calculates the PCs from the data given in table 14.1, adopting $\mathbf{Q}(\mathbf{\Delta})$ as the covariance matrix similar to the choice made in that chapter. Firstly, he centralises the data, shown in table 15.1.

	$\mathbf{g_1}(2y)$	$\mathbf{g_2}(5y)$	$\mathbf{g_3}(10y)$	$\mathbf{g_4}(30y)$	$\mathbf{g_1^c}$	$\mathbf{g_2^c}$	$\mathbf{g_3^c}$	$\mathbf{g_4^c}$
Day 10	-2.9	-3.3	-1.7	-1.6	-4.0	-4.0	-2.0	-1.6
Day 9	+1.8	+3.1	+1.1	-1.1	+0.7	+2.4	+0.8	-1.1
Day 8	-0.5	-1.5	+0.4	-1.1	-1.6	-2.2	+0.1	-1.1
Day 7	+1.2	+0.3	-0.4	+1.3	+0.1	-0.4	-0.7	+1.3
Day 6	+4.4	+2.0	+0.3	-0.9	+3.3	+1.3	+0.0	-0.9
Day 5	-1.6	-1.6	-2.7	-0.7	-2.7	-2.3	-3.0	-0.7
Day 4	-1.3	-0.3	-1.4	+0.6	-2.4	-1.0	-1.7	+0.6
Day 3	+3.0	+2.3	+4.0	+1.6	+1.8	+1.6	+3.7	+1.6
Day 2	+5.9	+5.3	+3.2	+2.0	+4.8	+ 4.6	+2.9	+2.0
Day 1	-	-	-	-	-	-	-	-
Mean	+1.10	+0.70	+ 0.31	+ 0.01	0.00	0.00	0.00	0.00

Table 15.1: Centralising the given data of daily rate changes.

$Q(\Delta)$ is necessarily the same as that calculated in equation 14.1, and the sorted eigenvalues and eigenvectors of that matrix are shown below.

$$[\lambda_i] = \begin{bmatrix} 19.5 & 1.53 & 1.06 & 0.55 \end{bmatrix},$$

$$\mathbf{E} = \begin{matrix} (2Y) \\ (5Y) \\ (10Y) \\ (30Y) \end{matrix} \begin{bmatrix} 0.65 & -0.41 & -0.06 & -0.64 \\ 0.59 & -0.26 & 0.18 & 0.74 \\ 0.44 & 0.73 & -0.53 & 0.03 \\ 0.20 & 0.49 & 0.83 & -0.19 \end{bmatrix}.$$

$\mathbf{H^c}$, which contains all the centralised PC multipliers for each day is calculated according to step five and shown in table 15.2.

We add the following class to our code repository[21, #9461f8] and ensure that `Swap` and `Portfolio` inherit it. Maintaining the same `market_movements` and `s_cv` object from chapter 14 we can then show,

---

[1]the mathematics of this is shown in the appendix in conjunction with the next section

[2]Excel addins or vba code is freely available online for the calculation of eigenvalues and eigenvectors of matrices for example [37], we use Python's NumPy in our implementation

	$\mathbf{h_1^c}$(PC1)	$\mathbf{h_2^c}$(PC2)	$\mathbf{h_3^c}$(PC3)	$\mathbf{h_4^c}$(PC4)
Day 10	-6.2	0.4	-0.8	-0.2
Day 9	2.0	-0.9	-0.9	1.6
Day 8	-2.5	0.7	-1.3	-0.4
Day 7	-0.2	0.1	1.4	-0.6
Day 6	2.7	-2.1	-0.7	-1.0
Day 5	-4.6	-0.8	0.7	0.1
Day 4	-2.8	0.3	1.3	0.6
Day 3	4.0	2.3	-0.4	-0.2
Day 2	7.5	-0.1	0.7	0.0
Day 1	-	-	-	-

Table 15.2: Centralised PC multipliers for each day.

```
class PCA_:

    def pca(self, Q):
        lambd, E = np.linalg.eigh(Q)
        return lambd[::-1], E[:, ::-1]

    def historical_multipliers(self, Q, data):
        lambd, E = self.pca(Q)
        centralised_data = data - data.mean(axis=0)
        return np.matmul(centralised_data, E)

>>> swap.pca(Q)
[19.58, 1.53, 1.07, 0.55],
[[-0.65  0.41, -0.06, -0.64],
 [-0.59,  0.26,  0.18,  0.74],
 [-0.44, -0.73, -0.53,  0.03],
 [-0.20, -0.49,  0.83, -0.19]]
```

Notice how the first two PCs in our code output are the negative of the above calculation. This is just a reflection of the different algorithms used to determine the eigenvectors. Both are valid but the negative signs will be transmissible through to the associated metrics, like PC multipliers in the code version.

The significance of PCs (eigenvectors) and patterns

The eigenvectors are the PCs. The PCs are ordered by dominance and they describe the most common pattern of daily changes in IRS rates. By design they are uncorrelated with each other. If 5Y and 10Y rates increased on any given day then it would be very likely, due to correlation, that 2Y and 30Y rates would also have increased. But this is not true for each PC. If the movement of rates is characterised by an increase in, say, PC1, this would have no bearing on the implied movement for any of the other PCs, due to their independence of one another. If we plot the four PCs the movement of rates during this ten day period is easier to understand.

Figure 15.1 shows that the dominant PC1 characterises the overall level of rates. If any rate moves up or down the other tenor rates are expected to move similarly with varying degrees of volatility. In this example the short end, particularly 2Y, is the most volatile with the largest movement and 30Y is the least volatile.

PC2 is characteristic of short to long curve steepening move; 2Y and 5Y have opposite sign to 10Y and 30Y. PC3 is characteristic of a 10s30s curve steepening move; 10Y has opposite sign to 30Y and the 2Y and 5Y components are small in comparison. The final and least dominant PC4 characterises a 2s5s curve steepening move.

These PCs are representative of the usual types of rate moves and PCs that are observed. Overall level of rates is always PC1, curve steepening is usually PC2 and PC3, and curve bowing

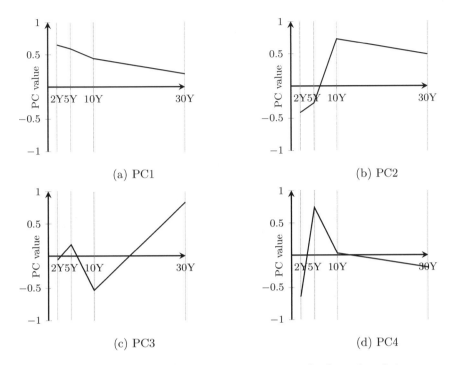

Figure 15.1: The four plotted PCs characterising volatility of each instrument with respect to that PC.

or micro steepening is PC3 and PC4. When more tenors are introduced each subsequent PC becomes less and less dominant, seeking to characterise highly specific (and probably unlikely to be repeated in subsequent time periods) rate movements simply as a result of mathematical consistency. Less dominant PCs are rarely of interest, particularly when many tenors have been included in the data. Less dominant PCs also become increasingly more random and subject to greater change with minor alterations to the data.

The significance of PC multipliers and the dataset

PCs themselves do not change for a given dataset because they are calculated from the given covariance matrix and reflect the dominant patterns of the variables. However, PC multipliers reflect the degree to which each PC explains any individual daily move with reference to each of these patterns. For example any arbitrary daily move might be made up of two PC1s, three PC2s, no PC3s and one PC4. These multipliers have to be introduced to represent each day to express the data as a whole. Sometimes in other texts these are called factor multipliers or loadings.

Example 15.3.
Suppose a centralised daily move is made up of 2×PC1, 3×PC2, and 1×PC4 then according to the PCs calculated from the covariance matrix one can calculate the centralised daily market move with reference to 2Y, 5Y, 10Y and 30Y instead:

$$\Delta \mathbf{r^c} = 2 \times \begin{bmatrix} 0.65 \\ 0.59 \\ 0.44 \\ 0.20 \end{bmatrix} + 3 \times \begin{bmatrix} -0.41 \\ -0.26 \\ 0.73 \\ 0.49 \end{bmatrix} + 1 \times \begin{bmatrix} -0.64 \\ 0.74 \\ 0.03 \\ -0.19 \end{bmatrix} = \begin{bmatrix} -0.6 \\ +1.2 \\ +3.1 \\ +1.7 \end{bmatrix}$$

The significance of eigenvalues and dominance

There is no doubt that the larger the eigenvalue for a given PC the more important that PC is to the observed data. Considering the sizes of all the eigenvalues collectively leads to the concept of PC dominance. There are some guides on PCA which will advise to determine a percentage dominance of any PC by dividing its eigenvalue by the sum of all the eigenvalues.

In terms of risk, this measure of dominance is as good as any. If, for example one happened to have an identical risk exposure to each PC then looking at the ratio of eigenvalues would be an accurate allocation of total risk in terms of VaR[3]. Looking back to example 15.2, the percentage dominance obtained by this measurement would be 86%, 7%, 5%, and 2% for each respective PC.

However, there is also a second approach. As is shown in the appendix the eigenvalues actually represent the variances of each PC multiplier giving rise to the underlying data. For considering market movements an alternative assessment of dominance is to proportion the square root of the eigenvalues, which are in fact the standard deviations of PC multipliers. If done in this way the dominance values obtained are 59%, 17%, 14% and 10%.

Even though these measures of dominance are valid determinations for the separate tasks of assessing risk or considering market movements, the fact they are different causes issues. It does unfortunately make it harder to conceptualise PCA and its application to trading IRDs. My personal opinion in this regard has been to treat dominance values somewhat apathetically, adopting the appropriate measure for use with risk or market movements, but overall not paying so much attention to their quantitative values but more their qualitative relations. On the other hand one of the purposes of PCA is to determine patterns in the data and to exclude supposed random noise to make constructive conclusions. Dominance values can be used to ascertain a threshold below which PCs become negligible. This does of course rely heavily on the subjectivity of the trader. For those familiar with machine learning principles the *elbow method* can be used to select an appropriate number of PCs for analysis.

Residuals and comparing to the original data

Leading on straight from the above, PCA is often used to remove what is perceived to be uncharacteristic data, i.e. the data which is not dominant, to attempt to discern outliers. Residuals are the values that are left over *if only* some of the more dominant PCs are used to explain the data. Residuals are the more unorthodox element of price levels and theoretically represent levels a trader can oppose by executing new trades in the hope of attaining value, when price levels revert to model normality.

Example 15.4.
The same trader perceives PC1 and PC2 as being the only PCs representative of the market. On Day 11 the market has moved in the following way, which he centralises exactly as before:

$$\boldsymbol{\Delta r} = \begin{matrix} (2Y) \\ (5Y) \\ (10Y) \\ (30Y) \end{matrix} \begin{bmatrix} +4.1 \\ +5.2 \\ +6.2 \\ +2.0 \end{bmatrix}, \qquad \boldsymbol{\Delta r^c} = \begin{bmatrix} +3.0 \\ +4.5 \\ +5.9 \\ +2.0 \end{bmatrix}.$$

The PC multipliers for this data calculated by $\mathbf{h^c} = (\boldsymbol{\Delta r^c})^T \mathbf{E}$, *give,*

$$\mathbf{h^c} = \begin{bmatrix} 7.6 & 2.9 & -0.8 & 1.2 \end{bmatrix}.$$

---

[3]this would actually represent the Aumann-Shapley value of allocating each PCs contribution of risk to the VaR multiplier.

If only the first two PC multipliers are used to explain this day's move and the last two are consciously neglected then the data that is explained is:

$$\widetilde{\Delta \mathbf{r}^{\mathbf{c}}} = \begin{bmatrix} +3.7 \\ +3.8 \\ +5.4 \\ +2.9 \end{bmatrix}.$$

The trader calculates the residuals, $\boldsymbol{\xi}$ by subtracting one from the other:

$$\boldsymbol{\xi} = \Delta \mathbf{r}^{\mathbf{c}} - \widetilde{\Delta \mathbf{r}^{\mathbf{c}}} = \begin{bmatrix} -0.7 \\ +0.7 \\ +0.5 \\ -0.9 \end{bmatrix}.$$

Based on these residuals the trader perceives 5Y and 10Y to have moved too high relative to 2Y and 30Y on the day and thus he receives some 2s5s and pays 10s30s as a short term trade.

In example 15.4 residual analysis has been used as the basis for executing RV trades. Personally, I would not have executed any trades based on that analysis. Even ignoring the fact that the covariance matrix was statistically insignificant being based on only nine days moves, and the fact that PC3 and PC4 together had a dominance of 24%, the residuals calculated did not appear to deviate much from the everyday norm. In fact the PC3 and PC4 multipliers of -0.8 and 1.2 respectively were well within the size of values that had been seen on previous days. There is simply not enough deviation here to be worth considering as the basis for executing new trades. These moves could well be reversals of previous day's outliers indicating that any analysis of this sort must be considered in conjunction with the overall theme of the market and in response to the reason why the market might have moved in that particular way.

Calculating residuals is a similar process that again uses matrix manipulations. From a column set of centralised daily market movements, $\Delta \mathbf{r}^{\mathbf{c}}$, the centralised row PC multipliers are obtained, as was seen in the example, by:

$$\mathbf{h}^{\mathbf{c}} = (\Delta \mathbf{r}^{\mathbf{c}})^{\mathbf{T}} \mathbf{E},$$

and the column centralised market movements are obtained from PC multipliers by:

$$\widetilde{\Delta \mathbf{r}^{\mathbf{c}}} = \mathbf{E} \big(\widetilde{\mathbf{h}^{\mathbf{c}}} \big)^{\mathbf{T}},$$

where in $\widetilde{\mathbf{h}^{\mathbf{c}}}$ some of the rightmost elements are set to zero reflecting any non-dominant PCs that one wishes to neglect. If none are neglected there will be no residual but if some have been neglected the residual is obtained as:

$$\boldsymbol{\xi} = \Delta \mathbf{r}^{\mathbf{c}} - \widetilde{\Delta \mathbf{r}^{\mathbf{c}}} = \mathbf{E} (\mathbf{h}^{\mathbf{c}} - \widetilde{\mathbf{h}^{\mathbf{c}}})^{\mathbf{T}}.$$

It is not possible to calculate residuals without the data being centralised so this step is important if that is the aim. Centralising is not necessary for the determination of the PCs but it is good practice in PCA.

In preceding sections we have focused on PCA of market movements from period to period and *not absolute price levels*. Performing PCA on absolute price levels introduces systematic bias to which we refer the reader to section 14.5.1 for more detailed comments in this regard.

15.2   Risk representation

Risk can also be expressed relative to PCs rather than the instruments of the risk model. The transformation,

$$\widetilde{\mathbf{S}} = \mathbf{E}^{\mathbf{T}}\mathbf{S},$$

gives the column vector of risk for each ordered PC.

Example 15.5.
The same trader starts Day 11 with the following risk:

$$\mathbf{S} = \begin{matrix}(2Y)\\(5Y)\\(10Y)\\(30Y)\end{matrix}\begin{bmatrix}-250\\150\\100\\60\end{bmatrix}, \qquad \widetilde{\mathbf{S}} = \begin{matrix}(PC1)\\(PC2)\\(PC3)\\(PC4)\end{matrix}\begin{bmatrix}-17\\166\\38\\263\end{bmatrix}.$$

The non-centralised market movements of tenor swaps and also the non-centralised PC multipliers are stated:

$$\mathbf{\Delta r} = \begin{matrix}(2Y)\\(5Y)\\(10Y)\\(30Y)\end{matrix}\begin{bmatrix}+4.1\\+5.2\\+6.2\\+2.0\end{bmatrix}, \qquad \mathbf{h}^{\mathbf{T}} = \begin{matrix}(PC1)\\(PC2)\\(PC3)\\(PC4)\end{matrix}\begin{bmatrix}+8.8\\+2.5\\-0.9\\+1.0\end{bmatrix}.$$

The estimated individual PnL components for each move and the total is stated:

$$P \approx \begin{matrix}(2Y)\\(5Y)\\(10Y)\\(30Y)\end{matrix}\begin{bmatrix}-1,025\\780\\620\\120\end{bmatrix}, \qquad P \approx \begin{matrix}(PC1)\\(PC2)\\(PC3)\\(PC4)\end{matrix}\begin{bmatrix}-150\\411\\-35\\269\end{bmatrix}.$$
$$\overline{\qquad\qquad\mathbf{495}\qquad\qquad} \qquad \overline{\qquad\qquad\mathbf{495}\qquad\qquad}$$

The example shows how the representation of risk as determined by PCs can be used for explaining the PnL in an alternatively understandable way. It is important to recognise that non-centralised PC multipliers are used in this regard, synchronous to non-centralised market movements, otherwise the PnL estimate produced will not be accurate.

Looking strictly at the par swap risk model approach the instinctive explanation of the gain might be to suggest that rates have moved higher with an overall total positive risk generating some PnL and the steepening risk between 2s5s and 2s10s has also generated some profit. It is difficult to discern much more than this or anything specific about 30Y.

On the other hand looking directly at the PCA approach the instinctive explanation of the gain might be to say that the overall level of rates has generated a loss, factoring in all of the relative volatilities of each tenor, but that the macro curve steepening captured by PC2 has generated the dominant amount of PnL which is reflective of 2s10s and 2s30s, and that PC4 which reflects 2s5s steepening has also contributed. PC3 which reflects 10s30s move has had little impact.

PC risk can also considered in conjunction with VaR and **each PC can be allocated a proportion of the VaR** that it represents[4]. For example 15.5 the VaR multiplier, c, can be

---

[4]the particular method proposed for allocating a proportion of the VaR against the respective risk in each PC is the same aforementioned application of Aumann-Shapley allocation theory. See section 17.2.6 and appendix section 17.6.1 for further discussion of allocation in general

calculated to be 296. To assign a proportion of this VaR to each PC, $\widetilde{c}_i$, perform the following calculation:

$$\widetilde{c}_i = (\widetilde{S}^i)^2 \frac{\lambda_i}{c} \, .$$

In this manner the apportioned VaR to each PC from the risk given in the example would be:

$$\widetilde{\mathbf{c}}_{\text{alloc}} = \frac{\begin{array}{cc} (PC1) \\ (PC2) \\ (PC3) \\ (PC4) \end{array} \begin{bmatrix} 19 \\ 142 \\ 5 \\ 130 \end{bmatrix} \begin{array}{c} (6\%) \\ (48\%) \\ (2\%) \\ (44\%) \end{array}}{\mathbf{296}} \, .$$

This is not the only way VaR could be apportioned but in this case appears to be supportive of the above assessment that PC2 and PC4 contribute the dominant amount of PnL and that PC3 is negligible. From this PC1 might have been expected to have less of an impact but this is only a statistical inference and still remains broadly accurate in an illustrative sense.

The PCA risk functions added[21, #52a7f3] to our `PCA_` class are,

```
 1  def pca_risk(self, curve, Q):
 2      S = self.risk(curve)
 3      lambd, E = self.pca(Q)
 4      return np.matmul(E.T, S)
 5
 6  def pca_covar_alloc(self, curve, Q):
 7      S_tilde = self.pca_risk(curve, Q)
 8      lambd, E = self.pca(Q)
 9      c = self.covar(curve, Q)
10      return (S_tilde[:, 0]**2 * lambd / c)[:, np.newaxis]
```

We demonstrate the use of these functions below.

```
 1  portfolio = Portfolio(objects=[
 2      Swap(datetime(2022,1,1), 12*2, 12, 12, notional=-1.272e6),
 3      Swap(datetime(2022,1,1), 12*5, 12, 12, notional=313545),
 4      Swap(datetime(2022,1,1), 12*10, 12, 12, notional=109931),
 5      Swap(datetime(2022,1,1), 12*30, 12, 12, notional=27160),
 6  ])
 7  >>> portfolio.risk(s_cv)
 8  [[-250],
 9   [150],
10   [100],
11   [60]]
12  >>> portfolio.pca_risks(s_cv, Q)
13  [[17],
14   [-166],
15   [38],
16   [263]]
17  >>> portfolio.pca_covar_alloc(s_cv, Q)
18  [[19],
19   [142],
20   [5],
21   [130]]
```

Note that CoVaR allocation is invariant to negative or positive eigenvectors so the allocation in code is the same as the allocation above in our textual example.

15.3 Drawbacks with using PCA

Previous sections have outlined using PCA to generate residuals. Plotting PC multipliers over time is also a charting technique comparable to simply plotting the level of rates over time, and using PCs to display risk has also been discussed. A benefit with using PCA is that for all the conceptual difficulty the implementation is fairly easy (with the right matrix tools package in

Excel or other programming languages such as Python), and provides an alternative view and assessment of risk. In my experience, however, there are some hindrances which prevented me from adopting PCA as a practical risk management tool:

(i) **Non-static PCs.** The PCs are dependent upon the covariance matrix chosen and when varied, either by altering the historical period of the data, or simply including or excluding instruments, the values of the PCs will change.

(ii) **No reference points.** PCs, being orthogonal, are standardised in a mathematical way which is not at all intuitive. Risk, measured against one PC, might be a small number and a large number versus another PC. Without factoring the volatility of each PC it is impossible to discern which is truly the riskiest position. PCA is then often needed to be used in conjunction with VaR.

(iii) **PCs are not tradable instruments.** It is impossible to hedge risk against any individual PC because one must trade each and every specific tenor in precisely the right proportion, which makes the knowledge of risk to some of the less dominant PCs redundant.

(iv) **Benchmark trades affect the risk of every PC.** When a simple trade is executed it will impact the risk representation of every PC, which makes it impossible to maintain any stable risks in specific PCs. This means that only the one or two most dominant PCs are able to be monitored.

(v) **Charting PCs provides no new information.** For a regular trader who monitors the markets daily, utilising charts created with PCA will not highlight anything that has not already been observed in the traditional manner, and is a more complicated approach to adopt.

(vi) **Residuals can be random.** Calculating residuals depends on the neglected PCs and if the PCs change due to an altered covariance matrix or simply if more or less PCs are chosen to be neglected then residuals can indicate the opposite to what they indicated previously.

(vii) **Conceptualising PCA is difficult.** Every time analysis changes, so do the PCs, and it requires some examination to be comprehended. In turn this has to be assimilated into the usual risk management process. This is too difficult and requires too many resources.

Unfortunately this is rather a long list, discovered in my personal attempts to use PCA more frequently for risk management principles, but failing. However, as already mentioned in this chapter, CoVaR approaches outlined in chapter 14 provide an alternate tool for risk management. CoVaR is based on the same principle of adopting a covariance matrix representing the correlation of instruments. It is by far my preferred tool for many reasons, and some of those reasons are the direct solutions to the above problems associated with PCA.

When using CoVaR a changeable covariance matrix will affect those trades suggested as VaR minimising trades but the impact is often much easier to comprehend. Additionally, rather than being held hostage to the changeable, mathematically generated PCs, CoVaR is designed around static instruments chosen individually by a trader. This is an advantage in that it establishes clear guidance and fixed reference points. These chosen instruments will often be benchmark trades or trade combinations giving direct control of risk through viable interbank market activity. CoVaR does not offer tools for charting or indicating RV, but, like PCA, it is useful for optimising the RV aspect of trades[5]. A convenient property of CoVaR is that everything revolves around a *single* metric, the VaR multiplier, making it effective when combined with all of the associated analysis.

---

[5]see section 23.1.2

15.4 Practical uses of PCA

In light of the above, one may very well query the overall use of PCA in IRD trading. It is a well recognised technique for dimension reduction of datasets and commonly utilised for machine learning techniques across many other disciplines. The following are sound uses for PCA that can be directly applied to IRD analysis and are the reasons it is included in the book in such detail. A further use is hedging trade directionality which is exemplified in section 23.1.1.

15.4.1 Correlation and covariance smoothing

Often, particularly when a large number of instruments are included in the analysis, the correlation and covariance matrices exhibit some random variation, if determined from historical samples. It can be beneficial to remove some of this noise to produce so called 'smoothed' matrices. This can be useful for avoiding idiosyncratic results when adopting covariance matrices for CoVaR methods or trade strategising.

One way of performing the smoothing is to select the more dominant PCs that one wishes to keep (some of the leftmost columns of $\mathbf{E}$ as $\hat{\mathbf{E}}$) and cross multiply by the respective eigenvalues. It is recommended to apply this technique to the correlation matrix[6], rather than the covariance matrix. The reason being that IRSs have an empirical structure to their correlation matrix, which is expected to be captured by the dominant PCs of a PCA performed on such correlation matrices. The smoothed correlation matrix is then determined as,

$$\mathbf{Q}^*_{\text{corr}} \approx \hat{\mathbf{E}} \, \mathbf{diag}(\hat{\boldsymbol{\lambda}}) \hat{\mathbf{E}}^{\mathbf{T}} \, .$$

It is normal that the diagonal of a smoothed correlation matrix will not contain precisely ones. This is due to the error introduced by neglecting some PCs. Applying scaling techniques to correct this whilst maintaining the smoothed structure is appropriate. This corrective scaling procedure is of a similar nature as that explained in the next paragraph and should be applied before the volatility scaling is applied.

The smoothed covariance matrix can be obtained by scaling the corrected, smoothed correlation matrix with the diagonal matrix of volatilities of each instrument (which can also be otherwise smoothed through methods such as spline interpolation or values implied by swaption markets),

$$\mathbf{Q}^* \approx \mathbf{diag}(\boldsymbol{\sigma}^*) \mathbf{Q}^*_{\text{corr}} \mathbf{diag}(\boldsymbol{\sigma}^*) \, .$$

Using PCA is not the only way of smoothing these matrices, nor might it be the best method given the circumstances or the objective. But it is an effective way nonetheless and readily implemented.

15.4.2 Multi-variate random walks

PCA has a definitive and easily implemented use in generating scenarios or random walks. This is something that is frequently used. But it is not the only way to generate random walks, nor might it be the fastest[7].

Continuing our scenario example, if we seek to simulate a random walk, or a typical set of random market movements, for the 2Y, 5Y, 10Y and 30Y rates we cannot simply generate a supposed market movement for each of the tenor rates independently. They are correlated to each other which means once the first market movement has been generated the second must be

---

[6]if applying PCA directly to a dataset ensure each variable has been standardised to have a unit s.d., which is equivalent to analysing the correlation matrix

[7]see the appendix for a note on the Cholesky decomposition

generated with a probability function that incorporates the data of the first into it. Similarly the third must incorporate the first and the second generated market movements, etc..

PCA solves this problem since each component is uncorrelated with each another. It is entirely possible to generate distinct random PC multipliers and then extract the market movements of the scenario from the PCs, see example 15.6.

We note that it is also common in this type of random walk to adopt only some of the dominant PCs, and classify them into specific types of market movement. Neglecting some of the components reduces the overall variation and may require a scalar adjustment in order to correctly quantify the full spectrum of market movement volatility.

Example 15.6.
Utilising the eigenvalues and eigenvectors from the previous example the trader wishes to simulate a market move scenario for Day 11.
Each centralised PC multiplier is calculated by a random variable sampled from a normal distribution with mean zero and s.d. equal to the square root of the eigenvalue:

$$H_i^c \sim N(0, \lambda_i).$$

The trader's sampling process returns the following variables:

$$\mathbf{h^c} = \begin{bmatrix} 4.0 & -1.6 & 1.6 & -0.2 \end{bmatrix}.$$

He converts these to centralised market movements and adds the mean to return non-centralised market movements and his desired random scenario:

$$\mathbf{\Delta r^c} = \begin{bmatrix} +3.3 \\ +2.9 \\ -0.3 \\ +1.4 \end{bmatrix}, \qquad \mathbf{\Delta r} = \begin{bmatrix} +4.4 \\ +3.6 \\ +0.1 \\ +1.4 \end{bmatrix}.$$

The trader can be confident that if he samples enough random scenarios the covariance matrix will asymptotically converge to the target covariance matrix, by design.

15.5 Appendix

15.5.1 Establishing PCA through eigenvalues and eigenvectors

Covariance matrices are real, symmetric, positive definite matrices. This implies that they are Hermitian and also that all of their eigenvalues are real and positive. This further implies all of their eigenvectors are real and orthogonal. Let $\mathbf{Q}$ be an $n \times n$ covariance matrix and let $\mathbf{e_i}$ be an eigenvector of $\mathbf{Q}$ with corresponding eigenvalue, λ_i. Then,

$$\mathbf{Q}\mathbf{e_i} = \lambda_i \mathbf{e_i} \ .$$

If $\mathbf{E} = [\mathbf{e_1} \ \dots \ \mathbf{e_n}]$ represents the $n \times n$ matrix composed of the column eigenvectors, then the transformation,

$$\mathbf{E^T Q E} = \begin{bmatrix} \mathbf{e_1^T} \\ \vdots \\ \mathbf{e_n^T} \end{bmatrix} \begin{bmatrix} \lambda_1 \mathbf{e_1} & \dots & \lambda_n \mathbf{e_n} \end{bmatrix} = \begin{bmatrix} \lambda_1 & 0 & 0 \\ 0 & \ddots & 0 \\ 0 & 0 & \lambda_n \end{bmatrix} = \boldsymbol{\lambda},$$

and thus a new covariance matrix has been established whose variables are completely uncorrelated with one another, where the variable transformation is adopted as below.

For a given array of centralised data (that is data which has been standardised to have zero mean), with random variables aligned column wise, for example,

$$\mathbf{G^c} = \begin{bmatrix} \mathbf{g_1^c} & \cdots & \mathbf{g_n^c} \end{bmatrix},$$

let,

$$\mathbf{H^c} = \mathbf{G^c E},$$

so that by the properties of covariance matrices under transformation of variables, the column wise random variables, $\mathbf{h_1^c}, \mathbf{h_2^c}, \dots, \mathbf{h_n^c}$, are uncorrelated with each other,

$$Cov(\mathbf{H^c}) = Cov(\mathbf{G^c E}) = \mathbf{E^T} Cov(\mathbf{G^c})\mathbf{E} = \mathbf{E^T Q E} = \boldsymbol{\lambda}.$$

This is actually the same if centralised data is used or not but calculating residuals is more difficult if the data is not centralised.

15.5.2 Cholesky decomposition

A covariance (or correlation) matrix is a real, symmetric, positive definite matrix and as a result can be deconstructed into a lower diagonal matrix multiplied by its transpose,

$$\mathbf{Q} = \mathbf{L L^T}, \quad \text{for} \quad \mathbf{L} = \begin{bmatrix} l_{11} & 0 & 0 & \dots \\ l_{21} & l_{22} & 0 & \dots \\ \vdots & & \ddots & \mathbf{0} \\ l_{n1} & l_{n2} & \dots & l_{nn} \end{bmatrix}$$

This is called a Cholesky decomposition. It is useful because a vector of independent standard normal random variables, $\mathbf{Z} = [Z_1, \dots, Z_n]^T$, can be multiplied by L to produce a vector of correlated and scaled random variables represented by the original covariance matrix,

$$\mathbf{X} = \mathbf{L Z}, \quad \implies \quad Cov(\mathbf{X}, \mathbf{X}) = \mathbf{Q} \ .$$

Customised Risk Management

The chapters of this book have outlined many different aspects of pricing and trading interest rate derivatives. The risk management of derivative portfolios is obviously one of the key and interesting topics. So far, numeric risk and multiple risk models have been discussed, the use of VaR, and more specifically perhaps, CoVaR, have shown separate techniques for being able to discern and react to market risk. In this chapter we seek to combine all of these elements with a trader's own preference, interpretation and perception of the IR market. Specifically, this chapter outlines;

- how to systematically treat risk management,
- how to create a personalised system for considering risks,
- how to combine all of the tools for risk management,
- what information an optimal trading risk summary will contain.

16.1 General risk management

Risk management for large portfolios containing many IRDs can be a difficult task. However, the goal of any such managerial process is fairly simple to define; hedge each and every risk except for those specific risks willingly and knowingly permitted. But this is quite a lofty goal. Certain unwanted risks might not be quantifiable or even possible to hedge. Otherwise, hedging in the absence of otherwise awkward risks might be possible given a static portfolio and ample time, but a dynamic portfolio with restricted timeframes mean that the elimination of each and every unwanted risk will almost certainly never occur. The managerial process that results, then, is one of prioritisation and focus.

To begin, we can first list the types of risk an individual trader is expected to recognise and control in his portfolio. See figure 16.1.

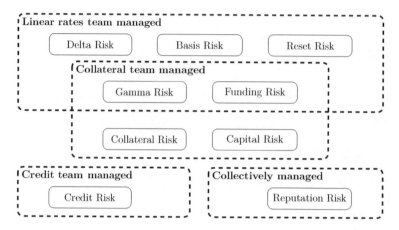

Figure 16.1: Major risk types of an IRD portfolio.

Gamma (more specifically cross-gamma) risk and funding risk are grey areas, and capital risk is such a new area of finance that it is probably not actively considered by all institutions. An individual trader might be expected to manage his gamma and cross-gamma risks or these might be assumed by another team. It might also be the case that an individual trader assumes responsibility for only a specific portion of the gamma and cross-gamma risks, but, regardless of whether the responsibility is owned or not, the fundamental understanding of the risks should exist to ensure correct division of labour.

Funding risk requires the management of one's cash balance in order to ensure the appropriate return (or interest) is achieved relative to the discounting methodology applied to all of the derivative's trades. Expecting an individual trader to be responsible for this is not sensible, since centralising the process gains economies of scale and potentially benefits from cross-netting. However, an individual trader should certainly be aware of the mechanics of any such process because it can have a direct impact on the accrual of PnL over a period of time without necessarily being particularly impactful on a day to day basis. It is most important for the trader to ensure that he prices trades relative to the funding rates that are automatically generated for his cash position(s), otherwise an economical inconsistency will arise. Along similar lines, it is important that an institution funds traders' cash positions in a systematic way factoring in appropriate collateral so that in turn the trader can price trades accurately and according to the details of specific CSAs. Additionally, if any automated process ever goes wrong I am certain the responsibility will always fall on the trader to recognise and correct it, thus he must understand it[1].

Capital risk is about managing an institution's capital position and ensuring it satisfies the limitations set forth by the regulator[2]. This requires information and action taken at an institution level and an individual trader cannot actively manage this, but one must understand the concepts and be capable of following the instructions laid down by the institution's management to trade in a capitally efficient way. Capital risk is one item which might also be

---

[1]these considerations were outlined in chapter 5
[2]see chapter 17 for a introduction to this topic

handled by the treasury department of a financial institution.

This leaves an individual trader directly responsible for their own delta, basis and reset risk. This is completely sensible because it allows a trader to be specialised in certain products and techniques and does not create an unreasonable workload otherwise diverting attention and resources away from this task. A core component of delta and basis risk management is being able to hedge with the most liquid products - interbank trades - and the specific trade combinations that are available.

16.2 Benchmark trade combinations

Benchmark trades underpin the efficiency of the interbank market. In this section we will explain why and provide some insight by outlining;

- the names and descriptions of benchmark trade combinations,
- the reasons why benchmark trade combinations exist,
- the association between trade combinations in fwd and par tenor spaces,
- how to think more deeply about trade combinations other than just at face value,
- pitfalls associated with apparent trade combinations, such as risk misconceptions and hedging cost considerations.

For those already aware of benchmark trade combinations the below will perhaps offer a novel way of thinking about them so is worth a quick perusal.

16.2.1 Types of trades

A regular and frequent trade is the **outright** trade where only a single trade is executed, for example to pay €100mm 10Y IRS. The following benchmark trade combinations exist which necessarily contain multiple outright trades:

Spread trade (-1/+1): this involves two trades of different maturities, each of equal and opposite analytic risk. For example paying $50k 5Y/10Y IRS, would involve receiving $50k pv01 5Y and paying $50k pv01 10Y IRS. Note that market terminology is always toward the action in the longest tenor swap.

Butterfly trade (-1/+2/-1): this involves three trades of different maturities. The middle maturity, termed the 'belly', has analytic risk equal and opposite to twice the risk of each of the 'wings'. For example paying £50k 2Y/5Y/10Y would involve paying £100k pv01 5Y IRS and receiving back £50k 2Y and £50k of 10Y. Paying and receiving is always expressed relative to the belly.

Condor trade (+1/-1/-1/+1): this involves four trades of different maturities, with the two trades at each extremity equal and opposite in analytic risk to the two middling maturity trades. For example paying $50k 5Y/6Y/7Y/8Y condor would amount to paying $50k 5Y and 8Y and receiving back $50k each of 6Y and 7Y. Condors rarely trade in the interbank market due to being more complicated, but one will observe they are simply a spread of spread trades; paying 7Y/8Y spread against receiving 5Y/6Y spread, which is how they would end up being executed. It is not a convention but often the longest tenor swap outlines the direction of paying or receiving the combination.

Pascal trade (-1/+3/-3/+1): this is by no means an official or conventional name but I once heard a trader call it this and given its structure seems very appropriate. Where a condor is a spread of spread trades, the pascal is a spread of butterfly trades. So paying \$10k 5Y/6Y/7Y/8Y pascal would amount to paying \$10k 8Y and \$30k 6Y and receiving back \$10k 5Y and \$30k 7Y. This is the same structure as receiving \$10k 6Y/7Y/8Y butterfly and paying back \$10k 5Y/6Y/7Y butterfly.

This list of standard trade combinations has evolved for two major reasons. Firstly, to execute multiple trades quickly and efficiently in an interbank market requires something that is universally understood. Spread trades and butterfly trades offer a simple structure, simple nomenclature and simple conventions which all aid trading. Even trade booking is relatively simple here because calculated notionals are achieved using an analytic delta approach so there are very rarely any disagreements. Secondly, trade combinations exist to express opinions about the market without taking large amounts of risk. Single outright trades are typically the most risky, but spread trades and butterfly trades usually offer much less risk and at the same time allow expression of market opinions in specialised ways. These simple structures are also readily available in charting packages so tracking historical trade performance graphically also becomes a simple task. They allow a simple, recognisable way of following the relative movements of the IR market and is universally understood by all participants.

A note on nomenclature

In order to shorten and make nomenclature more aesthetic we adopt the following rules in this book:

  (i) 5Y, 6Y, 10Y etc. represent par instruments and is the same as 0Y5Y, 0Y6Y etc.,

 (ii) 1Y5Y, 2Y10Y represent fwd instruments in the form start-date followed by tenor,

(iii) 2s5s, read twos fives, represents a spread trade the same as 2Y/5Y in the above description,

 (iv) 2s5s10s represents a butterfly trade the same as 2Y/5Y/10Y written above,

  (v) 2s3s4s5s represents a pascal trade, and 2s3s/4s5s represents a condor as a spread of spreads.

Example 16.1.

A trader has four instruments available to trade, 2Y, 5Y, 10Y and 30Y IRSs. He has established a covariance matrix of their daily moves so he can calculate a daily VaR multiplier, c:

$$\mathbf{Q} = \begin{bmatrix} 7.5 & 10.5 & 8.5 & 4.3 \\ 10.5 & 20.7 & 19.2 & 10.1 \\ 8.5 & 19.2 & 20.4 & 12.5 \\ 4.3 & 10.1 & 12.5 & 10.4 \end{bmatrix}$$

The below table shows the multiplier, and hence comparative riskiness, for some example trade types:

$\mathbf{S_A}$ (000s)	10Y	5s10s	2s5s10s	5s10s30s	2s5s/10s30s	2s5s10s30s
2Y	0	0	-50	0	-50	33
5Y	0	-100	100	-50	50	-100
10Y	100	100	-50	100	50	100
30Y	0	0	0	-50	-50	-33
c	452	164	149	123	238	91

16.2.2 Directionality

Benchmark trades present a relatively straightforward way of executing risk that is targeted to a specific part of the curve. Something often overlooked when executing benchmark trades, however, is their directionality. The most easily observed property of the overall interest rate market is whether it is rising or falling. This simple economic bias can affect spread, butterfly and all the other trade types simply because their constituent trades react in different proportions to the overall level of rates.

There are generally four (or five) macro sections of the interest rate curve:

Each of these curve sections usually has its own response mechanism to the overall level of rates. We highlight below the reasoning behind most of the typical reactions.

Medium tenor, containing the most liquid bond futures, is usually a fairly standard, volatile section. These futures contracts allow all market participants to speculate and trade in the interest rate markets and garners a lot of interest, and in turn this gives rise to a lot of supply and demand fluctuation for many economic reasons.

Longer tenor is usually more stable; small moves equate to reasonable percentage gains in bond prices which helps keep supply and demand in balance, the institutions that tend to trade this section have longer time horizons which helps reduce market panic or bubbles forming (not that it is avoided altogether), and finally events that trigger large moves in this section usually have to be significant to be considered impactful on such long dated trades.

Shorter tenors are dependent upon on the economic indicators and sentiment. These shorter sections can have periods of depressed volatility under conditions of economic certainty and periods of extreme volatility during uncertain times or after unpredictable events. Some historical analysis of various financial crises or global events will highlight this effect.

Trade combinations should always be considered against the backdrop of how various macro economic conditions are likely to impact them. We demonstrate detailed analysis in section 23.1.

16.2.3 Hedging considerations

A market-maker faced with the prospect of hedging a benchmark trade combination has always the same considerations as with any potential trade; **cost, effectiveness,** and **liquidity** of the hedge[3]. It would be reasonable to think that being a benchmark trade, the liquidity would be good, the cost minimal and the effectiveness would be complete because a benchmark trade hedged with the same benchmark trade is ideal. In some cases this is fully accurate. For example 2s5s and 10s30s are such common benchmark trade combinations, in any currency, that their ideal hedge is easily performed in the interbank market for minimal cost.

However, there exist particular combinations of trades that are not benchmark in the sense of the interbank market, for example 4s6s9s butterfly or 8s35s spread. These are benchmark trade combinations of what might be called off-the-run or non-standard tenors. It is more difficult to execute hedges for these trades in the interbank market and often creates a need to compromise between cost, liquidity and effectiveness.

---

[3]chapter 18 explores market-making considerations in more detail

Example 16.2.
A market-maker has executed an 8s35s spread trade with a price-taker and has the following considerations for his hedge:

(i) **Cost:** *he stands greater chance of executing more liquid interbank trades such as 8s10s, 10s30s and 30s35s in sequence at greater expense than he does of executing 8y35y in one trade for a lesser cost.*

(ii) **Liquidity:** *he can attempt to execute the illiquid 8s35s trade but will have to be patient and run the risk the trade is not executed in the necessary timeframe.*

(iii) **Effectiveness:** *he can choose to execute a single liquid trade such as 10s30s spread in a calculated amount leaving residual risk remaining in his portfolio, but this is likely the cheapest to execute.*

All of the above are valid considerations. In this instance the market-maker makes the decision that time is of the essence and he cannot afford to wait so he immediately executes a 10s30s spread trade as a proxy hedge leaving some residual risk. He decides to try to work the 8s10s and 30s35s spread trades at slightly favourable levels to mitigate the increased cost. This of course incurs risk but judged against other likely activity in his swap portfolio he deems this to be the most sensible option.

16.3   Trader risk models

16.3.1   Risk representation

Before going on to combine all risk management techniques to manage delta risk we introduce the final one that will be discussed; individual trader risk models. Psychology plays a huge part in trading and what is very helpful is when risk is perceived by a trader in a way that helps them visualise their actions in a manner that is permitted by the interbank market. This is more specific advice for market-makers managing large portfolios but understanding market-makers' processes can be enlightening and helpful for price-takers.

Trader risk models use Jacobian transformations to present risk in a form that is recognisable by individual traders, and is best demonstrated by example showing multiple options, none of which is *correct* per se but depends on personal preference.

Example 16.3.
A trader has the following risk strip:

$$\mathbf{S_A} = \begin{matrix}(2Y)\\(5Y)\\(10Y)\end{matrix}\begin{bmatrix}-65\\100\\-15\end{bmatrix}.$$

He may be comfortable viewing his risk as above in each individual swap tenor or he might prefer to view his risk with swaps relative to each another using benchmark trade combinations:

$$\mathbf{S_{A1}^*} = \begin{matrix}(2Y)\\(2s5s)\\(5s10s)\end{matrix}\begin{bmatrix}20\\85\\-15\end{bmatrix}, \quad \mathbf{S_{A2}^*} = \begin{matrix}(2Y)\\(2s5s10s)\\(10Y)\end{matrix}\begin{bmatrix}-15\\50\\35\end{bmatrix}, \quad \mathbf{S_{A3}^*} = \begin{matrix}(2s5s)\\(5s10s)\\(10Y)\end{matrix}\begin{bmatrix}65\\-35\\20\end{bmatrix}.$$

All of the trader models, $\mathbf{S_{A1}^*}, \mathbf{S_{A2}^*}, \mathbf{S_{A3}^*}$, represent the same risk as $\mathbf{S_A}$ in example 16.3 but they show it in relatively different ways. The calculation is shown later but here it is the concept that is of importance. Hopefully the numbers become self evident after a little consideration. Personally I don't recommend using more than one customised trader model, unlike above, because viewing what amounts to the same risk position in too many different ways will lead to confusion. It is best, in my opinion, to stick with a single trader model that is personally enlightening for any particular reason. As a guide as to who might adopt the above different models a short end trader who focuses on the outright market of short dated rates might find $\mathbf{S}^*_{\mathbf{A1}}$ the most useful because each tenor becomes relative to 2Y. A medium tenor trader might adopt $\mathbf{S}^*_{\mathbf{A2}}$ because he monitors short and medium tenors and visualising 5Y relative to 2Y and 10Y is quite sensible for this approach. A long tenor trader might adopt $\mathbf{S}^*_{\mathbf{A3}}$.

Constructing trader model risk representations is a task not dissimilar to that of using Jacobian transformations between risk models outlined in chapter 10. The only difference, perhaps, is that the instruments of the trader model are chosen by personal preference as opposed to being somewhat implicit. We will discuss some of these choices in the next section but beforehand we give an example to illuminate the concept.

Example 16.4.
A trader has the following par model risk strip and chooses to represent it with his own model:

$$
\mathbf{S}_{\mathrm{par}} = \begin{array}{c}(2Y)\\(3Y)\\(4Y)\\(5Y)\\(7Y)\\(10Y)\end{array}\begin{bmatrix}-80\\90\\-45\\20\\-40\\50\end{bmatrix}, \quad \mathbf{S}^*_{\mathrm{mod}} = \begin{array}{c}(2Y)\\(2s3s4s)\\(3s4s5s)\\(2s5s10s)\\(5s7s10s)\\(10Y)\end{array}\begin{bmatrix}?\\?\\?\\?\\?\\?\end{bmatrix}.
$$

To obtain the required risk he first has to construct the Jacobian, $\mathbf{J}_{\mathrm{mod}\to\mathrm{par}}$ (shown below).

$$
\mathbf{J}_{\mathrm{mod}\to\mathrm{par}} = \begin{array}{c}(2Y)\\(3Y)\\(4Y)\\(5Y)\\(7Y)\\(10Y)\end{array}\begin{bmatrix}1 & -1 & 0 & -1 & 0 & 0\\0 & 2 & -1 & 0 & 0 & 0\\0 & -1 & 2 & 0 & 0 & 0\\0 & 0 & -1 & 2 & -1 & 0\\0 & 0 & 0 & 0 & 2 & 0\\0 & 0 & 0 & -1 & -1 & 1\end{bmatrix},
$$

Then, with the assumption of a lossless transformation, the inverse is equivalent to the reciprocal transformation. This example is in fact lossless but that might not be the case in general. Not-lossless transformations can be useful but, as previously explained, they can introduce some unreliability.

$$
\mathbf{J}_{\mathrm{par}\to\mathrm{mod}} := \mathbf{J}^{-1}_{\mathrm{mod}\to\mathrm{par}} = \begin{bmatrix}1 & \frac{5}{6} & \frac{2}{3} & \frac{1}{2} & \frac{1}{4} & 0\\0 & \frac{2}{3} & \frac{1}{3} & 0 & 0 & 0\\0 & \frac{1}{3} & \frac{2}{3} & 0 & 0 & 0\\0 & \frac{1}{6} & \frac{1}{3} & \frac{1}{2} & \frac{1}{4} & 0\\0 & 0 & 0 & 0 & \frac{1}{2} & 0\\0 & \frac{1}{6} & \frac{1}{3} & \frac{1}{2} & \frac{3}{4} & 1\end{bmatrix}.
$$

Finally the risk strip is calculated using the traditional matrix multiplication:

$$\mathbf{S}^*_{\text{mod}} = \mathbf{J}_{\text{par}\rightarrow\text{mod}}\mathbf{S}_{\text{par}} = \begin{matrix} (2Y) \\ (2s3s4s) \\ (3s4s5s) \\ (2s5s10s) \\ (5s7s10s) \\ (10Y) \end{matrix} \begin{bmatrix} -35 \\ 45 \\ 0 \\ 0 \\ -20 \\ 30 \end{bmatrix}.$$

It becomes apparent that even though the trader has different risk in each of the six par tenor instruments when perceived under his own model he only has risk to four benchmark trade types, two outright trades in 2Y and 10Y and two butterfly trades; 2s3s4s and 5s7s10s.

When constructing trader risk models in this way it is important to recognise that the Jacobian matrices are square, that is the number of instruments in each model are the same. Also, for each instrument in the underlying model there must be at least one instrument in the trader model that incorporates it. In mathematical terminology the columns of the Jacobian matrix must be **independent** so that the matrix has **full rank**. As a somewhat useful means of protection, if the constructed Jacobian does not satisfy these rules it won't have an inverse so won't be capable of producing any (erroneous) results[4]. To conclude this section we give an example of two common problems of poorly constructed trader models and Jacobian matrices to illustrate these points.

Example 16.5.
The following model does not work because the third column is not independent, it is the result of the sum of the first and second columns. Intuitively this trader model cannot work because every instrument is a spread trade which leaves no possible way of representing outright risk in any single par instrument.

$$\mathbf{S}_{\text{par}} = \begin{matrix} (2Y) \\ (5Y) \\ (10Y) \end{matrix}, \quad \mathbf{S}^*_{\text{mod}} = \begin{matrix} (2s5s) \\ (5s10s) \\ (2s10s) \end{matrix}, \quad \mathbf{J}_{\text{mod}\rightarrow\text{par}} = \begin{bmatrix} -1 & 0 & -1 \\ 1 & -1 & 0 \\ 0 & 1 & 1 \end{bmatrix}.$$

Alternatively the following model does not work because the 2Y instrument has been neglected and the trader model has no way of representing 2Y risk in any form, the third column is again the sum of the first and second.

$$\mathbf{S}_{\text{par}} = \begin{matrix} (2Y) \\ (5Y) \\ (10Y) \end{matrix}, \quad \mathbf{S}^*_{\text{mod}} = \begin{matrix} (5Y) \\ (5s10s) \\ (10Y) \end{matrix}, \quad \mathbf{J}_{\text{mod}\rightarrow\text{par}} = \begin{bmatrix} 0 & 0 & 0 \\ 1 & -1 & 0 \\ 0 & 1 & 1 \end{bmatrix}.$$

These examples included here might seem obvious but when attempting to construct trader models from over a hundred underlying instruments, which is possible and practical, this basic understanding helps to alleviate a lot of frustration when the resultant matrix is singular and doesn't invert!

Increased usefulness

The above discussion and examples have described trader models from the point of view of being composed of benchmark trade combinations using instruments that are **exclusively available**

---

[4]advanced techniques can utilise the pseudoinverse but this is not recommended for those not already very familiar with the process

in the underlying risk model. But this is not strictly necessary. In fact, it is often more useful to introduce new instruments into the trader model, relative to the underlying instruments and incorporate those instead into the benchmark trade combinations. Example 16.6 shows the typical use of this technique. It can be extended to incorporate any kind of new instrument, such as a matched-maturity swap.

We do give the warning, however, that it is often better to introduce new instruments that align with the underlying model, in a lossless sense, since this minimises any introduced unreliability. The odd misaligned instrument here and there, though, shouldn't present much concern and can still be practical. On the other hand, a whole host of new, misaligned instruments is, in my experience, unreliable, unstable and not at all useful. As an anecdotal example I once developed a model with many matched-maturity swap instruments which were misaligned with respect to the benchmark par instruments, and it suffered from unreliability due to numerical precision errors of the inverse.

Example 16.6.
A trader has the following risk model, A, and chooses to represent it with his own model, which contains some new instruments not contained in the underlying model, A:

$$\mathbf{S_A} = \begin{matrix} (1Y) \\ (1Y1Y) \\ (2Y1Y) \\ (5Y) \\ (10Y) \end{matrix} \begin{bmatrix} -96 \\ -91 \\ -25 \\ 100 \\ 90 \end{bmatrix}, \quad \mathbf{S^*_{mod}} = \begin{matrix} (2Y) \\ (1s2s3s) \\ (2s3s5s) \\ (2s5s10s) \\ (10Y) \end{matrix} \begin{bmatrix} ? \\ ? \\ ? \\ ? \\ ? \end{bmatrix}.$$

In this case the first step is to express the new instruments in terms of the underlying risk model, A: [5]

$$\begin{matrix} (0Y1Y) \\ (1Y1Y) \\ (2Y1Y) \end{matrix} \begin{matrix} (2Y) & (3Y) \\ \begin{bmatrix} 0.513 & 0.346 \\ 0.487 & 0.329 \\ 0 & 0.325 \end{bmatrix} \end{matrix}$$

Then apply the same process as before substituting the values of the new instruments:

$$\mathbf{J_{mod \to A}} = \begin{matrix} (1Y) \\ (1Y1Y) \\ (2Y1Y) \\ (5Y) \\ (10Y) \end{matrix} \begin{matrix} (2Y) & (1s2s3s) & (2s3s5s) & (2s5s10s) & (10Y) \\ \begin{bmatrix} 0.513 & -0.320 & 0.179 & -0.513 & 0 \\ 0.487 & 0.645 & 0.171 & -0.487 & 0 \\ 0 & -0.325 & 0.650 & 0 & 0 \\ 0 & 0 & -1 & 2 & 0 \\ 0 & 0 & 0 & -1 & 1 \end{bmatrix} \end{matrix},$$

The results of risk (rounded) are calculated as before with the customary inversion and matrix multiplication, and are shown below.

$$\mathbf{S^*_{mod}} = \begin{matrix} (2Y) \\ (1s2s3s) \\ (2s3s5s) \\ (2s5s10s) \\ (10Y) \end{matrix} \begin{bmatrix} -143 \\ 0 \\ -38 \\ 31 \\ 121 \end{bmatrix}.$$

---

[5]these figures are calculated in example 10.1

This technique works, in particular, when expressing 1Y, 18M, 2Y, 30M and 3Y IRSs in terms of IMM instruments, which form a very common base of curveset constructions. In example 16.6 the instruments 1Y, 1Y1Y and 2Y1Y were broadly representative of the 'whites', 'reds' and 'greens' future contracts. Hopefully the reader can draw a parallel with this example and envisage how one would go about using the same technique for other tenor swaps, with respect to IMM instruments, instead of the chosen fwds used here. Expressly, the solution would be to represent 2Y and 3Y (or other tenors) in terms of the risk from those IMM instruments and then ensure that the trader model has enough information to link all of the instruments, i.e. by using spreads, butterflies or otherwise. Example 16.7 shows one way this can be done (of course it is subjective and there are other ways).

Example 16.7.
A typical risk model, B, containing the cash rate and first 8 IMM instruments is shown. A second, customised trader model is given illustrating the instrument mapping, whose transformation (rounded to 2 d.p.) is shown $(\mathbf{J} = \mathbf{J}_{\mathrm{mod}\to\mathrm{B}})$.

$$
\mathbf{S_B} = \begin{matrix}(3M)\\(1f)\\(2f)\\(3f)\\(4f)\\(5f)\\(6f)\\(7f)\\(8f)\end{matrix}\begin{bmatrix}-25\\15\\5\\10\\-10\\-20\\-20\\-5\\10\end{bmatrix}, \mathbf{S^*_{mod}} = \begin{matrix}(3M/1f)\\(1f)\\(1f2f3f)\\(1Y)\\(2f4f6f)\\(2Y)\\(4f6f8f)\\(4f5f6f)\\(6f7f8f)\end{matrix}\begin{bmatrix}28\\-22\\-7\\46\\-15\\-64\\-16\\-6\\2\end{bmatrix}, \mathbf{J} = \begin{bmatrix}-1 & 0 & 0 & 0.25 & 0 & 0.13 & 0 & 0 & 0\\1 & 1 & -1 & 0.13 & 0 & 0.06 & 0 & 0 & 0\\0 & 0 & 2 & 0.25 & -1 & 0.13 & 0 & 0 & 0\\0 & 0 & -1 & 0.25 & 0 & 0.13 & 0 & 0 & 0\\0 & 0 & 0 & 0.13 & 2 & 0.13 & -1 & -1 & 0\\0 & 0 & 0 & 0 & 0 & 0.13 & 0 & 2 & 0\\0 & 0 & 0 & 0 & -1 & 0.13 & 2 & -1 & -1\\0 & 0 & 0 & 0 & 0 & 0.13 & 0 & 0 & 2\\0 & 0 & 0 & 0 & 0 & 0.06 & -1 & 0 & -1\end{bmatrix}.
$$

16.3.2   PnL representation

When considering risk management, monitoring PnL is clearly of utmost importance. Understanding where one might be losing money is usually the first step toward preventing it happening repeatedly, and allowing profits to grow. It might seem obvious but understanding why and where one is losing money is actually a very common problem, which is often left undiagnosed. Utilising the right tools can considerably reduce the time it takes to navigate a portfolio, prevent ignorance and provide full diagnostics.

Chapter 10 outlined how to obtain market movements using Jacobian transformations and to provide consistent PnL estimates. To provide a practical example we continue from the one of the examples above.

Example 16.8.
The trader from example 16.4 calculates daily market movements for his par instruments and from that calculates a PnL estimate, shown in the table below.

$$
\begin{array}{c} \\ (2Y)\\(3Y)\\(4Y)\\(5Y)\\(7Y)\\(10Y)\end{array}
\begin{array}{c}\mathbf{S_{par}}\\ \begin{bmatrix}-80\\90\\-45\\20\\-40\\50\end{bmatrix}\end{array}
\begin{array}{c}\mathbf{\Delta r_{par}}\\ \begin{bmatrix}+1.1\\+1.4\\+1.5\\+1.6\\+0.6\\+0.2\end{bmatrix}\end{array}
\begin{array}{c}\mathbf{PnL}\\ \begin{bmatrix}-88\\126\\-68\\32\\-24\\10\end{bmatrix}\end{array}
$$

$$\quad -5 \qquad\qquad -12$$

He uses the transformation $\mathbf{\Delta r^*_{mod}} = \mathbf{J^T_{mod\to par}}\mathbf{\Delta r_{par}}$ *to display the market movements for his trader model and estimate an equivalent PnL, also shown in the table.*

$$
\begin{array}{c}
& \mathbf{S^*_{mod}} \quad \mathbf{\Delta r^*_{mod}} \quad \mathbf{PnL} \\
\begin{array}{r}
(2Y) \\
(2s3s4s) \\
(3s4s5s) \\
(2s5s10s) \\
(5s7s10s) \\
(10Y)
\end{array}
\begin{bmatrix}
-35 \\
45 \\
0 \\
0 \\
-20 \\
30
\end{bmatrix}
\begin{bmatrix}
+1.1 \\
+0.2 \\
0 \\
+1.9 \\
-0.6 \\
+0.2
\end{bmatrix}
\begin{bmatrix}
-39 \\
9 \\
0 \\
0 \\
12 \\
6
\end{bmatrix} \\
\hline
\mathbf{-12}
\end{array}
$$

The model representation clearly indicates to the trader that a dominant part of the loss is due to the movement of 2Y rates and particularly given 10Y rates have not moved by a similar amount. This can also be ascertained from the par risk model but it is more difficult to make that assessment in that model.

16.4 Market risk management

Although this section often explicitly references only delta risk management, the associated principles are also directly applicable to basis risks *and* for considering delta and basis risks collectively. That is, all of the principles discussed here are used to manage market risks to varying degrees. Extensions of any of the techniques simply involve building in more instruments to the risk models.

16.4.1 Prioritisation

The previous section explained how to build individual trader models. It made some references alluding to certain design choices. Here we expand a little on what makes good choices. The first necessary process when a risk manager begins to analyse his risk is that of prioritisation. Prioritisation means establishing which risks are the more pertinent to hedge, which is a subjective assessment.

To prioritise optimally one must use the collection of tools that have been presented already; multiple risk models including trader specific models, CoVaR techniques, principle component analysis, and perception and instinct. One might have heard the terms 'macro' and 'micro' before with respect to risk and have an idea what they refer to. This is a good start being a classification into two separate groups. Personally, I find that it is appropriate to make more of a distinction and utilise more subgroups. The example that follows is how to employ this technique, albeit with fewer instruments than in real practical trading but hopefully it is obvious how one might expand the premise.

Example 16.9.
A trader prioritises the par tenor instruments between 1Y and 10Y into groups benchmarked by perceived liquidity, volatility and tendency to drive the market. Table 16.1 outlines his view with more significant instruments occupying leftmost columns, and also details the new instruments he adopts in his trader model.

He arranges his summary trading view to display all relevant information aesthetically, see figure 16.2. He includes his risk position from his trader model as well as par and fwd model. He explains his PnL from his trader model only, because it neatly and efficiently groups risk into his categories; macro, sub-macro, micro and sub-micro.

Underlying	Macro	Sub-macro	Micro	Sub-micro
1Y			1s2s	
2Y	2Y			
3Y			2s3s4s	
4Y			3s4s5s	
5Y		2s5s10s		
6Y				5s6s7s
7Y			5s7s10s	
8Y				7s8s9s
9Y				8s9s10s
10Y	10Y			

Table 16.1: Prioritising tenor IRS

	S_{par}		S^*_{fwd}		S^*_{mod}	Δr^*_{mod}	PnL
1Y	-11	1Y	20	2Y	41	+1.3	54
2Y	87	1Y1Y	30	10Y	6	+1.4	8
3Y	36	2Y1Y	-13	2s5s10s	30	+0.7	21
4Y	-266	3Y1Y	-24	1s2s	11	+0.1	1
5Y	189	4Y1Y	40	2s3s4s	-65	-0.1	6
6Y	-56	5Y1Y	3	3s4s5s	-165	-0.2	33
7Y	42	6Y1Y	12	5s7s10s	64	+0.1	6
8Y	216	7Y1Y	6	5s6s7s	-28	+0.5	-14
9Y	-89	8Y1Y	-19	7s8s9s	114	+0.6	69
10Y	-101	9Y1Y	-9	8s9s10s	13	-0.7	-9
TOT	47	TOT	47	TOT			175

Figure 16.2: The trader's summary display.

The example begins to demonstrate how incorporating many techniques and tools makes understanding positions more clear. In the example each model shows the same risk but from slightly different perspectives, often creating synergies between the views. The fwd risk shows the 4Y1Y bucket to be the largest independent risk, supported by the par 4s5s position, and supported by the trader model's 3s4s5s bucket.

In terms of PnL, the distribution is fairly even across all categories; macro, sub-macro, etc.. Of particular note might be the 7s8s9s bucket where the market move is quite large relative to other days and has generated about 40% of the day's PnL, even though it is classed as a sub-micro position. A trader might recognise this as a position worth closing and recognising the profit if liquidity permits. Other contributors to PnL are fairly small or appropriately proportional. The portfolio is also making a profit and there are no positions showing disproportionate losses and therefore no need to question any stop losses on any individual positions.

16.4.2   Incorporating VaR

VaR can be incorporated into risk management practice in different ways. This guide uses the principles already established for CoVaR and the technique of analysing VaR minimising trades.

The VaR metric

The most basic way to incorporate VaR is to calculate the singular VaR multiplier and display the common c.i.s. Immediately a trader then knows the relative size of his positions in expected monetary value.

Example 16.10.
The trader obtains the covariance matrix, $\mathbf{Q}(\mathbf{\Delta r_{par}})$, in a similar manner to equation 14.1 but for instruments 1Y, 2Y, .., 10Y:

$$
\mathbf{Q}(\mathbf{\Delta r_{par}}) =
\begin{array}{c}
\\
(1Y) \\
(2Y) \\
\vdots \\
(9Y) \\
(10Y)
\end{array}
\begin{array}{c}
(1Y)\ (2Y)\ \cdots\ (9Y)\ (10Y) \\
\begin{bmatrix}
3.3 & 4.7 & \ldots & 7.4 & 7.2 \\
4.7 & 7.2 & & 11.5 & 11.2 \\
\vdots & \vdots & \ddots & & \vdots \\
7.4 & 11.5 & & 20.5 & 19.9 \\
7.2 & 11.2 & \ldots & 19.9 & 19.5
\end{bmatrix}
\end{array}.
$$

He calculates his VaR multiplier, $c = \sqrt{\mathbf{S_{par}^{T} Q_{par} S_{par}}}$, and the associated PnL c.i.s:

$c =$	259
$VaR_{5\%}$	425
$VaR_{1\%}$	602

By regularly observing the VaR multiplier one will quickly learn to recognise risk increasing and decreasing trades and levels of risk that one is comfortable running. It is very common for traders to run larger risk whilst the market is open, i.e. intraday, and close the day with smaller VaR multipliers because from one trading period to the next, where the market is closed, there is no opportunity to stop out and so this poses what is called a gap risk.

Simply observing the VaR multiplier might be enough for some traders with a large turnover in their portfolio and plenty of experience. Even so making more detailed analysis available is useful at times and is the topic of next discussion.

VaR minimisation

VaR can also be incorporated into risk management by utilising VaR minimisation trades provided by CoVaR techniques. By using these in conjunction with individual trader models the results can be much more useful than using it simply with par or fwd based risk models. Often if a trader has a dominant outright position then analysing a VaR minimising trade will show broadly the same thing for each and every par instrument.

Example 16.11.
From above the trader knows his total delta risk is 47(k) pv01. He also observes from figure 16.2 that the risk is mainly concentrated at the short end, say 2Y. He expects any par minimising trades to show between -25(k) and -50(k) of risk dependent upon the volatility of the instrument relative to 2Y, which is an offset for his overall delta position. Using CoVaR techniques from chapter 14 the trader calculates the single instrument VaR minimising trades for his par risk model, with the associated reductions in VaR:

	S_{par}	S_{par}^{trade}	Δc	$\frac{|\Delta c|}{c}$
1Y	-11	-96	-68	26%
2Y	87	-61	-57	22%
3Y	36	-41	-48	19%
4Y	-266	-34	-40	16%
5Y	189	-38	-60	23%
6Y	-56	-32	-45	18%
7Y	42	-33	-53	20%
8Y	216	-33	-47	18%
9Y	-89	-29	-37	14%
10Y	-101	-30	-36	14%

The results do not really highlight much to the trader. His intuition was correct, although it is interesting to observe he can achieve slightly better VaR minimisation trading either 1Y, 2Y, 5Y and 7Y which can reduce VaR by 20% or more.

Trading a single IRS really only contributes to VaR in one particular way which is to offset the directionality of the portfolio. This is specific to whether the risk of the portfolio favours interest rates rising or falling. Utilising CoVaR minimisation techniques with a trader's individual risk model can be more interesting. With a well designed model it will highlight more ways the risk can be reduced and some positions will be independent of the directionality of the portfolio, providing scope for more information.

Example 16.12.
The trader instead calculates the single instrument VaR minimising trades for his individual model risk:

	S_{mod}^*	S_{mod}^{*trade}	Δc	$\frac{|\Delta c|}{c}$
2Y	41	-61	-57	22%
10Y	6	-30	-36	14%
2s5s10s	30	-73	-65	25%
1s2s	11	-108	-26	10%
2s3s4s	-65	-59	-11	4%
3s4s5s	-165	98	-25	10%
5s7s10s	64	-69	-29	11%
5s6s7s	-28	78	-20	8%
7s8s9s	114	-10	-0	0%
8s9s10s	13	65	-7	3%

These results are more open to interpretation. The macro and sub-macro positions appear to dominate the VaR. It becomes apparent from the suggested minimising trade that 2s5s10s is a directional trade; paying it is correlated to paying an outright trade. The sub-micro positions have minimal impact on VaR and yet earlier it was apparent that 7s8s9s generated a good deal of PnL. This unusually large move but minimal apparent contribution to VaR further suggests taking some profit in this specific instrument. Additionally 3s4s5s and 5s7s10s appear to be reasonably independent trades whose risk could be reduced to lower VaR, without necessarily having an impact on the suggested minimising trade of any of the other instruments.

This process becomes dynamic and reactionary: to keep risk in a controlled state as new trades are added to the portfolio. Do not forget that these are single instrument minimising trades so that if one minimising trade is executed then the portfolio would have to be reassessed for the next set of minimising trades. That said, it is often reasonably practical to attempt a number of trades simultaneously. A useful tip to experiment with is to execute smaller proportions than the suggested single instrument minimising trades when attempting to trade multiple instruments. This, more often than not, ensures the VaR will at least decrease and sometimes to a large extent. Once the trades are booked the portfolio and subsequent VaR minimising trades can be reassessed and further strategies assessed.

Example 16.13.
The trader seeks to reduce his VaR. Using the above as a guide he considers executing three trades; receive 30(k) 2Y, receive 35(k) 2s5s10s and receive 35(k) 5s7s10s, which are roughly 50% of each of the suggested single instrument VaR minimising trades. Examining the risk as if he had executed these three trades the subsequent VaR minimising trades and new VaR multiplier are:

	$\mathbf{S}^*_{\mathbf{mod}}$	$\mathbf{S}^{*\mathbf{trade}}_{\mathbf{mod}}$	Δc	$\frac{|\Delta c|}{c}$
2Y	11	-1	0	0%
10Y	6	5	-1	1%
2s5s10s	-5	-10	-2	1%
1s2s	11	20	-1	1%
2s3s4s	-65	-16	-1	1%
3s4s5s	-165	120	-67	38%
5s7s10s	29	2	0	0%
5s6s7s	-28	63	-20	11%
7s8s9s	114	-46	-6	3%
8s9s10s	13	56	-8	5%

$c =$	175
$VaR_{5\%}$	287
$VaR_{1\%}$	406

The three trades under consideration would reduce the trader's VaR by 33%, a little more than any singular instrument hedge would have. The residual risk is clearly dominated by 3s4s5s where he could potentially reduce his VaR by a further 38%. The trader acknowledges this as a good strategy for further VaR reduction.

Covariance matrix for individual trader models

When calculating VaR minimising trades with CoVaR techniques the covariance matrix is an important element in the process. To calculate VaR for the trader's individual model a covariance matrix needs to be established for the market movements of those specific instruments. Chapter 10 outlines how to do this and section 10.6 lists the specific transformation formulae needed.

The VaR multiplier, like PnL, is an invariant quantity of the portfolio. That means the VaR should not alter no matter how one chooses to express the risk of any portfolio. This is mathematically consistent since,

$$c = \sqrt{\mathbf{S}^{\mathbf{T}}_{\mathbf{par}} \mathbf{Q}_{\mathbf{par}} \mathbf{S}_{\mathbf{par}}} = \sqrt{\mathbf{S}^{*\mathbf{T}}_{\mathbf{mod}} \mathbf{Q}^*_{\mathbf{mod}} \mathbf{S}^*_{\mathbf{mod}}} \, .$$

16.4.3 Simplified portfolio representation

In the context of our above example we have risk to each of the ten IRS tenors, 1Y through to 10Y. What if we want to express this risk to only the three most traded benchmark instruments, to give a kind of broad overview of the portfolio, and say those were chosen to be 2Y, 5Y and 10Y? Or more generally, in what way can we express the risk of a portfolio in much fewer instruments as a form of dimension reduction?

CoVaR minimisation offers an approach, and it also has some nice properties. Firstly, no matter how one were to derive the numbers, either analytically or numerically (from the same covariance matrix), there is only one unique solution to the question: what are the quantities of risk to trade in 2Y, 5Y and 10Y to minimise the VaR of the portfolio? Secondly the quality of the reduction can be assessed through the quantity of residual VaR that remains after the 2Y, 5Y and 10Y has been hypothetically traded to minimise VaR. Section 23.4.2, shows that the same results can be obtained by regressing the portfolio's risks against the smaller subset of instruments. An equivalent analysis would be to consider the variance of the residual under the multivariate least squares regression model.

If we perform all of the necessary calculations for multiple instrument VaR minimisation shown in chapter 14 for our par risk model and covariance matrix we obtain the following:

$$\hat{\mathbf{S}}^{\mathbf{trade}} = \begin{matrix} (2Y) \\ (5Y) \\ (10Y) \end{matrix} \begin{bmatrix} -56 \\ -98 \\ 94 \end{bmatrix} .$$

Since this is in fact the *trade* that will minimise risk, the *current* simplified portfolio risk itself can be represented as the opposite of this, so we can write:

$$\mathbf{S}_{\mathbf{simple}} := \begin{matrix} (2Y) \\ (5Y) \\ (10Y) \end{matrix} \begin{bmatrix} 56 \\ 98 \\ -94 \end{bmatrix} .$$

In our case this is *not* a particularly good representation of the portfolio because the resultant VaR shows that these hedges would only reduce VaR by about 36%. This supports the previous inference that many of the portfolio's risks are micro related, and cannot be captured by such a broad spectrum dimension reduction or simplification. Thus we should conclude that for this portfolio the simplified portfolio representation is of limited use. Occasionally, though, it can be very useful showing a simple way to reduce 80-100% VaR.

16.5   Consolidating everything

There is a distinct difference between good and bad risk management. A bad risk manager might still make a lot of money trading; he could be lucky or simply be well versed at predicting market movements and having enough risk to profit. On the whole though, bad risk managers do not make successful traders. The simple explanation for this is that when a portfolio loses money, and there will always be times when a portfolio will lose some money, a bad risk manager will not understand why and will not be able to prevent further losses. Stopping losses is one of the key components to long term success and understanding losses is really the only step that needs to take place before actually stopping them.

All of the techniques introduced and explained have been to aid a trader in their understanding of how their portfolio's PnL responds to movements in the market. We can summarise the list of tools that help a trader with this goal;

 (i) numeric risks against well designed, reliable risk models,

 (ii) visualising risk in both par and fwd instrument based models,

 (iii) the concept of VaR as a single metric representing the overall risk of a portfolio,

 (iv) PCA to highlight risks associated with typical market movements,

 (v) the use of individual trader risk models to express risk relative to benchmark trade combinations,

(vi) the use of PnL estimates to detail which risk positions in each risk model contribute to the PnL,

(vii) the concept of single instrument VaR minimising trades to make trading efficient,

(viii) the concept of multiple instrument VaR minimising trades used to create a simplified representation of the portfolio.

The knowledge and use of all of the above makes it easy for a trader to understand every facet of his portfolio with respect to market risks. Also it allows a trader to recognise where he might be losing money and be in a position to act. Not only that but a trader can also be proactive, he will instinctively be aware how unexpected market movements will affect the value of his portfolio and can execute hedge trades in the early stages of significant market sentiment shifts.

Looking back, figure 9.10 shows a practical view of a portfolio's market risks, shown against a single par risk model. It also shows how columns can be expanded to give greater detail, examining open risk, new risk, risk change due to gamma, the previous closing risk and the risk bleed. If we bring all of the risk management tools discussed previously together, then we can finally present a trading display, see figure 16.4.

At this point in the book each item visible has been methodically developed, so its calculation and purpose should now be clear. Hopefully one also recognises the difficulty in capturing a complete trading display, with multiple instruments and columns, on a single page of a book. Spreadsheets are ideal in this sense and provide useful ways of collapsing and expanding columns allowing more detail to be displayed or hidden on request. It is left to the reader to imagine how one would incorporate all of the below tools and build a spreadsheet to suit their own preferences. In practice, of course, there are many more instruments, and multiple currencies, that one will want to include to provide the level of detail needed to actively manage the market risks of a fully fledged IRD portfolio.

Anecdotally, I will highlight that these tools have not been developed in this book for the sake of academic rigour. Rather, I constructed my risk framework at Barclays and Nordea to include all of these elements and I referred to them all constantly in my capacity as a market-maker. Figure 16.4 is a genuine representation of part of my trading dashboard (reduced for number of instruments for pedagogical purposes).

Risk and PnL Estimate

	S_{par}		S^*_{fwd}		S^*_{mod}	Δr^*_{mod}	PnL
1Y	-11	1Y	20	2Y	41	+1.3	54
2Y	87	1Y1Y	30	10Y	6	+1.4	8
3Y	36	2Y1Y	-13	2s5s10s	30	+0.7	21
4Y	-266	3Y1Y	-24	1s2s	11	+0.1	1
5Y	189	4Y1Y	40	2s3s4s	-65	-0.1	6
6Y	-56	5Y1Y	3	3s4s5s	-165	-0.2	33
7Y	42	6Y1Y	12	5s7s10s	64	+0.1	6
8Y	216	7Y1Y	6	5s6s7s	-28	+0.5	-14
9Y	-89	8Y1Y	-19	7s8s9s	114	+0.6	69
10Y	-101	9Y1Y	-9	8s9s10s	13	-0.7	-9
Risk	**47**	Risk	**47**	PnL			**175**

VaR and PCA

	S^*_{mod}	S^{*trade}_{mod}	Δc	$\frac{\|\Delta c\|}{c}$
2Y	41	-61	-57	22%
10Y	6	-30	-36	14%
2s5s10s	30	-73	-65	25%
1s2s	11	-108	-26	10%
2s3s4s	-65	-59	-11	4%
3s4s5s	-165	98	-25	10%
5s7s10s	64	-69	-29	11%
5s6s7s	-28	78	-20	8%
7s8s9s	114	-10	-0	0%
8s9s10s	13	65	-7	3%

VaR	
$c =$	**259**
$VaR_{5\%}$	425
$VaR_{1\%}$	602

	$\widetilde{S_{par}}$	$\tilde{c}_i$	$\frac{\tilde{c}_i}{c}$
PC1	12	86	33%
PC2	97	49	19%
PC3	29	3	1%

Simplified Portfolio (VaR based)

Score 36%	S_{simple}
2Y	55
5Y	98
10Y	-94
Risk	**60**

Figure 16.4: An example trading display with all types of market risk management tools included.

Regulatory Capital, Leverage, and Liquidity

After the financial crisis of '07 and '08 regulation became a buzzword. In many ways it became about putting right what had been previously done wrong. Avoiding a complete financial collapse was imperative for governments, central bankers and regulators around the world. Regulation has become more stringent, and more technical. Its effect on fixed income markets is often pronounced because new regulation often forces all banking institutions to engage in the same kind of trading activity, moving markets through a supply and demand dynamic.

This chapter's overall aim is to convey the main topics of banking regulation. Regulation is an extensive subject with hundreds of pages of relevant documentation. It also evolves rapidly and this information may go out of date. Make a point of noticing this chapter was **written early in 2017**. My personal experience of this is primarily from Barclays Non-Core in 2014. Barclays Non-Core was an established entity whose sole, public purpose was to divest £110bn of RWAs. At the time, I portfolio managed their G7 linear rates part of this endeavour and sought to reduce the RWA usage from an IRD perspective. Additionally during 2016 I worked for Nordea who were beginning to consider cost of capital with regard to their IRD trading business. So the material in this chapter was relevant to those businesses. Please note that due a lack of working directly within this space within the last five years, this chapter remains the same as the previous edition and has therefore not been updated as is the case with other chapters.

To reduce the likelihood of material going out of date we focus on the following; overarching regulatory principles that are less likely to evolve significantly, and the key impact that some of this basic regulation has on IRDs. Additionally it is hoped that the reader will feel knowledgeable enough afterwards to research additional information in published Basel documents. This is important if the reader chooses to stay abreast of future developments.

In particular the topics covered here are;

- a high level summary of the Basel III Regulatory Framework, and of capital and liquidity,

- a list of the key publications detailing all of the imposed regulatory rules,

- understanding capital in terms of a typical bank's balance sheets and leverage, through examples,

- RWAs and associated capital ratios, including evolving calculation techniques,

- internal business management of RWAs and cost based performance metrics,

- capital requirements for market risk exposures,

- the leverage ratio as defined by Basel and its calculation,

- the liquidity coverage ratio (LCR) and description of high quality liquid assets (HQLAs),

- the net stable funding ratio (NSFR) and its treatment of IRDs,

- a holistic overview and collaboration of all items.

17.1   Basel Accords

The Basel Accords are a set of regulatory frameworks drawn up by the Basel Committee on Banking Supervision[1]. They are designed to be globally applicable across all jurisdictions and to allow for direct comparisons of the nature of banks' capital and liquidity strengths. These frameworks underpin the entire banking regulatory landscape across the world. This need not be so since the Basel Committee itself has no jurisdiction in all countries so their adoption by domestic regulators is voluntary. However their impressive depth and academic standing means that domestic regulators generally impose the substance of the accords. Therefore, they implicitly become mandatory for all financial institutions to adopt.

The Basel Accords focus on two major determinants on the health of an individual bank, and the wider banking community as a whole. These are **capital** and **liquidity**. To a newcomer to the finance industry, or even an experienced practitioner who might simply never have had previous guidance, the regulatory landscape can appear expansive and intricate. However, I want to address this misconception by always coming back to these two main focal points. We will also address the applicable areas of regulation for IRDs, in particular.

To begin, we form a high level overview of the complete regulatory framework. The most recent implementation are the Basel III Reforms[2].

---

[1] The Basel Committee has helpfully prepared a compilation of documents[38] that detail all aspects of their framework for regulation

[2] On their website the Basel Committee have published their own, single page summary of Basel III Reforms[39], which is well worth reviewing in context of this chapter

Capital

Regulation involving capital demands that banks hold enough capital relative to their RWAs and exposures. This defines a set of **minimum capital ratios** that all banks must demonstrate they adhere to, across the extent of their balance sheet.

Associated with the capital requirements is a structured set of rules defining how to measure and report **market risk** in stressed circumstances and how **credit counterparty risk** should be measured, in order to arrive at associated RWA values.

As an alternative, a **leverage ratio** is imposed, which is a another specific, but different, calculation on banks' market risk positions, with the aim of preventing excessive risk taking and leverage through exposures.

Liquidity

Liquidity is the ability of a bank to survive short term stress and be able to make its imminent short term commitments. To measure this, Basel proposes two different metrics.

The **LCR** requires all banks to have a sufficient amount of HQLAs to withstand a 30 day stressed funding scenario.

The **NSFR** is a longer term structural measure. It considers maturity mismatches across the entire balance sheet, and is designed to encourage banks to utilise stable sources of funding.

As well as defining the concepts and calculations of the above, Basel III also documents many aspects about how information should be disclosed and supervised internally. It also proposes a set of monitoring tools. We do *not* focus on these items at all in this book.

17.2 Capital

Beyond our summary, a thorough grounding in the understanding of capital for regulatory purposes can be attained by reviewing the appropriate Basel publications, particularly [20] and [40], as well as some of the ad hoc amendments. A broader view on banking capital in a philosophic sense can be gleaned by reviewing [41], and associated publications.

17.2.1 What is capital?

Basel Accords have very clear definitions of what they class as capital. Quoting directly from the publications[40, sec. 49];

> **Tier 1 Capital (T1)** (going-concern capital): is made up of two components,
>   **Common Equity Tier 1 Capital (CET1)** and,
>   **Additional Tier 1 Capital (AT1)**.
>
> **Tier 2 Capital (T2)** (gone-concern capital).

Common Equity Tier 1 Capital (CET1) is predominantly composed of ordinary share capital (*not market capitalisation*) plus retained earnings. Certain items, subject to criteria, are permitted to the category of Additional Tier 1 Capital (AT1). We do not expand on Tier 2 Capital (T2) in this book since it simply introduces further capital ratios, the theory of which we cover for Tier 1 Capital (T1).

There are several ways banks can raise new T1. The more obvious ways are to issue new share capital, and /or reduce dividend payments (to retain more as earnings). Another common example is the issuance of AT1 bonds, designed for this specific purpose. These bonds have to be sufficiently subordinated in the debt structure and have specific caveats to be allowed within this category.

17.2.2   Why is capital important to monitor?

To examine why capital is important as a measure of a bank's resilience we consider a series of progressive examples. First look at example 17.1, below. In it Bravo Bank's retail customers have some assurances that even if $\frac{1}{3}$ of the corporates default on their loans with 100% LGD, Bravo Bank will still have enough capital to (ultimately) repay the original depositors should they demand their money back[3].

Example 17.1.
Bravo Bank has been established with $100mm of ordinary share capital. It has secured $200mm in deposits from retail customers and loaned all available cash to the corporate sector earning 5% per year marginal interest (see table 17.1).

	Balance Sheet of Bravo Bank
	$ mm
Assets	
Loans to corporate sector	300
Liabilities	
Retail deposits	-200
Share Capital and Retained Earnings	
Retained earnings	0
Ordinary share capital	100

Table 17.1: Initial balance sheet example

Banks can act as creators of broad money supply. This means that they can issue new loans without actually having the basic deposits from retail customers to back them up. Essentially they create new entries on their balance sheet, and are permitted to facilitate this creation of money supply by the domestic central bank. To do so they create an asset, which is the loan, and credit the customer's account with new funds, which forms the liability. If a customer withdraws the funds this liability is replaced by the source of funding that the bank uses to pay out the money to the customer. This process exposes the bank to leverage, and was one of the initial reasons for the financial collapse in '07 and '08, when American banks extended too much credit, secured by real estate, to the broader economy[4].

Example 17.2.
Bravo Bank extends credit to individuals for the purpose of buying houses. See table 17.2.

Example 17.2 demonstrates a bank leveraging itself. The original retail depositors (and the new providers of funding) are more precariously positioned. If more than $\frac{1}{13}$ of the loans

---

[3]assuming no further losses and the loans could be used to raise funding at 100% face value through an agreement such as a repurchase agreement (repo), or that the depositors accept waiting until the loans have matured before being repaid.

[4]this is well documented as the American subprime mortgage crisis

Balance Sheet of	Bravo Bank
	$ mm
Assets	
Loans to corporate sector	300
Retail mortgages	1,000
Liabilities	
Retail deposits	-200
Other associated funding	-1,000
Share Capital and Retained Earnings	
Retained earnings	0
Ordinary share capital	100

Table 17.2: Balance sheet example with leverage created by new loan issuance.

and mortgages default with a 100% LGD then the available Tier 1 Capital will not be enough to service the entire amount of the remaining liabilities, and the bank could collapse without further injection of capital from share issues, subordinated debt or government bailout.

Of course one would hope that a defaulted asset would not have a LGD of 100%. Particularly in the example, the mortgages are backed by real estate. The collateral type is a general consideration for any asset, made in tandem with the general factors; the probability of default (PD) along with the associated exposure at default (EAD), the LGD and the time to maturity of the asset. Combined, these factors form a measure of the riskiness of the asset itself, or of a category of similar assets. Indeed, another important factor to consider would be the systemic risk of the entire asset class to correlated default behaviour.

With riskiness in mind, regulators design a metric called **RWA**, and they factor all the items mentioned. All RWA values can be summed to give a normalised measure of assets reported across different banks' balance sheets. In the particular case of the balance sheet of example 17.2 the total RWA value might be $650mm, dependent upon the bank's specific assessment and categorisation of types of risk. As an example of likely values, the corporate sector loans are assigned a full RWA value of $300mm whereas the retail mortgages are assigned a fractional RWA value of $350mm.

Not only does monitoring capital provide insight into the absolute standing of a bank, it also provides a comparison of relative standing comparing banks. Capital ratios incorporating RWA values aid in this direct comparison.

17.2.3 Capital ratios

A key metric that the regulators then monitor is the ratio of capital to RWAs. This is an official requirement of the Basel Accords regulation. They demand banks operate specific minimum capital ratios, which are calculated as,

$$\text{Capital Ratio} = \frac{\text{Capital Type}}{\text{Risk Weighted Assets}} , \quad \text{e.g.} \quad \text{T1 Ratio} = \frac{\text{T1}}{\text{RWAs}} .$$

At the time of publication these minimum ratios are[40, sec. 50]:

4.5% for CET1 and 6.0% for T1 and 8% for T2

Additionally from 2019 banks are required to hold additional capital buffers. These have the impact of raising the CET1 ratio further.

17.2.4   Risk weighted assets (RWAs)

As a key component in the capital ratio, it is sensible to introduce RWAs in more detail. In terms of IRDs' pricing this is also the component of the ratio that is variable with respect to the trades that a bank executes with its customers. Determining RWA values is an extensive topic and, also, different asset classes such as equities, commodities, and credit have other specific rules. But we won't discuss other asset classes.

IRDs are necessarily included in the scope of products that regulators consider. In example 17.2 we showed how a bank can leverage itself by creating broad money through the creation of loans, which are not a derivative product. A bank can also create leverage by using derivative instruments. See example 17.3. Since a bank can do this, regulators need to monitor and limit total activity.

Example 17.3.
Bravo Bank expands its business by synthetically restructuring (to fixed rate) some of the loans made to corporates, through the use of IRSs. Bravo bank hedges the resultant IR market risk with other, centrally cleared IRSs. See table 17.3.

Balance Sheet of	Bravo Bank
	$ mm
Assets	
Loans to corporate sector	300
Retail mortgages	1,000
IRDs with corporate sector	3
Margin and collateral posted to CCP	2
Liabilities	
Retail deposits	-200
Other associated funding	-1,002
IRDs with CCP	-1
Share Capital and Retained Earnings	
Retained earnings	2
Ordinary share capital	100

Table 17.3: Balance sheet example with leverage created by IRSs.

The balance sheet example in table 17.3 states the immediate asset and liability values of the IRSs. This is a very poor indicator of actual RWA value because it does not account for many factors. Specifically not the credit risk of the counterparty, nor the expected future values of the derivatives, nor the sensitivity of these factors to IR market movements.

Example 17.4 gives an illustration of how the balance sheet might change in a stressed market scenario. Although the market risk is hedged so no PnL is earned on market movements overall, it shows that Bravo Bank's assets can deteriorate to become much riskier, and additionally it becomes exposed to liquidity problems because collateral must be sourced to post to the CCP. Capital ratios are reduced in this scenario, so this outcome must be captured in the method of calculating derivative RWAs.

Example 17.4.
Market interest rates fall by 200bps and the value of the IRSs changes. In this instance all IRSs with the corporate sector are uncollateralised, but become large assets. The IRSs with the CCP become large liabilities and the required collateral must be funded. See table 17.4

	$ mm
IRDs with corporate sector	25
Margin and collateral posted to CCP	24
Other associated funding	-1,024
IRDs with CCP	-23

Table 17.4: Adjusted balance sheet entries following stressed market movements.

17.2.5 Basel rules for RWA calculation

At a counterparty level, calculating an RWA value under Basel III requires determining three aspects;

$$RWA = \text{Exposure at Default (EAD)} \times \text{Risk Weight (RW)} + \text{CVA Vol Charge}.$$

EAD calculation under different methods

Historically, the EAD value was permitted to be assessed by way of three methods[40, Annex 4]; either by adopting the regulator's *standard rules* or adopting the *current exposure method*, which are both classed as non-internal model methods, or using an **internal model method** designed by a financial institution and signed off by the regulator.

Recent modifications have combined the non-internal model methods to produce the single **Standardised Approach (to CCR) (SA-CCR)**[42] to be used alongside the internal model method. Regulators now require calculation under both methods and will restrict the internal model method to return values not less than a fixed percentage of the SA-CCR.

The **SA-CCR method** ascribes a formula to EAD of;

$$EAD = \alpha \times (RC + PFE), \quad \alpha = 1.4.$$

The approach here is quite similar to that explained in chapter 5 on credit risk. For well collateralised counterparties the replacement cost (RC) is often zero, and the potential future exposure (PFE) component takes account of market risks to gauge the possible mismatches in the collateral lag and period of transition - what Basel refers to as the margin period of risk. Precise details of the PFE calculation are seen in the examples of the previous citation, and section 17.3.1 gives a specific example.

The **internal model method** is constructed by an individual bank. Again, details from chapter 5 are required, in particular the definition of EEPE, as the principle is to calculate,

$$EAD = \alpha \times EEPE \quad 1.2 \le \alpha \le 1.4.$$

Since RWA is a balance sheet measure the entire tenor of a trade is not necessarily considered in an attempt to make this measure more present day focused. In fact, Basel allows the EEPE to be measured over a maximum of 5Y maturity or less depending on the characteristics of the netting portfolio of the counterparty.

For the margin period of risk Basel specifies the use of a ten day window for most generic linear IRDs, and requires adopting 'stressed' market conditions in part of the assessment.

Example 17.5.
Bravo Bank's swap restructuring amounts to an uncollateralised $100mm 2Y8Y IRS trade, the same as in example 5.11. Using the same model parameters to generate scenarios as in that example[5] the EEE value is determined from the given EE values. The EEPE is then determined from those EEE values taken over the first five years. The EEPE is determined as $3.4mm, which Bravo multiplies by 1.25 to achieve a full EAD of $4.25mm.

Rules for RWs

The risk weight (RW) value can also be assessed with two general approaches, either 'standard rules' or 'advanced internal ratings based'.

Standard rules classify products, differentiating them by ratings assigned by ratings agencies, for example cash is considered to have a RW of 0% but a BBB rated corporate bond might have a RW of 100%. For derivatives the assessment is standardised against the counterparty and whether the trade is collateralised or not. Derivatives traded through a clearing house have special rules, contained in [43], which typically amount to a 2% RW in most cases.

Advanced internal ratings based (AIRB) is the second method. It must also be regulator approved. Commonly this model will devise an analytic function based on the assumed PD of a counterparty, and on the LGD, to devise the RW. The LGD varies dependent upon the level of securitisation or collateralisation of the product. This method offers a more continuous application of RWs rather than the standard rules which aim to group products into specific categories and assign discrete RWs.

Example 17.6.
Bravo Bank applies standard rules for risk weights to assess the RWA of its uncollateralised derivative asset.
$$\text{EAD} = \$4.25mm \ , \quad \text{RW} = 100\% \ .$$

CVA vol charge calculation

The Basel III Accord introduced more stringent regulations, one of them being the CVA volatility charge in the calculation of RWAs. This element of the RWA formula is to account for the variability of a credit counterparty's loss parameters, such as PD and LGD. This factor limits the scope of an RWA value being estimated lower than it should due to these parameters being conservatively estimated.

Recent consultative Basel documents [44] outline how these calculations are expected to evolve.

The holistic concept of the CVA volatility charge is to capture the associated RWA value of a synthesised portfolio of corporate bonds or credit default swaps that replicates the movement of the CVA associated with the specific IRDs. Since CVAs are values that are directly dependent upon a counterparty's assumed PD and LGD, as shown in section 5.3, and these are precisely the same parameters that determine the pricing of corporate bond spreads and credit default swap protection premiums, it is sensible to use these as proxies.

---

[5]to be technically correct the horizon should be replaced with a 10D horizon instead of the 1D horizon used in the previous chapter, but for the sake of example this is overlooked. Stressed conditions should also be considered

Calculating the correctly synthesised position of credit bonds or credit default swaps is quite technical mathematically, but having simulated the CVA portfolio with assumed notionals of bonds or credit default swaps, RWA assessment is then made easier with the typical methodology applied to these synthesised positions. For the RWs either standard rules can be applied or advanced internal ratings based calculations can be made, subject to approval by regulators after scenario testing.

[2, 'Credit risk' and 'Credit derivatives'] outlines the relationship between credit pricing with PD and LGD, which we use here to present a simplified example using only one tenor since exact details of this section are not important in our context in favour of the wider concept.

Example 17.7.
The CVA of Bravo Bank's swap restructuring has been determined to be $25,593 (see example 5.14). If the PD of the counterparty increased by 0.1% per year then the CVA would increase to $51,354. Therefore we need to synthesise a portfolio of the counterparty's bonds which would decrease in value by $25,761 when its credit pricing is impacted by this increased PD.

With 10Y zero-coupon risk free rates at 2%, a zero-coupon bond with a yield of 2.171%, priced at par, implies an unconditional PD of 1.7% over ten years[6], consistent with the initial CVA assumption (with 100% LGD). If the PD is increased by 0.1% per year then the mid-market yield on the bond moves to 2.274%, and its price falls to $98.98. In order for this $1.02 fall in bond price to reflect the same CVA losses the synthetic position must be a notional of $2.536mm bonds.

Applying a 100% RW to this synthetic bond position results in an RWA value of $2.536mm applicable for the CVA vol charge component. The total RWA value factoring the EAD from above is calculated to be $6.786mm.

17.2.6 Management of RWAs

Spot versus lifetime RWA values

The RWA value described above is a measure made against existing balance sheet items and positions. Although it takes into account future movements these are still done to determine a value today. In this sense it is an immediate, or spot, assessment. However, a single trade might exist for one year and attract an RWA value for that one year, or a trade might exist for ten or fifty years and carry an RWA value for its entire life. The RWA value calculable today says little about what the RWA value might be for that trade in one year's time, or ten, or fifty.

At this stage it is sensible to introduce the concept of earnings, or PnL, in context with regulatory capital. It is hopefully clear that given two IRD trades with the same proposed PnL and spot RWA value it would be more advantageous from a capital perspective to trade the one which matures the earliest. Once a trade has matured it cannot obviously contribute to any further RWA value, and will not incur capital costs on an ongoing basis.

To account for this so-called *duration* of RWA value, a concept can be developed with that in mind. We call this the lifetime RWA. The value we assign to the lifetime RWA is the discounted expectation of yearly future RWA values of any derivative asset, as opposed to the spot RWA value which is the more easily calculated RWA value measured today[7].

If financial institutions desire to be managed in a competent and future proof manner then they must consider the future availability of capital and its use to generate returns in future years. It is not sensible to make a large amount of profit upfront, record it in the PnL account

---

[6]for this approximation we have used the principles described in [2, 'Credit risk']

[7]this lifetime RWA value could be made more continuous by choosing to sample more frequent valuations other than one yearly and accounting for the fraction of the year over which they are applicable

for that financial year and then spend many years afterwards managing the capital requirements of those trades that were executed previously. This is why spot and lifetime RWA values are both important considerations for an institution.

We highlight that Basel do not make any reference of regulation with respect to lifetime RWA. This is only introduced by responsible banks, due to its importance for long term financial planning and management of regulatory capital.

Example 17.8.
Bravo Bank's has a set target to return 15% on Tier 1 capital in any financial year. It has also stated it will maintain a minimum Tier 1 capital ratio of 10% targeting 12.5% as an operating level. This means that given the initial Tier 1 capital of $100mm, its RWA target is set at $800mm, but must not exceed $1,000mm so its ratio does not fall below the minimum. Since Bravo Bank desires to return $15mm earnings in a given year then this is reflective of 1.875% of the targeted yearly operating RWA value.

Bravo Bank analyses whether it is prudent to execute the suggested 2Y8Y uncollateralised swap restructuring with the corporate entity(ies) as a hedge for the loan. Under Basel III it has calculated the spot RWA value to $6.956mm. By estimating future RWA values at subsequent years of the IRSs, and discounting them, Bravo Bank arrives at a lifetime RWA value of $41.0mm[8]. Using the aforementioned 1.875% earnings target then the IRS would need to have a PnL of $769k. Since the PnL is $2mm this deal is well above those minimum earnings levels, and recommended at least from a capital perspective.

Limiting and minimising RWA values from a point of view of an IRD portfolio is a sensible starting point for considered management. But, this view must be placed in context with business as a going-concern. RWA management needs to be treated politically to maintain appropriate relationships with the right clients.

Individual trades have specific mid-market prices and usually transparent, hard facilitation fees. But the charges for capital usage due to RWA are less transparent and require a softer approach, measured on a portfolio basis over a period of time and cannot be accurately assessed for an individual trade taken in the context of a regularly changing portfolio, regularly changing market and the importance of the client to the bank as a whole.

A good example of a soft concession with respect to RWA fees is that some types of client of a bank, particularly hedge funds, are very strategic and execute trades with short term time horizons. In such circumstances executing trades, particularly, long dated trades which attract very high spot and lifetime RWA values can be permitted because there is near certainty that the trade will be exited, or unwound, after a short period and then its RWA impact disappear. If some earnings are generated in the meantime for facilitation then this is likely to be a favourable outcome measuring the cost of capital over the very short term of the trade.

This inevitably leads to a logical extension; the *expected* lifetime RWA, which factors in the likely time horizon of the trade, including client intentions and purpose, and not simply its physically contracted maturity.

A sound and reasonable manner for a bank to operate under is for it to **set an earnings target against expected lifetime RWAs**. Each year some RWAs will drop off the balance sheet as trades mature or clients unwind them. These are replaced by new business which also brings in new earnings for that financial year. A steady state of RWAs recycled by a systematic stream of new targeted business creates the optimum balance of a performing business.

---

[8]this value is hypothetical, roughly assuming spot RWA values of $7,7,7,6,5,4,3,2,1,0.5 and 0mm at the respective starts of years 1 to 11 respectively and some typical DFs

Allocation of RWAs

For any institution to be capitally efficient, it must have a good understanding of where all of its RWAs are generated. It might have, for example, in excess of one million trades each having an individual impact on the total RWA calculation. Evaluating which trades are the best candidates for early termination, or what are the best new trades to execute is important for ongoing business management, in light of the principles above. Of course, various calculation methodologies, with either standard rules or with an AIRB approach, make the idea of a universal approach to capital management quite remote. In fact, we are in the early stages of this type of capital management, so there are likely to be many possible approaches that one institution might make. Some of these will be far more complex than others.

It is important for an institutions's individual business units to be collectively aligned to the same goal of effective capital control. This means costs must be allocated to business units based on their consumption of RWAs. The reason for this is that one business unit cannot be allowed to run up a large amount of RWAs without generating an appropriate return. On the other hand, a business unit that successfully achieves reduction in RWAs should be recognised, otherwise incentives are misaligned and leads to moral hazard of employees.

Overall this is not an easy task to achieve. Consider an example scenario to highlight the problems involved.

Example 17.9.
Two traders (or business units) of Delta Bank have executed three and two trades, respectively, of a total of five facing Charlie Bank. Delta Bank aggregates the trades as part of netting set when calculating the final RWA value. In this case, with a risk weight of 100%, the total spot RWA value is stated as $2.29mm, and the lifetime RWA is $12.94mm. As a guide the individual spot and lifetime RWA values are also given, measured as if each trade was isolated and not part of the netting set.

($mm)	Notional	MTM	Spot Alloc.	Life Alloc.	Ind. SpotRWA	Ind. LifeRWA
Trade 1	50	1.2	x_1	y_1	1.95	8.70
Trade 2	30	-3.2	x_2	y_2	0.45	5.40
Trade 3	10	0.2	x_3	y_3	0.35	2.45
Trade 4	5	-1.1	x_4	y_4	0.08	0.45
Trade 5	73	3.9	x_5	y_5	5.00	11.57
TOTAL		1.0	2.29	12.94	7.82	28.57

Table 17.5: List of trades by details with supposed, netted RWA allocation values, and also the isolated, individual RWA values.

Table 17.5 remains undetermined with the question; how do we determine the allocation values, given that trade netting provides a good deal of offset within the total portfolio?

To do this we suggest some principles that we would like to capture in any allocation procedure. These principles are not restricted to RWA allocation but can be thought of in lieu of other forms of allocations such as funding costs, operation costs, market risk capital charges, etc..

Efficiency is the principle that the allocation values should sum to give the overall RWA value, so that $\sum x_i =$ spot RWA and $\sum y_i =$ lifetime RWA. The RWA value, be it spot or lifetime, is fully distributed across the five trades, no more and no less.

Symmetry is next; it would be helpful if two trades that are exactly the same are assigned the same allocation. This means, for example, that the date on which a trade was executed is not relevant. Whether one trade comes first or last in the set should have no impact on its cost allocation. This also means that the order in which trades are processed for allocation is irrelevant.

We can also define **ignorance of null trades**; it is important that introducing a null trade, one with say a notional of zero and a MTM of zero, would not impact the allocation. This might seem obvious but imagine if the allocation was done by simply averaging across all of the trades. If there were six trades instead of five then each trade would be assigned a different allocation and that sixth, null trade, would have impacted everything else simply by its existence.

No undercut is the principle whereby an allocation never assigns more than an individual trade's isolated RWA value. This is useful to avoid the scenario where a strategic business unit might seek to fragment from the collective and demand isolated treatment, undermining the allocation principles in general.

So, is it possible to allocate RWAs amongst all of the traders, or business units, satisfying all of the desired properties above? Unfortunately not. Efficiency, symmetry and ignorance of null trades are staple ingredients to an allocation procedure but no undercut may or may not be sensible or achievable.

The way we recommend to allocate RWA values here is by using the Aumann-Shapley value[9], applied on a trade by trade basis. We can adjust (iteratively) the Aumann-Shapley value to adhere to the no undercut principle by distributing 'surplus' allocation in the case of 'undercut' trades evenly amongst the others.

In fact, [46], co-authored by some of my former colleagues at Barclays, gives an excellent further description of advancing these principles, and of those used in practice.

The Aumann-Shapley approach works on a marginal basis. That means it measures how a reduction in one of the trades by an infinitesimal amount affects the overall RWA measure, and then scales that reduction to account for the removal of the entire trade. Taken across all trades it gives an efficient and symmetric value which is ignorant of null trades. Once adjusted for no undercut the allocations of example 17.9 are stated in table 17.6.

($mm)	Notional	MTM	Spot Alloc.	Life Alloc.	Ind. Spot RWA	Ind. Life RWA
Trade 1	50	1.2	1.95	8.70	1.95	8.70
Trade 2	30	-3.2	−3.73	−6.75	0.45	5.40
Trade 3	10	0.2	0.35	2.45	0.35	2.45
Trade 4	5	-1.1	−1.28	−3.03	0.08	0.45
Trade 5	73	3.9	5.00	11.57	5.00	11.57
TOTAL		1.0	2.29	12.94	7.82	28.57

Table 17.6: Trades with assigned allocation values.

The allocation is practical. Negative allocations represent capital releases as opposed to capital costs. The first trader's trades have a total spot allocation of $-1.435mm versus the second trader's $3.725mm. The respective lifetime totals are $4.40mm versus $8.54mm. Within each portfolio the traders can determine which trades are the largest consumers of capital requirement.

---

[9]the appendix gives a brief summary of this method but the cited paper [45] gives a much more in depth analysis of a similar problem for interested readers

Costs of allocated RWAs

Once RWAs have been allocated to each trader or business unit it is sensible to then assign an overall cost associated with the capital usage. This lends itself to benchmarking a trader, or business unit, against a target consumption and measuring their return on capital employed.

Real costs by an institution will be borne each year on a spot basis, but implicit costs arise from the build up of lifetime RWAs. Thus any costs divided amongst the utilisation of RWAs must be careful to factor spot against lifetime. For example, if spot RWA was the sole metric examined then a moral hazard might exist to minimise a business unit's spot RWA value with no due regard paid to the increases in lifetime RWAs. Similarly if the focus was on lifetime then the spot value might balloon affecting the capital ratios of balance sheets and be immediately displeasing from an investor's and regulator's perspective.

The following formula is suggested to provided a benchmark profit target in consideration of RWA allocation, factoring both spot and lifetime values from slight different perspectives:

$$\text{Benchmark Profit} = \text{Profit Factor} \times \left(\frac{\text{Spot}_{\text{start}} + \text{Spot}_{\text{end}}}{2} + \text{Lifetime}_{\text{end}} - \text{Lifetime}_{\text{start}} \right) .$$

Example 17.10.
Similar to Bravo Bank, Delta Bank has a 10% Tier 1 capital ratio, with a 15% return on Tier 1 capital target. This means that Delta Bank must earn 1.5% on its RWAs on an ongoing basis to achieve its targets. The trades from example 17.9 are all new with respect to Delta Bank's financial year, with no spot or lifetime RWA values assigned at the start of the year. Using the benchmark profit formula the traders are expected, within the financial year, to have made the following profits from the resultant trades:
   Trader one: $\$55.2k = 1.5\% \times \left(\frac{-1.435mm}{2} + 4.400mm \right) .$
   Trader two: $\$156.0k = 1.5\% \times \left(\frac{3.725mm}{2} + 8.540mm \right) .$

Effect of market movements on RWAs

A reader should legitimately query how any business unit or individual trader can be expected to have benchmark profit targets when the allocated RWA value of their trades varies with market movements.

In example 17.10, the first trader has a lower benchmark profit target, because his allocated RWA usage is lower, which in turn is because the MTM value of his trades are negative. It is completely feasible, however, that all trades were executed originally with zero MTM, hedged with cleared trades, and after the effect of market movements take distinct MTM values which affect their RWA calculations. The hedge trades will likely have the opposing MTM values. So in this scenario trader one will have benefited from the direction of the market move and trader two has been disadvantaged.

This is not ideal from the perspective of an institution's overall management team. It leads to arbitrary determination of profit targets due to factors that are out of any of the individual trader's or business unit's control. In order to reduce, or eliminate, the arbitrary nature of this effect, it is useful to try to disseminate any increases, or decreases, in spot RWA or lifetime RWA values into two categories; change due to market movements, and change due to new business positions. In turn it would be expected that a business unit could at least control its RWA change due to new business, thus targets should be based on those to be optimal.

One way of asserting this dissemination is to use averages, calculated using market levels from the start of a period and market levels at the end of a period. Whilst this is not a perfect solution as it doesn't account for trades executed at interim market levels, it is better. Using a tighter period, i.e. reducing the time between sampled start and end dates will also limit this margin of error. Figure 17.1 demonstrates this by highlighting two paths which isolates these components, with the suggested approach to average the two.

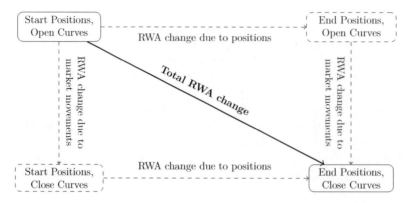

Figure 17.1: Two possible paths to disseminate total RWA change.

Market movements are not the only factor that can affect RWA values of course. Modelled market volatility, and parameters such as PD and LGD can, and do, also change. The same considerations can be made in the figure 17.1 substituting the word 'curves' for 'parameters'.

17.2.7   Capital requirements for market risks

Previous capital requirements have been specific to the credit risk of counterparties and individual netting portfolios from the perspective of default risk. There is an additional component to consider - that of market risk and MTM losses.

A portfolio might have no market risk but many RWAs if it has many equal and offsetting trades with many different counterparties. In that case there will be no additional capital requirement. But this is unlikely in large market-making portfolios. Commonly there will be residual market risks to consider. And other types of portfolio may have specific mandates to run large market risks, such as treasuries.

Basel specifies ([47]) an institution must hold (additional to other capital requirements) an amount of capital that covers an almost worst case scenario in terms of adverse market movements. As usual, there are multiple methods of calculation; a standardised approach and an internal model method.

The standardised approach classifies and aggregates delta, basis, gamma and vega risks into buckets across currencies and provides a formula for calculating the capital charge.

The internal model method works along the principle of requiring an amount of capital that is equal to the $ES_{2.5\%}^{10D}$, assessed in stressed market conditions and scaled by a factor that considers the intricacy of a portfolio (whether it has lots of offsetting bucket risks or is due to simple outright trades). As was shown in section 14.9.5 we can approximate this ES with that of the $VaR_{1\%}^{10D}$, and make some estimates for the additional factors to form an estimation of the capital requirements due to market risks.

In order to standardise the approach, and for the correct calculation of capital ratios, one must convert the market risk capital charge into an equivalent RWA value by multiplying the capital charge by 12.5 (which is the inverse of the 8% T2 ratio).

Example 17.11.
Bravo bank has $75,000 pv01 10Y IRS delta risk. The normal one-day volatility, $\sigma_{BP} = 5bps$ and from this the $VaR_{1\%}^{10D}$ is calculated to be $2.76mm, which approximates the $ES_{2.5\%}^{10D}$. We

*double this as a consideration of stressed markets to give an **estimate of \$5.52mm capital requirement** for Bravo's overall market risk position. As a standardised RWA value this equates to \$69mm, of which \$5.52mm represents the 8% T2 ratio.*

17.3 Leverage Ratio

The leverage ratio is the second capital measure regulators use to monitor and limit the activity of banks. The purpose of have two different measures is to compliment each other; to promote greater financial stability when one ratio restricts certain trading activity that the other measure does not necessarily capture.

For the case of derivatives the leverage ratio tends to be more impactful for shorter maturities where the notionals are quite large, similarly to other products of the same nature such as repurchase agreements (repos). For longer tenor IRDs, RWAs and the capital requirements for market risk tend to be the limiting factors.

The requirement is for this ratio to **be a minimum of 3% at all times**. G-SIBs have more stringent requirements, for example US G-SIBs are subject to 6% minimum values by US regulators. The ratio is defined as:

$$\text{Leverage ratio} = \frac{\text{T1}}{\text{Exposure measure}} \, .$$

17.3.1 Basel rules for the exposure measure calculation

Generally speaking exposures are taken at face value, i.e. their balance sheet values. IRDs are measured differently, however.

At the time of publication of this book the leverage ratio bases its calculation for IRDs on the current exposure method (CEM), but the introduction of the SA-CCR and consultative documents[48] suggest imminent changes by Basel. We ignore the CEM method (actually discussed in the first edition of this book) in favour of these expected changes.

For IRDs the leverage ratio defines the exposure measure as:

$$\text{Exposure measure} = \alpha \, \times \, (RC + PFE), \quad \alpha = 1.4 \, .$$

Broadly speaking for collateralised IRDs, secured by cash and 100% HQLAs, the RC is set to zero, and uncollateralised IRDs or IRDs collateralised with weaker forms of collateral have a value of $\max(MTM, 0)$.

Leverage ratio PFE calculation

The PFE addon's purpose is to capture the effect of leverage due to market movements, even for collateralised IRDs that exist in the margin period of risk.

[42, para 166-169] specifies the calculation. We summarise the steps below;

(i) each IRD trade is assigned to a hedging set. Each counterparty netting set provides a distinction and, within those, each different currency and different index provide further distinction, see figure 17.2. XCSs are also part of distinct hedging sets,

(ii) calculate the start and end dates of each IRD in the hedging set in years (minimum of zero years),

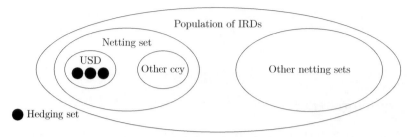

Figure 17.2: Identification of hedging sets as subsets of netting sets and currency sets.

(iii) determine the **adjusted notional,** for each trade, i, with the formula,

$$\text{Adjusted notional, } AN_i = \text{Notional} \times \frac{e^{-0.05 \times \text{Start date}} - e^{-0.05 \times \text{End date}}}{0.05},$$

(iv) determine the margin period multiplication factor, MF_i, of risk for each trade (likely the same within a hedging set) with the following rules;

- 0.175 for centrally cleared derivatives,
- 0.25 for non-centrally cleared collateralised derivatives,
- 0.35 for non-centrally cleared collateralised derivatives in netting sets with more than 5000 trades,
- $\sqrt{\text{End date}}$ for uncollateralised trades with an end date less than 1Y,
- 1.0 for uncollateralised trades with an end date greater than 1Y.

(v) group the trades into three categories by end date; less than 1Y, 1Y to 5Y, and greater than 5Y, and determine the netted effective notional of each category, E_1, E_2 and E_3 with formula,

$$E_k = \sum_i \text{Direction}_i \times AN_i \times MF_i , \quad \text{for trades in category } k = 1, 2, 3 ,$$

(vi) combine the effective notionals of each category and multiply by the regulatory factor of 0.5% to give the PFE add-on amount for each hedging set, j,

$$\text{PFE}_j = 0.5\% \times \sqrt{E_1^2 + E_2^2 + E_3^2 + 1.4E_1E_2 + 1.4E_2E_3 + 0.6E_1E_3} .$$

(vii) sum all of the PFE add-ons of each hedging set to give the total PFE add-on for regulatory purposes.

The leverage ratio is **not** an additive measure of capital required after analysing the capital ratios in the preceding sections. Provided the leverage ratio and the capital ratio are satisfied independently a financial institution is said to be compliant.

Example 17.12. *Bravo Bank's $100mm 2Y8Y uncollateralised swap, as part of the loan arrangements, is considered under the leverage ratio. The effective notional, E_i, of the trade is calculated to be $597mm. From that the PFE is $2.98mm, and the EAD, $4.18mm. This compares very closely with example 17.5.*

17.3.2   A note on centrally cleared counterparties (CCPs)

The goal of the regulatory push to trade through CCPs is to minimise credit exposure between counterparties and limit the inter-reliance of one institution to the next. This is a sensible approach to protect the financial system, assuming those central clearing houses are themselves well managed, capitalised and capable of continuing to operate in the event of any default.

The better credit standing of an approved CCP is reflected with respect to capital usage by categorising these trades with an RW of 2%[10]. So, trades with done through a CCP generally have far lower RWA values than other types of counterparty. Better treatment of cleared trades is visible under the leverage ratio where the multiplication factor of risk is the lowest (0.175) reflective of a five day margin period of risk opposed to other types which are ten days or longer.

Example 17.13.
Bravo Bank's net risk position with the CCP amounts to $150,000 pv01 10Y IRS delta, or approximately $140mm notional. Repeating calculations outlined above gives a $0.027mm RWA value and a $1.35mm leverage exposure.

17.4   Liquidity

Liquidity is the second key measure of the resilience of a bank in a downturn. The following liquidity measures give an impression of a bank's immediate ability to finance payments and traded positions. Again, these measures take into account all items of a bank's balance sheet and operations. We will highlight the impact to IRDs after their summaries.

17.4.1   Liquidity coverage ratio (LCR)

The LCR [49] is a basic measure put in place to ensure a bank manages its ultra short term obligations. There are two components, the stock of HQLAs, and cash outflows occurring in the next 30 days. The ratio states that the HQLAs should be at least as large as the supposed cash outflows, mandating a bank to have enough liquidity to at least withstand a short period of time.

$$\frac{\text{Stock of HQLAs}}{\text{Net cash outflows in next 30 calendar days}} \geq 100\%$$

Although this is a fairly simple concept, the devil is in the details of the definition of the items. Basel documents go into great detail defining HQLAs, in terms of their liquidity, ease of conversion to cash, low correlation with risky assets, etc.. Some assets might only qualify for HQLA status in a percentage of their nominal value. For purposes here, however, it is reasonably safe to assume that HQLAs comprise cash and high credit worthy sovereign debt to the full extent of their nominal value. Indeed nothing is superior to cash (in the appropriate currency) in this sense. HQLAs represents the safety capital of a bank to withstand immediate shocks.

Cash outflows are more complicated. The measure does *not* only represent the forecast net cash payments of a bank, but it is also designed to be reflective of cash outflows under a stressed market scenario. This is the item which IRD trading impacts the most and we will focus on that in a moment, but first we give an example of one of the scenario events that this item is supposed to capture. This is capital loss through a bank run.

Any bank that wishes to calculate their LCR must factor in some cash outflows from an assumed run on their capital base. Different proportions are assumed for different types of

---

[10]more complex rules of being an intermediary clearing broker can extend this to 4%

deposits by retail investors or wholesale investors for example. As a concrete example retail deposits which are fully covered by a government guarantee scheme have a run off rate of 3% (or higher at the discretion of different jurisdictions' regulators). Retail deposits above the guaranteed amount are set to run-off at 10% (or higher).

Example 17.14.
Bravo bank has $50mm of fully guaranteed retail deposits and $150mm of non-guaranteed retail deposits. It must factor a cash outflow, due to run-off, under a stressed scenario of $16.5mm (3% of 50mm, 10% of 150mm) over the next 30 calendar days, therefore hold HQLAs to the value of at least $16.5mm.

Now we direct attention to IRDs. Derivatives can be considered on a netted basis where there is a formal netting agreement in place. This means cash inflows from scheduled payments can offset outflows. It also means that collateral received as a result of making a scheduled payment on a derivative can also be considered a netting item. Therefore the LCR is generally unaffected by collateralised IRDs (where the collateral is high quality).

However, uncollateralised trades do not have this benefit. Their outflows are real outflows and need to be added into the sum. Probably the most pertinent aspect for IRDs is potential valuation changes of trades with lower quality forms of collateral or no collateral at all; large cash outflows that might be generated for adverse market movements which create a high quality collateral liability versus a lower quality collateral, or uncollateralised, asset. The particular size of the cash outflow will depend upon the extremity of the scenario imposed, which affects the trade valuations.

Example 17.15.
In example 17.4 Bravo Bank's IRDs positions move such that $22mm more of cash collateral has to be posted to the CCP, with no equivalent receipt of collateral because the other IRDs are uncollateralised. Using this as the example stressed scenario produces an outflow of the same amount within 30 calendar days. Therefore to satisfy the LCR Bravo Bank would need to hold at least $22mm HQLAs. Unfortunately its balance sheet of the same example showed that it was not and hence Bravo Bank is in breach of the LCR requirement. It is recognised as being exposed to liquidity problems.

Historically the LCR had a sizeable impact on IRD pricing is single currency basis. This is due to its nature of favouring unsecured funding which extends beyond the 30 calendar day limit. If such funding can be sourced then it provides cash recognised as a HQLA for the period of time when the repayment is not classed as an outflow in the next 30 days. For example a rolling $100mm 1M loan will always have an outflow in the next 30 days so provides no benefit to the LCR. But, three rolling $33.3mm, well spaced and overlapping, 3M loans provide permanent funding totalling $99.9mm but only ever a 30 day outflow of $33.3mm, making $66.6mm available in HQLAs to facilitate the LCR. Similarly six rolling $16.7mm 6M loans, totalling $100.2mm, make $83.5mm HQLAs available. This created a supply and demand dynamic for 1M, 3M and 6M IBOR related products where 1M was always skewed much lower to reflect that limited demand.

17.4.2   Net stable funding ratio (NSFR)

The NSFR is a measure designed to ensure that any financial institution's funding requirements, over a longer timeframe than the LCR, are well met. Like the LCR the requirement is fairly straightforward but, again, the complexity is in the definitions of each item, and how each asset and liability, on and off balance sheet, is categorised.

$$\frac{\text{Available amount of stable funding (ASF)}}{\text{Required amount of stable funding (RSF)}} \geq 100\%$$

Key characteristics that Basel focus on when categorising all forms of banking activity are **funding tenor** (how long an activity has until maturity) and **funding type and counterparty** (the specific banking activity involved and the credit worthiness of counterparty). Types of asset and liability, and their contributions to each element, are neatly outlined in Basel's own publications [50]. How banks should disclose this information is explained in [51].

For IRDs the rules have evolved in the last few years and the general expectation is that they will evolve further. Under current rules IRDs will never contribute to available stable funding (ASF), they will only weaken the ratio by contributing to the required stable funding (RSF) in various amounts outlined in table 17.7.

Collateral	Net Liability	Net Asset
HQLAs	RSF increased by 20% of net liability value.	No impact.
None or weak forms of collateral	RSF increased by 20% of net liability value.	RSF increased by 100% of net asset value.

Table 17.7: The impact of an IRD netting set's value to the NSFR.

Example 17.16.
Bravo Bank's uncollateralised IRSs with the corporate sector have an asset value of $3mm. This increases the RSF by that amount. Bravo Bank's IRSs with the CCP have a liability value of $1mm increasing the RSF by $0.2mm. Bravo Bank's loans to corporates increase the RSF by $255mm given their classification at 85%.

17.5 Overview

Regulation	Measure	Minimum Requirement
Capital Ratio	$\frac{\text{Capital}}{\text{RWAs}}$	4.5% CET1, 6% T1, 8% T2
Leverage Ratio	$\frac{\text{Capital}}{\text{Exposures}}$	3% basic, 6% US G-SIBs
LCR	$\frac{\text{Stock of HQLAs}}{\text{Net cash outflows in next 30 calendar days}}$	100% coverage
NSFR	$\frac{\text{Available amount of stable funding (ASF)}}{\text{Required amount of stable funding (RSF)}}$	100% coverage

Table 17.8: Overview of outlined regulatory control measures of banks.

Preceding sections have systematically introduced individual concepts. Here we present a holistic overview of the structure of a bank and how it meets its regulatory requirements. We stress this is only an example to give the reader context of capital and liquidity control and how IRDs impact various elements. A summary of the regulatory controls of a bank is also given in table 17.8.

Example 17.17.

The state of Bravo Bank outlined in example 17.3 is not regulatory compliant. It fails the LCR and the NSFR. To correct this Bravo Bank sources term funding. In addition to its existing funding structure it issues $50mm of AT1 bonds at 5% interest and it raises $50mm through other, less subordinated, bank debt at 2.5%. It invests the proceeds in domestic sovereign bonds and central bank deposits[11]. After Bravo's actions the regulatory metrics are shown in table 17.9.

Regulation	Measure
Capital Ratio	$\frac{102}{725.813} = 14.1\%$ CET1 and $\frac{152}{725.813} = 20.9\%$ T1
Leverage Ratio	$\frac{152}{1407.53} = 10.8\%$
LCR	$\frac{100}{72.16} = 138.6\%$
NSFR	$\frac{1092}{1088.9} = 100.3\%$

Table 17.9: Calculated regulatory metrics of Bravo Bank's example balance sheet.

Table 17.10 demonstrates each item's contribution to the various measures of regulatory requirements to demonstrate Bravo Bank's compliance. A positive line item denotes value to the numerator and a bracketed item denotes value to the denominator.

As a final consideration of Bravo Bank we can estimate its profitability given its structure and some broad based assumptions. See table 17.11

Bravo Bank's outlook is positive.

---

[11]this has the additional benefit of ensuring a minimum percentage of retail deposits is held as central bank reserves as a stipulated requirement by most central banks

[12]see section 17.2.2 and example 17.16

[13]retail mortgages are given a 65% RSF classification, but $500mm are encumbered for greater than one year as security for the covered bond liabilities attracting 100% RSF. See section 17.2.2 for RWA value

[14]for uncollateralised IRDs see examples 17.5, 17.7, 17.12, 17.15, and 17.16

[15]CCP collateral given an 85% RSF classification

[16]domestic sovereign bonds have an RW of 0% and a 5% RSF classification

[17]central bank reserves have 0% RW and a 0% RSF classification

[18]this is capital charge for market risk, see example 17.11

[19]retail deposits have a 95% ASF classification. See also example 17.14 for LCR value

[20]see examples 17.13 and 17.16

[21]$\frac{1}{6}$ of total liability assumed to be a cash outflow in the next 30 days. Interbank unsecured loans less than 6M given 0% ASF classification

[22]unsecured interbank loans given a 50% ASF classification

[23]AT1 bonds increase T1 and given a 100% ASF classification

[24]covered bonds given a 100% ASF classification

[25]other term debt given a 100% ASF classification

Balance Sheet of	Bravo	Rate	CR	LR	LCR	NSFR
	$ mm					
Assets						
Loans to corporate sector[12]	300	5%	(300)	(300)	0	(255)
Retail mortgages[13]	1,000	2%	(350)	(1000)	0	(825)
IRDs with corporate sector[14]	3	-	(6.786)	(4.18)	(22)	(3)
Collateral with CCP[15]	2	0.1%	0	(2)	0	(1.7)
HQLAs[16]	80	0.5%	0	(80)	80	(4)
Central bank reserves[17]	20	0%	0	(20)	20	0
Extraneous[18]	-	-	(69)	-	-	-
Liabilities						
Retail deposits[19]	-200	0%	-	-	(16.5)	190
IRDs with CCP[20]	-1	-	(0.027)	(1.35)	0	(0.2)
Other funding subtotal	-1,102	0.79%	50	50	(33.66)	800
unsecured <6M [21]	*-202*	*0.2%*	*-*	*-*	*(33.66)*	*0*
unsecured 6M-1Y [22]	*-200*	*0.4%*	*-*	*-*	*0*	*100*
AT1 bonds [23]	*-50*	*5%*	*50*	*50*	*0*	*50*
covered bonds [24]	*-500*	*0.25%*	*-*	*-*	*0*	*500*
other term debt [25]	*-150*	*2.5%*	*-*	*-*	*0*	*150*
Share Cap. and Earnings						
Retained earnings	2	-	2	2	-	2
Ordinary share capital	100	-	100	100	-	100

Table 17.10: Balance sheet example highlighting the regulatory values.

Profit and loss item	Amount, $mm
Accrual interest income	35.4
Expected IRD activities	4.0
Interest payments	-8.7
Operating expenses	-20.0
Net profit before tax	10.7
Corporation tax	-2.5
Net profit after tax	8.2

Table 17.11: Bravo Bank's expected profit and loss figures.

Regulation out of scope

Different jurisdictions typically introduce other, more stringent regulation, for either cultural, commercial or political reasons. New regulation often evolves through consultation periods, and this makes it suitable to exclude here. The specificity of its nature is also too narrow a focus for this book.

However it is useful to say that these specific regulations can have large impacts on certain markets due to international asymmetries. For example the increased leverage ratio on US G-SIBs has been a large influencer in European funding market (repo market) liquidity. Another example is the **stability fee** levied on Swedish banks' liabilities. This has been an influencer of SEK/USD XCSs and SEKUSD FX rates in recent times.

17.6   Appendix

17.6.1   Aumann-Shapley allocation concept

The Aumann-Shapley allocation method atomises or attempts to extend the concept of Shapley values to an infinitesimal scale. It is otherwise referred to as marginal contribution to describe the infinitesimal contribution of a particular item value as part of some overall metric, and multiply that contribution to account for the whole item.

In general suppose that $F(t_1, \ldots, t_n)$ is a metric based on some items, t_i; F could be VaR based on a set of bucket risks for example, or an RWA value based on a set of trades. If we introduce $x \in (0, 1]$ as a parameter by which to globally scale the items then, derived from the fundamental theorem of calculus,

$$F(t_1, \ldots, t_n) = \int_0^1 \frac{dF(xt_1, \ldots, xt_n)}{dx} dx , \quad \text{where} \quad F(0, \ldots, 0) = 0$$

If each item, instead of being scaled by x, is assigned its own scalar, $\lambda_i(x) = x$, then,

$$F(t_1, \ldots, t_n) = \int_0^1 \frac{dF}{dx} dx = \int_0^1 \left(\sum_{z=1}^n \frac{\partial F}{\partial \lambda_z} \frac{d\lambda_z}{dx} \right) dx = \sum_{z=1}^n \int_0^1 \frac{\partial F(\lambda_1 t_1, \ldots, \lambda_n t_n)}{\partial \lambda_z} dx .$$

Each item; risk bucket or trade, t_i, is assigned the marginal allocation, $a_i = \int_0^1 \frac{\partial F}{\partial \lambda_i} dx$. This method is **symmetrical** since identical trades will be assigned the same allocation, and it is **efficient** because the sum of all allocations are equal to F. It is completely **ignorant of null trades**. However, **no undercut** is not guaranteed, but can be considered an after adjustment if required.

F is not necessarily a smooth function, particularly given the non-linearity of RWA calculations, and so $\frac{\partial F}{\partial \lambda_i}$ will often need to be determined numerically. For further reading on this see citations [45], [46] and [52].

Allocation of VaR

For the CoVaR multiplier, c we have that (using Einstein summation convention),

$$c(\boldsymbol{\lambda}, \mathbf{S}) = c(\lambda_1 S^1, \ldots, \lambda_n S^n) = \sqrt{S^i \Lambda_i^j Q_{jk} \Lambda_l^k S^l}, \quad \Lambda_i^j = \begin{bmatrix} \lambda_1 & & \mathbf{0} \\ & \ddots & \\ \mathbf{0} & & \lambda_n \end{bmatrix} = \delta_i^j \lambda_i, \quad \text{so that,}$$

$$c(\mathbf{S}) = \sum_{z=1}^n \int_0^1 \frac{S^i \delta_{iz} Q_{zk} \Lambda_l^k S^l}{c(\boldsymbol{\lambda}, \mathbf{S})} dx = \sum_{z=1}^n \frac{S^i \delta_{iz} Q_{zl} S^l}{c(\mathbf{S})}, \quad \text{for} \quad \lambda_i = x .$$

Therefore expressed as a vector equation, the above gives,

$$\mathbf{c}_{\text{alloc}} = \frac{1}{c} \mathbf{diag}(\mathbf{S}) \mathbf{Q} \mathbf{S}, \qquad \mathbf{diag}(\mathbf{S}) = \begin{bmatrix} S^1 & & \mathbf{0} \\ & \ddots & \\ \mathbf{0} & & S^n \end{bmatrix}$$

Chapter

18

Market-Making and Price-Taking

Making prices is the reserve of market-makers, who traditionally try to maintain risk neutrality. Price-takers have to decide whether a price given to them is reasonable enough to be accepted and traded, and generally run portfolios with varying degrees of speculative risk. The dominant part of this chapter discusses the aspects of pricing from a market-maker's perspective but we include suggestions how a price-taker might act in certain circumstances. Knowledge of how a market-maker and a price-taker rationalise their decisions is useful information to either party.

The items dealt with in this chapter include;

- general principles of market-making placed in context,

- a list of considerations that a market-maker should have when quoting a price,

- a guide on how to treat each of the considerations,

- an assessment of the actions of price-takers and market-makers when making deals.

18.1 Context of the whole market

Two-way business is important because it means profit is generated from the margins with risks being offset. See the example below.

Example 18.1.

*Delta Bank is only registered to clear EUR IRS trades with EUREX, whilst the other market-makers, Alpha, Bravo and Charlie Banks are registered to clear with both LCH and EUREX. The 10Y LCH mid-market is 1% and the 10Y EUREX is 1.02% (i.e. the 10Y EUREX-LCH basis price is 2bps). A price-taker requests a 10Y price from all four market-makers (the trade will **not** be cleared and the price-takers's CSA with any market-maker is the usual EUR RFR).*

Delta has a difficult problem, since it can only hedge with interbank trades cleared through EUREX it can either;

i) price the requested trade based on the EUR:1D.ESTR-EUREX curve,

ii) or price the requested trade based on based on the EUR:1D.ESTR-LCH curve.

If Delta uses the EUREX curve and quotes the two-way market 1.01% / 1.03%, whilst the other market-makers quote 0.99% / 1.01%, based on the LCH curve, then Delta will only ever trade in one direction, it will always pay fixed to the non-cleared customers, since it is always the highest bid. Consequently it will receive fixed versus EUREX on its hedge. Its trades, will show positive EUR cashflows (paying at 1.01% versus receiving at 1.02%) but it will build up a systematic position against EUREX, which may prove to be more and more costly in terms of allocated clearing house marging requirements and cost of capital.

On the other hand, if Delta uses the LCH curve and quotes a two-way market similar to other banks it will have a 25% likelihood of trading, and importantly if the distribution of customer flows is neutral it will likely trade in both directions, and its exposure to EUREX should net over the course of multiple deals. Importantly, its cashflows will also show positive values, since the non-cleared two-way business will have rates paying 0.99% and receiving 1.01%, whilst the EUREX hedges will all be transacted at 1.02% and where paying and receiving nets.

Thus actions, and opinions, of others must be a factor to any market-maker. If every market-maker prices an instrument, or a market effect, differently to another market-maker with an alternative assessment that other market-maker must adjust his line of thinking to become more associated with the collective. This is particularly acute if the status quo of other market-makers is unlikely to change in the short term due to a lack of any such catalyst to provoke a reassessment. Two-way business is valuable and allows risks to be offset.

18.2   Market-maker considerations

Given the scope of all possible considerations it is helpful to categorise them, shown in figure 18.1. Each can then be explained in turn.

18.2.1   Curve model & pricing curves

A more accurate, intricately designed, curve model will yield a more accurate price. Sometimes the concept of a better curve, though, is ill defined because simulating the overall belief of the market for interpolated points is subjective and there is no right answer. Section 6.1.9 has highlighted this already when discussing curveset constructions. Additionally knowledge of the whole market's way of interpolating and constructing curves is never available so it is difficult to gauge prices in the context of the whole market in that respect. But that being said, a trader does their best to characterise the market and design a good curve model. After doing so, they must then exhibit some confidence in it. Subject to the below considerations, actually deriving the mid-market price of a request is usually straight forward. For requests that more closely resemble benchmark trades this process often takes a minimal amount of time, and can be read directly from screens.

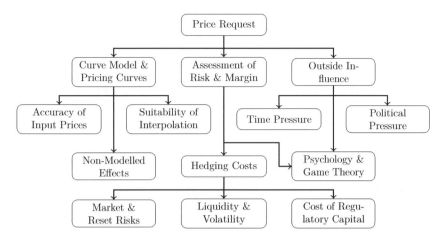

Figure 18.1: Illustrating the considerations of market-makers following price requests by price-takers.

Accuracy of input prices

The pricing curves will only be as accurate as the accuracy of the input prices to the curve model. If they lag the market by a number of milliseconds that can ultimately prove costly. If an input price has been entered incorrectly or miscalibrated this may lead to an incorrect price and be costly also. All that can be said about this topic is that a trader should have some kind of sanity check. A tip is to cross reference a price, generated from the pricing curves, of a benchmark tenor swap with the real market traded price. If they are the same then a market-maker should have confidence that the price is accurate with respect to his curve model and traded market prices.

Suitability of interpolation

Price requests are sometimes made specifically to certain market-makers so that the price-taker can benefit from the particular type of interpolation style used to produce the price. Different interpolations for non-benchmark, intermediate tenor swaps across market-makers can yield vastly different results. Practically a trader must consider this in the context of the whole market and question whether adjustments need to be made to become less of an outlier. Recording the number of times prices were accepted or rejected, and in which direction price-takers tended to favour trading can give a steer on this types of effects. Also analysing the amount of roll-down on the trade request can give an impression as to the direction the price-taker may want to trade and permit a more fundamental assessment of the price.

Non-modelled effects

A curve model hopefully captures all of the effects one wishes to price, but sometimes a curve model is not technical enough, not up to date, or simply incapable of pricing the effect. For example, a price generated by a curveset that does not price year end or quarter end turns might need a manual adjustment for a trade with those rolls. Alternatively a product that experiences a different quantity of gamma to the products it will be hedged with, for example a ZCS or an in-arrears IRS, will need a manual adjustment. These types of effects need alternative models to be consulted to generate their accurate adjustments[1]. Perhaps the CSA of the counterparty is highly specialised demanding discounting considerations, and there might also be a large amount of optionality of the CSA to be factored in. There are too many ad-hoc items that could be categorised in this section, but it is always worth sparing a though about a price request to think if there is anything about the price that won't be captured by the curve model. Often educated guesses give manual adjustments that are fit for purpose and within acceptable margins or error, and it is always worth performing some kind of sanity check as a trader to make sure a price is within a broad expectation.

18.2.2 Outside influence

Outside influence is a factor that will affect prices that are characterised as not being part of the pricing theory or of the interaction between the market-maker and the price-taker. There are two main influences in this regard.

Time pressure

A market-maker is time pressurised to respond to price requests usually because the price-taker is keen to execute a trade without the level of the market changing before the price quote is received. Additionally other market-makers, that are competing for the price-taker's business, who respond more expediently create a need to act in a timely manner. The only effect that time pressure can have is to force certain considerations to be overlooked. This creates a need for a subjective assessment by a market-maker.

Political pressure

Political pressure results when colleagues of the market-maker want the quoted price to carry a good chance that the price-taker will accept the quote. For example, this could come from management looking to promote synergies across other businesses from the same price-taker, or sales teams promoting their own agenda with regard to increasing volumes. Each form of political pressure is different and may require different treatment.

18.2.3 Assessment of risk and margin

Trading is ultimately about making a profit. For a market-maker and in the context of thousands of trades, avoiding losing money on any price request is as important as making profits on others. Assessment of risk and margin is a broad assessment of two factors; the costs associated with hedging a trade and deciding what fee over and above the hedging costs to charge the price-taker for facilitating it.

Assessing the hedging costs can take a good deal of time. For simple trades obviously it can take no time at all, the phrase 'business as usual' is quite apt. But more bespoke price requests need consideration. If a market-maker underestimates the hedging costs this might result in him making a loss when executing the hedge in practice. If a market-maker overestimates the hedging cost then this might result in the price-taker rejecting the quote because the resultant margin is too wide and a competing market-maker supplies a more favourable quote to the price-taker. Perhaps this is then a missed opportunity.

To be clear, the term *margin* is the distance from the mid-market price that a market-maker will quote to a price-taker to execute the trade in a particular direction. In this context

---

[1]see chapter 21 for a description and examples of some of these

it should not be confused with margin as collateral posted to exchanges and clearing houses. *Bid-offer* is sometimes used as a term with a similar meaning, but is slightly different in that bid-offer is actually the distance from the bid price to the offer price. Bid-offer is actually the bid-margin plus the offer-margin, which might not be equal where a market-maker chooses to skew his prices about the mid-market for one reason or another. The margin must include the anticipated hedging cost plus the fee that the market-maker wants to charge for transacting the trade and attempting to hedge it.

Assessments of risks and margin is an area of IR trading which is actively being researched. Algorithms are well suited to advance this aspect of trading practice and gone are the days when market-makers can provide a default response of "charge one bp of margin as always". Indeed we explore these ideas in section 19.3.

The design of algorithms does not detract from the need of a trader. It does not mean that a computer takes his job and makes him redundant, but rather it shifts his focus to provide accurate calibration of the models and to the role of risk management rather than being an assessor of price requests.

18.2.4 Reset risk hedging costs

One of the great aspects of the transition from IBOR is the almost complete elimination of the need to hedge reset risks, and as such we have relegated previous edition material in this regard to the end of the book. The RFR market experiences much less of this risk for the following, combined reasons:

i) for the same swap notional a daily RFR fixing constitutes approximately the same risk as $\frac{1}{30}$'th of a floating 1M IBOR fixing, $\frac{1}{90}$'th of a 3M IBOR fixing, $\frac{1}{182}$'th of a 6M IBOR fixing and $\frac{1}{365}$'th of a 12M IBOR fixing.

ii) since the tenor on a daily RFR fixing is 1D, there is much less variability in this fixing, compared to say tenor IBORs which suffer from the variability of future rates expectations within the tenor window,

iii) since RFRs have been designed to be more effective with regards to the transmission mechanism they more closely track the central bank deposit rate and therefore have less variability than IBORs which also suffered from interbank liquidity scarcity events.

For these reasons, we do not labour the point on reset risks hedging costs as was necessary in previous editions. However, market-makers should still be vigilant towards trade packages that can combine to yield reset ladders across central bank meeting dates which can offer excessive volatility.

18.2.5 Market risks hedging costs

Before ever giving a quote a market-maker should model a price request and analyse its market delta and basis risks and its reset risks. Then a determination should be made about the likely costs associated with hedging the risks. Of course this needs to be done against the backdrop of liquidity and volatility but it is practical to make an assessment of cost assuming a standard, average market state. This can still be quite subjective because many variables might affect the decision. Being able to make good assessments in this regard comes from data. Garnering lots of experience of trades that have been successful and others that have been failures gives some perspective about where one should pitch the cost level.

Whilst it is not sensible to try and list or categorise every single thought that might go through a trader's mind the below list presents some considerations worth making. The leftmost item is traditionally what will result in the lowest expected hedging cost and the rightmost item the highest;

(i) is the price request of benchmark or non-standard tenors?

(ii) do the risks require few or many different benchmark instruments in the interbank market to hedge?

(iii) are the risks smaller than or larger than the average request?

(iv) are the reset risks exposed to any isolated calendar events such as central bank meetings or speeches?

18.2.6   Liquidity and volatility hedging costs

To extend the cost assessment the real state of the market must be factored in, relative to standard conditions. The two key components of a market used for hedging is its liquidity and its volatility. There is generally some correlation between these two, and a market will have a state of lower volatility if it is more liquid and vice versa. Referencing *normal* market conditions requires a definition of the concept. Undoubtedly there are numerous ways of establishing a benchmark in such a broad concept as the volatility and liquidity of a market. As an example a measure of an IR market's liquidity might be to observe the number of bond futures for the specific currency that have traded relative to the average number that have traded up to that timestamp on any given day. To assess the volatility perhaps, a similar measure could be made considering the standard deviation of one minute historical price intervals compared to an average.

It will generally be more difficult to hedge a trade in a less liquid market, and in liquidity vacuums might even be impossible. This will usually result in estimating a higher hedging cost.

18.2.7   Regulatory capital hedging costs

Every trade carries some intrinsic cost of capital for an institution[2]. If an institution has a choice of executing one of two trades; one with an expected PnL of $100 and regulatory capital requirement of $1,000, or another with a PnL of $150 and regulatory capital of $3,000, then it has a difficult decision to make. Does it trade for maximal upfront profit? Or does it trade to maximise profit relative to capital usage? Historically the choice was always to favour the bottom line, taking the profit upfront and worrying about capital later. But, modern approaches categorise this viewpoint as being entirely unacceptable. The usage of capital of an institution often becomes the main concern, and maximising profit relative to its use of capital is the key goal. In this way margin on trades can sometimes be dictated by simply representing enough to cover the costs of utilising regulatory capital.

---

[2]for example see chapter 17

18.2.8   Strategy and game theory

The remaining aspect of margin from a market-maker's perspective, having considered what are the costs of the trade, is what fee to charge in order to extract some profit for facilitating the trade. This is where strategic psychology and game theory plays a part, and is the competitive nature of financial markets.

The appendix of a previous edition [53], constructed a model of a traditional price-taker /market-maker interaction to treat decision making strategically. In light of electronic platforms and a variety of possibilities, regarding interaction types, here we just present its suggestions and qualitative reasoning supporting its conclusions.

We assume that trade requests have two latent properties;

i) **transparency**, which is observability and confidence in a mid-market price,

ii) **information**, which may include an imminent market impact or offers a source of liquidity privately, and not publicly, known.

If we consider *transparency* first, it reflects model uncertainty in the price of the requested portfolio or trade. The EUR IRS market is liquid with various exchange based and central limit order book (CLOB) pricing. The mid-market price of, say, 5Y should be universal, or at least have minimal variation. On the other hand, the SEK 5Y IRS, which has no exchange based or CLOB pricing, might be modelled based on comparisons with EUR and USD IRS and/or other markets and other factors. There is much higher model uncertainty in the 5Y SEK mid-market price than the 5Y EUR. Quantifying it relies upon knowledge of all market-makers true mid-marker prices, which is not available and why we classify it as latent. But estimates can be made, for example consider data of figure 18.2. It shows a standard deviation of 0.07bps for 5Y EUR and 0.65bps for 5Y SEK of non-transparency.

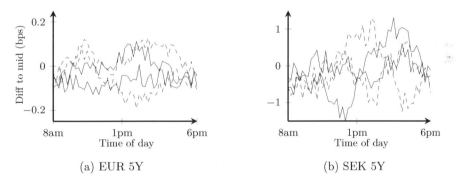

(a) EUR 5Y   (b) SEK 5Y

Figure 18.2: Differences between four selected brokers' prices and an institution's mid-market 5Y IRS measured at different times throughout a one day period.

Transparency has an impact on margin, since in a competitive market price-takers will take the *best* price. That is, if you assumed that every market-maker has the same bid-offer margin, $2X$, without skew, then the tradable margin available to the price-taker could be shown to be[3], $2(X - g(N)T)$, where T is the standard deviation of the different mid-market prices, and, N, the number of market-makers and $g(N)$ is from the table below,

---

[3]modelling approximations of maximums and minimums of normal random variables (see https://quant.stackexchange.com/a/55703/29443)

N	g(N)	N	g(N)	N	g(N)
2	0.564	5	1.163	8	1.423
3	0.846	6	1.127	9	1.485
4	1.029	7	1.352	10	1.539

Table 18.1: Tabulated values for the pricing margin formula.

Considering *information*, a market-maker is expected to account for this in the price quotation shown to the price-taker, as well. We give an example of such inclusion in section 19.4.1. Information is certainly a latent variable since it is not observable and we cannot really suggest any empirical estimators either, beside collecting pricing data of executed trades over the long term, but even this is difficult to structure and reliably interpret.

Upon combining information and transparency, the citation derived equilibrium prices between the strategic actions of price-takers and market-makers, under the assumed conditions of the model interaction. The result was that a market-maker would calculate, X, as follows;

$$X = \max\left(Z + 1.15T, \quad C + 1.7I + 0.5T\right)$$

The leftmost value is used for trades with low informational content and higher uncertainty, the rightmost dominates when trades have higher informational value.

Figure 18.3 shows four different trade categorisations, and contours of the above pricing formula. The trade categorisations shown are as follows,

1) No information and completely transparent, e.g. small trades in benchmark products, such as MAT IRSs,
2) High informational value and completely transparent, e.g. very large trades in benchmark products,
3) No information and non-transparent, e.g. small trades in off-the-run, obscure, or less liquid instruments,
4) High informational value and non-transparent, e.g. large trades in off-the-run, obscure, or less liquid instruments.

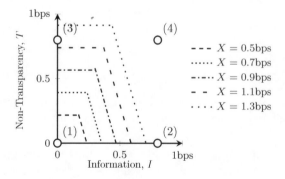

Figure 18.3: Trade categorisation by transparency and informational value, including contours of pricing margins for various combinations of values.

For trade category (1) a price-taker is expected to achieve the same price quotation via any approach he chooses to take when requesting. This is because this trade type carries no informational value and is completely transparent. In that sense it is fully standardised and effectively automated. The price quoted is, $X = Z$, which is the minimum marketable price whereby a market-maker is expected to remain in business, winning a fair proportion of trades in competition with other, rational, market-makers.

For trade category (3) a price-taker is expected to ask a competitive quote from as many market-makers as possible, and be dishonest by saying that he is asking only two market-makers in competition. If operating in an electronic market that would be strategically equivalent to, for example, submitting 3 different price requests to 2 market-makers simultaneously, instead of a single price request to 6 market-makers. Electronic data capture and trade execution statistics might reveal this over the long term though so care would be needed. The rationale for this is that this trade is non-transparent so every market-maker will have a different mid-market value, potentially to the advantage of the price-taker. Rational market-makers should generally assume that this price request is broadcast to as many as possible, however and therefore factor this in.

For trade categories (2) and (4) a price-taker is expected to fluctuate between asking a competitive quote of just two market-makers and a non-competitive quote from a single market-maker. The price-taker should, where possible, try to convey the notion that the quote is competitive between two market-makers, even if he is actually asking non-competitively. The rationale for this is that a price-taker wishes to withhold the high informational content from as many market-makers as possible, but keep up the appearance of competition to evoke better prices forced by competition.

Example 18.2.

A price-taker requests a price in 50mm 5Y SEK IRS from five market-makers. One market-maker, Alpha Bank, has the following assessment:

$$R_{5Y} = 1.00\%, \qquad T = 0.65, \qquad I = 0.1, \qquad C = 0.1, \qquad Z = 0.35$$

where T is determined by estimation as previously, C is brokerage on interbank hedging, Z is a typical market wide equilibrium, I is a considered market impact akin to section 19.4.1. The margin from mid he then determines and the quoted two way are,

$$X = \max(0.35 + 0.7475, 0.1 + 0.17 + 0.325) = 1.0975bps, \quad \textit{Quote: } 0.989/1.011\%$$

The price-taker's best market, aggregated over all market-makers, is 0.994 / 1.0015%, being 0.75bps wide. Alpha Bank is cover bid meaning that its bid of 0.989% is second best.

A reverse calculation using values from table 18.1 to determine the price a market-maker must show with, $T = 0.65$, to arrive at a bid-offer margin of 0.75bps for a price-taker across five market-makers is $X = 1.13bps$. This is similar to the example 18.2 and that is not surprising since the same assumptions of normal distributions of the mid-market are factored into the strategic interactions deriving the pricing formula.

The above was an example of trade category 3). To conclude this section I will share a real anecdote of an interaction I had roughly around 2012 as a sterling market-maker at Barclays, with trade category 2). Its purpose is to show how real world activity can be described by these parameters even if they are not used specifically to determine the price.

Example 18.3.

A price-taker, at a hedge fund, requested a price in 200mm 10Y GBP. Typical market size of this instrument is 25 to 50mm. Say I had a mid-market of 1.30% then I quoted a price of

1.25bps from mid yielding a market, 1.2875 / 1.3125%. In terms of the pricing parameters above this would reflect something like, $T = 0.15, I = 0.66, C = 0.05$.

I traded with the price-taker in that instance and I recall that the market impact of this trade was significant. Broker prices and gilt futures activity was quick to reflect the trade, and the 10Y GBP mid-market price was impacted about 2bps overall in a short timeframe. The same thing happened again a week or so later with the same price-taker and same market impact, albeit I was cover in that second instance.

The activity was so pronounced in the market that the informational value of these trades had to be increased. If the price-taker was trading in multiple places simultaneously so that his full volume was, in fact, two or three times larger, this would warrant that reassessment.

Upon being asked a third and fourth time for a price quotation I offered a market 1.75bps from mid, with a total bid-offer of 3.5bps. I did not trade with that price-taker again. This reflected my assumption that the volume was twice as large as stated, and a repeated market impact likely, i.e. effectively we had, $I = 0.94$.

It was rumoured that that specific price-taker damaged his firm's ability to source liquidity, since the activity he engaged in was then assumed to be replicated by his price-taker colleagues, who suffered by receiving worse price quotations than they otherwise should have. Internal discussions were reportedly taken!

Electronic Trading

This chapter aims to;

- discuss algorithmic means of determining mid-market prices from electronic order books,

- demonstrate processes to minimise the processing time for curve calculation and price generation,

- propose an automated pricing engine which includes parametrised market-maker margin calculations.

19.1 Mid-market

The concept of mid-market for any financial instrument is much more difficult than one would expect to define. For a start, we have different asset classes, which, in accounting and for regulatory purposes, are usually assigned one of three labels;

i) **Level 1**: these are products with a directly tradable market with observable bid and offer quotations, such as exchange traded products, listed equities, liquid bonds, MAT IRS, etc.

ii) **Level 2**: these are products which do not have observable bid and offer quotations but whose price is derived and has a direct link to level 1 assets. For example bespoke IRSs prices depend upon an IR curve which is parametrised by level 1 assets. Swaptions follow a similar principle.

iii) **Level 3**: these are products not falling within the above categories whose prices are more difficult to determine, for example unlisted equities.

Our scope is level 1 and level 2 assets. The products covered in this book are **not** level 3 assets.

19.1.1   Level 1 assets

As above, level 1 assets are characterised by a transparent market with observable bid and ask quotations. Since our level 2 assets are essentially dependent upon the pricing of the level 1 assets we will focus on their prices here. Within this category there is actually a reasonable amount of discretion for some of these assets. For example, EUR benchmark IRS are a very liquid product with high volumes and numerous data venues with multiple contributors. This leads to very tight pricing that is validated by frequent trading, so minimal uncertainty. NOK benchmark IRS, on the other hand, have few contributors, often wide markets and frequently periods of no trading at all, questioning the uncertainty in those prices. Regulators are well aware of such considerations and their rules regarding prudent valuation assessment for capital requirements cover making such quantitative assessments of all asset classes and products [54].

With this knowledge we can begin to analyse level 1 assets and categorise certain properties. Instruments may have structured price levels which are relatively wide, for example SOFR futures, where CME permits tick increments of 0.5bps. Alternatively, IRS CLOBs may be very granular pricing, allowing tick increments of 0.05 or even 0.01 bps. With a wider pricing structure usually comes a greater amount of volume at those specific levels, but with more granular pricing there is usually volume dispersed across a wider array of distinct prices. The relevancy of this will become apparent when we start looking at different calculations for the mid price.

It is not always the case but typically level 1 assets will have some form of order book pricing as follows, where the bid prices, $b_i > b_{i+1}$, and the ask prices, $a_i < a_{i+1}$, and the sizes $w_i > 0$, $v_i > 0$.

Bid Size	Bid Price	Ask Price	Ask Size
w_1	b_1	a_1	v_1
w_2	b_2	a_2	v_2
w_3	b_3	a_3	v_3
w_4	b_4	-	-

Table 19.1: Structure of a typical order book.

When a price-taker chooses to hit a bid (or lift an offer) some of the volume at the respective bid (or offer) will be filled. Whose specific bids (or offers) are filled will depend upon the prioritisation algorithm implemented by the order book owner, which may be an exchange. The features of this prioritisation algorithm are important and, generally speaking, are designed to encourage early order placement and to discourage order spoofing. **Spoofing**, which is illegal, is the practice of entering orders to an order book with the intention of never trading those orders. Typically these orders will be pulled when they are more at risk of being filled, such as evolving price dynamics make them more attractive to trade or their time prioritisation places them at the front of the queue.

19.1.2 Single instrument pricing algorithms

This section will describe some of the most common techniques used to derive mid-market prices from the given information of **an electronic order book**.

Last traded price

$$p_{lt} = last\ traded\ price$$

Under a last traded price rule, the mid price is set to be the most recently traded price. This is a useful metric in the case of high-frequency trading, perhaps for FX or other super liquid markets, since at the timescales involved its accuracy in determining the mid is effective. For our purpose though, since interest rate markets are not high frequency (and not 24hour markets), the disadvantage here is that in the absence of trading the last traded price quickly becomes obsolete, and should not really be relied upon. It may be the case that the last traded price is neither b_1, nor a_1, or in fact remotely close to these values.

Arithmetic first depth average

$$p_{afda} = \frac{b_1 + a_1}{2}$$

This is a simple rule which might also be reasonably effective for frequently traded markets where the sizes on the bid and ask vary frequently and the price discrepancy between bid and ask is narrow, e.g. EUREX bund futures. The problem with this rule for instruments with wider price discrepancy, e.g. CME SOFR futures, is that it is very sensitive to high variance when a lot of trading occurs at a particular price point.

Example 19.1.
A 3M CME SOFR future has a well bid price of 98.01 and a well offered ask price of 98.02, and p_{afda} is therefore 98.015. Seconds later a small bid of 98.015 comes to market, forcing p_{afda} to 98.0175. A few more seconds later and these lots at 98.015 are sold and are offered on in a small quantity, and p_{afda} jumps to 98.0125. This variance of the mid price is unwarranted given that trading is taking place at 98.015 and, heuristically, that appears to be the true mid-market.

Weighted first depth average

$$p_{wfda} = \frac{v_1 b_1 + w_1 a_1}{v_1 + w_1}$$

The above problem and example would be mitigated somewhat by using information about the bid and ask size. When the price discrepancy is narrow, e.g. in the case of EUREX bund, the difference between an arithmetic average and a weighted average might be considered negligible, and in the case of wide price discrepancies is open to manipulation from spoofing.

Example 19.2.
Suppose, from the previous example, the bid at 98.01 is 5000 lots and the ask price of 98.02 is 6500 lots, and p_{wfda} is therefore 98.0143. The incoming bid of 98.015 in 10 lots forces p_{wfda} to

98.0150. The subsequent offer at 98.015 in 20 lots maintains p_{wfda} at 98.0150. The variance in the mid price here deviates less from the assumed 98.015 mid-market.

Example 19.3.
Suppose the bid in the (now obsolete) ICE GBP 3M LIBOR future at 98.01 is 2000 lots and the ask price of 98.02 is 4500 lots, and p_{wfda} is therefore 98.0131. A fund, looking to receive 1Y GBP IRSs, tries to manipulate rates higher by increasing the size of the offers on the futures contracts. The fund adds 3000 lots to the offer, knowing that the first 4500 have a priority so those additional 3000 lots are unlikely to be traded, even if 98.02 is paid. This causes the p_{wfda} to adjust to 98.0121, i.e. by 0.1bps higher in rate. After the fund has received a quotation for the 1Y IRS it pulls its offers on the futures.

Example 19.3 is included because, anecdotally, this is exactly what our trading team at Barclays observed around 2010. The price discrepancy, at the time, in short sterling contracts was 1bp, which was wide (it has since reduced in SONIA futures contracts to 0.5bps), and certainly wide enough to easily add sufficient contracts to the bid or ask size to influence the weighted mid. There was low inherent risk to such strategies especially when coupled with the prioritisation algorithm determined by the exchange, which meant priority was given to earlier orders so later orders were unlikely to be filled. As a result of the perceived distorted mids our trading team switched from using **weighted first depth average** as an algorithm to instead use **multi-instrument least squares regression**, incorporating spread and butterfly prices between contracts, to better assess our mid-market prices of all short sterling contracts, protected from the effects of spoofers.

Weighted maximum first depth average

$$p_{wxfda}(z) = \frac{\min(v_1, z)b_1 + \min(w_1, z)a_1}{\min(v_1, z) + \min(w_1, z)}$$

Another potential way of avoiding the above issue is to cap the volume on one side of the price, so that adding volume above a certain parameter, z, does not impact the calculation. This algorithm will vary between the arithmetic first depth average (for small values of z) and weighted first depth average (for large values of z).

Intrinsic depth average

$$p_{ida}(z) = \frac{p_{bida}(z) + p_{aida}(z)}{2}$$

where p_{bida} is the *bid intrinsic depth average* and p_{aida} is the *ask intrinsic depth average* for chosen depth, z. To calculate these values one must choose an intrinsic depth, say 3000 lots, and calculate the bid and ask prices that would be achieved if that volume of the instrument was to be hit, or lifted, directly at each of the relevant prices in the volume they are immediately bid or offered in. Below we give the formulae for these prices for intrinsic amount, z.

$$p_{bida}(z) = \frac{\sum_{k=1}^{n-1} b_k w_k + b_n(z - \sum_{k=0}^{n-1} w_k)}{z}, \quad \text{where} \quad \sum_{i=0}^{n-1} w_k < z \le \sum_{i=0}^{n} w_i : \; w_0 = 0$$

$$p_{aida}(z) = \frac{\sum_{k=1}^{n-1} a_k v_k + a_n(z - \sum_{k=0}^{n-1} v_k)}{z}, \quad \text{where} \quad \sum_{i=0}^{n-1} v_k < z \le \sum_{i=0}^{n} v_i : \; v_0 = 0$$

36	169.70	169.71	53
78	169.69	169.72	88

Example 19.4.
The order book of the EUREX bund at a given moment is as follows,
For an intrinsic 65 lots,

$$p_{bida} = \frac{169.70 * 36 + 169.69 * 29}{65} = 169.6955$$

$$p_{aida} = \frac{169.71 * 53 + 169.72 * 12}{65} = 169.7118$$

$$p_{ida} = 169.7037$$

Example 19.5.
The order book data given in example 19.2 would give p_{ida} values of 98.0150 initially, then 98.0150 as the small bid appeared and also 98.0150 as the small offer appeared, using a parameter value, $z = 1000$.

This algorithm demonstrates a robust nature against variance in comparison to the previous arithmetic average and weighted average in certain cases, such as the example 19.5. Clearly it is dependent upon the subjective choice of the intrinsic size which would have to be cross validated against training data if this algorithm were to be implemented in production. This parameter specification is this algorithm's weakness since it can demonstrate reasonable variance dependent upon that choice (see figure 19.1).

Mean intrinsic depth average

An extension to the previous algorithm is to avoid choosing a specific intrinsic amount and instead average over all quantities up to a specified maximum, Z, which serves as the parameter for this algorithm.

$$p_{mida} = \frac{1}{Z} \int_0^Z p_{ida}(z)dz = \frac{1}{2Z} \left(\int_0^Z p_{bida}(z)dz + \int_0^Z p_{aida}(z)dz \right)$$

Appendix section 19.5.1 expands this formula as a closed form solution and the code repository [21, #2421b3] contains python executable functions.

Comparison of methods

Consider the following order book,

10	99.05	99.06	5
5	99.04	99.07	10
10	99.03	99.08	15
5	99.02	99.09	10
10	99.01	99.10	5

Which algorithm is best depends upon the structure and properties of the specific order book. The wall clock runtimes of the slower algorithms are only marginally so. Indeed, even in Python, it requires only 3 micro seconds to compute the above order book.

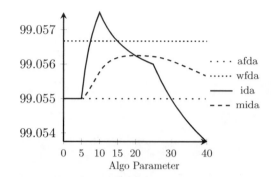

Algorithm	Python time
afda	0.5 μs
wfda	1.0 μs
ida	2.7 μs
mida	3.2 μs

Figure 19.1: Algorithm properties including runtime and calculated mid-market price for various parameter settings.

Anecdotally, in 2017, iSwap kindly donated one day's worth of anonymised order book data for the EUR 10Y IRS. I analysed the arithmetic, weighted and mean intrinsic depth algorithms, and found that the latter was indeed a much more stable price measured over the high frequent variations throughout the day. This is because that order book has a very narrow price discrepancy, so including multiple depths added to its overall performance in my assessment.

19.1.3   Least squares regression

In the previous section we possessed order book data for a single instrument and devised ways of determining the mid-market price from that information. Typical exchanges and CLOBs often define additional instruments which are combinations of the single instruments we seek mid-market prices for. For example, given 12 STIR futures (the conventional whites, reds, and greens) there are potentially 66 spread instruments that have individual order books, and even more butterfly instruments, although some will not be offered and many won't have liquid order books. There are also potentially pack and bundle prices. Therefore, there is more information to be gleaned by considering the extent of all order books.

In this process we use a single instrument algorithm to determine the mid-market price of each of the individual order books, and then use an additional algorithm afterwards to include this information and combine these prices to affect the core (or target) instrument prices.

Suppose we have used order book data and an appropriate algorithm to derive the mid-market price of the order books for the M2, U2, and Z2, SOFR futures. Additionally we have derived mid-market prices of the M2-U2, M2-Z2 and U2-Z2 spread prices and the M2-U2-Z2 butterfly price from their respective order books. The implied prices of these instruments, as calculated using the mid-price from the combination of individual instruments, may differ to the mid-price of the instruments as calculated from their own, specific, order books.

Instrument	Single instrument algo mid price	Core implied mid price	Difference ($\pm$bp)
M2	**98.2120**	$\leftarrow$	
U2	**98.1160**	$\leftarrow$	
Z2	**98.0440**	$\leftarrow$	
M2-U2	0.0950	0.0960	0.1
M2-Z2	0.1665	0.1680	0.15
U2-Z2	0.0740	0.0720	0.2
M2-U2-Z2	0.0220	0.0240	0.2

Table 19.2: Spread and butterfly prices derived from specific order books and by implication from the individual instrument mid-market price.

In this scenario we seek core instrument prices, $\mathbf{p}$, that will return the minimal squared difference to all our single instrument mid prices, $\mathbf{s}$. Here, $\mathbf{A}$, is a transformation that maps core prices, $\mathbf{p}$, to the combined prices in $\mathbf{s}$.

$$\min_{\mathbf{p}} f(\mathbf{p}) = ||\mathbf{A}\mathbf{p} - \mathbf{s}||_2 = (\mathbf{A}\mathbf{p} - \mathbf{s})^{\mathbf{T}}(\mathbf{A}\mathbf{p} - \mathbf{s})$$

This has the solution, via a typical Moore-Penrose pseudoinverse,

$$\nabla_{\mathbf{p}} f = 0 \quad \implies \quad \mathbf{p}^* = (\mathbf{A}^{\mathbf{T}}\mathbf{A})^{-1}\mathbf{A}^{\mathbf{T}}\mathbf{s}$$

Thus for our supposed order book above,

$$\text{with} \quad \mathbf{A} = \begin{bmatrix} 1 & 0 & 0 \\ 0 & 1 & 0 \\ 0 & 0 & 1 \\ 1 & -1 & 0 \\ 1 & 0 & -1 \\ 0 & 1 & -1 \\ 1 & -2 & 1 \end{bmatrix}, \quad \mathbf{s} = \begin{bmatrix} 98.212 \\ 98.116 \\ 98.044 \\ 0.095 \\ 0.1665 \\ 0.074 \\ 0.022 \end{bmatrix}, \quad \mathbf{p}^* = \begin{bmatrix} 98.2114 \\ 98.1167 \\ 98.0439 \end{bmatrix}$$

where we notice that the single instrument algorithm mid price, of the three core instruments, differs slightly with these results as it has adjusted to better suit the determined mid prices of the extraneous instruments, i.e. the spreads and butterfly.

Least square regression models are also suitable in (and can be combined with) the case that multiple mid-market prices may be supplied for the *same* single instrument from different sources. For example, suppose the iSwap and TradX CLOB order books were used to derive 5Y and 10Y IRS mid-market prices. This may lead to the following system,

$$\text{with} \quad \mathbf{A} = \begin{bmatrix} 1 & 0 \\ 1 & 0 \\ 0 & 1 \\ 0 & 1 \\ -1 & 1 \\ -1 & 1 \end{bmatrix}, \quad \mathbf{s} = \begin{bmatrix} s_{\text{5Y iSwap}} \\ s_{\text{5Y TradX}} \\ s_{\text{10Y iSwap}} \\ s_{\text{10Y TradX}} \\ s_{\text{5s10s iSwap}} \\ s_{\text{5s10s TradX}} \end{bmatrix}, \quad \mathbf{p}^* = \begin{bmatrix} p^*_{\text{5Y}} \\ p^*_{\text{10Y}} \end{bmatrix}$$

It is also an option to aggregate order book data for the *same* instrument before computing a single instrument mid-market price algorithm. However, this might contain its own source of error, since the same prices might be supplied to multiple order books by the same party whose systems are capable of pulling, or adjusting, prices rapidly if one of the venues trades, therefore the *true* depth of the market may not be as reported by an aggregated order book.

Weighted least squares regression

The addition of weights as a diagonal matrix to the problem yields,

$$\min_{\mathbf{p}} f(\mathbf{p}) = (\mathbf{Ap} - \mathbf{s})^{\mathbf{T}} \mathbf{W}(\mathbf{Ap} - \mathbf{s})$$

with the adjusted solution,

$$\mathbf{p}^* = (\mathbf{A}^{\mathbf{T}} \mathbf{WA})^{-1} \mathbf{A}^{\mathbf{T}} \mathbf{Ws}$$

Suppose our weights, $\mathbf{W}$, were $\mathbf{diag}([1, 1, 1, 0.2, 0.2, 0.2, 0.1])$, then the solution would be impacted marginally to,

$$\mathbf{p}^* = \begin{bmatrix} 98.2116 \\ 98.1165 \\ 98.0439 \end{bmatrix}$$

The above algorithms provide some discretionary ways of determining a mid-market price of core level 1 instruments that provide the basis for a model which then prices level 2 assets, such as an interest rate curve(s) pricing bespoke IRSs. This assumes one has access to, and visibility of the order books. Of course it is entirely possible to specify the prices according to some other rule. With less liquid markets, it may be necessary to manually input some of the prices due a lack of other valid data, although we also suggest a predictive method below.

One should also note that in the case that the matrix, $\mathbf{A}$, is square and has full rank, the system is no longer least squares but is in fact a linear system with a unique solution. For example, supplying the 10Y and 5s10s prices will yield 10Y and 5Y core prices (provided $\mathbf{A}$ is correctly configured).

19.1.4   Bayesian inference

The nature of IRD markets, particularly across different currencies, is such that some markets might be fully transparent with deep and voluminous order books supporting an accurate assessment of mid-market prices. Others might be opaque with limited visibility (or none) on an electronically traded screen. In such circumstances one may choose to use these other, transparent, markets as a guide to the determined market movements in the opaque instruments.

This method is **parametric** since we will assume a statistical distribution. In this case we assume a **multivariate normal distribution**, and parametrise the mean and covariance of the market movements that we want to infer, and that act as our conditional variables.

Suppose that USD, EUR and GBP are three transparent markets with liquid futures order books and accurate methods for determining the 2Y, 5Y, 10Y and 30Y mid-market rates in those markets. Now suppose that NOK is an opaque market with few, if any, electronic order books from which to determine mid-market pricing. Let, $\mathbf{Q}$, be the, 16 by 16, covariance matrix of the 2Y, 5Y, 10Y and 30Y market movements in each currency USD, EUR, GBP, and NOK. For simplicity we can further assume this is centralised and that mean market movements are zero in each instrument, thus, $\mathbf{\Delta R} \sim N(\mathbf{0}, \mathbf{Q})$.

In our case, the first 12 market movements in $\mathbf{\Delta R}$ are known, since these correspond to the transparent instruments in USD, EUR and GBP: we denote these *known* market movements as, $\mathbf{x}$. The latter 4 are *unknown*, which we denote by, $\mathbf{Y}$, and we derive, in appendix section 19.5.2, the maximum likelihood estimator for these, conditioned on the known values under the assumed distribution. We find that,

$$(\mathbf{Q}^{-1})_{\mathbf{YY}} \mathbf{Y} = -(\mathbf{Q}^{-1})_{\mathbf{Yx}} \mathbf{x}$$

where $(\mathbf{Q}^{-1})_{\mathbf{Yx}}$ is the sub-matrix of the inverted covariance matrix corresponding to rows of the $\mathbf{Y}$ instruments and columns of the $\mathbf{x}$ instruments, and this is, therefore, a solvable linear system.

In practice, since we are dealing with market movements, one must be careful as to the timely application of this formula. As market movements are defined by the difference between initial prices and terminal prices the choice as to the initial price is important. If one were, for example, inferring NOK prices from a combination of USD, EUR, and GBP there would, at some point, be some reported (or observed) real mid-market trading levels which would dominate any Bayesian inferred market movements. Moving forward, it would then be sensible to 'reset' the measured market movements in USD, EUR, GBP and NOK from that observation time onwards to maintain the most likely mid-market under the assumed correlation model, subject to the most up to date information.

The following code, where H is a list of indexes which we want to infer, is added to our repository [21, #78b66e].

```
 1  def bayes_inferred_market_moves(Q, H, x, mu_x=None, mu_Y=None):
 2      n, Q_inv = Q.shape[0], np.linalg.inv(Q)
 3      mu_x = np.zeros((n-len(H), 1)) if mu_x is None else mu_x
 4      mu_Y = np.zeros((len(H), 1)) if mu_Y is None else mu_Y
 5      H_ = list(set(range(n)).difference(set(H)))
 6      Y = np.linalg.solve(Q_inv[np.ix_(H, H)], -np.matmul(Q_inv[np.ix_(H, H_)], x-mu_x))
 7      Y += mu_Y
 8      delta_r = np.zeros((n, 1))
 9      delta_r[H, :], delta_r[H_, :] = Y, x
10      return delta_r
```

Example 19.6.
Suppose that a NOK trader is trying to assess where the 2Y NOK IRS market will open at 0900hrs CET on a given day. He considers the USD, EUR, and GBP markets, which have liquid and transparent STIR futures markets which derive accurate 2Y mid-market rates. He knows the 2Y rate in all currencies as of 1615hrs CET the previous trading day, and he knows the current mid-market rates in three of those currencies,

$$\mathbf{r}_{2Y:t_0} = \begin{matrix} USD \\ EUR \\ GBP \\ NOK \end{matrix} \begin{bmatrix} 2.20 \\ 0.43 \\ 1.54 \\ 2.02 \end{bmatrix}, \quad \mathbf{r}_{2Y:t_1} = \begin{matrix} USD \\ EUR \\ GBP \\ NOK \end{matrix} \begin{bmatrix} 2.22 \\ 0.44 \\ 1.56 \\ ? \end{bmatrix}, \quad \mathbf{x} = \begin{bmatrix} 2.0 \\ 1.0 \\ 2.0 \end{bmatrix}$$

Measured over a historical sample he also has a covariance matrix of the 2Y rate in each of these currencies, and can therefore derive the Bayesian inferred market movements,

$$\mathbf{Q} = \begin{bmatrix} 1.00, 0.80, 0.85, 0.75 \\ 0.80, 1.00, 0.87, 0.84 \\ 0.85, 0.87, 1.00, 0.82 \\ 0.75, 0.84, 0.82, 1.00 \end{bmatrix}$$

```
1  >>> x = np.array([[2.0, 1.0, 2.0]]).transpose()
2  >>> bayes_inferred_market_moves(Q, [3], x)
3  [[2.0],
4   [1.0],
5   [2.0],
6   [1.294]]
```

Thus $\mathbf{Y} = [1.294]$ and the 2Y rate in NOK at time, t_1, is inferred as 2.0329%.

Suppose further that at time, t_1, the 2Y NOK market is observed to trade at 2.0275%. This creates a new referential data point, so that at time, t_2, which may be, for example 45 minutes after t_1, a new inference can be made between t_1 and t_2,

$$\mathbf{r}_{2Y:t_2} = \begin{matrix} USD \\ EUR \\ GBP \\ NOK \end{matrix} \begin{bmatrix} 2.225 \\ 0.425 \\ 1.56 \\ ? \end{bmatrix}, \quad \mathbf{x} = \begin{bmatrix} 0.5 \\ -1.5 \\ 0.0 \end{bmatrix}$$

```
1  >>> x = np.array([[0.5, -1.5, 0.0]]).transpose()
2  >>> bayes_inferred_market_moves(Q, [3], x)
3  [[0.5],
4   [-1.5],
5   [0.0],
6   [-0.710]]
```

Thus the new inferred mid-market at time, t_2, is now 2.0204% (2.0275 - 0.0071).

19.2   Slow and fast calculation

In fast and liquid markets, such as for EUR, USD and GBP IRSs, there may be a distinction made between fast and slow curveset calculation. The above calculation for mid-market prices, as well the then necessary curve construction process, may take an amount of processing time that is considered too slow and lead to delayed pricing. Even quarter of a second (250ms) might be too slow at times. In these cases, a solution we look to employ is parallelised calculation, where multiple processes are working simultaneously to provide the most accurate and timely curveset possible. In this framework we will propose the following worker processes that operate continually,

   i) **Data collector**: this process has direct connections to the exchanges, CLOBs, and any pricing data sources. Its purpose is to collect electronic, synchronous order book data and pass the data to the processor as quickly as possible.

  ii) **Data processor**: this process is configured to calculate mid-market prices according to the subjectivity and algorithms selected from sections 19.1.2 and 19.1.3. It may also make comparisons to the last synchronous dataset that was used in the construction of the most recent slow, full curveset.

 iii) **Curve builder**: this process accepts data from the processor and builds a curveset using the iterative curve solvers, for example from chapter 12. This curve is passed to the transformer.

  iv) **Transformer**: this process makes first order transformations, via a configured Jacobian matrix and matrix multiplication, to either the streamed market prices or a portfolio PV.

Figure 19.2 attempts to demonstrate the effect of these processes by means of a chronological chart. Initially, at time T_1, we need to construct our first curve of the day. Data is collected from the market, all of it is processed and passed to the curve builder, and after construction time the curve is built, at T_2. However, during this time, the market has moved - we now need a fast way to update the curve we just constructed reflecting new market data, and which doesn't go out of date as we execute that process.

After T_2, the data collector will collect, at time T_3, and pass a smaller subset of data to the data processor, along with the cached data in the same instruments which was used to build

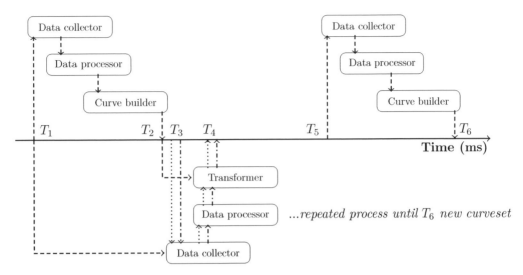

Figure 19.2: Illustrating parallel processes to construct curves as reactive to market data as possible.

the original curve. This time the data processor has the job of only calculating and comparing the most recent data with that used to build the curve. The differences are passed to the transformer. The transformer accepts the curve, or a portfolio PV with its risk sensitivities, and makes a linear transformation to those prices based on the differences it received from the data processor. The output is received at T_4.

The market lag is identified as $T_4 - T_3$. According to the figure this is approximately 25% of the time it takes to calculate a full curve build, which is $T_2 - T_1$. However, the chart is not necessarily to scale, and the objective is to minimise this lag as much as possible.

These processes repeat as scheduled all throughout the day. The fast process and transformer should be active as frequently as computationally feasible. The curve builder process is shown in the figure to repeat at time, T_5. This is approximately twice the length of time after T_1 as T_2 generally occurs, i.e. $T_5 \approx T_1 + 2(T_2 - T_1)$, giving more than enough time for the calculation to occur and then restart.

Example 19.7.

A curve has been constructed and is available at time, T_2, representing market rates from time, T_1. The calculated IRS rates are given below as a vector, $\mathbf{R_1}$, The original data, from time, T_1, cached in the data collector had bobl and bund mid-yields of 0.5000% and 1.0000% respectively.

$$\mathbf{R_1} = \begin{matrix} (4Y) \\ (5Y) \\ (6Y) \\ (7Y) \\ (8Y) \\ (9Y) \\ (10Y) \end{matrix} \begin{bmatrix} 0.750 \\ 0.765 \\ 0.779 \\ 0.782 \\ 0.783 \\ 0.782 \\ 0.781 \end{bmatrix}$$

The data collected from time, T_3, has bobl and bund mid-yields of 0.5005% and 1.0015%, meaning that the market movement approximating vector is $\mathbf{\Delta\tilde{R}_{1,3}} = [0.0005, 0.0015]^{\mathbf{T}}$. The static transformation matrix and the market adjusted rates valid for time, T_3, are calculated, *by the transformer process, as follows,*

$$\mathbf{R}_3 = \mathbf{R}_1 + \mathbf{J}\Delta\tilde{\mathbf{R}}_{1,3} = \begin{bmatrix} 0.7500 \\ 0.7650 \\ 0.7790 \\ 0.7820 \\ 0.7830 \\ 0.7820 \\ 0.7810 \end{bmatrix} + \begin{bmatrix} 1 & 0 \\ 1 & 0 \\ 0.8 & 0.2 \\ 0.6 & 0.4 \\ 0.4 & 0.6 \\ 0.2 & 0.8 \\ 0 & 1 \end{bmatrix} \begin{bmatrix} 0.0005 \\ 0.0015 \end{bmatrix} = \begin{bmatrix} 0.7505 \\ 0.7655 \\ 0.7797 \\ 0.7829 \\ 0.7841 \\ 0.7833 \\ 0.7825 \end{bmatrix}$$

Note that in this case the Jacobian has been statically encoded to map a linear proportion of the bobl and bund yield moves to the 4Y through to 10Y IRS rates. These calculated values, $\mathbf{R}_3$, are available at time, T_4.

19.3   Automated pricing model

This rest of this chapter is dedicated to discussing a model to price, from a market-maker's perspective, an arbitrary portfolio of IRSs upon request from a price-taker. Previous sections have discussed methods of determining accurate and timely mid-market prices and curvesets, thus we now **assume** that we have these at our disposal, and therefore we are confident that the mid-market of such trade requests can be priced accurately. We must now calibrate the margin, according to the risks of the portfolio and other factors such as the market conditions in which a market-maker is expected to hedge the trade request, although we begin by considering just the element, **market and reset risks**, depicted in figure 18.1.

Before we begin, I will comment on my own philosophy regarding software and model design. In my opinion, as one may have noticed with a number of items throughout this book, the best general approach to any programmatic solution is a **decoupled** one. This means that all tasks that can be appropriately isolated, separated and individually developed should be. The less dependence any process has on another will simultaneously make it easier to improve, either in efficiency or in scope, and easier to maintain from a developer's point of view when factoring employee turnover. This often has the additional benefit of having separate controlling parameters that are understandable to a model operator, i.e. a trader, as opposed to the model developer, i.e. the quantitative analyst.

Therefore our proposed model contains a core idea with decoupled, add-on components that serve to enhance that core. Mathematically, this may not be fully consistent, but the minor mathematical inefficiency is warranted by avoiding a complex black box algorithm in favour of a simple, transparent pricing mechanism. Consider the following analogy to give this context.

Example 19.8.
A baker requires 10 bags of salt and 12 bags of flour. From a vendor salt costs $2 and flour costs $4. As a bundle, a bag of each costs $5. The cheapest order the baker can place for his requirement is a simple, linear optimisation problem.

$$\min_{\mathbf{x}} \mathbf{c}^{\mathbf{T}}\mathbf{x}, \quad \text{subject to,} \quad \begin{bmatrix} 1 & 0 & 1 \\ 0 & 1 & 1 \end{bmatrix} \mathbf{x} = \begin{bmatrix} 10 \\ 12 \end{bmatrix}, \quad \text{where} \quad \mathbf{c} = \begin{bmatrix} 2 \\ 4 \\ 5 \end{bmatrix}, \ \mathbf{x} \geq \mathbf{0}. \tag{19.1}$$

The solution, by inspection (although this linear programming problem can be solved with the simplex algorithm), is $\mathbf{x}^* = [0, 2, 10]^{\mathbf{T}}$, which indicates it is best to order 2 individual flour bags and 10 bundles, for a total cost of $58.

Suppose that the vendor offered a discount for bulk orders. Instead of charging his prices on the total volume, he applied prices to the volume taken to the power of $\frac{4}{5}$, which, heuristically, gives an increasing discount of 10%, 30%, 40% and 45% on order sizes of 2, 5, 10 and 20 respectively. This changes the objective function (where the vector power is taken element-wise),

$$\min_{\mathbf{x}} \mathbf{c}^{\mathbf{T}} \mathbf{x}^{\frac{4}{5}}, \quad \text{subject to,} \quad \begin{bmatrix} 1 & 0 & 1 \\ 0 & 1 & 1 \end{bmatrix} \mathbf{x} = \begin{bmatrix} 10 \\ 12 \end{bmatrix}, \quad \text{where} \quad \mathbf{c} = \begin{bmatrix} 2 \\ 4 \\ 5 \end{bmatrix}, \mathbf{x} \geq \mathbf{0}. \quad (19.2)$$

This change has significant impact to the problem. It converts from a linear program into a non-linear problem with equality and inequality constraints. The latter requires a more complex and computationally intensive algorithm, most likely relying on sequential quadratic programming.

*If we choose to **approximate** 19.2 with 19.1 and apply an after adjustment using the approximated solution to determine an approximated minimum cost, we obtain,*

$$cost = \underbrace{\mathbf{c}^{\mathbf{T}}\mathbf{x}^*}_{\text{approximate cost}} - \underbrace{(\mathbf{c}^{\mathbf{T}}(\mathbf{x}^* - \mathbf{x}^{*\frac{4}{5}})}_{\text{adjustment}} = \$58 - \$19.5 = \$38.5$$

In example 19.8 the approximate solution of 19.2 is actually identical to the real solution. One can verify this either manually or by using a sequential quadratic program solver. In general, however, we won't know if the approximated solution is the true minimum, without further analysis. But the advantage in this case is that the decoupled nature of approximate solution and adjustment gives a more a comprehensible answer. The 'discount' of $19.5 is made obvious. In the following sections one will observe parallels between this basic example and our adopted approach.

For pedagogical purposes our curve and risk instruments will only be the 2Y, 5Y, 10Y, and 30Y IRSs, but it is, of course, expected that a practical model would be extended to the full set of market tradable tenors.

19.3.1 Equivalence of portfolios

We reiterate that IRSs portfolios are only a series of fixed and floating cashflows in their basic form. How trades are presented to our automated pricing model should not be a differentiating factor in the output price. For example consider the following three portfolios;

i) receiving 100mm 5Y5Y IRS,

ii) paying 100mm 5Y and receiving 100mm 10Y IRSs,

iii) receiving 5s10s (100mm 5Y versus 50mm 10Y) and receiving 50mm 10Y IRSs.

Assuming that all the fixed rates are the same on all trades (different fixed rates only introduce minimal annuity discounting differences and don't affect the general concept here), these portfolios are identical in terms of their cashflows and their market risk sensitivities. Therefore, any price that the model outputs should be identical. This reflects an application of the no arbitrage principle, since otherwise rational price-takers would selectively present one of three portfolios above to the pricing model to secure the most favourable price.

On the other hand, a human trader might naturally respond to the above three portfolios differently. For example; for portfolio i) he might quote a margin for the delta risk, such as 1bp, for portfolio ii) he might apply margin to the 5Y and to the 10Y, such as 0.35bps on each, for portfolio iii) he might apply margin to the 5s10s, such as 0.25bps and to the 10Y, such as 0.5bps. A human trader might also recognise these portfolios as being equivalent, since they are quite basic, and therefore might always show a consistent margin. However, when portfolios grow to include many more swaps this basic level of recognition is lost and therefore the next section attempts to reconcile our model with understandable parameters from a human perspective.

19.3.2   Parametrising the model

The margin price output of our model will be **risk based**. All portfolios will be reduced to a set of risks against benchmark tradable instruments, which ensures all equivalent portfolios are treated identically. In price terms we allow a human trader to determine margin for these benchmark trades which will act as parameters. We have three trade types to parametrise; outright trades, spread trades and butterfly trades.

Trade	Margin (bps)		Trades	5Y	10Y	30Y		Trade	Margin (bps)
2Y	0.4		2Y	0.25	0.45	0.85		2s5s10s	0.5
5Y	0.5		5Y	-	0.25	0.7		5s10s30s	0.6
10Y	0.5		10Y	-	-	0.55			
30Y	0.6								

Figure 19.3: Input model margin pricing parameters

Figure 19.3 contains twelve pricing parameters determined from mid-market. There are some **inherent constraints** that should be observed. For example 2s10s margin cannot be greater than the margin for 2s5s plus 5s10s, otherwise this would break the no arbitrage principle. For example if 2s5s cost 0.1bps, 5s10s cost 0.1bps, and 2s10s cost 0.25bps, our model would never use 2s10s, since the combination of 2s5s and 5s10s replicates 2s10s for a cheaper 0.2bps total margin. It is also not sensible to permit ambiguous solutions either, so 2s10s margin should really be strictly less than the sum of 2s5s and 5s10s to ensure that when 2s10s is required it is not, in some solutions, returned as 2s10s while in others returned as 2s5s combined with 5s10s, for an identical cost.

19.3.3   Solving the system

When a price request is submitted to our pricing model for a portfolio, P, the model will make two immediate calculations. Firstly it will calculate the risk, $\nabla_{\mathbf{S}} P$, and then it will calculate the PV of the portfolio using the most recent curve with the transformer adjusting the price based on those calculated risk sensitivities, according to section 19.2. That provides the mid-market price.

Next we derive the margin based on the above parametrisation. We will be solving a linear programming problem with equality constraints,

$$\min_{\mathbf{x}} f(\mathbf{x}) = \mathbf{c}^T |\mathbf{x}| \qquad \text{subject to} \qquad \mathbf{A}\mathbf{x} = \nabla_{\mathbf{S}} P$$

where $\mathbf{x} =$ *the allocation of risk amount to each parametrised instrument*

$\mathbf{A} =$ *mapping of each parametrised instrument to the risk model*

$\mathbf{c} =$ *hedge cost parameters associated with each instrument*

This optimisation problem finds the lowest cost combination of instruments that, combined, will replicate, or hedge, the requested portfolio of trades. We need to use the element-wise absolute value of $\mathbf{x}$ since the margin cost is positive regardless of positive or negative risk amounts.

In order to solve this using the simplex algorithm it must be transformed to an equivalent problem of standard form, using $\mathbf{t}$ as an associated slack variable, since absolute value problems are not solvable under the simplex algorithm:

$$\min_{\mathbf{x,t}} f_2(\mathbf{t}) = \mathbf{c}^T \mathbf{t}$$

$$\text{subject to} \quad \begin{bmatrix} \mathbf{A} & \mathbf{0} \end{bmatrix} \begin{bmatrix} \mathbf{x} \\ \mathbf{t} \end{bmatrix} = \boldsymbol{\nabla}_{\mathbf{S}} P$$

$$\begin{bmatrix} \mathbf{I} & -\mathbf{I} \\ -\mathbf{I} & -\mathbf{I} \\ \mathbf{0} & -\mathbf{I} \end{bmatrix} \begin{bmatrix} \mathbf{x} \\ \mathbf{t} \end{bmatrix} \leq \mathbf{0} \tag{19.3}$$

The following code, when inherited by our `Portfolio` class, will perform this optimisation. It is included in the code repository [21, #358d5c].

```
from scipy import optimize as op

class Margin_:

    def model_margin(self, c, A, S):
        n = c.shape[0]
        I = np.eye(n)
        ret = op.linprog(
            c=np.block([np.zeros(n), c[:, 0]]),
            A_eq=np.block([A.T, np.zeros(A.T.shape)]), b_eq=S[:, 0],
            A_ub=np.block([[I, -I], [-I, -I]]), b_ub=np.zeros(2*n),
            bounds=[(-1e10, 1e10)] * n + [(0, 1e10)] * n,
            method="highs-ds"
        )
        return ret.fun, ret.x[:n], ret
```

The simplex algorithm is not computationally intensive and will usually complete in negligible time for the limited number of instruments for which one will typically solve in this problem.

Example 19.9.
Our above portfolio of a single 100mm 5Y5Y IRS yields the below risk for a given curve,

$$\boldsymbol{\nabla}_{\mathbf{S}} P = \begin{matrix} (2Y) \\ (5Y) \\ (10Y) \\ (30Y) \end{matrix} \begin{bmatrix} 23 \\ 47,433 \\ -90,529 \\ 0 \end{bmatrix}.$$

Using the parameters from figure 19.3 , if we enter this into our margin calculator model we return the result,

```
>>> pf = Portfolio([Swap(datetime(2027, 12*5, 12, 12))])
>>> df = DataFrame({
        "2Y": [1, 0, 0, 0, -1, -1, -1, 0, 0, 0, -1, 0],
        "5Y": [0, 1, 0, 0, 1, 0, 0, -1, -1, 0, 2, -1],
        "10Y": [0, 0, 1, 0, 0, 1, 0, 1, 0, -1, -1, 2],
        "30Y": [0, 0, 0, 1, 0, 0, 1, 0, 1, 1, 0, -1],
        "c": [0.4, 0.5, 0.5, 0.6, 0.25, 0.45, 0.85, 0.25, 0.7, 0.55, 0.5, 0.6],
    })
>>> c, A = df[["c"]].to_numpy(), df[["2Y", "5Y", "10Y", "30Y"]].to_numpy().T
>>> S = pf.risk(curve)
>>> output = pf.model_margin(c, A, S)
>>> output[0]  # this is the calculated margin from mid
33,405
>>> df["x"] = output[1]
>>> df
```

Instrument	2Y	5Y	10Y	30Y	c	x^*
2Y	1	0	0	0	0.40	0
5Y	0	1	0	0	0.50	0
10Y	0	0	1	0	0.50	-43,073
30Y	0	0	0	1	0.60	0
2s5s	-1	1	0	0	0.25	0
2s10s	-1	0	1	0	0.45	-22
2s30s	-1	0	0	1	0.85	0
5s10s	0	-1	1	0	0.25	-47,433
5s30s	0	-1	0	1	0.70	0
10s30s	0	0	-1	1	0.55	0
2s5s10s	-1	2	-1	0	0.50	0
5s10s30s	0	-1	2	-1	0.60	0

$\mathbf{c^T x^*} = 33,405$ *is equivalent to basic margin on the analytic delta of the 5Y5Y of 0.78bps.*

19.4   Model extensions

The above model provides a basic introduction and a very efficient algorithm to determine a pricing margin. Anecdotally, this is not only useful in this context but, in a consultative capacity, I have also applied this model to calculate the prudent valuation margin for a large Nordic bank's IRS and FX risks, for inclusion in its regulatory and financial disclosures.

We will now present a few ideas to demonstrate some additional features that can be incorporated. These included proposals are made as decoupled add-ons to the above model.

An automated pricing model tends to eliminate the **outside influence** factors, especially **time pressure** and **political pressure**, that are highlighted in figure 18.1. The other factors we try to highlight below are items such as **non-modelled effects**, **liquidity and volatility** and **cost of regulatory capital**.

19.4.1   Volume and market impact

Our pricing model is ignorant of the impact of large portfolios, i.e. those that require market hedges with large volumes. Under the above, scaling up the size of a portfolio linearly scales the designated margin amount (since the margin model proposed is a linearly homogeneous function). Studies, such as [55] and [56], indicate that large orders leave an impact on prices following a square root law, i.e.

$$\text{Market impact (bps) of instrument, } i = \alpha_i \sqrt{|x_i|}$$

Suppose this is also true for IRS markets then we should factor in the cost of the market impact into our hedging considerations, which will increase the total margin. In order to calculate the incremental, additional hedge cost associated with market impact we integrate the above,

$$\text{Additional hedge cost (bps) of instrument, } i = \frac{1}{|x_i|} \int_0^{|x_i|} \alpha_i \sqrt{z} dz = \frac{2\alpha_i}{3} \sqrt{|x_i|}$$

For simplicity, assume that every market instrument in our model experiences the same impact and that the parameter, $\alpha = \frac{1}{1000}$. This gives an impact of 1bp for a risk amount of 1mm. The additional hedge cost in local currency can be calculated as,

$$\text{Volume add-on (ccy)} = \frac{2}{3} \boldsymbol{\alpha^T} |\mathbf{x^*}|^{\frac{3}{2}}$$

If we apply this same technique to the solution instruments in example 19.9 we result in additional charges, which increase the calculated margin from 33,405 to 46,252, or from 0.78bps of delta risk to 1.08bps. See table 19.3

Instrument	Risk	Market Impact (bps)	Added cost (bps)	Added Cost (Ccy)
10Y	-43,073	0.21	0.138	5,959
2s10s	-22	0.00	0.00	0
5s10s	-47,433	0.22	0.145	6,887

Table 19.3: Additional hedging costs after market impact considerations.

The astute mathematician will recognise that this is a similar issue as with our vendor's discount in example 19.8. The add-on could be incorporated into the original optimisation problem in the previous section. However doing so would convert the linear program to a non-linear optimisation problem requiring a more complex algorithm. The incorporation of further add-ons that will be proposed below might also have the effect of converting the optimisation problem into more of a 'black-box' solution that might be difficult to interpret, and/or validate.

19.4.2 Inventory hedging

Adjusting margin for trade requests that either offset, or add to, the existing market-maker's positions should be a considered extension. This requires, obviously, the knowledge and input of the existing market-maker's positions and a guarantee that it is up to date and accurate. For example this means that any trades that have been executed but not booked into the system, e.g. voice brokered interbank trades, must somehow be included or 'slated' in the risk. This is not impossible to do but it requires a very organised, structured and efficient internal trading platform. Anecdotally, of all the market-making banks I have experienced, this was only barely, technically possible to achieve at one of them.

Technical issues aside, another reason this is a valid consideration is to avoid being arbitraged when a price-taker submits a trade numerous times to build up volume and 'average in'. For example, consider two cases, using our parametrised model from above;

i) a price-taker submits a request with 10Y risk of 100,000 pv01. This returns a margin, in normal conditions, of,

$$\underbrace{50,000}_{\text{core margin}} + \underbrace{21,081}_{\text{volume add-on}} = \underbrace{71,081}_{\text{total margin}} , \quad \text{or 0.71bps from mid-market.}$$

ii) a price-taker submits a request with 10Y risk of 50,000 pv01. This returns,

$$25,000 + 7,453 = 32,453, \quad \text{or 0.65bps from mid-market.}$$

If the price-taker submitted item ii) twice, in rapid succession, (with the intention of always trading 100,000 pv01) one of two outcomes would be likely;

i) either the market-maker has not had time to execute any hedge and thus no market impact is visible and the market-maker is still holding the risk from the first trade. Without further adjustment, the price-taker secures an executable price of 0.65bps, again, averaging this same price for the full size of 100,000 pv01 from the original mid-market.

ii) or the market-maker has hedged the trade rapidly which has (over statistical averages) left a market impact of 0.22bps. The second trade is priced 0.65bps from the impacted mid which totals 0.87bps from the original mid-market. Averaged over two trades the total price from the original mid-market is 0.76bps.

All of these outcomes for the price-taker, 0.71, 0.65 or 0.76 bps from the original mid-market, in 100,000 pv01, are different. Clearly the price-taker would favour the second where the market-maker has no time to hedge, nor impact the market, and repeatedly offers the same price without accounting for increasing volumes. Therefore, we must propose that the market-maker's inventory is considered.

Suppose the market-maker's current risk inventory is, $\mathbf{S_{inv}}$, then performing the same optimisation as in equation 19.3 would give the inventory risk in equivalent instruments in our margin model, $\mathbf{x^*_{inv}}$. When we perform our volume add-on instead of calculating relative to the trade request we add, and subtract, the existing inventory,

$$\textit{Volume add-on (ccy)} = \frac{2}{3}\boldsymbol{\alpha}^{\mathbf{T}}\left(|\mathbf{x^*} + \mathbf{x^*_{inv}}|^{\frac{3}{2}} - |\mathbf{x^*_{inv}}|^{\frac{3}{2}}\right)$$

Example 19.10.
A price-taker requested 50,000 pv01 of 10Y with a market-maker, received a price of 0.65bps from mid and executed. The market-maker's risk inventory, which was initially zero, now includes this executed risk. The same price-taker immediately makes a repeated request for another 50,000 pv01. The volume add-on in this case is calculated to be,

$$\frac{2}{3}\frac{1}{1000}\left((50,000+50,000)^{\frac{3}{2}} - 50,000^{\frac{3}{2}}\right) = 13,628, \quad \textit{or 0.27bps}$$

Measured over his two price quotations the price-taker averages, $\frac{1}{2}(0.65+0.77) = 0.71bps$, which is exactly the same price he would have received had he requested only a single price for 100,000 pv01, when the market-maker's inventory was initially zero.

This proposed method for accounting for inventory has the advantage that the volume add-on cost is consistent with a no arbitrage principle: there is no longer a distinction between submitting a price request for the full size, or repeated price requests in smaller volumes, with no intermediate hedging. There is an inconsistency if two trades are requested and the market-maker performs hedges in between, but this is acceptable since the market impact is a model of a random variable and in this case the second price request comes after the market impact is known, i.e. more information is available to the trader in a Bayesian context.

This inventory accounting also ensures that trades which can reduce the inventory are favourably priced, i.e. the volume add-on is reversed. This leaves the market-maker with profit equivalent to the parametrised margin from mid only, and creates a system with an embedded preference to target zero inventories.

19.4.3   Correlation

Correlation occurs when our solved model generates tradable instruments that would be difficult to execute simultaneously. Similarly, the market impact of trading one of these instruments might be expected to also cause market impact in another instrument, which is not directly priced into our volume add-on. In the case of example 19.9 we have risk in 10Y and 5s10s. It might be worse if we had 10Y, 2s10s, 5s10s and 10s30s all with same direction in the 10Y bucket.

To make an assessment of the correlation risk here we can use the CoVaR techniques from chapter 14, as well as taking, $\mathbf{Q}$, from that chapter. We will calculate the CoVaR multiplier

Inventory	Requested	Volume Add-on
0	50,000	7,454
50,000	50,000	13,628
50,000	-50,000	-7,454
50,000	-100,000	0
100,000	-50,000	-13,628
100,000	-100,000	-21,082
100,000	0	0

Table 19.4: Example volume add-on amounts for combinations of inventory and requested risk.

using the full covariance matrix, and secondly with only the diagonal elements, which asserts the correlation between all instruments is zero. We can extend the covariance matrix, $\mathbf{Q}$, from that including only the 2Y, 5Y, 10Y and 30Y instruments to include all of our model instruments by reusing the $\mathbf{A}$ matrix of the optimisation constraints in equation 19.3,

$$\mathbf{Q}_{\mathrm{model}} = \mathbf{A}^{\mathrm{T}}\mathbf{Q}\mathbf{A}$$

and then the CoVaR multiplier as normal, and assuming no correlation, can be calculated, using the data from example 19.9, as,

$$c = \sqrt{\mathbf{x}^{\mathrm{T}}\mathbf{Q}_{\mathrm{model}}\mathbf{x}} = 126,091$$

$$c_{\mathrm{zero\ corr}} = \sqrt{\mathbf{x}^{\mathrm{T}}\mathbf{diag}(\mathbf{diagonal}(\mathbf{Q}_{\mathrm{model}}))\mathbf{x}} = 123,434$$

This shows that our tradable instruments are only very slightly correlated. The residual VaR increase of 2,657, compared with the uncorrelated VaR, we choose to multiply by an additional parameter, say 15%, and add that to the previously calculated margin.

This extension is likely to benefit from a more rigorous and robust quantitative metric, but this serves a pedagogical purpose and suffices in the current absence of a better idea. One should be careful that this add-on does not reduce the margin by too large a value in the case of negatively correlated instruments. But, in this respect I will offer the conjecture that a well parametrised margin model, combined with the optimisation solution of equation 19.3 will result in risk instruments with a minimal degree of negative correlation. Statistical sampling strongly supports this conjecture.

19.4.4 Liquidity and Volatility

Liquidity and volatility go hand in hand. Our current pricing model only outputs a margin based on static trader parameters. Of course these parameters can be updated by a human trader but this requires constant monitoring and potentially heavy workload. Suppose that we would like our model to dynamically update we then need to develop a method for assessing the liquidity and volatility of the market at a given moment.

For explanatory purposes we will propose using transparent instruments, such as EUREX bund or bobl futures or CBOT treasury futures, as a means to proxy the liquidity of associated IRS markets and make a margin add on adjustment. Consider the two order books in figure 19.5. In order to assess them we plot the width between the intrinsic depth average bid and ask against intrinsic volumes.

Empirically this shows that the lower liquidity conditions, in this case, yield approximately twice the margin of intrinsic volumes than normal conditions. We will make the assumption

112	169.70	169.71	145
145	169.69	169.72	189
165	169.68	169.73	199
156	169.67	169.74	212
198	169.66	169.75	215
256	169.65	169.76	278

(a) normal conditions

36	169.70	169.71	53
78	169.69	169.72	88
86	169.68	169.73	79
111	169.67	169.74	102
121	169.66	169.75	198
189	169.65	169.76	213

(b) lower liquidity conditions

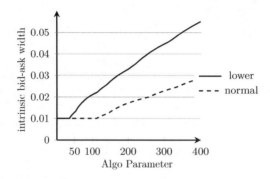

Figure 19.5: Comparative order books and intrinsic margin widths.

here to use this liquidity factor and multiply our volume add-on and correlation add-on to adjust them dynamically.

Although this mechanism is valid it is especially subjective;

i) using bond futures as a liquidity proxy for IRSs needs statistical support,

ii) using this particular intrinsic depth algorithm to assess liquidity is one of many possible approaches,

iii) assuming a linear relationship between liquidity and volatility is spurious and needs statistical evidence,

iv) proper model cross-validation should be performed to define *normal* conditions,

v) scaling just the add-ons and not the basic margin is an unjustified model choice.

We highlight this for thoroughness, and to point out that we are not cavalier with respect to data driven models but, for the sake of brevity of section, this is the approach we adopt.

One final point to make in this regard is about negative volume add-on. We may need to set a minimum to avoid too low prices.

Example 19.11.
A price-taker receives a price of 0.65bps from mid-market from an inventory neutral market-maker in 50,000 pv01 10Y and executes. This included a volume add-on charge of 7,454 (0.15bps). Liquidity worsens significantly to a quarter of the recent, normal conditions. A new price-taker requests a price in -50,000 pv01 and the market-maker's inventory includes the risk from the previously executed trade. The model calculates a negative add-on to offset inventory and a total margin of,

$$50,000 * 0.5 - 7,454 * 4 = -4,816$$

which is converted to zero as a protective measure. The second price-taker therefore executes the trade at mid-market and the market-maker's inventory is reverted to neutral. By executing two trades (assuming the same mid-market price) the market-maker has made 32,454 in profit. Ordinarily this would have been 50,000 profit but the profit was reduced by the failure to predict worsening liquidity conditions, which ultimately came at a cost to the market-maker.

19.4.5 Other possible extensions

Here will propose some additional ideas of aspects that should be incorporated but are also subjective in their approach.

Toxic flow

Toxic flow is generally described as that which loses money almost the instant that it executes. Commonly it occurs when price-takers aim to profit from spurious market pricing. One method of avoiding this is, of course, to have a margin that sufficiently compensates for this phenomenon, but, on the other hand, for regular fair pricing this is likely to be too conservative and potentially price a market-maker out of a competitive market.

Anecdotally, the most success I have had in this regard has been using historical time series of trades and tending to mean revert prices that deviated significantly from their recent history. This was especially effective with regard to pricing hedge fund RV price requests in GBP and EUR.

Off-the-run trades

The example trade we have used throughout this chapter was a 5Y5Y, which has risk exactly to the 5Y and 10Y buckets. Suppose that the trade was 4.5Y5Y instead. This would still yield similar risk structure in the 5Y and 10Y buckets but it is not exactly the same trade. In fact, it is worse, since hedging the portfolio with 5Y and 10Y buckets will leave interpolation risk and the portfolio will experience risk bleed as explained in section 9.3.5. As explained in that section one way of identifying this is to use a more granular risk framework. A residual risk model can be constructed that functions as an add on to identifying these types of off-the-run risk and appropriately charge more than if the requested portfolio can be perfectly hedged with benchmark trades.

Regulatory capital

The pricing of regulatory capital and of other forms of pricing adjustments should also be a concern. If these are required to be included in the margin priced for electronic trades a system capable of efficiently calculating these numbers should be developed. For this reason, it is quite common to restrict electronic trades only to those that are cleared through a CCP to provide consistency.

The code repository [21, #9d1193] contains an alternative example that is worth exploring in a Jupyter Notebook.

19.5 Appendix

19.5.1 Mean intrinsic depth average

$$p_{mida} = \frac{1}{Z} \int_0^Z p_{ida}(z) dz = \frac{1}{2Z} \left(\int_0^Z p_{bida}(z) dz + \int_0^Z p_{aida}(z) dz \right)$$

where the integral is decomposed into the separate parts between the relevant values of bid and ask sizes,

$$\int_0^Z p_{bida}(z) dz = \sum_{j=1}^{n-1} \int_{\sum_{k=0}^{j-1} w_k}^{\sum_{k=0}^{j} w_k} p_{bida}(z) dz + \int_{\sum_{k=0}^{n-1} w_k}^Z p_{bida}(z) dz$$

Let, $W_j = \sum_{k=0}^{j} w_k$, be the cumulative sum of w for different depth levels, and, $B_j = \sum_{k=1}^{j} b_k w_k$, be the cumulative sum of price-volumes for those same depth levels. Then the above is more concisely written as,

$$\int_0^Z p_{bida}(z) dz = \sum_{j=1}^{n-1} \int_{W_{j-1}}^{W_j} \frac{b_j(z - W_{j-1}) + B_{j-1}}{z} dz + \int_{W_{n-1}}^Z p_{bida}(z) dz$$

$$= \sum_{j=1}^{n-1} b_j(W_j - W_{j-1}) + (B_{j-1} - b_j W_{j-1})(\ln W_j - \ln W_{j-1})$$

$$+ b_n(Z - W_{n-1}) + (B_{n-1} - b_n W_{n-1})(\ln T - \ln W_{n-1})$$

Note the same method applies to the ask sizes and the ask volumes.

19.5.2 Bayesian inference of market movements

Suppose a covariance matrix, $\mathbf{Q}$, of IRS market movements. Furthermore assume a mean, $\boldsymbol{\mu}$, which may well be zero and an **assumed multivariate normal distribution** such that,

$$\boldsymbol{\Delta R} \sim N(\boldsymbol{\mu}, \mathbf{Q}), \quad \implies \quad f_{\boldsymbol{\Delta R}}(\boldsymbol{\Delta r}) = det(2\pi \mathbf{Q})^{-\frac{1}{2}} exp\left((\boldsymbol{\Delta r} - \boldsymbol{\mu})^\mathbf{T} \mathbf{Q}^{-1} (\boldsymbol{\Delta r} - \boldsymbol{\mu}) \right)$$

where, $\boldsymbol{\Delta R}$, is a vector of random market movements of length, n. Suppose that the first, m, market movements of $\boldsymbol{\Delta R}$ are *known* and denote these by, $\mathbf{x}$, and furthermore suppose that the latter $n - m$, market movements are *unknown* and denote these by $\mathbf{Y}$.

We seek the maximum likelihood estimators, $\hat{\mathbf{Y}}$, given $\mathbf{x}$, which are the solution of the optimisation problem,

$$\max_{\mathbf{Y}} \; f_{\boldsymbol{\Delta R}}(\boldsymbol{\Delta r}|\mathbf{x}) = \max_{\mathbf{Y}} \; \ln f_{\boldsymbol{\Delta R}}(\boldsymbol{\Delta r}|\mathbf{x})$$

which reduces, after neglecting constants and expanding the matrix multiplication, to,

$$\max_{\mathbf{Y}} g(\mathbf{Y}, \mathbf{x}, \boldsymbol{\mu}) = \max_{\mathbf{Y}} \; 2(\mathbf{Y} - \boldsymbol{\mu_Y})^\mathbf{T}(\mathbf{Q}^{-1})_{\mathbf{Yx}}(\mathbf{x} - \boldsymbol{\mu_x}) + (\mathbf{Y} - \boldsymbol{\mu_Y})^\mathbf{T}(\mathbf{Q}^{-1})_{\mathbf{YY}}(\mathbf{Y} - \boldsymbol{\mu_Y}) \,.$$

where $(\mathbf{Q}^{-1})_{\mathbf{Yx}}$ is the sub-matrix of the inverted covariance matrix corresponding to rows of the $\mathbf{Y}$ instruments and columns of the $\mathbf{x}$ instruments. This is an unconstrained quadratic program, with solution available via usual calculus techniques,

$$\nabla_{\mathbf{Y}} g(\mathbf{Y}, \mathbf{x}, \boldsymbol{\mu}) = 0 \quad \implies \quad (\mathbf{Q}^{-1})_{\mathbf{YY}}(\mathbf{Y} - \boldsymbol{\mu_Y}) = -(\mathbf{Q}^{-1})_{\mathbf{Yx}}(\mathbf{x} - \boldsymbol{\mu_x}) \,.$$

Swaptions and Volatility

Swaptions are IRDs, but they are not classed as part of the 'linear rates product set'. This book's focus is on those linear rates products; swaps in particular. Thus, the approach we take here is to introduce swaptions from the point of view of the linear rates trader, and not the swaptions trader. Swaptions are important because they are the simplest product which permit the trading of volatility. They also allow the volatility surface to be calibrated. In turn, volatility is important because of its implications to the term structure of the yield curve and to the PnL of portfolios containing gamma and cross-gamma risks.

Option pricing theory is used in a few instances in this book so a basic grounding is helpful. What we will specifically avoid, though, is to discuss stochastic equations and the derivation of the Black-Scholes equation (and others) for pricing options. For interested readers there is a wealth of published material easily researched in this regard, and [2], [3] and [57] provide far more detail than discussed here.

Instead, we remain focused on practicality and specifically aim to advise linear rates traders on how to monitor and use volatility. We show here;

- what call and put options are and what the equivalent payer and receiver swaptions are,
- basic terminology of general options and swaptions in particular,
- an overview and a little history of the underlying no arbitrage argument that ultimately derives a swaption price,
- how assumptions of probability distributions affect the price of swaptions,
- formulae necessary to price swaptions, and Python code to achieve this which can be found in the code repository[21, #8ff128]
- why swaptions permit trading of an asset class of its own; IR volatility,
- various definitions of volatility, and aspects such as the vol surface, smile and skew,
- methods for calculating the volatility of fwds, and forward volatility,
- definitions of other 'greeks', and extraneous topics.

20.1   Option basics

Premium, strike, exercise and expiry

A simple, generic option allows the purchaser of the option contract to enter a new financial transaction at some point in the future, at a pre-agreed price or rate, if he chooses to do so.

The amount of money paid by the buyer to purchase the option is known as the **premium**, or price of the option. The premium is often paid upfront, but it can also be paid at a future date. Similar concerns about credit and collateral that were discussed in chapter 5 are relevant to option premiums and the PV of options.

The precise moment in the future when the buyer chooses to exercise his option and enter a new financial transaction is known as the **exercise time**. The pre-agreed price or rate of the new financial transaction is known as the **strike**.

Options are only offered to their buyers for a set period of time. After a contractually agreed amount of time the option is said to have expired, at the **expiry time**. After this time the buyer has no available claim to enter into a new financial transaction at the previously agreed strike.

Options can also be described as American or European (or Bermudan). European options are the most simple options, due to the fact they can only be exercised at the precise point at which they expire. American options have a specific time period leading up to expiry, during which they can be exercised at any time at the discretion of the option buyer. Bermudan options are blend of the former types permitting multiple discrete opportunities when exercise is permitted.

In this chapter we only discuss the European style since this is the standard for interbank swaptions. This means that for purposes of European options and swaptions the terms exercise time and expiry time are synonymous.

Direction and settlement type

For options on equities, commodities, and other securities one can purchase either an option to buy that specific security, or sell that specific security at an agreed strike price at expiry. These are called **call options** and **put options** respectively.

In the interest rate market one can buy an option to pay fixed on an IRS, or receive fixed on an IRS, at a pre-agreed strike rate at expiry. These are called **payer swaptions** and **receiver swaptions** respectively. Sometimes these swaptions are referred to simply as 'payers' and 'receivers'. It is very common for books describing option pricing to graphically illustrate the 'pay-offs' of each option direction at expiry. The traditional 'hockey stick' chart is shown in figure 20.1. The charts show the pay-off for the buyer of each type of swaption. The pay-off to the seller can be obtained simply by reflecting the graph vertically, i.e. about the x-axis.

Swaptions can also be either cash settled, or physically settled. Physically settled means that the underlying IRS is executed and booked on the expiry date between the counterparties (or through a CCP) at the agreed strike price. Cash settled means that, at expiry, the difference in PV between the exercised IRS and prevailing mid-market IRS in the same notional is assessed[1] and paid to the buyer.

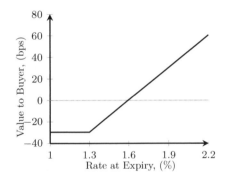 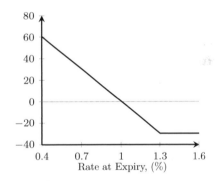

(a) A payer swaption with a strike of 1.30%.   (b) A receiver swaption of strike of 1.3%.

Figure 20.1: The pay-offs to the buyer of the swaption, in bps, at expiry with an initial premium of 29.5bps.

Terminology

Like other interest rate products some terminology needs to be established to reference different swaptions. Market convention is to discuss swaptions in the form, "expiry, swap, strike, type". A couple of examples are,

1M 5Y 1.0% Payer: a payer swaption on a 5Y IRS with a strike of 1.0% expiring in 1M.
4Y 5Y5Y 1.5% Receiver: a receiver swaption on a 5Y5Y IRS with a 1.5% strike, expiring in 4Y.
Note also that common market terminology sometimes calls the underlying IRS the **tail**. So, for a 1Y10Y swaption, the tail is identified as a 10Y par IRS.

A standardisation that is made for swaptions is the **expiry time** on a given day. Recall that for European swaptions, which make up the bulk of the market, this expiry time is also the exercise time and makes it very important for risk management and settlement. Swaptions

---

[1]this 'assessment' is determined by calculating an analytic pv01 for the underlying IRS using the ISDA fix for discounting in an IRR style, shown in the appendix

with an expiry on any given day will do so **at a specific time local to their currency** alongside all other swaptions adhering to the same ISDA documentation.

In order to standardise settlement for cash settled options, ISDA fixings for a set of tenor IRSs rates are compiled and published. These fixings represent the par IRS rates at the precise moment that swaptions expire, and therefore provide reference points for making cash settlement determinations.

For swaptions with underlying IRSs that do not form part of the set of tenors for which ISDA fixings are published, such as fwd IRSs, then physical settlement is the most common approach to exercise.

History

Option pricing really took off in the late '70s and '80s. This was after Black and Scholes published their famous paper[57].

The original idea Black and Scholes proposed was to continually trade the market in the underlying product (or continually delta hedge) so that at the point of expiry the pay-off of the trading strategy would precisely match that of the option. They were creating a synthetic option through their specifically designed trading strategy. Having designed their strategy they argued that the overall cost of it should mirror the premium on an option with the same target strike price and expiry. This is another application of the no arbitrage principle. Theoretically if the price of the option were higher than their strategy implied it would be better to sell the option and delta hedge in the respective direction. If the price of the option was too low then it would be better to buy the option and delta hedge in the other respective direction.

It is due to this fundamental idea that the pricing of options is so dependent upon the assumed volatility of the market. When the market is volatile the continual delta hedging becomes expensive for buyers, and when it is not volatile much less delta hedging is needed overall to synthesise the structure of the option. Specifically the Black and Scholes strategy depends on having a precise delta exposure, for a particular market price relative to the strike, with a specific time until expiry. For volatile markets the frequent changes in required delta exposures leads to frequent delta hedging at different executable levels. The costs of permitting this strategy mount and equivalently the respective option prices increase.

20.2   Swaption pricing

20.2.1   Pricing formulae

As highlighted, the **volatility** of an underlying IRS rate is an important parameter for pricing its swaptions. A second important parameter is the assumed **statistical distribution** of the underlying IRS rate. The distribution assumption, combined with the volatility assumption, allows an assessment to be made of the likelihood of that swaption being ITM or OTM at expiry, and of the delta hedging cost in the interim period until expiry.

It is possible (using different mathematical techniques) to price a swaption from the point of view of *any* supposed underlying probability distribution, but here we give examples of two; the normal distribution and the log-normal distribution[2]. We use these distributions to describe interest rates because their formulae are analytic and, secondly, because they form a market standard.

---

[2]see section 1.3.1 for description of these distributions

For simply monitoring swaption markets the choice(s) of distribution is often redundant, provided the assumptions of either are understood.

Pricing swaptions can be confusing because of how the prices are quoted, for example in absolute cash terms or in rate percentage terms or in percentage of notional. The formulae we show below are in **rate percentage terms**. To produce an absolute cash price, the rate percentage price and analytic delta of the fwd IRS should be multiplied together (see examples 20.1 and 20.1). The absolute cash price can then be readily converted a percentage of the notional as the third pricing label. Swaption traders are used to quoting prices in percentage of notional terms, which are rarely quoted here, so be careful of this distinction.

We give the formulae for **physically settled payer swaptions** using the following notation;

F is the mid-market rate of the underlying fwd IRS,

K is the strike rate set on the swaption,

σ is the volatility per period, usually expressed annually,

T is the number of periods until expiry, usually in years,

$\Phi(x)$ is the cumulative standard normal distribution[3].

Under a **normal distribution**, $F \sim N(F, \frac{\sigma_N}{100})$, with volatility given in absolute bps, σ_N, the price, given in percentage point terms, is,

$$O_p = (F - K)\Phi(x) + \frac{\sigma_N\sqrt{T}}{100\sqrt{2\pi}}e^{-\frac{1}{2}x^2}, \quad \text{where,} \quad x = \frac{100(F - K)}{\sigma_N\sqrt{T}}.$$

Under a **log-normal distribution**, $F \sim \ln N(F, \frac{\sigma_{LN}}{100})$ with volatility in (approximate) relative percentage terms, σ_{LN}, the price, given in percentage point terms, is,

$$O_p = F\Phi(x) - K\Phi\left(x - \frac{\sigma_{LN}\sqrt{T}}{100}\right), \quad x = \frac{100}{\sigma_{LN}\sqrt{T}}\left(\ln\left(\frac{F}{K}\right) + \frac{1}{2}\frac{\sigma_{LN}^2 T}{10,000}\right).$$

20.2.2 Receiver-payer (put-call) parity

A commonly known result from option pricing theory is the so-called put-call parity. In swaption terminology this is equivalently receiver-payer parity. Suppose a trader buys a physically settled payer and sells a physically settled receiver with the same strike price, say 2%. Then the pay-off diagram at expiry is simply a straight, 45° upward line, identically replicating the pay-off of paying the underlying IRS. Of course, there can be no arbitrage so the difference between the strike rate and the mid-market fwd rate must be accounted for. This results in the receiver-payer parity equation below and allows the determination of the respective receiver price,

$$O_p - O_r = F - K.$$

Note that these pricing formulae are only valid for physically settled swaptions. Cash settled swaptions have small pricing adjustments which we do not cover here, although the concept is outlined in section 21.5.3.

---

[3]this value is not analytically determinable but many excellent approximations exist to calculate it, here we will use the Python SciPy package

20.2.3   Python code for swaption pricing

The following outlines a simple Python function to price physically settled swaptions, incorporating all of the information above regarding their pricing theory.

```
1 from math import pi, log, exp
2 from scipy.stats import norm
3
4 def swaption_price(forward, strike, expiry, ann_vol, option, distribution):
5     adj_vol = ann_vol * expiry ** 0.5 / 100
6     if distribution == "log":
7         x = (log(forward / strike) + 0.5 * adj_vol**2) / adj_vol
8         n1, n2 = norm.cdf(x), norm.cdf(x-adj_vol)
9         payer_price = forward * n1 - strike * n2
10    elif distribution == "normal":
11        x = (forward - strike) / adj_vol
12        n1 = norm.cdf(x)
13        payer_price = (forward - strike) * n1 + (adj_vol / (2*pi)**0.5) * exp(-x**2/2)
14    else:
15        raise ValueError("`distribution` must be in {'log', 'normal'}.")
16
17    receiver_price = payer_price - (forward-strike)
18    if option == "payer":
19        return payer_price
20    elif option == "receiver":
21        return receiver_price
22    elif option == "straddle":
23        return payer_price + receiver_price
24    else:
25        raise ValueError("`option` must be in {'receiver', 'payer', 'straddle'}.")
```

Input parameters

Before we discuss the output of the pricing formula and function, it is wise to explain the inputs. The **forward** and **strike** prices are simply the current mid-market rates of the underlying IRS and the strike is as defined. These must be input in percentage terms, i.e. 1.3 represents a rate of 1.3%.

The **time to expiry** is commonly expressed as a fractional number of years. A standardised annual volatility is used here because it is what financial markets watch and follow. This is true for interest rate markets, commodity and equity markets, and is thus a worthwhile benchmark. It is also highlighted because it can have a subtle nature. Calendar days versus business days is one such subtlety that creates pricing differentials. Suppose that a volatility parameter has been estimated based on an annual period of 252 business days and 365 calendar days. One might attempt to price a swaption that expires in one month's time, say in 31 calendar days. But, if Easter falls within that month then there are fewer business days than normal until expiry. In calendar terms the time to expiry is $\frac{31}{365} = 0.0849$ periods, and in business day terms it is perhaps $\frac{19}{252} = 0.0754$ periods. How this is interpreted as an input is a subjective assessment of the trader. Arguably business days, on which the market is open to trade, are what give rise to most of the volatility, yet more calendar days permit the chance of news events occurring on holidays to impact the market and cause jumps or 'price gaps'.

The **volatility** is an input that differs dependent on whether the pricing distribution is chosen to be normal or log-normal. If the intended distribution is normal then the volatility should be input in bps, e.g. 50bps. This represents precisely one s.d. of the underlying normal probability distribution. If the distribution is log-normal then the volatility input should be entered in (approximate) percentage terms of the underlying mid-market rate. For example, an input of 25(%) and a mid-market rate of 2.00(%) is, in approximate optical terms at least, the equivalent 50bps.

The **option type** can be "Payer", "Receiver", and "Straddle" and the **distribution type** can be "Normal" and "Log".

Output data

This pricing formula and function yields the swaption price in the same terms as the input forward and strike rates, i.e in rate percentage terms. To obtain an actual cash premium amount payable upfront, the output should be converted to bps (by multiplying by 100) and multiplied by the analytic pv01 of the underlying IRS.

Example 20.1.
A trader prices a $100mm 5Y30Y 1.5% payer, using a normal distribution with assumed volatility of 52bps annually. The mid-market rate of the 5Y30Y IRS is 1.325% and the analytic pv01 of the underlying $100mm 5Y30Y IRS is $230,500. The swaption price returned is,

```
>>> swaption_price(1.325, 1.500, 5.0, 52, "payer", "normal")
0.3816
```

This represents 38.16bps and corresponds to an upfront cash premium of $38.16 \times 230,500 =$ $8,795,880, which is 879.6bps payable on the $100mm notional.
    Under the terms of the CSA the option seller will post an equivalent amount of collateral back to the buyer representing this swaption's asset value, and exchange further collateral based on MTM valuations.

Example 20.2.
A trader prices a $10mm 3M5Y 3.1% receiver, using a log-normal distribution with assumed volatility of 13% annually. The mid-market rate of the 3M5Y IRS is 2.8% and the analytic pv01 of the underlying IRS is $4,520. The swaption price returned is,

```
>>> swaption_price(2.80, 3.10, 0.25, 13, "receiver", "log")
0.3048
```

Converting 30.48bp to an upfront cash premium gives $137,770, or 137.8bps of notional.

20.2.4 Intrinsic and optionality value

The price of a general option is sometimes thought of with respect to two components; its **intrinsic** value and its **optionality** value.

$$\text{Swaption Price} = \text{Intrinsic Value} + \text{Optionality Value} .$$

The intrinsic element is the difference between the strike rate and the mid-market fwd rate. An option is said to have some intrinsic value if the strike is more advantageous than the prevailing mid-market rate, otherwise there is no intrinsic value. For example, a payer swaption with a 1.3% strike would have 20bps of intrinsic value if the mid-market rate on the underlying were 1.5%. It would have zero intrinsic value if the mid-market rate were lower than the strike of 1.3%.
    For normal distributions, without introducing skew, the optionality value is symmetrical about the mid-market fwd rate. It declines as the strike becomes further from that mid-market rate.

20.2.5 Log-normal distribution and shifting

Originally, option pricing theory was developed for options on equities. Equities have the distinct property that prices cannot be less than zero. When the theory was developed it was

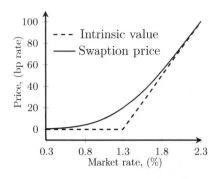 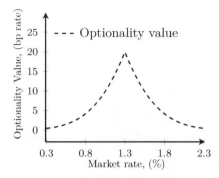

Figure 20.2: The swaption price, and intrinsic and optionality value components of a 1.3% payer swaption for different market rates with a 50bp normal vol and 1Y expiry.

also assumed that an equity price followed a multiplicative process. This meant that its daily percentage moves were distributed normally, and as a result the distribution of the underlying equity price must be log-normally distributed.

Log-normally distributed random variables require their volatility, as the input to the pricing formula, to take a specific form. They require it to be expressed in (approximate) percentage terms of the underlying. This makes it a *relative* parameter and hence as the price of the underlying gets lower the volatility must rise to permit the same absolute value. For example, an IRS with a 1% mid-market rate and a 20% volatility has an anticipated absolute volatility of approximately 20bps, but for an IRS with a mid-market rate of 0.2% to have the same absolute volatility then the log-normal volatility must be 100%. And as that rate becomes lower toward zero the volatility should get larger and larger toward infinity.

Modelling interest rates becomes problematic because they can, and do, go below zero. One solution that markets have adopted in this regard is to use log-normal **shifting**. Shifting, as the name suggests, moves all rates into positive (or more positive) territory by adding a constant amount, subjectively chosen, and then perform the calculations. These calculations must be done with an adjusted volatility that yields the intended absolute value. Afterwards the distribution is shifted back to the previous rate levels to obtain the appropriate probability distribution that permits some negative rates. Figure 20.3 shows how the log-normal probability distribution is affected, in practice via shifting, for a mid-market rate of 0.2% whose absolute annual volatility is assumed to be 20bps.

This is only required for the assumption of log-normally distributed rates. If a normal distribution is assumed then no shifting is required because the volatility parameter is an *absolute* number in that case.

20.2.6   Implying distributions from swaption prices

Since the price of a swaption is naturally characterised by the assumed distribution of the underlying IRS rates, it stands to reason that a set of swaption prices for different strikes should say something about that underlying distribution. And indeed they do. The appendix outlines a way of approximating the assumed distribution of IRS rates given a set of swaption prices for different strikes.

In practice this might be difficult to assess, since swaption prices are not usually made available with the level of transparency needed to utilise this method. Nonetheless, knowledge of the method's existence might yet prove to be of use to the reader.

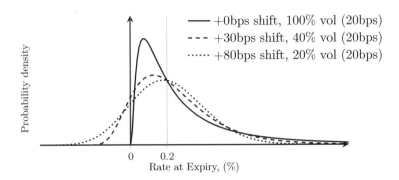

Figure 20.3: Log-normal probability distribution for a 0.2% rate and 20bps absolute volatility under different shifts.

20.3 Volatility

Volatility is a key component of financial markets. It impacts VaR and is directly related to the liquidity of financial instruments available to trade. In chapter 8 we also discuss its impact on the term structure of yield curves.

The previous section was written from the point of view of determining swaption prices from a known volatility. This section is about **implied volatility**. This means determining market volatility from the knowledge of swaption prices.

20.3.1 At-the-money (ATM) straddles

To begin analysing volatility we need to explain at-the-money (ATM) straddles. These are a particular type of swaption strategy, or a specific combination of different swaptions for want of a better term.

A straddle means buying a payer and receiver swaption, both with the same strike price. The pay-off of a straddle is shown graphically in figure 20.4. Although straddles of any strike can be constructed, an ATM straddle means that the strike price is set to be the current mid-market rate of the underlying fwd IRS rate. So, for figure 20.4 to be an ATM straddle, the underlying mid-market rate must be 1.30%.

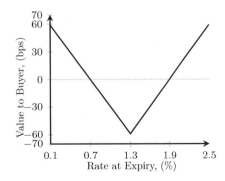

Figure 20.4: The pay-off at expiry of a 1.30% straddle (strikes are 1.30%) with a 59bps premium.

ATM straddles are important because they are the market benchmark product for implying volatility. An ATM straddle has a delta of approximately zero, meaning its price is largely dictated solely by volatility making it suitable for this purpose.

Visually they are quite helpful. Figure 20.4 indicates that the profit regions on either side of the chart are more likely to be reached if volatility increases. On the other hand if the volatility is depressed then the rate is more likely to remain within the centre of the chart around the strike, so the straddle will expire at a loss for the buyer. These conditions force the price of ATM straddles up and down respectively.

The total premium of an ATM straddle is the minimum pay-off value, which in the case of figure 20.4 is 59bps (rate value, not of notional). This, therefore, also represents the amount the mid-market rate must move before the straddle would show any profit at expiry.

When the volatility for a specific expiry on a specific underlying IRS is quoted in isolation, say for example the volatility of a 1Y10Y, or a 2Y5Y5Y, then the context will always be in reference to an ATM straddle of the same structure. Of course one can quote the volatility of any swaption or swaption strategy with any strike price, ATM, ITM or OTM, but this will then always be explicitly stated in the context.

20.3.2   Python code for implied volatility

There is not necessarily a clean formula for implying volatility given a swaption price, or straddle price. It is common to take numerical, iterative approaches to calculate it. The simplest numerical approach is to use Newton-Raphson iteration, where, for the known price, O_s, of a straddle in percentage terms,

$$\sigma_{i+1} = \sigma_i + (O_s - O_s(\sigma_i)) \left(\frac{\partial O_s(\sigma_i)}{\partial \sigma_i} \right)^{-1} \ , \quad \text{for some initial guess, } \sigma_0 \ .$$

For a reasonable initial volatility guess, say 20bps or 20% for normal and log-normal distributions respectively, then this method is almost always stable and converges in minimal iterations (2 to 4). Below we describe a simple Python function for implementing this method to imply volatility from either a payer, receiver or straddle swaption price.

```
1  MAXITER = 25
2  VOLTOL = 1e-4
3
4  def swaption_implied_vol(price, forward, strike, expiry, ini_vol, option,distribution):
5      v1 = ini_vol
6      for i in range(MAXITER):
7          v0 = v1
8          c0 = swaption_price(forward, strike, expiry, v0, option, distribution)
9          c1 = swaption_price(forward, strike, expiry, v0 + 1, option, distribution)
10         v1 = v0 + (price - c0) / (c1 - c0)
11         if abs(v1 - v0) < VOLTOL:
12             return v1
13     raise ValueError(f"Failed to converge to tolerance after {MAXITER} iterations.")
```

Example 20.3.

For figure 20.4 we can assume the time to expiry is 1 year, the distribution is normal and the price has fallen to a bp rate premium of 15bps. The implied volatility given the straddle price of 15bps is calculated to be,

```
1  >>> swaption_implied_vol(0.15, 1.3, 1.3, 1.0, 20, "straddle", "normal")
2  18.80
```

This gives, $\sigma_N = 18.80bps$ annualised absolute volatility.

20.3.3 Measures of volatility

So far in this chapter we have been very careful not to use potentially ambiguous terminology. Market terminology with respect to swaptions, however, can appear ambiguous. Less ambiguous is 'volatility' often shortened to 'vol'. But more ambiguous perhaps are the terms **'normal vol'** and **'normalised vol'**. But these are quite prevalent terms in financial markets, so worth clarification.

We begin with the common names of the volatilities we have already used, and add on the others.

(i) **Normal vol (σ_N):** this represents the s.d. of the assumed normal distribution describing the underlying IRS rate. It is expressed in bps per annum either on a calendar day or business day basis.

(ii) **Log vol (σ_{LN}):** represents the approximate percentage of the underlying IRS on a per annum basis. Sometimes also called the **Black vol**, since this is the parameter entered into the traditional Black-Scholes model developed using a log-normal distribution.

(iii) **Normalised vol (σ_N^*):** given the log vol, an approximation can be made to retrieve an absolute measure of vol, akin to the normal vol[4] that would reprice the swaption under an assumed normal distribution instead. We stress this does not represent the s.d. of the log-normal distribution originally assumed for the underlying rate, but in certain circumstances is close to it.

$$\sigma_N^* \approx \sigma_{LN} F \ .$$

(iv) **Daily bp vol ($\sigma_{BP}^{(*)}$):** this is the simple average implied volatility measured across one of the assumed 252 trading days of the year. It can be determined from normal vol or normalised vol.

$$\sigma_{BP}^{(*)} = \frac{1}{\sqrt{252}} \sigma_N^{(*)} \ .$$

(v) **Daily breakeven vol ($\sigma_{BE}^{(*)}$):** this is average daily volatility needed, repeatedly, to give an expectation of breaking even, i.e. returning no PnL, on an unhedged ATM straddle.

$$\sigma_{BE}^{(*)} = \sqrt{\frac{2}{\pi}} \sigma_{BP}^{(*)} \ .$$

(vi) **Realised vol:** this is the volatility that is actually observed over a given period of time, say three months or one year. It is often quoted in annual terms even if the period sampled is not a year. Obviously this can only be measured from a historical perspective

(vii) **Implied vol:** as above, this is a function of swaption prices. This is representative of expected future realised vol.

The inclusion of these terms is made so a generalist trader can identify with information distributed by swaptions traders. Importantly one should recognise the inherent assumptions that are carried with the use of each term. For example a normal vol implies a normal distribution has been used in the pricing of a swaption, or a daily bp vol implies that each day within a year is treated identically and assumed to have the same expected volatility as any other. Of course, the log-normal shifting is also a feature that affects the assumed distribution of the underlying rate, and therefore it is always important to clarify the amount of shifting used.

---

[4]the appendix expands on this approximation giving a more accurate but uncommonly used variant

Since log vol is a relative concept and normal vol is absolute we can often infer how markets price their swaptions by observing the respective parameters over time. If a price were to trade log-normally then the log vol would typically remain constant given movements in rates - consequently, in this model, normal vol would rise and fall as mid-market rates rise and fall respectively. Alternatively a swaption price might trade normally ('normal' in the sense of distributions not in the sense of stereotypical behaviour), meaning the normal vol remains fairly static as rates rise and fall - so that log vol falls and rises as the the rates rise and fall respectively.

Example 20.4.
A 2.0% 1Y10Y ATM straddle has a price of 25bps. Using the `swaption_implied_vol` *function we calculate the normal vol of the underlying rate to be 31.33bps annually. Similarly the log vol is calculated with the same function to be 15.68% annually. Normalising this volatility by multiplying by the mid-market rate of 2% yields the normalised vol of 31.36bps.*

20.3.4   Volatility smiles and skew

All preceding sections have been built upon the premise of adopting normal or log-normal distributions for the underlying fwd IRS rates. Whilst it will probably always be impossible to actually state for certain what distribution an IRS rate will take, there is evidence and a large consensus to suggest that neither of these distributions capture one very important aspect of rate movements. And that aspect is of the probability of extreme events. Extreme events occur much more frequently than either the normal or log-normal models predict. This leads to other distributions being proposed which have "fat-tails", meaning greater probability density values for underlying rates which are far from the current mid-market rate (larger kurtosis).

The under-predictive nature of extreme events would suggest that our two distributions permit swaption prices of extreme events that are too low. It would be advantageous to buy swaptions with strikes far from the mid-market rate, in anticipation of more frequent extreme events, that yield large pay-offs for these swaptions. But this would present a pseudo-arbitrage opportunity and as such the market has calibrated to remove this systematic pricing dynamic.

This calibration takes the form of option prices that increase relatively for certain ranges of strikes further from the mid-market rate, producing the so-called **implied volatility smile**. This leads naturally to higher implied volatility for those strike ranges. There is no set parameter that states by how much a volatility should "smile", rather it is something that increases and decreases as market sentiment shifts. See figure 20.5.

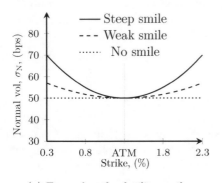
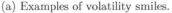
(a) Examples of volatility smiles.

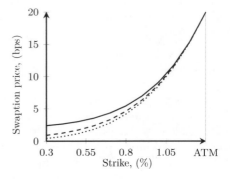
(b) Prices of 1Y expiry receiver.

Figure 20.5: Showing the effect of volatility smiles on swaption prices.

Furthermore, there is no requirement for the smile to be symmetric. If it is not symmetric, then the asymmetry is termed the **volatility skew**. A skew will arise if one particular "tail-risk" is more dominant than another. For example if it is believed that the extreme event which sees rates fall dramatically is more likely than the opposing extreme event, then OTM receivers would be in higher demand. In figure 20.5 this would be reflected with a higher smile left of the ATM rate and a lower smile to the right of the ATM rate.

There are limits to the size of the smile, though. A smile that is too great will result in pricing anomalies. For example a swaption which is more OTM than another, similar, swaption might still have a higher price. Under any scenario this would represent an arbitrage opportunity since the more expensive swaption could be sold to fund the purchase of the cheaper one, generating a purely positive pay-off. Smiles do not extend indefinitely though, and at some point the kurtosis has to be curtailed.

In summary volatility skew is an adjustment to the normal and log-normal models of swaption pricing to account for the fact the underlying distribution is not actually taken to be precisely either of these.

20.3.5 Volatility surface

We have described the different measures of volatility that are used in practice. And also the fact that, in order to characterise the likelihood of extreme events, volatilities must increase as the strike deviates from the mid-market rate on any underlying IRS, creating smiles and skew.

Now we highlight that the volatilities of different expiries on the same underlying IRS vary, dependent upon market expectations. For example a 1M10Y might have a normal vol of 60bps but a 3M10Y might have a normal vol of 50bps. This is plausible if an event is expected within the next month that might create a large amount of volatility but won't be repeated within the next 3M. For example, a political vote or referendum, or anticipated quarterly news release such as gross domestic product (GDP).

Similarly, we point out that the volatilities of different tenor swaps for the same expiry deviate. So for example a 1Y10Y might have a normal vol of 50bps, but a 1Y30Y might have a normal vol of 75bps. This, of course, reflects the volatility of the underlying IRSs market.

The result of this means the number of calibration points for swaption pricing is quite large; ATM straddles for different expiries on different underlying IRSs are needed to estimate volatility. This information about the ATM normal vols of different tenor IRSs with different expiries forms a matrix array. If each of these mesh points in 3D-space is interpolated with a suitable interpolating function this results in a **volatility surface**, from which all intermediate tenors or expiries can be derived, in order to construct a pricing system. See figure 20.6[5].

Market terminology applicable to this surface is to call the **top-left** the short dated expiries with short tenor tails, the **top-right** is short dated expiries with long tenor tails, the **bottom-left** is longer expiries with shorter tenor tails and the **bottom-right** is, finally, longer expiries with longer tenor tails.

It is beyond the scope of this book to suggest mathematical techniques in which the volatility surface is interpolated, or to what degree spikes and jumps can be incorporated as a result of specific news or market calendar events.

An astute reader will also recognise the need to combine volatility surfaces with volatility smile and skew. An ATM surface of volatility is created as a two dimensional object visualised in three dimensions parametrised by expiry and tail, solving for the implied volatility. Similarly implied volatility can also be the fourth dimension of a three dimensional parameter space; expiry, tail and strike. Visually this would constitute a volatility density function inside a cube

---

[5]this figure contains real data from the EUR swaption market of July 2016.

Exp./Tail	1Y	2Y	...	25Y	30Y
3M	22	25		72	75
6M	23	26		70	73
$\vdots$			$\ddots$		
25Y	60	60		47	46
30Y	56	57		44	43

(a) Market implied ATM normal vols by expiry and tail.

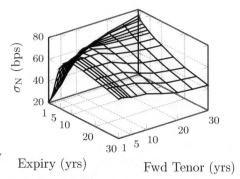

(b) Interpolated volatility surface for the provided dataset.

Figure 20.6: Construction of a volatility surface.

- the **volatility cube**. It requires an associated three dimensional interpolation function to permit a consistent trading model.

20.3.6   Volatility of forward rates and correlation

The volatility surface (and cube) described above, are applicable to, and calibrated by, par IRSs with the various expiries (and strikes). However, we have mentioned that swaptions can also be written on any underlying IRS, e.g. a 1Y5Y5Y is a 1Y expiry swaption on a 5Y5Y IRS. But the volatility surface created above, for all its complexities, still does not contain enough information to price a 1Y5Y5Y swaption. It can in fact only determine prices for any interpolated *par tenor* IRS with any expiry, but not a fwd IRS measured to be fwd from the point of the chosen expiry.

We can be more explicit with an example. The volatility surface of figure 20.6 has 1Y5Y and 1Y10Y ATM normal vol of 39bps and 59bps respectively. What can we infer about 1Y5Y5Y volatility from this? Intuitively one would suggest that in order for the 1Y10Y to have a volatility higher than the 1Y5Y, the 1Y5Y5Y component must also be higher than the 1Y5Y. If we naively assumed the 1Y10Y volatility was made up of 50% 1Y5Y and 50% 1Y5Y5Y then the 1Y5Y5Y normal vol would have to be 79bps to produce the arithmetic average of 59bps. But this does not account for the respective weightings of the pv01s of each trades, nor does it account for the correlation of the 1Y5Y rate with the 1Y5Y5Y rate that will ultimately combine to create the volatility of the 1Y10Y rate, nor does it account for assumed differences in the distributions of all of the respective IRS rates.

If we **assume** information about the correlation, the attribution of pv01, and a normal distribution, then we can derive the implied volatility of the 1Y5Y5Y. The information on correlation is best provided for the 1Y5Y rate correlated with the 1Y10Y rate, since that aligns nicely with the given data on volatility for both the 1Y5Y and 1Y10Y rates. The information on attributed pv01s is supplied by a Jacobian transformation.

Example 20.5.
A trader has the following normal vol and correlation information regarding 1Y5Y and 1Y10Y IRS.

$$(\text{ATM 1Y expiry}) \; \boldsymbol{\sigma}_N = \begin{bmatrix} \sigma_N^{1Y5Y} \\ \sigma_N^{1Y10Y} \end{bmatrix}, \quad \boldsymbol{\rho}_{(1Y5Y,1Y10Y)} = \begin{bmatrix} 1 & \rho \\ \rho & 1 \end{bmatrix}.$$

He can construct a covariance matrix from that information[6], $\mathbf{Q}_{(1Y5Y,1Y10Y)}$. He has also constructed the Jacobian transformation[7],

$$\mathbf{J}_{\text{fwd}\rightarrow\text{par}} = \begin{bmatrix} 1 & 1 - \frac{A_{1Y10Y}}{A_{1Y5Y5Y}} \\ 0 & \frac{A_{1Y10Y}}{A_{1Y5Y5Y}} \end{bmatrix}, \quad \text{for } A = \text{Analytic PV01.}$$

The trader calculates $\mathbf{Q}_{(1Y5Y,1Y5Y5Y)}$ with the transformation,

$$\mathbf{Q}_{(1Y5Y,1Y5Y5Y)} = \mathbf{J}_{\text{fwd}\rightarrow\text{par}}^{\mathbf{T}} \mathbf{Q}_{(1Y5Y,1Y10Y)} \mathbf{J}_{\text{fwd}\rightarrow\text{par}}.$$

The desired result (the normal vol of the 1Y5Y5Y rate) can be gleaned from the bottom right element of the resultant covariance matrix, $\mathbf{Q}_{(1Y5Y,1Y5Y5Y)}$. That element represents the variance of the 1Y5Y5Y, so to obtain the normal vol the trader takes the root,

$$\sigma_{\text{N}}^{\text{1Y5Y5Y}} = \sqrt{\left((1-L)\sigma_{\text{N}}^{\text{1Y5Y}}\right)^2 + 2(1-L)L\rho\sigma_{\text{N}}^{\text{1Y5Y}}\sigma_{\text{N}}^{\text{1Y10Y}} + \left(L\sigma_{\text{N}}^{\text{1Y10Y}}\right)^2},$$

where the leverage of the fwd, $L = \frac{A_{1Y10Y}}{A_{1Y5Y5Y}}$.

Using data already determined, so (ATM) $\boldsymbol{\sigma}_N = \begin{bmatrix} 39 \\ 59 \end{bmatrix}$, and $L = 2.10$, we can plot the 1Y5Y5Y normal vol against the correlation of the 1Y5Y and 1Y10Y IRS rates in figure 20.7. For a high, expected correlation of, say, 0.95 then the 1Y5Y5Y normal vol is 84bps.

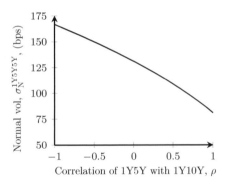

Figure 20.7: Illustrating the implied forward vol relationship with correlation.

The above matrix representation was given as a means of calculating multiple forward volatilities simultaneously if a larger correlation matrix is provided. The single line formula gives the method of calculating an individual forward volatility from the two respective par tenor IRSs that instruct it.

One will note the inclusion of the leverage variable, L, which is dependent upon the analytic pv01s of the IRSs in question. This actually changes with market rates so makes this overall approach an approximation and not precise in a stochastic sense. However, given the context of the unknown correlation parameter, which has such a large influence, the small changes that the leverage variable might have is of negligible concern. Especially for the range of considered products and analysis in this book's scope.

---

[6]see chapter 1

[7]see example 10.5

Generic formula for the volatility of a fwd rate

Calculating the volatility of a fwd IRS is simpler than the procedure of the next section because it involves only a single expiry. This means that the volatility of a fwd, to be calculated for a given expiry, needs the volatility of par tenor swaps with **only the same expiry** for the calculation. The formula of example 20.5 was not expressed in general terms because it was thought to obfuscate the overall concept. Figure 20.8 is included to reinforce the concept of the volatility of a fwd, and provides general variables which can be reinserted into the equation if the reader prefers the substitution. Do not forget the inherent assumption of correlation, static pv01 ratios and normally distributed market movements.

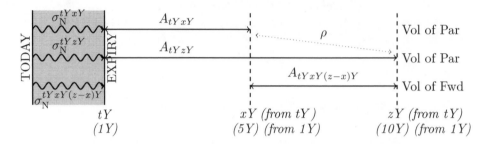

Figure 20.8: Necessary values to calculate the vol of a fwd.

$$\sigma_N^{tYxY(z-x)Y} = \sqrt{\left((1-L)\sigma_N^{tYxY}\right)^2 + 2(1-L)L\rho\sigma_N^{tYxY}\sigma_N^{tYzY} + \left(L\sigma_N^{tYzY}\right)^2},$$

where t is the expiry, x, z are tenor tails, $z - x$ is the tenor of the fwd, and the leverage of the fwd, $L = \frac{A_{tYzY}}{A_{tYxY(z-x)Y}}$.

This section on forward volatility has been included because the implied volatility of fwd IRSs is relevant for PnL calculations of IRS trade strategies incorporating cross-gamma (chapter 23). Also it is useful for devising better covariance matrices (chapter 14) and it is recommended to be considered in the context of the term structure (chapter 8).

20.3.7   Forward volatility

Now we are in a position to broach forward implied volatility. What does this mean? Let us consider from the point of view of an example. A 2Y7Y swaption settles to a 7Y IRS expiring in 2Y time. From that swaption one can imply an annualised volatility. But, that implied annualised volatility is just an average measure of the volatility over the two year period. It may very well be expected that the volatility is the same on every trading day, or that in the first year there is no volatility at all and then all of the assumed volatility takes place in the second year until expiry. It can be useful to assess what the market is implying about volatility in the near term and volatility further into the future. Often this can provide an assessment of the importance of a market event.

Given other swaption information available we can calculate some inferences about how the market expects volatility to evolve, again assuming normal distributions. See example 20.6.

Example 20.6.
The 2Y7Y implied normal vol in the interbank market, σ_N^{2Y7Y}, is 50bps. And the 1Y1Y7Y implied normal vol, σ_N^{1Y1Y7Y} is 44bps. This, the vol of a fwd, has been calculated in the manner akin to the previous section. With this information we can infer the 1Y7Y implied normal vol

in 1Y's time, i.e. the forward vol, $\sigma_N^{1Y7Y\_1Y}$.

$$\sqrt{2} \times 50 = \sqrt{44^2 + (\sigma_N^{1Y7Y\_1Y})^2} \implies \sigma_N^{1Y7Y\_1Y} = 55bps .$$

The expected distribution of volatility over the two years is not constant. The first year is expected to have less volatility than the second year.

For any underlying IRS the forward volatility, in general terms, can be measured with the following formula[8],

$$\sigma_N^{(t-f)YzY\_fY} = \sqrt{\frac{t\left(\sigma_N^{tYzY}\right)^2 - f\left(\sigma_N^{fY(t-f)YzY}\right)^2}{t - f}} , \quad f < t , \qquad (20.1)$$

where f is the number of years forward and t is the number of years to expiry of the basic swaption. Be aware though that $\sigma_N^{fY(t-f)YzY}$ is the volatility of a fwd which means the previous section must be used to calculate it, highlighted as the first three rows of figure 20.9. The figure shows the calculation is reasonably involved, but is included as well to reinforce the concept. Note how pricing information on **multiple expiries** is needed for the result.

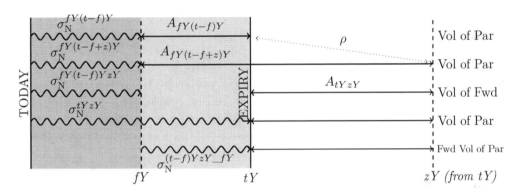

Figure 20.9: Necessary values to calculate forward volatility of a par IRS.

Often traders use simplifications and assumptions to make this more manageable, which is precisely what we do in example 20.7.

Example 20.7.
A market event will occur in just over a month's time. For example's sake let it be the UK's leave-remain referendum on EU membership. The swaption market is currently pricing a 1M10Y normal vol at 25bps and 2M10Y normal vol at 69bps.

Optically, this suggests a large amount of volatility is priced dependent upon the result of the referendum. There is no further granularity available in the swaption market so the trader uses these prices to proxy the market implied volatility around the single referendum event.

The trader first seeks to calculate the 1M1M10Y normal volatility. Since this is the volatility of a fwd he needs; the 1M(10Y+1M) and 1M1M normal vols, the correlation between them, and the apportioned risk via a Jacobian transformation. He simplifies this by assuming the correlation is zero, the leverage is 1, and the 1M(10Y+1M) vol is the same as the 1M10Y. All of these assumptions reduce so that the 1M1M10Y is assumed to be the same as the 1M10Y, which intuitively seems like a sensible conclusion.

---

[8]the derivation is shown in the appendix

Now the trader can apply the formula for forward volatility,

$$\sigma_N^{1M10Y\_1M} = \sqrt{\frac{\frac{2}{12}69^2 - \frac{1}{12}25^2}{\frac{2}{12} - \frac{1}{12}}} = 94bps \ .$$

The trader acknowledges that this value is a volatility assessing a 1M expiry time, but the referendum's result is likely to cause volatility on only a few days, perhaps only a single trading day. If the trader assigns all of the referendum premium volatility to a single day, and he assumes all other days in the 2M period have the same volatility of 1.57bp per day[9], then the daily volatility on the day of the referendum needs to be 26.21bps[10] to satisfy these market prices.

Furthermore there might be an expected and unexpected outcome, i.e. polls might show a Brexit to be more unlikely than a remain. An unexpected outcome might give rise to a more volatile market than an expected one. From which it might be inferred that a Brexit vote will cause more than 26bps daily vol and a remain vote will cause less, although this is a more speculative assessment.

20.4   Greeks

The 'greeks' are the names given the values describing a swaption's price relationship with respect to different market variables. The **delta** and **gamma** of a swaption are the first two greeks. For linear IRDs we have specific sections introducing delta and gamma as the first and second derivatives of the PV of the derivative asset with respect to the movements of underlying rates. The reader is referred to those chapters for a more in depth discussion.

Analytic functions for the delta and gamma of swaptions priced under a normal and log-normal distribution exist[58]. The practical nature of this book means that the included numerical functions (below) serve to calculate delta and gamma for each "payer", "receiver" and "straddle" type, in a broad sense. These should be accurate enough for practical purposes.

The **'vega'** of a swaption is another greek. Vega is not relevant to linear derivatives since their pricing is not explicitly dependent upon volatility. Vega describes how a swaption price changes as the volatility changes. Formulaically, the vega on a swaption is,

$$\text{Total vega risk} = \frac{DO}{D\sigma} = \frac{\partial O}{\partial \sigma_1} + \ldots + \frac{\partial O}{\partial \sigma_{mn}}$$

Multiple ATM volatilities might be relevant to a given swaption's price due to the nature of the surface construction being an interpolation of calibrated mesh points (m expiries and n tails), similar to how a 4.5Y IRS might display delta risk to say 3Y, 4Y, 5Y, 6Y, etc. IRS buckets for a curve calibrated by those instruments.

It is also possible, of course, just consider the vega of a swaption from the point of view of just the volatility of the specific underlying rate, like it would be possible to consider the delta of a 4.5Y IRS with respect solely to the 4.5Y bucket. The basic Python function below does it this way, measuring the swaption price change either relative to an increase by 1bp normal vol or 1% log vol. We could use the Dual class[11] for automatic differentiation to produce these values, but since these functions are dependent to so few variables we have calculated the derivatives using forward difference numerical differentiation.

---

[9]this is equivalent to 25bps annually

[10]this is equivalent to 416bps annually and calculated as the result of sums of independent normal random variables, see section 1.3.4

[11]see chapter 11 for the implementation of automatic differentiation

A fourth greek, **'theta'** is the last we discuss. There are other greeks, along with correlation risk, but these are considered too technical for this book's scope. Theta measures the change of a swaption price as the time to expiry changes. The function below is calibrated to determine the value change of a swaption after the passing of a single trading day[12].

20.4.1   Python code for swaption greeks

We provide a function to return these four greeks for a specified swaption type. The delta and gamma are output as percentage values of the analytic delta of the underlying IRS. The vega is output in the same manner representing 1bp or 1% move higher in the normal or log-vols respectively. Theta is measured as value acquired holding the position for a single trading day.

```python
def swaption_delta(forward, strike, expiry, ann_vol, option, distribution):
    d0 = swaption_price(forward-0.0005, strike, expiry, ann_vol, option, distribution)
    d1 = swaption_price(forward+0.0005, strike, expiry, ann_vol, option, distribution)
    return (d1 - d0) * 1000

def swaption_gamma(forward, strike, expiry, ann_vol, option, distribution):
    g0 = swaption_delta(forward-0.0005, strike, expiry, ann_vol, option, distribution)
    g1 = swaption_delta(forward+0.0005, strike, expiry, ann_vol, option, distribution)
    return (g1 - g0) * 10

def swaption_vega(forward, strike, expiry, ann_vol, option, distribution):
    v0 = swaption_price(forward, strike, expiry, ann_vol-0.0005, option, distribution)
    v1 = swaption_price(forward, strike, expiry, ann_vol+0.0005, option, distribution)
    return (v1 - v0) * 1000

def swaption_theta(forward, strike, expiry, ann_vol, option, distribution):
    t0 = swaption_price(forward, strike, expiry, ann_vol, option, distribution)
    t1 = swaption_price(forward, strike, expiry-1/252, ann_vol, option, distribution)
    return t1 - t0

def swaption_greeks(*args):
    return [swaption_delta(*args), swaption_gamma(*args),
            swaption_vega(*args), swaption_theta(*args)]
```

Example 20.8.
A trader buys a $100mm 1Y10Y 1.3% payer. Using a normal distribution with volatility of 50bps annually, current mid-market rate of the 1Y10Y IRS at 1.1%, and the analytic pv01 of the underlying $100mm 1Y10Y IRS being $93,200, the swaption greeks returned are,

```python
>>> swaption_greeks(1.10, 1.30, 1.0, 50, "payer", "normal")
[0.34458, 0.00737, 0.00368, -0.00037]
```

This translates to $32,115pv01 delta, $686pv01/bp gamma, $343pv01vol vega, -$34 per trading day theta.

Example 20.9.
A trader buys a $100mm 1Y10Y 1.1% straddle with same parameters as above. The swaption greeks returned are,

```python
>>> swaption_greeks(1.10, 1.10, 1.0, 50, "straddle", "normal")
[0.00000, 0.01596, 0.00798, -0.00079]
```

This translates to no delta, $1,487pv01/bp gamma, $744pv01vol vega, -$74 per trading day theta.

---

[12]a trader adopting a calendar day mentality might tweak the formula to represent 365 days instead of 252

20.5   Market-making and price-taking

Having discussed volatility cubes, and making inferences to volatility driving events, in addition to supposing correlations, it should be clear that there are many parameters needed to construct a system to accurately price swaptions. This is even before the choices about how to interpolate all of the parametrised mesh points are made.

In addition to this, the swaption market is not transparent, meaning that for all of the 1000-2000 parameters needed to calibrate the volatility cube, only 10-50 prices are available in the interbank market at any time to gauge these parameters against. Educated guesswork and approximations fill in the gaps.

This has an impact on the prices made by market-makers. In section 18.2.8 we showed how information and transparency should affect market-makers' prices in a game theoretic sense. As a comparison to swaptions' prices suppose we take the same example (that was shown in that section) of a $5mm 13Y2Y IRS and consider this as the underlying for a swaption with 13Y expiry. Falling in an interpolated part of the surface the non-transparency of the normal vol might be 1bp, and the non-transparency of the forward rate we maintain is the same 0.6bps. Combining these gives a non-transparency of an ATM receiver of 0.7bps (calculated through price sampling). The hedge cost plus minimum increment we assume to be 0.75bps, and thus the theory in that previous section would yield a price from mid of 1.55bps. This is 50% larger than the bid-offer quoted for the underlying IRS in the same example.

20.5.1   Named strategies

Strangles: similar to a straddle, a strangle is to purchase a payer and receiver with different strikes (receiver strike less than the payer). This has a less costly premium than a straddle since each swaption has reduced intrinsic value compared with its equivalent in a straddle.

Payer spread (call spread on options):   buy a lower strike payer and sell a higher strike payer. The combination of buy and sell usually lessens the upfront premium, but caps the upside if rates move higher.

Receiver spread (put spread on options):   buy a higher strike receiver and sell a lower strike receiver. Same as the payer spread but a reversed direction. Selling a receiver spread has a similar pay-off profile to buying a payer spread.

Collar: paying an outright IRS and selling a higher strike payer caps the upside potential. Then buying a lower strike receiver limits the downside. This pay-off profile is similar to a payer spread. Reversing the details produces a pay-off profile similar to a receiver spread.

Caps: buying a series of payers, with different expiries but the same strike, on single period IRSs (caplets) provides an upper bound to interest payments for those with floating leg exposures.

Floors: buying a series of receivers, with different expiries but the same strike, on single period IRSs (floorlets) provides the comparative lower bound, useful to protect those who are receiving interest payments.

20.6 Extraneous topics

Like swaps, swaptions are a technical product. One could most likely write a comparable practical guide to trading swaptions. However this book is not aiming to give swaptions a detailed treatment, nor do I feel I currently have the depth of knowledge to do so. To conclude this chapter some brief comments on extraneous topics will have to suffice to encourage the reader to research further.

Swaption **expiry management** is similar to reset risk management. When a swaption expires risk often needs to be replaced, if it is a cash settled expiry, for example. Gamma on swaptions increases for those that have strikes close to ATM rates with short expiries. This commands technical delta management specifically around these times.

Volatility estimation is widely practised. Various statistics can be drawn comparing implied vols to realised vols. It can be helpful to also define a third term in this context; historical vols. One must be quite careful to not misinterpret the meaning of each. As an example suppose it is 1st Jan and the 3M10Y has a normal implied vol of 50bps. In three months time, when the swaption expires, we will have the actual data about the real market movements in January, February and March and therefore will be able to state the realised vol of that period and can make a judgement about how well the swaption forecast the market. On the other hand as at 1st Jan we have market data available for the last three months of October, November and December, which gives us the historical (realised) vol. A significant deviation in the historical vol with the implied vol suggests the market is expecting a significant change of conditions or a particular market event.

From time to time one may hear reference to the **SABR (Stochastic Alpha Beta Rho) model**. This is one of the more common volatility models used by IRD traders. The three parameters α, β, ρ, characterise the model by controlling the level of volatility and skew for calibrated mesh points (1M5Y, 1M10Y, 3M5Y, 3M10Y, etc.). The original paper describing its development is cited [59].

20.7   Appendix

20.7.1   IRR formula for cash settlement

For the settlement of cash settled swaptions ISDA specifies a zero coupon curve must be constructed to discount cashflows. The formula, taken from market practice, for doing this is as follows,

$$A_n = \sum_{i=1}^{fn} \left(\frac{1}{f(1 + \frac{R_n}{f})} \right)^i ,$$

for n the number of years, R_n the ISDA fixing rate, and $f \in \{1, 2, 3, 4, 6, 12\}$ the frequency of the fixed rate, of the underlying IRS.

This is a typical geometric series which reduces to,

$$A_n = \frac{1}{1 - f(1 + \frac{R_n}{f})} \left(\frac{1}{f(1 + \frac{R_n}{f})} \right)^{fn} - 1 .$$

20.7.2   Implying distributions from swaption prices

This result is taken from [60]. The price of a payer swaption with strike, K, is given by,

$$O_p(K) = \int_K^\infty (r - K)g(r)dr ,$$

where r is the underlying IRS at expiry, and $g(r)$ is the risk-neutral probability density function of r. We then have,

$$\frac{\partial O_p}{\partial K} = -\int_K^\infty g(r)dr , \quad \frac{\partial^2 O_p}{\partial K^2} = g(K) .$$

For small δ, $g(K)$ can be approximated by,

$$g(K) = \frac{O_p(K - \delta) - 2O_p(K) + O_p(K + \delta)}{\delta^2} .$$

20.7.3   Estimating $\sigma_{\mathbf{N}}$ given ATM swaption implied $\sigma_{\mathbf{LN}}$

For an ATM swaption, say a payer, where $K = F$ is assumed, the price implicit under a normal distribution reduces to,

$$O_p = \frac{1}{\sqrt{2\pi}} \frac{\sigma_N \sqrt{T}}{100} .$$

The same price implicit under a log-normal (Black) distribution is,

$$O_p = 2F \left(\Phi(x) - \frac{1}{2} \right) , \quad x = \frac{1}{2} \frac{\sigma_{LN} \sqrt{T}}{100} .$$

It can be shown by taking the Maclaurin series of the normal cdf, $\Phi(x)$, expressed in terms of the mathematical *error function*, that,

$$\Phi(x) = \frac{1}{2} + \frac{1}{\sqrt{2\pi}} \left(x - \frac{1}{6}x^3 + O(x^5) \right) .$$

Thus by equating the payer swaption prices we have,

$$O_p = \frac{1}{\sqrt{2\pi}} \frac{\sigma_N \sqrt{T}}{100} \approx F \frac{\sqrt{2}}{\sqrt{\pi}} \left(x - \frac{1}{6} x^3 \right) \ .$$

This reduces on substitution of x to,

$$\sigma_N^* = F \sigma_{LN} \left(1 - \frac{\sigma_{LN}^2 T}{24} \right) \ .$$

20.7.4 Deriving forward volatility

Under a normal distribution the rate of an tYzY IRS at expiry is modelled as,

$$R^{tYzY} \sim N \left(\mu, t \left(\sigma_N^{tYzY} \right)^2 \right) \ ,$$

where μ is the ATM rate.

On the other hand, create a subdivision between today and the expiry, tY, at a forward point fY ($0 < f < t$). **Assume** that the market movements in each subdivision are themselves **normally distributed and independent**, and that they sum to produce that total visible at expiry. By the properties of sums of normal random variables,

$$R^{tYzY} \sim N \left(\mu, f \left(\sigma_N^{fY(t-f)YzY} \right)^2 + (t-f) \left(\sigma_N^{(t-f)YzY\_fY} \right)^2 \right) \ .$$

Comparing the two yields equation 20.1, in section 20.3.7.

Gamma and Cross-Gamma Risk

Gamma and cross-gamma are important properties of trades and portfolios. This chapter aims to qualitatively address the topic providing intuitive reasoning without complicated mathematics. The next chapter is reserved for a more mathematical description. In this chapter we;

- introduce gamma by definition and give classical and modern descriptions of its effects,
- similarly, define cross-gamma and explain how and why it arises in derivatives portfolios,
- state why the pricing of different product types is affected by the existence of cross-gamma,
- show how cross-gamma risks can be neatly expressed for portfolios,
- outline why cross-gamma can be disadvantageous and suggest hedging strategies.

21.1 Defining gamma

Gamma, or convexity as it is referred to in bond terminology, has been alluded to a number of times already in this book but has not been properly introduced or explained. Particularly table 9.1 gives a visual description of gamma.

Gamma risk is the exposure of delta risk to increases or decreases as the outright IR market changes by one bp, respectively. Gamma risk is sometimes referred to as *second order* risk because it is the second derivative of the PV of an IRD with respect to rates, *scaled to a single bp*:

$$\text{Total Gamma risk is,} \quad \frac{D^2 P}{D\mathbf{r}^2} = \sum_i \sum_j \frac{\partial^2 P}{\partial r_i \partial r_j} \;,$$

For example if the gamma risk is 5 pv01/bp then the delta risk of a trade would be seen to increase by 5 for every bp that rates move up, and decrease by 5 for every bp that rates move down.

If the gamma of a trade is known then a more accurate, second order estimate to PnL can be obtained by extending the first order estimate that was introduced in chapter 9, using only the bp change in market rates, Δr:

$$P \approx \frac{DP}{D\mathbf{r}} \Delta r + \frac{1}{2} \frac{D^2 P}{D\mathbf{r}^2} \Delta r^2 \;.$$

Example 21.1.
Alpha has received 1bn 3M3M IRS at the market rate of 2%. The delta and gamma risks are calculated as:

$$\frac{DP}{D\mathbf{r}} = -24,800 \;,$$

$$\frac{D^2 P}{D\mathbf{r}^2} = 2 \;.$$

The IR market moves 10bps higher and the PnL estimate is determined as:

$$P \approx -248,000 + 100 = -247,900 \;.$$

In example 21.1 the gamma risk has negligible impact in terms of the overall PnL. In many derivative portfolios this might well be common place, and gamma risks might not factor into any real considerations for risk management. For some products, some specific effects, and some larger derivatives portfolios, gamma and cross-gamma risks can be important and certainly non-negligible. In the above example, whilst '+100' was negligible to the overall PnL of 247,900, we highlight that this '+100' was generated through a gamma risk of only '+2', which demonstrates that when portfolios begin to exhibit more gamma, or the market movements are larger (say over longer periods of time), the impact can mount up.

21.2 Classical description of gamma

Other texts, particularly those discussing bond convexity, commonly present a traditional figure. Here we do the same. Figure 21.1 illustrates both how delta changes with respect to IR market movements, and how the PnL of a portfolio changes is similar respects. In the leftmost figure the shaded area represents the PnL of the portfolio with rates having moved 10bps lower. The gamma risk itself is the gradient of the line and it amounts to 5 pv01/bp.

Single period RFR IRSs are an excellent product to use as examples to introduce gamma since it is simpler to qualitatively describe the mechanics. IRSs have two possible directions; paying fixed, or receiving fixed. Paying fixed incurs negative gamma risk, and receiving incurs positive gamma. Considered from the point of view of having received; if rates go up then one will lose money on the derivative contract, and if rates go down one will have a MTM gain.

Because the (only) cashflow is discounted to give the PV of the IRS, this yields a benefit for the receiver of the contract for either movement in rates.

When rates move higher, DFs decrease, and thus the loss is not quite as much because it is discounted more heavily. And when rates move lower, DFs increase, meaning the gain is amplified because it is discounted less heavily. Figure 21.1 gives the graphical depiction of having received an IRS (albeit the units are overly simplified and more typical in example 21.1). The characteristic curved PnL line which always lies above the straight line is visible.

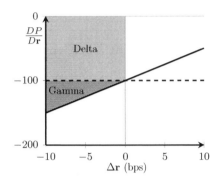 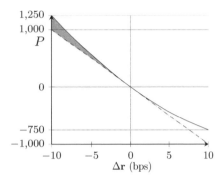

Figure 21.1: Graphing delta and PnL with respect to market movements due to the effect of gamma.

IRSs and ZCSs both exhibit gamma. Receiving fixed on any of these products generates positive gamma risk and paying fixed results in negative gamma. The longer tenor, and the more forward starting an instrument is, the more gamma they exhibit, because the more influence rate changes and compounding have on the DFs used to PV those IRDs.

Unlike conventions for delta and basis risks, which have no accepted sign for market direction, gamma does have a convention. Positive gamma is an advantage; one's risk increases as profit is generated, and negative gamma is unfavourable; one's risk increases as losses are incurred.

21.3 Modern description of gamma

In order to completely understand gamma in a modern sense, with reference to different CSAs or different products, we explain here precisely where gamma comes from. There are essentially two components that create gamma on IRDs;

(i) **level of rates:** with lower rates come higher DFs and an amplified sensitivity to market movements. This leads to increased risk on any IRD for lower rates rather than higher rates (see table 9.1),

(ii) **mark-to-market (MTM):** a trade that is ITM or OTM contains a form of annuity due to the PV that is sensitive to market movements, which then creates risk to further market movements.

Example 21.2.
At a given time, say t_1, a trader receives 100mm 10Y IRS at the mid-market rate of 2%. The pv01 of this IRS is measured as -90,000.
At another time, t_2, a trader receives 100mm 10Y IRS at the prevailing mid-market rate of 4%.

Due to lower DFs at higher rates the sensitivity of the swap is reduced and the pv01 is measured as -81,000.

Even though both IRSs were executed at mid-market and had no initial PV in example 21.3 different amounts of measured risk are due the level of mid-market rates.

With regard to ii), any trade that is ITM or OTM can be represented as, or decomposed into, two separate trades; a basic mid-market trade plus an annuity component representing the PV. These separate components can then be individually risked.

Example 21.3.
A trader has received 100mm 10Y IRS at 4%, the current mid-market is 2%.
A 100mm 10Y IRS at 2% plus a 200bps annuity stream on 100mm exactly replicates the cash-flows on the former.
The mid-market component has pv01 -90,000, and the annuity has pv01 -9,000, totalling -99,000 pv01.

In this representation the mid-market IRS at 2% generates a default amount of risk, for the basic structure of the trade. The annuity stream generates an amount of risk dependent upon the PV that it represents.

The reason why this description is labelled as modern is because separating the delta change into these components allows one to characterise the risk change in terms of discount delta and forecast delta. Discount delta is the risk that is created due to the PV of the derivative from the annuity, and forecast delta is the risk of the underlying derivative product measured at mid-market rates. Discount delta will necessarily give rise to discounting basis risk in addition, and forecast delta will necessarily give rise to forecast basis risk. The combination of all of these different risk changes leads to cross-gamma, which we will come on to presently.

21.4   Defining cross-gamma

Cross-gamma, similar to gamma, is a measure of how risk changes as the market moves. In the case of cross-gamma a move in one of market instrument, such as the outright market in 1Y, creates risk to a different market instrument, say the outright market in 1Y1Y. Technically, we have already seen these in our total definition of gamma above, where all of these were summed. For example the the change in risk to instrument, r_i, when instrument, r_j, moves is expressed as,

$$\frac{\partial}{\partial r_j}\left(\frac{\partial P}{\partial r_i}\right) = \frac{\partial^2 P}{\partial r_j \partial r_i} = \frac{\partial^2 P}{\partial r_i \partial r_j} = \frac{\partial}{\partial r_i}\left(\frac{\partial P}{\partial r_j}\right)$$

Cross-gamma risk is symmetric meaning the same change is experienced by instrument, r_j, when instrument, r_i, moves.

Cross-gamma is a broad term that encompasses risk creation in one variable when another variable moves, whatever they might be. For example if 10Y USD IRS rates move and that creates risk to the 2Y EUR IRS rates then this would be an example of cross-gamma. In our formulae in the next chapter our instrument space will be restricted to the following types of cross-gamma in a single currency only;

(i) **Delta/Basis Cross-Gamma:** this occurs when basis spreads move and it gives rise to new outright delta risks, or equivalently when the outright market moves and it gives rise to new basis risks.

(ii) **Inter-curve Delta/Delta Cross-Gamma:** this occurs when part of the outright interest rate curve moves, say at the short end, for example rates r_1, r_2 or r_3, and this gives rise to outright risk against other parts of the curve, say to rates, r_{10}, r_{20} or r_{30}.

(iii) **Inter-curve Basis/Basis Cross-Gamma:** this occurs the same as inter-curve delta/delta but for different tenor basis spreads, instead of outright rates.

(iv) **Multiple Basis/Basis Cross-Gamma:** this occurs when one type of basis moves, for example 6M IBOR/3M IBOR basis and the risk in another basis changes, for example 3M IBOR/OIS basis.

After the transition from IBOR, the use of a single RFR curve in a currency negates any of these *basis* effects. **FX/Delta and FX/Basis Cross-Gamma** is a further category including FX exposures, applicable to XCSs and trades with CSAs in other currencies. But we don't explore that further here.

The above categorises different types of cross-gamma for the sake of explanation but in a mixed IRD portfolio all of the above are likely to be found. Making the distinction is less important than understanding the concept of which types of product combinations give rise to which type of cross-gamma and why.

To be consistent with some of the terminology used earlier, delta/basis cross-gamma of IR instruments is defined as[1]:

$$(\text{Delta/Basis}) \text{ Cross-Gamma risk is,} \quad \frac{D^2 P}{D\mathbf{r} D\mathbf{z}} = \sum_i \sum_j \frac{\partial^2 P}{\partial r_i \partial z_j} \ .$$

$$\text{Total (Basis) Gamma risk is,} \quad \frac{D^2 P}{D\mathbf{z}^2} = \sum_i \sum_j \frac{\partial^2 P}{\partial z_i \partial z_j} \ .$$

The general **PnL formula** that incorporates all gamma and cross-gamma elements is stated as:

$$P \approx \mathbf{S} \cdot \mathbf{\Delta x} + \frac{1}{2} \mathbf{\Delta x}^{\mathbf{T}} \mathbf{G} \mathbf{\Delta x} \ , \quad \text{for} \quad \mathbf{\Delta x}^{\mathbf{T}} := [\Delta z_1, \dots, \Delta z_n, \Delta r_1, \dots, \Delta r_m] \ ,$$

for $\mathbf{S}$ the risk strip of basis risks and delta risks, $\mathbf{\Delta x}$ the array of basis market movements and delta market movements, and $\mathbf{G}$ the cross-gamma grid between each and every instrument. Specifically an individual element of $\mathbf{G}$ is, $G_{ij} = \frac{\partial^2 P}{\partial x_i \partial x_j}$, where x_i, x_j can be either a basis or delta instrument.

21.5 Gamma and cross-gamma risks in portfolios

If one hedges a trade with the same instrument then all the delta risks and gamma risks are offset, because the two trades have the opposite risks of each other and therefore cancel out in a portfolio.

Often, though, certain trades are hedged with products of a different nature. This means that the first order, delta (and basis) risks might be hedged **but that the second order, gamma risks are not**. Without complicated, numerical scenario analysis it can be difficult to determine whether a portfolio has a lot of cross-gamma risks, particularly if one does not have a technical grasp of the types of products present in the portfolio and that have been used for hedging.

Additionally, the nature of hedging one type of product with another and creating gamma or cross-gamma gives rise to the concept of **pricing adjustments**. This is because trading some products are more preferable in some directions relative to others. The following sections

---

[1] we denote any basis instrument, including discounting basis risk, with z_j. In the following chapter this separation is made distinct.

describe and explain some of the most common product combinations that result in any form of gamma. We summarise the items covered in table 21.1.

Calculating pricing adjustments for any type of gamma effect means applying a no arbitrage argument to assert that a portfolio cannot generate statistically expected profits through any kind of strategy. These are always theoretical adjustments since the practical application of ever trying to capture such profits is fraught with transaction costs of any kind of re-hedging strategy, in a dynamic market.

Trading combination	Pricing adjustment
STIR futures hedged with IMM IRSs	Futures convexity adjustment (FCA)
ZCSs hedged with IRSs	Zero coupon swap convexity adjustment (ZCA)
Cash settled swaptions hedged with physically settled swaptions or IRSs	Zero-wide collar premium
IRDs with a non-benchmark CSAs hedged with similar IRDs with a benchmark CSA	Subjective adjustment based on correlation (and optionality)
IRDs with misaligned payment schedules hedged by standard IRDs	IRD convexity bias for payment dates
Non-MTM XCSs hedged with MTM XCSs	XCS convexity adjustment

Table 21.1: Product combinations whose cross-gamma signature will be explained.

21.5.1   STIR futures hedged with IMM IRSs

An IRS has gamma. Its risk changes as the market moves. A STIR future does not, the risk of a single contract is always the same for a one bp move. Therefore a portfolio containing an IMM IRS offset by a STIR future (over the same dates) will need to be continually re-hedged as the outright market moves to maintain a total delta neutrality.

Since receiving an IRS creates positive gamma that translates to positive PnL in the portfolio. This means it is always more favourable to receive an IRS and sell a STIR future as a hedge for the portfolio. To put it another way, STIR futures are oversold (in price terms) relative to IRSs, and thus display higher rates than the respective IRS which is, similarly, oversold (in yield terms) relative to rate implied by the future.

This price differential between the two is known as the FCA. It represents the upfront value of the total amount of PnL that a portfolio would be expected to accrue, through its lifetime, until the IRS and STIR futures contract expired simultaneously. It is expressed in basis point terms. This adjustment is needed to make the price of each fairer such that it is not possible to generate any theoretical arbitrage of PnL.

Calculating FCAs is a difficult, stochastic, problem[2]. Models exists in other literature and in Bloomberg terminals for example. However, each model has their own inherent assumptions about the current and future volatilities of the market, the expected level and statistical distribution of rates, and the inclusion or not of discounting basis correlated to the outright market movements, and the correlation inputs. Some models may also choose to add in an assumption of mean reversion to market movements. The choice of assumptions can have a very big impact to the overall calculations. A reader is encouraged to understand the assumptions that are included in any model before adopting its results.

---

[2]see the appendix for an introductory mathematical approach to the calculation of FCAs

Of course in trading, FCAs prices, like any instrument, are at the mercy of supply and demand. The much higher liquidity of futures compared to that of IMM IRSs can create distortions, implying market based FCA prices far from the theoretical no arbitrage price.

21.5.2   ZCSs hedged with IRSs

This effect is negated by the transition from IBOR and use of RFR curves

Hedging ZCSs with IRSs creates cross-gamma and a very small amount of outright gamma (specifically inter-curve delta/delta cross-gamma). To outline why, we create a simple scenario.

Suppose at inception a mid-market ZCS is hedged with precisely the right amount of single period fwd mid-market IRSs. Because all these IRDs have a single cashflow, and because they are all executed at mid-market, there is no initial forecast of any cashflow.

If the outright market now rallies or falls neither the ZCS, nor any of the IRSs, will be valued at mid-market any more. The PnL of the portfolio is effectively zero, since it was delta hedged and the PnL of the IRSs offsets that of the ZCSs but there will be new discounting basis risks. This is due to the new distribution of future cashflows within the portfolio.

Supposing the ZCS became ITM then that would create a large, positive, single cashflow expected at maturity of the portfolio. Consequently, each of the IRSs are OTM and expected to generate a series of smaller, negative cashflows distributed all throughout the portfolio, which all sum up to the value of the positive cashflow so the total PV is zero.

After each period with a negative cashflow the future PV of the remaining cashflows becomes more and more positive reflecting that large cashflow at maturity becoming more dominant. This means it becomes more and more advantageous to discount the cashflows less heavily further into the future, being reflected as increasing fwd discounting basis risks, see figure 21.2

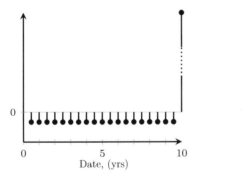
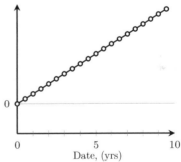

(a) Distribution of PV cashflows after a market move.

(b) Discounting basis risk exposure in fwd space beyond each cashflow.

Figure 21.2: Illustrating the generation of delta/discounting basis cross-gamma for a 10Y 6M-IBOR ZCSs hedged with IRSs.

The very small amount of outright gamma that arises is more complicated to explain. We have explained why the portfolio creates discounting risk as the market moves due to the position of relative cashflows, and one might legitimately query whether this discounting risk is also delta risk, and not just basis risk. But there is an offsetting element.

Each IRS has a fixed notional so that when the outright market moves the delta risk of each IRS changes. This is because the notional is discounted more or less heavily depending on the direction of the market move. For the ZCS the notional of each period is not fixed, and instead is dependent upon the level of the market due to the compounding effect of the floating leg. If rates fall then the future notionals are predicted to be lower but the resulting higher discount factors negates this.

Table 21.2 tries to capture this idea using very simplified numbers. The very small amount of delta gamma results if the discount curve and the outright forecasting curve are not at the same level (i.e. there is a basis). Where there is a slight difference between them, the offsets that have been qualitatively described above are very, very close but are not precisely the same; the notionals are compounded by IBOR rates but the discount factors are dependent upon the OIS rates (or whatever the CSA dictates).

Instrument	Forecast risk change	Discounting risk change	Total (Delta) change
ZCS	0.00	+2.02	+2.02
IRSs	-1.00	-1.01	-2.01
Portfolio	-1.00	+1.01	+0.01

Table 21.2: Example of risk changes under market movements of a portfolio of a ZCS hedged with IRSs.

Calculating zero coupon swap convexity adjustments (ZCAs) is more difficult than calculating FCAs for a number of reasons[3]. Firstly, ZCAs are applicable to much longer maturity instruments which gives a greater period of time for assumptions to deviate from reality, and therefore more variance in a statistical sense. Secondly, ZCAs are dominated by the delta/discounting basis cross-gamma term, which is more difficult to analyse or suppose correlations for, and is itself dependent upon on the supply and demand of these types of positions. This means it is potentially self-prophesying.

The amount of cross-gamma and gamma inherent in a portfolio of ZCSs and IRSs can be calculated accurately and directly from the outright and basis delta risks of each specific product type. The algorithms for this analytic approach are developed in chapter 22.

21.5.3 Cash settled swaptions hedged with physically settled swaptions, and zero-wide collars

This effect is negated by the transition from IBOR and use of RFR curves

An important aspect of cash settled swaptions is how the cash at expiry is calculated. It is not the same as how the PV of the underlying IRS is calculated[4]. This difference causes a number of properties, one being the fact that cash settled swaptions and physically settled swaptions have different PVs.

This difference also gives rise to changing risks throughout the life of the IRDs and therefore cross-gamma. Again we will outline a simple scenario[5]. Consider a trader who has sold a 10Y expiry, cash settled payer swaption and hedged it by buying a 10Y expiry, physically settled payer swaption with the same strike. We can also assume that the strikes are sufficiently lower than current mid-market rates so that the delta is high, and that peripheral hedges are in place resulting in a portfolio that is initially hedged.

What now happens if rates move higher by one bp? The cash settled swaption will lose value, and the physically settled one will gain. The IRR formula for cash settlement has no dependence upon the discount curve, i.e. the discounting basis. It only has dependence to the

---

[3] see the appendix for an introductory mathematical approach to the calculation of ZCAs

[4] see section 20.7.1

[5] in this scenario the cash settled swaption is hedged with a physically settled swaption but the reasoning is also applicable for IRS hedges as substitutes

underlying IRS rate (which is the ISDA fixing rate at expiry). The portfolio's value will remain effectively zero due to the initially hedged portfolio. But since the physically settled swaption's value is more exposed to discounting basis this must be exhibited as new discounting basis risk.

To maintain a similar theme of explaining the effects through cashflows we can reflect this as a negative cashflow for the cash settled swaption payable at expiry and a series of positive cashflows representing the annuity of the underlying IRS. See figure 21.3.

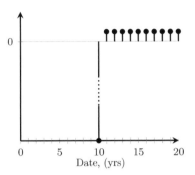 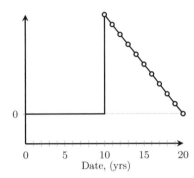

(a) Distribution of PV cashflows after a market move.

(b) Discounting basis risk exposure in fwd space beyond each cashflow.

Figure 21.3: Illustrating the generation of delta/discounting basis cross-gamma for a 10Y10Y cash settled swaption hedged with the same physically settled.

The nature of swaptions being a non-linear product, and the fact that the IRR formula for cash settlement is an approximation to analytic delta also introduces other forms of cross-gamma and valuation adjustments. The technical effect of these other elements is too complicated for the scope of this section but discussed in [61] and [62].

The second of these citations considers, what is termed, a zero-wide collar. If one buys a payer swaption and sells a receiver swaption at the same strike (i.e. zero-wide), both cash settled, then the pay off that is replicated is that of a cash settled IRS, sometimes termed a cash IRS. Hedged with a regular IRS this replicates the same structure as above and leads to the same cross-gamma effects. In swaption markets zero-wide collars occasionally trade which calibrates the pricing adjustments that need to be made to account for all of these cumulative effects.

21.5.4 Trades with different CSAs

Chapter 13 outlines how trades with CSAs in a currency other than the underlying product type can create cross-currency basis risk. It specifically gave an example of how the discounting of the PV was translated into XCS risk. It also inferred that the mid-market level of the trade can be affected depending upon the shape of the curve, and that, in turn, can result in more XCS risk.

This represents yet another way that cross-gamma can creep into an IRD portfolio. A portfolio of two trades; one trade hedged with the same trade but contracted under a different CSA, will exhibit risk changes as the IR market moves. This is due to the aggregation of PV and mid-market levels which are dependent upon different discount curves constructed to represent the different CSAs.

Example 21.4.

A trader has a received $1mm pv01 mid-market 30Y GBP QQ IRS with a USD cash only

CSA and has hedged this trade by paying $1mm pv01 mid-market 30Y GBP QQ IRS with a benchmark GBP CSA. All of the trader's delta and basis risks are initially zero by coincidence or other peripheral hedges.

GBP outright market yields rise by one bp. The PVs of each respective trade are now $\mp$*$1mm and they give rise to equal and opposite discounting risks in different currencies, which are estimated to be:*

IRSs: $\frac{\pm\$1mm \times 30}{2 \times 10,000bps} = \pm\$1,500$ pv01.

The trader's risk view now shows the following:

($ per bp)	IRS	SBS	XCS	IRS	SBS
Tenor	GBP 3M	GBP 3M/OIS	GBP/USD	USD 3M	USD 3M/OIS
30Y	0	1,500	-1,500	0	-1,500

The positive $1,500 figure relates to the discounting risk of the positive PnL on the trade with the GBP CSA and the negative $1,500 figure relates to the discounting risk of the trade with a USD CSA. Initially all risks were zero and have been created as a result of the market move.

Suppose instead that the GBP/USD XCS spread had decreased by one bp (or equivalently that the USD 3M/OIS spread had decreased by one bp or that the GBP 3M/OIS spread had increased by one bp) then this would have an impact on the GBP 3M delta risk. This is because the portfolio is now better positioned to have positive cashflows under a GBP CSA and negative cashflows under a USD CSA. In this case the trader's risk view now shows the following:

($ per bp)	IRS	SBS	XCS	IRS	SBS
Tenor	GBP 3M	GBP 3M/OIS	GBP/USD	USD 3M	USD 3M/OIS
30Y	1,500	0	0	0	0

This example also **highlights the symmetric nature of cross-gamma risks**.

A very common example of where this type of cross-gamma is accrued is in XCS portfolios. The benchmark CSA for XCSs is USD cash, so when a XCS trader looks to hedge one of the fixed legs on a fixed/fixed or fixed/floating XCS with an IRS in the local currency, which has a local currency benchmark CSA, then the result is of that above.

Example 21.5.
Relating to a corporate hedge of a newly issued fixed rate corporate bond, a market-maker has paid a fixed/floating EUR/USD XCS with a benchmark USD cash CSA. The market-maker hedges the cross-currency basis risk with a MTM EUR/USD XCS with the same USD cash CSA, and the EUR fixed rate delta risk with a EUR IRS with a benchmark EUR cash CSA. The trader experiences cross-gamma akin to example 21.4 due to the different CSAs of the trades in the portfolio relative to the fixed legs in EUR.

Calculating adjustments for this type of cross-gamma is again difficult. The same approach used for FCAs and ZCAs shown in the appendix can be used but of course with slightly different analytics for each product traded and hedged with an equivalent product of a differing CSA.

In the context of cross-gamma an important consideration for calculating pricing adjustments is correlation between all of the instruments. This is difficult to predict and, in some cases, have a systematic explanation or economic rationale for.

There may be a valid argument, especially in the case of the cross-instruments involved in the cross-gamma due to different CSAs, that certain correlations are zero and will remain at zero. Consequently no correlation results in no statistical expectation of PnL due to cross-gamma risks on those pairs. This naturally leads to no theoretical mid-market adjustments.

However, one should recognise the increased variation of potential PnL if the realised correlation is not zero, by coincidence or otherwise. This means that there exists a risk that greater losses may be incurred, even if they are not the statistical expectation. This can result in typical margin (i.e. bid-offer) increases.

21.5.5 Misaligned payment dates

When customising trades, for example IRSs, it is possible to deviate from using the standard reset and payment schedules. Interbank market trades are always standardised to use the same conventions and therefore this can create another source of discrepancy in the portfolio.

Standard IRSs pay their cashflows at the end of each accrual period, but suppose a customised version was traded to pay them five days (or another number) later than standard. In which direction would it be more favourable to trade the customised IRS hedged by a standard IRS?

Considering this in terms of cashflows, when the market moves the trades generate equal and opposite PV cashflows payable at two different dates. Suppose that the customised IRS happens to have a positive cashflow, paid five days later than the standard IRS's negative cashflow, then it is more advantageous if that later cashflow is discounted less heavily, i.e. if the fwd rate between the two cashflows moves lower.

Separating payment dates by only a few days will not make much of a difference, but the effect builds up with longer tenor swaps the more fwd starting. This is because longer tenor swaps have more periods which to consider, and a fwd start allows the effect to generate more PnL over time.

Example 21.6.

A trader hedges a customised $1bn USD 30Y QQ IRS with standard IRSs, so that he has precisely no risk initially. The customisation is as above so cashflows are paid five business days in arrears of standard payment dates.

The trader makes the following, ordered, estimates to arrive an at adjustment;

(i) *each bp that the outright market moves creates equal and opposite cashflows in each period of $25,000 separated by five days,*

(ii) *the raw (non-discounted), fwd discounting risk between each cashflow is $\frac{\$25,000}{10,000bps} \times \frac{5}{365} = \$0.034$ pv01, which represents the positive amount of gamma per bp in the case the customised IRS is received and the standard IRS is paid,*

(iii) *the assumed, mean daily market movement, σ_{BP}, 4 bps in each swap period, and so the expected raw PnL created by gamma effects is $\$0.034 \times 4^2 \times \frac{1}{2} = \$0.272$ in any given period,*

(iv) *for the duration of any 3M period with 63 business days this amounts to a total $17.14 per swap period,*

(v) *the total number of swap periods over the lifetime of the trade is 7,260. This is 30Y × 4 initially and then $29\frac{3}{4}Y \times 4$ after 3M and then $29\frac{1}{2}Y \times 4$ after another 3M period continuing until maturity. Thus the raw PnL expected to be captured by this gamma effect over the lifetime of the trade is $\$17.14 \times 7,260 = \$124,436$,*

(vi) *an arbitrary estimate at the effect of discounting all of the above raw values is to use the average mid time over the life of every swap period, arriving at the DF of 22.5Y. We take this to be 0.50, so the upfront PnL that accounts for the adjustment is $62,218,*

*(vii) if the analytic delta of the original $1bn IRS is $2,250,000, then this reflects **an upfront adjustment of -0.03 bps on the mid-market rate of the customised IRS.***

The example gives a result that is a typical of standard adjustments of this nature, albeit with a very approximate calculation. It serves to highlight how tiny amounts of gamma, in this case $0.03 pv01/bp per period can produce more meaningful numbers over the course of time (even if the final adjustment of -0.03 bp is not very much either).

As with many of these types of calculation it is theoretical, assuming that hedging is done exactly and daily, which is of course practically impossible when the risks are so minimal.

21.5.6   Non-MTM XCSs hedged with MTM XCSs

Another combination that creates cross-gamma risks in portfolios are non-MTM XCSs hedged with MTM XCSs. This is because XCSs have a multitude of variables; the cross-currency basis, the level of forecast rates in each currency, the discounting basis spread and the spot FX rate.

Analysing and anticipating appropriate hedges really requires numeric risk and scenario analysis revealing the cross-gamma risks. For all of the previous combinations of products in this section it is possible, if not a cumbersome and lengthy process, to consider all of these risks analytically and accurately. To give a qualitative impression of how cross-gamma interacts with FX risk we have included example 21.7.

Example 21.7.

To build a simple scenario, suppose that the EUR/USD mid-market cross-currency basis is zero and that all the EUR forecast rates are equal to USD forecast rates at 2.0%, and discounting rates are the same, so that any fwd EURUSD FX rate equals the spot FX rate of 1.20.

A trader pays a €1bn 5Y EUR/USD MTM XCS at a spread of zero bps and hedges it by receiving €1bn 5Y EUR/USD non-MTM XCS at the same zero spread. The initial EURUSD FX fixing used in both cases is 1.20.

In this portfolio, the EUR leg cashflows are completely equal and opposite at all times, and, although initially equal and opposite, the USD leg cashflows are changeable, due to the MTM nature of only one of the trades.

If the spot FX rate deviates from 1.20, say to 1.25, then this changes the cashflow profile. The trader will have to make a $50mm MTM USD payment at the next payment date, repayable at maturity, and of course this affects the notional on which interest is calculable throughout the life of the MTM trade, see figure 21.4.

Similarly to all the previous examples this new cashflow profile creates USD discounting basis risk. A discounting basis risk estimate is around -$25,000 pv01, and since it has been explicitly created from the movement of the FX rate, this represents FX/basis cross-gamma. It is tempting to think this might also represent FX/delta cross-gamma risk due to a similar argument, but in fact if the outright USD market movements this alters the fwd FX rates and MTM payments to negate any PnL impact.

Finally since cross-gamma risks are symmetric we can consider this from the opposite perspective. If USD discounting basis were to move one bp lower then portfolio would benefit if EURUSD FX rates were to move higher. The specific amount of FX exposure created would be €500,000, since if the FX rate moves from 1.20 to 1.25 this reflects a profit of $25,000.

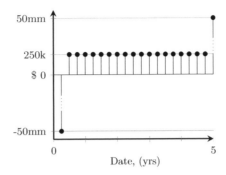

Figure 21.4: Portfolio's net USD cashflows after a spot EURUSD FX rate move to 1.25 from 1.20 (the net EUR cashflows all remain at zero).

21.6 Hedging gamma and cross-gamma

There are two possible meanings to the term *hedging* here. The first means actually hedging the gamma and cross-gamma risks themselves. The second refers to some form of dynamic hedging strategy that neutralises the delta and basis risks as they arise as the result of gamma and cross-gamma risks and market movements.

Hedging all risks, delta, basis, gamma and cross-gamma alike, is only achievable by trading identical products in the opposing directions. Only hedging with the same product results in a portfolio that remains statically hedged regardless of market movement. Clearly this is the simplest and best option but it might be impossible due to liquidity, or come at a price one may judge to be too high.

When precise matching is not possible a proactive approach to the risks is needed. This also means a way of characterising those cross-gamma risks is required. A good way of representing the gamma and cross-gamma risks in a portfolio is to do so in grid form. For historical context we describe this in a legacy IBOR environment.

21.6.1 Cross-gamma grids

A cross-gamma grid shows how much exposure one instrument has, in pv01 terms, to the movement of any other instrument, and in the particular case of gamma risk to the movement of itself. In practice cross-gamma grids can be large matrices. Anecdotally, at Barclays I calculated 30 risk buckets in each of the following risk types; 3M delta, and basis in the following index pairs, 3M/6M, 6M/12M, 3M/OIS, 3M/1M and 3M/uncollateralised. This was a 180 x 180 grid of 32,400 cross-gamma elements, just for the single currency I traded.

Example 21.8.
A trader has obtained the cross-gamma grid for his portfolio. Four of the many elements of it are shown.

($ pv01/bp)	$\cdots$	3M 4Y1Y	$\cdots$	3M/OIS 15Y5Y	$\cdots$
$\vdots$	$\ddots$				
3M 4Y1Y		12		-101	
$\vdots$			$\ddots$		
3M/OIS 15Y5Y		-101		-4	
$\vdots$					$\ddots$

The cross-gamma grid is interpreted as follows; if the rate on the outright 4Y1Y IRS increases by 1bp the risk in that same bucket will increase by $12 pv01, and thus make an additional $12 profit if the rate were to increase by 1bp again. This represents a favourable long gamma position.

Similarly if the 15Y5Y 3M/OIS basis were to increase by 1bp the risk in that bucket would reduce by $4. This represents an unfavourable short gamma position.

Cross-gamma wise, the trader observes that if the outright 4Y1Y IRS rate increases by 1bp then the 15Y5Y 3M/OIS basis risk reduces by 101 pv01 meaning the portfolio will make $101 profit if the OIS rate were to subsequently rise by 1bp relative to the 3M rate. This is a symmetric cross-gamma risk so that if the 15Y5Y basis increases by 1bp the outright risk in the 4Y1Y bucket reduces by $101 pv01. Positive or negative cross-gamma can be favourable depending if the correlation being the two instruments is positive or negative, respectively.

In the context of so many grid elements, each one usually making such a small contribution, it is practical to group many of these elements to provide traders with a useful, aggregated summary. This can be done in different ways, but we explain the two most frequently used methods.

Simple summation

The simple summation method groups each bucket into either 3M outright, 6M/3M basis, 3M/OIS basis etc. Probably also subdivided into curve segments; less than 5Y, 5Y to 10Y, greater than 10Y, etc. Table 21.3 demonstrates this.

	($ pv01/bp)	3M 0Y1Y	3M 1Y1Y	3M 2Y1Y	3M/OIS 0Y1Y	3M/OIS 1Y1Y	3M/OIS 2Y1Y
	0Y1Y	4	18	19	-5	0	0
3M	1Y1Y	18	3	17	-89	-4	0
	2Y1Y	19	17	2	-89	-89	-3
	0Y1Y	-5	-89	-89	0	-11	-10
3M/OIS	1Y1Y	0	-4	-89	-11	0	-10
	2Y1Y	0	0	-3	-10	-10	0

($ pv01/bp)	3M	3M/OIS
3M	117	-279
3M/OIS	-279	-62

Table 21.3: Simple summation applied to a cross-gamma grid to provide a simple overview by risk type.

Simple summation has the advantage of being quick and easy to calculate (provided a complete cross-gamma grid is available). The downside of this method is that without the comparative volatility metrics it is difficult to make an assessment of VaR.

PCA weighted scenario summation

The second method is to weight cross-gamma elements using PCA vectors and take the sum. This is, of course, more complicated, but is more realistic in terms of market movements.

How one might perform the PCA is subjective. Here we choose to use only the first PC. One might choose to analyse more PCs representing further scenarios but this is probably excessive for most practical purposes relating to cross-gamma grids. We also use the first PC of each category generated through separate, individual analysis of either outright rates or basis.

Performing only a single PCA is often distorted because the variance of outright market movements dominates basis movements. Attempting a single *correlation* PCA instead can correct this but since we are choosing to use only the dominant PCs, and interested in relative volatility, I suggest it is easier to perform the PCAs separately.

Table 21.4 gives the comparative overview. Summation is performed after adopting the stated PCs and their s.d.s and multiplying the relevant cross-gamma grid elements, table 21.3, by these values.

Creating an overview in this manner gives some further useful information. Incorporating the standard deviation of each 3M or 3M/OIS PC creates a 'standard scenario' assessment of the amount of new risk expected to be generated through a standard market move dictated by the dominant PC. The resultant summary should be read row wise; a one s.d. move higher in 3M outright rates will generate an expected \$425 pv01 of 3M risk and -\$1,294 pv01 of 3M/OIS basis risk. On the other hand a typical higher basis movement will result in -\$158 pv01 3M outright risk and -\$36 pv01 basis risk. The typical symmetric appearance of the grid has been lost because the relative, standard market movements of each instrument type have been factored into the analysis.

	3M PC1	3M/OIS PC1
0Y1Y	0.20	0.55
1Y1Y	0.75	0.60
2Y1Y	0.63	0.58
s.d.	7.0	0.9

(\$ pv01/bp)	3M	3M/OIS
3M	425	-1,294
3M/OIS	-158	-36

Table 21.4: PCA weighted summation applied to a cross-gamma grid to provide a standard scenario overview by risk type.

21.6.2 Cross-gamma hedging strategies

Having an understanding of the evolution of a portfolio's risks is one thing. Knowing how to react is another. It is sensible to consider methods of proxy hedging when methods of directly hedging delta and/or basis risks are not viable options, either due to liquidity or to the cost of the hedge.

The nature of cross-gamma means basis risks can sometimes be accumulated in quantities or tenors which might be particularly illiquid or have a large margin costs in order to execute the required amount. The logical remedy in this kind of scenario is to employ VaR minimisation techniques, trading other instruments which are far more liquid and cheaper to transact. Of course, these will be inferior hedges since a large amount of residual risk will still remain in the portfolio.

Overall, a trader must make an acute decision between the quality of the hedge they wish to put in place and the amount of loss they are willing to either commit to upfront or risk taking. This leads to a high degree of subjectivity and is a reason why cross-gamma risks can be difficult to deal with.

Example 21.9.

A trader has a portfolio with cross-gamma risks. Yesterday his portfolio was completely hedged, delta and basis wise, but following a large market movement he has acquired the following risks:

$$\mathbf{S_{par}} = \begin{matrix} \text{(3M 10Y)} \\ \text{(3M 30Y)} \\ \text{(3M/OIS 10Y)} \\ \text{(3M/OIS 30Y)} \end{matrix} \begin{bmatrix} -4,000 \\ -18,000 \\ -110,000 \\ -290,000 \end{bmatrix}.$$

The trader recognises two things; firstly the 3M/OIS basis market for both the 10Y and 30Y tenors has large margin and is therefore expensive to repeatedly trade. Secondly, the size of his position in those risk buckets is large relative to the liquidity generally available. On the other hand, the 3M outright market is liquid and cheap to trade so the trader to decides to minimise his portfolio's VaR with respect to those instruments. The trader determines the following covariance matrix for the four instruments (by analysing a suitable historical time period, or otherwise):

$$\mathbf{Q(\Delta)} = \begin{matrix} \text{(3M 10Y)} \\ \text{(3M 30Y)} \\ \text{(3M/OIS 10Y)} \\ \text{(3M/OIS 30Y)} \end{matrix} \begin{bmatrix} 30.3 & 13.1 & 0.29 & 0.16 \\ 13.1 & 8.41 & 0.09 & 0.10 \\ 0.29 & 0.09 & 0.16 & 0.07 \\ 0.16 & 0.10 & 0.07 & 0.05 \end{bmatrix}.$$

The trader's initial VaR multiplier, $c = 133,153$, but if he executes the following multiple instrument VaR minimising trade, which includes only 3M delta instruments, then his VaR multiplier is reduced approximately 25% to $c = 101,958$:

$$\mathbf{S^{trade}} = \begin{matrix} \text{(3M 10Y)} \\ \text{(3M 30Y)} \end{matrix} \begin{bmatrix} 5,790 \\ 19,838 \end{bmatrix}.$$

This hedge will leave the portfolio slightly paid in delta terms which, given the small correlations of basis with delta, should reduce losses if market yields rise and basis is expected to narrow marginally.

Analytic Cross-Gamma

The previous chapter discussed gamma and cross-gamma qualitatively. In this chapter we explain, mathematically, the nature of gamma and cross-gamma risks. The latter part of the chapter is devoted to showing how to make use of the formulae even if their derivation is of no interest. The mathematics in the first part gives the overall topic of gamma and cross-gamma risk greater clarity, but it is possible to skip ahead to section 22.7. We will implement the analytic formula within the code base we have constructively developed throughout the book.

In this chapter the following items are shown;

- the mathematical framework for calculating accurate cross-gamma, including how analytic cross-gamma can be expressed as a linear combination of first order risks,

- algorithms for calculating the cross-gamma risks of different trade types,

- examples of how to apply the algorithms to obtain the analytic cross-gamma,

- a reiteration of how to transform a fwd based cross-gamma grid into a par based one,

- how PnL estimates can be improved with knowledge of cross-gamma risks,

- determining gamma and its value for use in other chapters of the book.

22.1   Historical context

This book's release is ten years after the events I will describe and the Sterling IRS market has completely transitioned from LIBOR to SONIA, which means the effects which gave rise to all of this development no longer have an impact in that market.

Between '07 and '14 I traded the medium and long term maturity, Sterling IRS portfolio at Barclays. During that time pension funds were a significant client and typically traded ZCSs against LIBOR. Exclusively, those pension funds would receive fixed and all interbank hedging could only ever be done with IRSs. This meant that the portfolio built a sizeable position of medium to long dated ZCSs hedged with IRSs, during those years and preceding years. When CSA discounting and multicurve frameworks were established these trading positions generated significant cross-gamma risks.

Unfortunately, the technology at the time (which I do not believe had implemented automatic differentiation) took around one hour to numerically compute the delta risks of just my portfolio since it possessed around 75,000 trades. This was for approximately 3 risk models of 200 bucket risks each. Therefore it averaged about 15ms to risk a single trade in a single risk model. In order to calculate the cross-gamma to the same degree of bucket granularity for one model, and to the same degree of accuracy that the following formulae give, would have taken that same technology around 2 days to numerically compute.

Therefore, I was forced to consider other solutions, and with the mathematics of this chapter it was conveniently discovered that one could express cross-gamma risks in terms of the known quantities that the technology *could* produce: first order delta risks. This then meant a live risk and PnL framework, incorporating cross-gamma, could be developed and deployed for traders. So all of the following development was inspired from a practical requirement, and was implemented and used for years.

22.2   Discounting risk

Before we begin we will present a qualitative explanation of discounting risk. The basic principle here will be visible in the subsequent formulae (and table 22.5) so will help to give perspective and intuitive understanding.

Consider investing \$1mm in a bank account for one year. What is the exposure to a 1bp rise in your deposit rate? $\$1mm \times 1bp \times 1 = \$100$ (discounted for 1Y), and what about two years? That's \$200 discounted for 2Y. Suppose instead that a cashflow *worth* \$1mm was due to be received in one year. What is the exposure to the discounting curve? Exactly the same concept: if it falls by 1bp the impact to the PV is to increase by \$100.

Discounting risk only ever appears as a result of economic cashflows in the future. For a completely flat yield curve, with IRDs never forecast to pay any net cashflows, the discounting risk will be zero. So we have already established now that formulae for discounting risk will show dependency to cashflows and PV.

Suppose we now introduce an IRD which has two fixed cashflows, receive \$4.5mm at one year and pay \$3mm at two year. Using the same estimate as above we tabulate the discounting basis risk in fwd space.

Instrument	+$4.5mm @1y	-$3mm @2y	IRD
1Y	-$450	+$300	**-$150**
1Y1Y	0	+$300	**+$300**
Total	$-450	+$600	**+$150**

The PV of the IRD measured at the one year point (which includes both cashflows) is +$1.5mm, and the PV measured at the two year point is -$3mm, alluding to the calculation of the rightmost column.

For general trades we often do not have the future expected PVs available and instead only have the current PV. For different types of trade we can use basic assumptions to yield the following **approximations of discount delta**. For annuity based trades, such as IRSs or SBSs one can assume that the PV is attributable in equal instalments over time, therefore the future PVs can be expected to decline with a regular structure. For ZCSs with only a single payment the future PVs are obviously all the same because there are no intermediate payments. For forward starting annuity instruments one can mix the techniques of annuity based instruments and ZCSs.

IRSs and annuity based instruments:

$$\text{Total Discounting risk,} \quad \frac{DP}{Ds} \approx \frac{-P \times \text{tenor}}{2 \times 10,000bps} \; .$$

ZCSs:

$$\frac{DP}{Ds} \approx \frac{-P \times \text{tenor}}{10,000bps} \; .$$

Forward starting instruments:

$$\frac{DP}{Ds} \approx \frac{-P \times \text{fwd tenor}}{10,000bps} + \text{IRS approximation above} \; .$$

Example 22.1.
Suppose a 10Y10Y IRS has a PV of $10mm. The discount delta approximation is:

$$\frac{DP}{Ds} \approx \frac{-10mm \times 10Y}{10,000bps} + \frac{-10mm \times 10Y}{2 \times 10,000bps} = \$15,000 \text{ pv01} \; .$$

22.3 Mathematical basis

To progress we now need to lay down some mathematical groundwork. Notation in the book's introduction gives instruction on how the IR curve can be segregated. We choose to do this by invoking indexed, forward, zero coupon rates, and indexed, forward, basis spread levels. By the nature of these variables being in fwd space (and not overlapping), then they are, by definition, independent for the purposes of the mathematical formulae[1]. This allows us to formulate a way to derive the cross-gamma grid.

Since delta and gamma are by definition the derivatives of PV with respect to outright market movements or basis movements we start by establishing these derivatives of DFs.

---

[1]they might not be independent with respect to correlations, but this can be considered in the context of section 21.6.1, using summation or PCA for risk assessment

Discount factors (DFs) and continuously compounded (CC) rates

DFs, relating to a benchmark CSA, are defined by the RFR rates in the local currency. Other DFs representing the outright curve and forecasting curve can also be expressed, using the respective formulae (of course for RFRs these are typically the same curve where the basis spreads are always zero),

$$v_i = \frac{v_{i-1}}{1 + d_i(r_i + s_i)} \;, \qquad v_0 = 1 \;,$$

$$w_i = \frac{w_{i-1}}{1 + d_i r_i} \;, \qquad w_0 = 1 \;,$$

$$x_i = \frac{x_{i-1}}{1 + d_i(r_i + z_i)} \;, \qquad x_0 = 1 \;.$$

For the purpose of calculating derivatives, that is determining how DFs change with respect to market movements, it is more helpful to define discount factors in terms of CC rates. We can then write,

$$v_i = v_{i-1} e^{-d_i(\bar{r}_i + \bar{s}_i)} \;,$$

$$w_i = w_{i-1} e^{-d_i \bar{r}_i} \;,$$

$$x_i = x_{i-1} e^{-d_i(\bar{r}_i + \bar{z}_i)} \;.$$

These show a relationship between the per annum rates, r_i, and spreads, s_i and z_i, and their CC equivalents, $\bar{r}_i$, $\bar{s}_i$ and $\bar{z}_i$. The row element of the table 22.1 defines the partial derivative denominator and the column is the partial derivative numerator. I find it is easier to visualise all derivatives at once in the prevailing table.

$\dfrac{\partial COL}{\partial ROW}$	$\partial \bar{r}_i$	$\partial \bar{s}_i$	$\partial \bar{z}_i$
∂r_j	$\delta_i^j e^{-d_i \bar{r}_i}$	$\dfrac{\partial \bar{s}_i}{\partial s_j} - \dfrac{\partial \bar{r}_i}{\partial r_j}$	$\dfrac{\partial \bar{z}_i}{\partial z_j} - \dfrac{\partial \bar{r}_i}{\partial r_j}$
∂s_j	0	$\delta_i^j e^{-d_i(\bar{r}_i + \bar{s}_i)}$	0
∂z_j	0	0	$\delta_i^j e^{-d_i(\bar{r}_i + \bar{z}_i)}$

Table 22.1: Derivatives of CC rates with their discrete rate equivalents.

The Kronecker delta is included to highlight the independent nature of variables; an i variable is never dependent on a j variable, but can be dependent on other i variables. This result is only due to the way the curveset has been segregated into forward, non-overlapping, instruments. This is by choice and, partly, is the reason for the design.

Next, we differentiate the DFs with respect to the outright rates, r_j, and the discount basis spreads, s_j and the forecasting basis spreads, z_j.

When the *analytic delta* was calculated previously in section 9.2.1 we stated explicitly that it didn't represent risk in the *true* sense. We stated how the fixed rate on the derivative contract was assumed to be the variable, when, in fact, it is not in practice. Market rates themselves were held constant in that estimate, as were DFs, and in turn this gave an easily calculable value, with its own merits.

Here we are correctly allowing the market rates to move, and in turn the DFs change with market movements. The above formulae explicitly describe these relationships, with the first column of table 22.2 the most relevant because that is the DF for valuing cashflows, under the appropriate CSA.

$\frac{\partial COL}{\partial ROW}$	∂v_i	∂w_i	∂x_i
∂r_j	$-\alpha_j^i d_j \frac{\partial \bar{s}_j}{\partial s_j} v_i$	$-\alpha_j^i d_j \frac{\partial \bar{r}_j}{\partial r_j} w_i$	$-\alpha_j^i d_j \frac{\partial \bar{z}_j}{\partial z_j} x_i$
∂s_j	$-\alpha_j^i d_j \frac{\partial \bar{s}_j}{\partial s_j} v_i$	0	0
∂z_j	0	0	$-\alpha_j^i d_j \frac{\partial \bar{z}_j}{\partial z_j} x_i$

Table 22.2: Derivatives of DFs with respect to discrete rates and spreads.

Make a point of noting that any given discount factor is never affected by the movement of any rate or basis spread that succeeds it. Hence the inclusion of the α_j^i term which is zero in the case that $j > i$ and one otherwise. Broadly speaking, DFs are affected in the same way given a movement of any precedent rate or spread variable. The overall RFR for any given period affects how much a DF will change on a 1bp market movement, though. If rates are low (and consequently DFs generally higher) then a 1bp market movement to either a forecasting or discounting basis spread will have a more pronounced effect than if rates were higher initially.

Example 22.2.
The DF at the 10Y date is 0.7, $v_{10} = 0.70000$. A trader estimates what that DF will be if the 3Y1Y fwd rate moves higher by 1bp:

$$\frac{\partial v_{10}}{\partial r_4} = \frac{\partial v_{10}}{\partial s_4} \approx -1 \times 1 \times 1 \times 0.7 = -0.7 (\times \frac{1}{10,000}) \, .$$

For simplicity the trader has assumed that s_4 and $\bar{s}_4$ vary with each other identically, and that the DCF of the 3Y1Y rate is precisely 1.0.

Thus for a 1bp move higher in r_4 (or s_4) then the DF, v_{10}, will change by approximately $-0.7 \times \frac{1}{10,000} = -0.00007$, so that the new DF would be 0.69993.

Suppose instead that the trader assumes that the 10Y IRS rate moves higher by 1bp. He approximates the change in the DF by summing each change affected by the movement of each fwd OIS, be it the 1Y, 1Y1Y, 2Y1Y, etc. rates by 1bp. This means that,

$$\frac{\partial v_{10}}{\partial r_{10Y}} \approx \frac{\partial v_{10}}{\partial r_1} + \ldots + \frac{\partial v_{10}}{\partial r_{10}} \approx -7.0 \, (\times \frac{1}{10,000}) \, .$$

Hence the approximate new DF in this scenario is 0.69930.

Furthermore, since this chapter deals with gamma and cross-gamma specifically the second derivatives of all the above formulae will be needed. Their derivations are standard calculus results, and we state them in table 22.3.

22.4 Trade types

The products that we analyse in this chapter are the standard, single currency IRD contracts. We do not consider XCSs due to the added complexities of dealing with more variables and more partial derivatives, but the logic of this chapter can be extended and applied to them in turn.

The products here have also been standardised to a specific set of aligned dates. There is no benefit attempting to account for all of the variability in bespoke swaps or IR products,

$\frac{\partial^2 COL}{\partial^2 ROW}$	$\partial^2 \bar{r}_i$	$\partial^2 \bar{s}_i$	$\partial^2 \bar{z}_i$
$\partial r_j \partial r_k$	$-d_i\frac{\partial \bar{r}_i}{\partial r_j}\frac{\partial \bar{r}_i}{\partial r_k}$	$-d_i\left(\frac{\partial \bar{s}_i}{\partial s_j}\frac{\partial \bar{s}_i}{\partial s_k} - \frac{\partial \bar{r}_i}{\partial r_j}\frac{\partial \bar{r}_i}{\partial r_k}\right)$	$-d_i\left(\frac{\partial \bar{z}_i}{\partial z_j}\frac{\partial \bar{z}_i}{\partial z_k} - \frac{\partial \bar{r}_i}{\partial r_j}\frac{\partial \bar{r}_i}{\partial r_k}\right)$
$\partial r_j \partial s_k$	0	$-d_i\frac{\partial \bar{s}_i}{\partial s_j}\frac{\partial \bar{s}_i}{\partial s_k}$	0
$\partial r_j \partial z_k$	0	0	$-d_i\frac{\partial \bar{z}_i}{\partial z_j}\frac{\partial \bar{z}_i}{\partial z_k}$
$\partial s_j \partial r_k$	0	$-d_i\frac{\partial \bar{s}_i}{\partial s_j}\frac{\partial \bar{s}_i}{\partial s_k}$	0
$\partial s_j \partial s_k$	0	$-d_i\frac{\partial \bar{s}_i}{\partial s_j}\frac{\partial \bar{s}_i}{\partial s_k}$	0
$\partial s_j \partial z_k$	0	0	0
$\partial z_j \partial r_k$	0	0	$-d_i\frac{\partial \bar{z}_i}{\partial z_j}\frac{\partial \bar{z}_i}{\partial z_k}$
$\partial z_j \partial s_k$	0	0	0
$\partial z_j \partial z_k$	0	0	$-d_i\frac{\partial \bar{z}_i}{\partial z_j}\frac{\partial \bar{z}_i}{\partial z_k}$

Table 22.3: Second derivatives relating CC rates to their discrete rate equivalents.

in terms of any arbitrary date schedules, for the purposes of evaluating analytic cross-gamma. Simplification is a huge advantage and allows the derivation of the key results which can then be made applicable to other, more complex examples.

Before progressing to the derivatives tables, defining first and second order risks, the reader must be prepared for how the information will be presented. It is important to note that all of the IRDs in this book, and the ones we focus specifically on in this chapter, have particular aspects in common. They contain either fixed rate legs, and /or floating rate legs. Legacy products such as SBSs only include floating rate legs. A subset of products contain compounded floating rate legs, for example ZCSs. Historically the separation between an IBOR IRS and an IBOR ZCS in terms of being non-compounded and compounded, respectively, was more distinct. RFR IRSs are a product whose settlement is to compounded daily RFR fixings over the period, but these are classed as non-compounded relative to our curve segregation. The distinction we emphasise, between non-compounded and compounded trades, is that compounded trades will have only a single cashflow at maturity regardless of their maturity and tend to have tenors that are greater than one year, or at least span multiple sections over which the curve has been segregated into. Section 22.10.4 is also relevant to this consideration.

The way that the formulae are developed for cross-gamma risks is done by separating trades into their constituent legs (of which there are fewer types than there are tradable products). This is highlighted to the reader because, once completed, each different trade type can then be constructed from the basic principles of these legs.

Also, we design two very distinct measures of risk; forecasting basis risk and discounting basis risk. Forecasting basis risk is the risk to the movement in the spread above an arbitrary curve, which we deem the outright market curve, to arrive at the level of rates that defines the index, $(r_i + z_i)$. Discounting basis risk is the equivalent risk to a movement in the spread above that same arbitrary outright curve to arrive at the level of rates that defines the discount curve of a benchmark CSA $(r_i + s_i)$. Again, this is highlighted in figure 1.

In our definition, the arbitrary outright curve is defined to be the RFR curve. For any forecasting basis risk that references the RFR the approach is still to use the forecasting basis spread variable, z_i, in the formulation but with the knowledge that to achieve back the RFRs then this spread will be stable at 0bps.

The reason that these two distinct risks are chosen to be represented in this way is so that the delta risk to a particular segment of the curve, r_i, can be expressed as the linear sum. That is,

$$\text{Delta risk} = \text{Discounting basis risk} + \text{Forecasting basis risk} ,$$

$$\frac{\partial P}{\partial r_j} = \frac{\partial P}{\partial s_j} + \frac{\partial P}{\partial z_j} .$$

This considerably reduces the scope needed to calculate all cross-gamma pairs, since those involving the outright, r_i, variables can be reduced to those of the spread, s_i, z_i, variables. In particular,

$$\frac{\partial^2 P}{\partial r_j \partial r_k} = \frac{\partial^2 P}{\partial s_j \partial s_k} + \frac{\partial^2 P}{\partial s_j \partial z_k} + \frac{\partial^2 P}{\partial z_j \partial s_k} + \frac{\partial^2 P}{\partial z_j \partial z_k} ,$$

$$\frac{\partial^2 P}{\partial r_j \partial s_k} = \frac{\partial^2 P}{\partial s_j \partial s_k} + \quad 0 \quad + \frac{\partial^2 P}{\partial z_j \partial s_k} + \quad 0 \quad ,$$

$$\frac{\partial^2 P}{\partial r_j \partial z_k} = \quad 0 \quad + \frac{\partial^2 P}{\partial s_j \partial z_k} + \quad 0 \quad + \frac{\partial^2 P}{\partial z_j \partial z_k} .$$

This means that in order to calculate all of the analytically desired cross-gamma risks we need only to design functions that produce the three specific cross-gamma pairs;

(i) discounting basis / discounting basis cross-gamma, $\frac{\partial^2 P}{\partial s_j \partial s_k}$,

(ii) discounting basis / forecasting basis cross-gamma, $\frac{\partial^2 P}{\partial s_j \partial z_k}$,

(iii) forecasting basis / forecasting basis cross-gamma, $\frac{\partial^2 P}{\partial z_j \partial z_k}$.

(note that the fourth element, forecasting basis / discounting basis cross-gamma, $\frac{\partial^2 P}{\partial z_j \partial s_k}$, can be determined from the transpose of the discounting basis / forecasting basis cross-gamma).

Product formulation

The trade types and constituent legs that are examined and their respective PV formulation are shown in table 22.4.

Trade Type (direction)	PV Formulation, P
1. Single fixed cashflow (receiver)	$P_{\cdot,i}^{\{\text{cashflow}\}} = C_i v_i$
2. Standard fixed leg (receiver)	$P_{h,i}^{\{\text{fixed leg}\}} = NR \sum_{j=h}^{i} d_j v_j$
3. Standard non-compounded floating leg (receiver)	$P_{h,i}^{\{\text{float leg}\}} = N \sum_{j=h}^{i} (r_j + z_j) d_j v_j$
4. Standard IRS (receiver)	$P_{h,i}^{\{\text{IRS}\}} = P_{h,i}^{\{\text{fixed leg}\}} - P_{h,i}^{\{\text{float leg}\}}$
5. Standard compounded floating leg (receiver) [2]	$P_{h,i}^{\{\text{comp. leg}\}} = v_i N \left(\prod_{j=h}^{i} (1 + d_j r_j) - 1 \right)$
6. Standard ZCS (receiver)	$P_{h,i}^{\{\text{ZCS}\}} = P_{\cdot,i}^{\{\text{cashflow}\}} - P_{h,i}^{\{\text{comp. leg}\}}$

Table 22.4: Relevant formulae and notation for generic trade constituents.

22.5   First order risks

First order risks define the discounting basis and forecasting basis risks collectively. If these are
linearly combined they sum to give the specific delta risk. Table 22.5 displays the determined
partial derivatives.

Trade Type	$\frac{\partial P}{\partial s_j}$	$\frac{\partial P}{\partial z_j}$
1. Fixed cashflow	$-d_j \frac{\partial \bar{s}_j}{\partial s_j} \alpha_j^i P_{\cdot,i}^{\{\text{cashflow}\}}$	0
2. Fixed leg	$-d_j \frac{\partial \bar{s}_j}{\partial s_j} P_{\max(h,j),i}^{\{\text{fixed leg}\}}$	0
3. Non-compounded leg	$-d_j \frac{\partial \bar{s}_j}{\partial s_j} P_{\max(h,j),i}^{\{\text{float leg}\}}$	$+\alpha_h^j \alpha_j^i d_j N v_j$
4. IRS	$-d_j \frac{\partial \bar{s}_j}{\partial s_j} P_{\max(h,j),i}^{\{\text{IRS}\}}$	$-\alpha_h^j \alpha_j^i d_j N v_j$
5. Compounded leg	$-d_j \frac{\partial \bar{s}_j}{\partial s_j} \alpha_j^i P_{h,i}^{\{\text{comp. leg}\}}$	$+\alpha_h^j \alpha_j^i d_j \frac{\partial \bar{z}_j}{\partial z_j}(N v_i + P_{h,i}^{\{\text{comp. leg}\}})$
6. ZCS	$-d_j \frac{\partial \bar{s}_j}{\partial s_j} \alpha_j^i P_{h,i}^{\{\text{ZCS}\}}$	$-\alpha_h^j \alpha_j^i d_j \frac{\partial \bar{z}_j}{\partial z_j}(N v_i + P_{h,i}^{\{\text{comp. leg}\}})$

Table 22.5: Discounting basis and forecasting basis risks, as the two linear components of delta
risk, for each generic trade constituent.

What can we say about these discounting and forecasting basis risks qualitatively?

Firstly, fixed cashflows have no forecasting basis risk, because they do not depend on an
index fixing, e.g. IBOR, OIS, or RFR. They only depend on the discount curve.

Only floating legs, and therefore IRSs and ZCSs which contain floating legs, depend, explicitly, on the index fixings and thus exhibit forecasting basis risk.

Secondly, the discounting basis risk is completely dependent upon the immediate and future
PVs of any cashflow or leg. Any positively valued cashflow, or leg, benefits if yields fall and
DFs increase and of course vice versa. So, this is major influencer in the determination of
discounting basis risks.

Example 22.3.
*A cashflow of €10mm is due to be received in 5Y time. The DF at that point, $v_5 = 0.90$. The
delta and discounting basis risks for each annual instrument (i.e. $d_j \approx 1.0$), 1Y, 1Y1Y, 2Y1Y,
3Y1Y and 4Y1Y, are all approximately the same and are approximately -900 pv01,*

$$\frac{\partial P}{\partial r_j} = \frac{\partial P}{\partial s_j} = -900 , \quad \text{for j = 1, .. ,5 } .$$

*The total delta risk is estimated as the sum of each of the 5 annual delta risks to be -4,500
pv01, which is the same as the total discounting basis risk,*

$$\frac{DP}{D\mathbf{s}} = \frac{DP}{D\mathbf{r}} = \sum_j \frac{\partial P}{\partial r_j} = -4,500 .$$

$^2 P_{h,i}^{\{\text{comp. leg}\}} = v_i N \left(\prod_{j=h}^{i} (1 + d_j r_j) - 1 \right) = v_i N \left(e^{\sum_{j=h}^{i} d_j \bar{r}_j} - 1 \right) .$

22.6 Second order risks

The second order risks *are* the calculations of gamma and cross-gamma. These are precisely the formulae that all the preceding sections of this chapter have been steered to produce, and those that will be used in the next section regarding simple, practical algorithms that can be implemented. To obtain them, we take the relevant partial derivatives of the first order risks.

Discounting / discounting basis cross-gamma, $\frac{\partial^2 P}{\partial s_j \partial s_k}$

This value is the same formula for all trade types. This is due to the fact that it is sensitive only to monetary PV. It can be assessed in terms of the risks, $\frac{\partial P}{\partial s_j}$ and $\frac{\partial P}{\partial s_k}$. For all of the above trade types,

$$\frac{\partial^2 P}{\partial s_j \partial s_k} = -(1 + \delta_j^k) d_{\min(j,k)} \frac{\partial \bar{s}_{\min(j,k)}}{\partial s_{\min(j,k)}} \frac{\partial P}{\partial s_{\max(j,k)}} .$$

Discounting / forecasting basis cross-gamma, $\frac{\partial^2 P}{\partial s_j \partial z_k}$

Since this form of cross-gamma involves the forecasting basis we can immediately eliminate fixed cashflows and fixed legs. They are not dependent on the forecasting basis.

For non-compounded floating legs and, implicitly, standard IRSs, this cross-gamma is linearly related to the forecasting basis risk, provided that the specific discounting basis instrument sampled, comes before the forecasting basis risk instrument.

For compounded floating legs and, implicitly, ZCSs, this cross-gamma has the same linear dependency to the forecasting basis risk, provided the discounting basis instrument sampled comes before the maturity of the trade. This small difference is reflected in the resultant formulae - note the 'k's and 'i's,

$$\frac{\partial^2 P}{\partial s_j \partial z_k} = \begin{cases} 0, & \text{for trade types 1 \& 2,} \\ -\alpha_j^k d_j \frac{\partial \bar{s}_j}{\partial s_j} \frac{\partial P}{\partial z_k} , & \text{for trade types 3 \& 4,} \\ -\alpha_j^i d_j \frac{\partial \bar{s}_j}{\partial s_j} \frac{\partial P}{\partial z_k} , & \text{for trade types 5 \& 6.} \end{cases}$$

Forecasting / forecasting basis cross-gamma, $\frac{\partial^2 P}{\partial z_j \partial z_k}$

For this form of cross-gamma we can immediately eliminate fixed cashflows, fixed legs, non-compounded floating legs and IRSs. The only trade type we don't eliminate are those with compounded floating legs and ZCSs. The reason being that compounded legs are interdependent on forecasting basis. If any single forecasting basis moves then, due to the compounding effect, it can affect the forecasting risks of other periods. Thus for trade types 5 and 6 the cross-gamma formulae are explicitly,

$$\frac{\partial^2 P}{\partial z_j \partial z_k} = \begin{cases} 0 & \text{for types 1, 2, 3, 4,} \\ \alpha_h^{\min(j,k)} (1 - \delta_j^k) d_{\min(j,k)} \frac{\partial \bar{z}_{\min(j,k)}}{\partial z_{\min(j,k)}} \frac{\partial P}{\partial z_{\max(j,k)}} , & \text{for types 5 \& 6.} \end{cases}$$

22.7   Practical algorithms

A reader uninterested in the derivation of formulae, but keen to analyse gamma and cross-gamma of trades and portfolios in a practical sense, should focus attention from this point of the chapter onwards.

The above formulae for analytic cross-gamma are highly accurate when applied to an entire portfolio, or just an individual trade. They are practical because of a single, convenient property; that second order (cross-gamma) risks can be determined from a linear combination of the first order risks. Meaning, if one has a system capable of outputting first order risks (which almost all institution's numeric risk systems can), then the cross-gamma risks can be determined analytically.

However, this does require that these first order risks are provided in the format designed for performing the calculations. Firstly they must be zero coupon **fwd risks** *not* par risks[3]. Secondly, a trade or portfolio's **first order risks must be separated into** the following constituent parts; **discounting basis risk**, **forecasting basis risk of non-compounded legs** (i.e. on IRSs), and **forecasting basis risk of compounded legs** (i.e. on ZCSs).

As was explained in the previous sections, compounded or non-compounded legs prove to be fundamentally different in terms of their cross-gammas, due to the positioning of cashflows, which is all important for discounting basis risks. This is one of the reasons why the preceding sections approached the problem by segregating trade types into their constituent legs.

To demonstrate how these required risks can be computed we will adapt our code base to risk swaps in the appropriate manner, by;

   i) augmenting a new `Swap2` class that uses separate curves for forecasting and discounting,

   ii) implementing a specific function to output the relevant risks.

22.7.1   New swap class

The previous `Swap` we implemented, in section 11.1.3, calculated rates and PV using a single curve, the RFR curve. This meant we were able to make some mathematical reductions to simplify the code. Since we now need to derive risks to two curves we can no longer permit these and must code the rates and PV to evaluate the periods individually, with forecasting and discounting curves. We implement [21, #7d1d8b] a `Swap2` class inheriting basic structure from the previous `Swap` class. This time we use the following formula for determining the rate,

$$R = \frac{\sum_j^{T_2} r_j d_j v_j}{\sum_i^{T_1} d_i v_i}$$

```
1  class Swap2(Swap):
2      def __init__(self, *args, **kwargs):
3          super().__init__(*args, **kwargs)
4
5      def rate(self, curve: Curve, disc_curve: Curve = None):
6          disc_curve = disc_curve or curve
7          if self.notional == 0:
8              self.notional = 1
9              fixed_delta = self.analytic_delta(disc_curve) * 10000 / self.notional
10             self.notional = 0
11         else:
12             fixed_delta = self.analytic_delta(disc_curve) * 10000 / self.notional
13         floating_leg = 0
```

---

[3]in fact they should be zero coupon fwd risks and not IRS fwd risks. Appendix section 22.10.4 highlights this distinction with practical guidance

```
14        for period in getattr(self, f"schedule_float").data:
15            _ = (curve[period[0]] / curve[period[1]] - 1)
16            floating_leg += _ * disc_curve[period[1]]
17        return floating_leg / fixed_delta * 100
18
19    def npv(self, curve: Curve, disc_curve: Curve = None):
20        disc_curve = disc_curve or curve
21        self.set_fixed_rate(self.fixed_rate, curve, disc_curve)
22        rate_diff = (self.rate(curve, disc_curve) - self.fixed_rate)
23        return rate_diff * self.analytic_delta(disc_curve) * 100
24
```

22.7.2 Forward zero coupon risks

Next, we implement a method to output the relevant risks. Observe that our `Curve` object is constructed in such as way as to define DFs on given node dates. Therefore the risks we seek will be to the forward zero coupon risks between these specific node dates, i.e. we seek,

$$\frac{\partial P}{\partial r_j}, \frac{\partial P}{\partial s_j}, \frac{\partial P}{\partial z_j} \quad \forall j$$

Since our `Swap2` PV function is capable of accepting two separate curves, one for forecasting and one for discounting, we can evaluate derivatives by varying each of these relevant curves individually and holding the other static. Technically, if our curves were defined with `Dual` number implementation that does not hard code the DFs with same 'v' label, then we could extract automatic derivatives simultaneously. But in this case, performing two separate calculations avoids having to restructure the previous code to avoid this hard coded naming clash.

As with section 11.4 our automatic differentiation does not quite yield the full calculation. Instead, it gives derivatives with respect to DFs that must be transformed, via the chain rule,

$$\nabla_\mathbf{r} P = \nabla_\mathbf{r} \mathbf{w}^\mathbf{T} \nabla_\mathbf{w} P, \qquad \nabla_\mathbf{s} P = \nabla_\mathbf{s} \mathbf{v}^\mathbf{T} \nabla_\mathbf{v} P, \qquad \nabla_\mathbf{z} P = \nabla_\mathbf{z} \mathbf{x}^\mathbf{T} \nabla_\mathbf{x} P$$

where the Jacobians, $\nabla_\mathbf{r} \mathbf{w}^\mathbf{T}, \nabla_\mathbf{s} \mathbf{v}^\mathbf{T}, \nabla_\mathbf{z} \mathbf{x}^\mathbf{T}$, were determined in tables 22.1 and 22.2, and in the case of RFR curves are all identical, which we label, $\nabla_\mathbf{r} \mathbf{v}^\mathbf{T}$, for consistency with code naming. So we have all of the information available from the separate curves to perform this calculation using automatic differentiation. First we calculate $\nabla_\mathbf{r} \mathbf{v}^\mathbf{T}$, which is a static property of the `Curve`,

```
1  class Curve:
2      ...
3
4      @property
5      def grad_r_v(self):
6          if getattr(self, "grad_r_v_", None) is None:
7              v, dsds, d, n = self.var_collection
8              v = v[1:, :]
9              alpha = np.triu(np.ones((n, n)))
10             self.grad_r_v_ = -np.matmul(np.diag(dsds[:, 0]), np.matmul(d, v.T)) * alpha
11         return self.grad_r_v_
12
13     @property
14     def var_collection(self):
15         def val(v):
16             return v.real if isinstance(v, Dual) else v
17         v = np.array([val(v) for v in self.nodes.values()])
18         n = v.shape[0] - 1
19         dsds = np.array([v[i + 1] / v[i] for i in range(n)])
20         dates = [k for k in self.nodes.keys()]
21         d = np.array([
22             (dates[i + 1] - dates[i]) / timedelta(days=365) for i in range(n)
23         ])
24         return v[:, np.newaxis], dsds[:, np.newaxis], d[:, np.newaxis], n
```

Then we calculate $\nabla_r P$ using the above, and the derivatives with respect to the DFs calculated via automatic differentiation,

```
class Swap2(Swap):
    ...

    def risk_fwd_zero_rates(self, curve: SolvedCurve, disc_curve: SolvedCurve = None):
        disc_curve = disc_curve or curve
        stat_crv, stat_disc_crv = copy(curve), copy(disc_curve)
        for crv in [stat_crv, stat_disc_crv]:
            crv.nodes = {k: v.real for (k, v) in crv.nodes.items()}
        n = len(curve.nodes.keys())
        npv_fore = self.npv(curve, stat_disc_crv)
        grad_zv_p = np.array([npv_fore.dual.get(f"v{i}", 0) for i in range(1, n)])
        npv_disc = self.npv(stat_crv, disc_curve)
        grad_sv_p = np.array([npv_disc.dual.get(f"v{i}", 0) for i in range(1, n)])

        grad_z_p = np.matmul(curve.grad_r_v, grad_zv_p[:, np.newaxis])
        grad_s_p = np.matmul(disc_curve.grad_r_v, grad_sv_p[:, np.newaxis])
        return grad_z_p / 10000, grad_s_p / 10000
```

If we assume that we have constructed a `SolvedCurve` with nodes points at 1Y, 2Y, 3Y, 4Y and 5Y we can now use the new methods to calculate our relevant risks,

Example 22.4.
Receiving a 5Y IRS in 830mm notional with a fixed rate vastly off market at 25% creates a large PV and a large amount of exposure to the discounting curve.

```
>>> curve = SolvedCurve(...)  # iterated and valid
>>> swap = Swap2(datetime(2022, 1, 1), 5*12, 12, 12, fixed_rate=25.0, notional=-8.3e8)
>>> dPdz, dPds = swap.risk_fwd_zero_rates(curve)
>>> DataFrame(
        {"dPdz": dPdz[:,0], "dPds": dPds[:,0], "dPdr": (dPdz+dPds)[:,0]},
        index=["1Y", "1Y1Y", "2Y1Y", "3Y1Y", "4Y1Y"]
    )
```

Instrument	$\frac{\partial P}{\partial z_j}$	$\frac{\partial P}{\partial s_j}$	$\frac{\partial P}{\partial r_j}$
1Y	-82,178	-94,111	-176,289
1Y1Y	-81,203	-74,435	-155,638
2Y1Y	-80,295	-55,378	-135,673
3Y1Y	-78,967	-36,544	-115,511
4Y1Y	-77,913	-18,178	-96,091

22.7.3   Cross-gamma of fixed and non-compounded trade types

This section implements the code and presents an example of the application of the algorithms for IRSs, being the most common product for which cross-gamma (or gamma) is likely to be sought. For strategising trades or evaluating the term structure of the yield curve it is IRSs which are usually of most interest.

For compounded trades, and of course ZCSs, the algorithms are slightly more involved but of precisely the same nature. The algorithms for calculating the cross-gammas of compounded IBOR trades are included in the appendix.

With all of the necessary preliminaries in place from previous sections the addition of a `Gamma` class for IRSs is only an additional ten lines of code [21, #95f76d], to implement all of the formulae derived.

```
class Gamma_:

    def cross_gamma(self, curve, disc_curve=None):
        disc_curve = disc_curve or curve
        v, dsds, d, n = disc_curve.var_collection
```

```
6    dz, ds = self.risk_fwd_zero_rates(curve, disc_curve)
7    U = np.matmul(np.triu(np.ones((n, n)) * dsds * d), np.diag(ds[:, 0]))
8    dP_dsds = -(U + U.T) / 10000
9    U = np.matmul(np.triu(np.ones((n, n)) * dsds * d), np.diag(dz[:, 0]))
10   dP_dsdz = -U / 10000
11   dP_dzdz = np.zeros((n, n))
12   return dP_dsds, dP_dsdz, dP_dzdz
```

We can then extend example 22.4 and use the above to display the full cross-gamma grid, **G**.

Example 22.5.

```
1  >>> ss, sz, zz = swap.cross_gamma(curve)
2  >>> G = np.block([[ss, sz, ss + sz],
3                    [sz.T, zz, sz.T + zz],
4                    [(ss + sz).T, (sz.T + zz).T, ss + sz + sz.T + zz]])
5  >>> labels = ["s1", "s2", "s3", "s4", "s5",
6                "z1", "z2", "z3", "z4", "z5",
7                "r1", "r2", "r3", "r4", "r5"]
8  >>> DataFrame(G, index=labels, columns=labels)
9  # see following figure
```

	s_1	s_2	s_3	s_4	s_5	z_1	z_2	z_3	z_4	z_5	r_1	r_2	r_3	r_4	r_5
s_1	19	7.4	5.5	3.6	1.8	8.1	8.0	8.0	7.8	7.7	27	15	13	11	9.5
s_2	7.4	15	5.5	3.6	1.8	0	8.0	7.9	7.8	7.7	7.4	23	13	11	9.5
s_3	5.5	5.5	11	3.6	1.8	0	0	7.9	7.8	7.7	5.5	5.5	19	11	9.5
s_4	3.6	3.6	3.6	7.2	1.8	0	0	0	7.8	7.7	3.6	3.6	3.6	15	9.5
s_5	1.8	1.8	1.8	1.8	3.6	0	0	0	0	7.7	1.8	1.8	1.8	1.8	11
z_1	8.1	0	0	0	0	0	0	0	0	0	8.1	0	0	0	0
z_2	8.0	8.0	0	0	0	0	0	0	0	0	8.0	8.0	0	0	0
z_3	8.0	7.9	7.9	0	0	0	0	0	0	0	8.0	7.9	7.9	0	0
z_4	7.8	7.8	7.8	7.8	0	0	0	0	0	0	7.8	7.8	7.8	7.8	0
z_5	7.7	7.7	7.7	7.7	7.7	0	0	0	0	0	7.7	7.7	7.7	7.7	7.7
r_1	27	7.4	5.5	3.6	1.8	8.1	8.0	8.0	7.8	7.7	35	15	13	11	9.5
r_2	15	23	5.5	3.6	1.8	0	8.0	7.9	7.8	7.7	15	31	13	11	9.5
r_3	13	13	19	3.6	1.8	0	0	7.9	7.8	7.7	13	13	27	11	9.5
r_4	11	11	11	15	1.8	0	0	0	7.8	7.7	11	11	11	23	9.5
r_5	9.5	9.5	9.5	9.5	11	0	0	0	0	7.7	9.5	9.5	9.5	9.5	19

Figure 22.1: Complete cross-gamma grid, **G**.

Note that the cross-gamma risks shown are small in comparison to the delta and basis risks. In fact they are $O(10^{-4})$ of those first order risks. They do not necessarily sum to large numbers either, since each grid (in this case) is only dimension 5×5. However portfolios of greater maturities have quadratically increasing amounts of cross-gamma, as the dimension of the grid increases. And don't forget that cross-gamma impacts PnL proportional to the square of market movements. It certainly should not be disregarded out of hand, since during periods of volatility cross-gamma can dominate some portfolios.

For RFR IRSs it is the bottom right quadrant, $\frac{\partial^2 P}{\partial \mathbf{r}^2}$, that is of interest since, if one recalls, the spreads s_j and z_j are fixed at zero in the single, self discounted curve framework.

22.7.4 Jacobian transformations

Chapter 10 discusses Jacobian transformations in general and specifically states a matrix equation for transforming a cross-gamma grid from one risk model to another. The formula was shown to be,

$$\mathbf{G_B^*} = \mathbf{J_{A\to B}}\mathbf{G_A}\mathbf{J_{A\to B}^T} \,.$$

The way that the theory of this chapter has been constructed is entirely based upon using fwd zero coupon rates. This is to permit coherent algebra. This book has, however, persistently highlighted a useful distinction between par and fwd rates. Cross-gamma grids are no different in this respect. It may be useful to understand one's cross-gamma in terms of par rate movements, for no less a reason than to design hedging strategies, or for better observability with the interbank market which trades in par tenor products.

Given an RFR `Curve` we can calculate a Jacobian between the instruments parametrising the curve and the fwd zero coupon rates we have constructed, by observing,

$$\nabla_\mathbf{s}\mathbf{r^T} = \nabla_\mathbf{s}\mathbf{v^T}\nabla_\mathbf{v}\mathbf{r^T}$$

where $\nabla_\mathbf{s}\mathbf{v^T}$ was already calculated in section 11.4, and $\nabla_\mathbf{v}\mathbf{r^T}$ is the inverse of $\nabla_\mathbf{r}\mathbf{v^T}$ which we have calculated in section 22.7.2. Although, just for completeness, we can demonstrate that $\nabla_\mathbf{v}\mathbf{r^T}$ can also be calculated directly from its definition,

$$r_i = \frac{1}{d_i}\left(\frac{w_{i-1}}{w_i} - 1\right) \quad \Longrightarrow \quad \frac{\partial r_i}{\partial w_i} = \frac{-w_{i-1}}{d_i w_i^2}, \quad \frac{\partial r_i}{\partial w_{i-1}} = \frac{1}{d_i w_i}, \quad \frac{\partial r_i}{\partial w_j} = 0 \ \forall j \notin \{i, i-1\}$$

and whose calculations can be added directly to the code repository[21, #715d65]

```
1  class Curve:
2      ...
3
4      @property
5      def grad_v_r(self):
6          if getattr(self, "grad_v_r_", None) is None:
7              v, dsds, d, n = self.var_collection
8              diag0 = -v[:n, 0] / (d[:, 0] * v[1:, 0] ** 2)
9              diag1 = 1 / (d[:, 0] * v[1:, 0])
10             self.grad_v_r_ = np.diag(diag0) + np.diag(diag1[1:], 1)
11         return self.grad_v_r_
```

For our RFR curve we can use this same Jacobian for basis and delta, although note that the calculation is only relevant for the delta cross-gamma elements, $\frac{\partial^2 P}{\partial r_j \partial r_k}$. We can add an option to our `cross_gamma` method to output the cross-gamma represented as the swap input instruments making up the curve,

```
1  def cross_gamma(self, curve, disc_curve=None, swaps=False):
2      ...
3      if swaps:
4          J = np.matmul(curve.grad_s_v, curve.grad_v_r) * 100
5          transform = lambda G: np.matmul(np.matmul(J, G), J.T)
6          return transform(dP_dsds), transform(dP_dsdz), transform(dP_dzdz)
7      return dP_dsds, dP_dsdz, dP_dzdz
```

With the above additions we can now calculate accurate cross-gamma, to the input instruments of a `SolvedCurve`, efficiently and without repeated numerical differentiation via the automatic differentiation from our library.

Example 22.6.
A trader calculates the delta/delta cross-gamma of receiving a mid-market, 100mm 5Y IRS to the instruments parametrising his curve, which are 1Y, 2Y, 3Y, 4Y and 5Y.

```
1  >>> swap = Swap2(datetime(2022, 1, 1), 5*12, 12, 12, fixed_rate=1.270, notional=-100e6)
2  >>> ss, sz, zz = swap.cross_gamma(curve, swaps=True)
3  >>> G = ss + sz + sz.T + zz
4  >>> labels = ["1Y", "2Y", "3Y", "4Y", "5Y"]
5  >>> df = DataFrame(G, index=labels, columns=labels)
6  >>> df["Total"] = df.sum(axis=1)
7  >>> df.loc["Total", :] = df.sum(axis=0)
```

	1Y	2Y	3Y	4Y	5Y	Total
1Y	2	-2	0	0	0	0
2Y	-2	8	-6	0	0	0
3Y	0	-6	18	-12	0	0
4Y	0	0	-12	32	-20	0
5Y	0	0	0	-20	48	28
Total	0	0	0	0	28	28

He observes that if the whole curve moves in parallel his risk change will only be to the 5Y bucket, however, if the curve steepens for flattens he is also exposed to changes in other buckets.

22.8 Cross-gamma and PnL estimates

The first order PnL estimate of a trade or portfolio is restated as,

$$\Delta P \approx \mathbf{S} \cdot \mathbf{\Delta x} = \sum_j S^j \Delta x_j , \quad \text{for} \quad \mathbf{\Delta x} := [\Delta s_1, \ldots, \Delta s_n, \Delta z_1, \ldots, \Delta z_n, \Delta r_1, \ldots, \Delta r_n]^{\mathbf{T}} .$$

This estimate is good for small market movements. But, if a portfolio has a reasonable amount of cross-gamma (due to possibly different trade types) then the estimate will be less accurate, especially for larger market movements. For these cases we can extend the PnL estimate to incorporate second order risks,

$$\Delta P \approx \mathbf{S} \cdot \mathbf{\Delta x} + \frac{1}{2} \mathbf{\Delta x}^{\mathbf{T}} \mathbf{G} \mathbf{\Delta x} = \sum_j S^j \Delta x_j + \frac{1}{2} \sum_j \sum_k G^{jk} \Delta x_j \Delta x_k .$$

This estimate is very accurate. Daily market movements will certainly be small enough to permit high accuracy for this estimate. However, larger market movements (those measured on the scale of months or years) may be susceptible to some inaccuracy, but will still produce superior estimates than those from first order only.

Due to the linearity of the formula it is possible to separate each contributing element of cross-gamma PnL to improve the usefulness of the PnL explain. Alongside chapter 16, which examines PnL explains in terms of risk managing first order risks, it is sensible to add cross-gamma PnL explains. It is recommended to sum each sub-grid to give a meaningful measure. As previously mentioned for RFRs, $\mathbf{\Delta s} = \mathbf{0}$ and $\mathbf{\Delta z} = \mathbf{0}$, so this may be redundant, albeit was highly relevant for the legacy IBOR framework.

Example 22.7.
Continuing example 22.5, some daily market movements are suggested (outside of the pure RFR framework), and the cross-gamma component of the PnL estimate is calculated in figure 22.2. The PnL grid shows a total of 1,271 PnL generated by the cross-gamma risks of the portfolio. Specifically, the traditional gamma component (delta / delta cross-gamma) can be seen to produce the majority of the PnL, but the delta / forecasting basis cross-gamma has also contributed since the forecasting basis has had a reasonable daily market movement (at least compared with the discounting basis).

22.9 Gamma of IRSs

A successful portfolio manager will, of course, strategise his trading positions. Factors affecting the decisions of this nature are economic conditions, tradable levels, carry and roll-down, VaR

Δs_j	Δz_j	Δr_j
+0.2	-1.1	-5.2
+0.3	-1.2	-4.1
+0.2	-1.1	-2
+0.1	-0.8	2.4
-0.1	-0.5	7.8

1,271	Δs	Δz	Δr
Δs	2.4	-10	-20
Δz	-10	0	147
Δr	-20	147	1,035

Figure 22.2: PnL explain for cross-gamma risks of the portfolio of IRSs.

and gamma. Chapter 23 discusses this more generally. This chapter has provided the complete set of tools to calculate the complete cross-gamma grid of a trade or portfolio. What remains is to describe a common, practical scenario where gamma analysis is used and how it fits into the wider context of other chapters of this book.

It can be useful to calculate the gamma of a single trade in isolation. **By 'gamma' we mean the sum of all of the delta / delta cross-gammas,**

$$\frac{D^2 P}{Dr^2} = G = \sum_{j=1}^{i} \sum_{k=1}^{i} \frac{\partial^2 P_{h,i}}{\partial r_j \partial r_k} \ .$$

The reason that this quantity is useful is that it allows a better statistical assessment of the true PnL of those trades (see section 23.3.4), for given market movements. Gamma, as a single number, means that this is an estimate, and assumes a parallel curve market movement. It is generally a good estimate, and provides sound information to draw conclusions when comparing trade strategies with one another.

To factor more than a simple parallel market movements will require numerical simulations rather than analytical formulae. Scenario analysis and Monte Carlo techniques are likely to be overly complicated for the context of more typical studies. Certainly that kind of advanced analysis would require knowledge of the complete cross-gamma grid.

Example 22.8.
A trader pays fixed on a 29Y IRS and receives fixed on a 30Y IRS in the same delta, S pv01. The gamma of the 29Y IRS is estimated to be $\frac{-30S}{10,000}$, and of the 30Y it is estimated to be $\frac{31S}{10,000}$. The total delta and gamma of the two trades is therefore,

$$\frac{DP}{Dr} = +S - S = 0, \qquad \frac{D^2 P}{Dr^2} = G = \frac{S}{10,000} \ .$$

The swaption market is pricing an annualised normal volatility of $\sigma_N = 60bps$. The expected PnL over the course of the year can be estimated as[4],

$$E[\Delta P] = \frac{DP}{Dr} E[\Delta \mathbf{r}] + \frac{1}{2} G E[\Delta \mathbf{r}^2] \ ,$$

$$= 0 + \frac{1}{2} \cdot \frac{S}{10,000} 60^2 = 0.18S \ .$$

This is not necessarily an insignificant amount of expected PnL, as it does represent 0.18bps of the risk. A no arbitrage hypothesis might suggest the 30Y rate should be lower that 29Y rate to compensate (see section 8.2.1).

---

[4]assuming a parallel market move where $E[\Delta \mathbf{r}] = 0$ and identical volatility of the 29Y and 30Y IRSs

In example 22.8 the gamma of the 29Y and 30Y IRSs has been approximated with a simple formula developed in appendix section 22.10.1. Alternatively, with knowledge of all rates, DFs and trade notionals, we could have calculated the forecasting and discounting basis risks of each IRS using the formulae from table 22.5, or numerically. Then, with those, used the cross-gamma functions to derive the relevant cross-gamma grids and sum the respective elements.

We summarise that simple approximation here as,

$$\frac{D^2 P}{Dr^2} = G \approx -\frac{h+i}{10,000} S \,.$$

The appendix also improves this formula to account for the term structure of interest rates. **Of all methods for single figure gamma estimation the improvement to the simple formula is my preferred method, balancing accuracy with relative ease.** For rule of thumb calculations I still use the simple formula because of its accessibility and reasonable accuracy.

22.9.1 The value of gamma

Throughout this book, gamma has often been used to calculate expected values of PnLs. The component of PnL due to gamma is the term, $\frac{1}{2}G(\Delta r)^2$. To derive the expectation of gamma we have often assumed it equals[5] $\frac{1}{2}G\,(\sigma_N^{\Delta r})^2$.

However, if we were to be completely consistent with the swaption market we actually need to think a little more about what the value of gamma is, and how we should assess its value. We will see that the impact of the volatility smile, which is designed to skew probability distributions towards fatter tails (i.e. higher kurtosis), can be significant.

In chapter 20 on swaptions we discussed how they are valued according to a strategy of trading the underlying IRS in such a manner as to replicate the pay-off of the swaption itself. The cost of the trading strategy was equated to the cost of the option. We can adopt a similar approach with respect to gamma. The intention is to purchase a precise set of swaptions at different strikes such that the PnL, that would be achieved through the gamma value alone, is replicated. See figure 22.3.

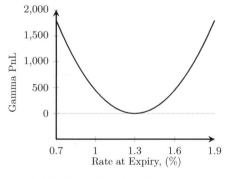
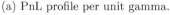

(a) PnL profile per unit gamma.

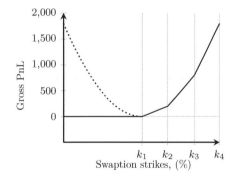

(b) Gross PnL profile of a series of payers.

Figure 22.3: The pay-off profiles of the value of gamma and of a series of payer swaptions (gross of premiums).

---

[5]if the mean of Δr is not zero (for example if roll-down is assumed) then this is $\frac{1}{2}G\left((\sigma_N^{\Delta r})^2 + (\mu^{\Delta r})^2\right)$

The figure only shows one half of the construction. To the left-hand side of the ATM or mid-market rate we would synthesise the PnL profile with a series of receiver swaptions, instead of payers.

The notional amounts of each swaption are important and must be precisely devised to replicate the shape of the PnL profile. The calculation of these notionals is given in the appendix. One will observe that the more strikes that are chosen, i.e. the more swaptions are utilised, then the better the replication will be, otherwise a rather clunky, approximation will be the result. Figure 22.3's strikes were chosen wide enough to demonstrate the lack of accuracy, but close enough to demonstrate the key point. In practice, when using this technique, it would be a simple extension to utilise far more strikes to get higher accuracy.

We will also point out that the gamma PnL profile is a convex function, which means the profile constructed of linear segments due to the payer swaptions' pay-offs will always be higher. This makes that profile more valuable, which is why using many strikes to replicate the gamma's PnL profile more precisely is important to negate inaccuracy of the final calculation of the value of gamma. The purpose of making this calculation is to discover how much more value the volatility smile associates to gamma, but not taking enough strikes will overestimate this addition.

In the final calculation, to measure the value of gamma one must determine the upfront premium that would be paid for all of the payer and receiver swaptions that have been used to synthesise the profile of the PnL of gamma. As the payers and receivers get further OTM their price falls so that the sum of a theoretically infinite amount of swaptions does exist. If there is no volatility smile and the swaptions are priced with a normal distribution then the value of gamma will equal $\frac{1}{2}G(\Delta\sigma_N^{\Delta r})^2$ as we have frequently assumed. But, if a volatility smile or skew exists then the value of gamma will increase as more extreme market movements become more likely. **This can be an important consideration, for example, when calculating Sharpe ratios of trade strategies or the consideration of the term structure of the yield curve.**

The last point we make here is that this value of gamma has been determined for a precise time of expiry. The receiver and payer swaptions have been designed with only one, discrete expiry date. When initialising a trade or trading strategy, however, the precise point at which the trades will likely be unwound, or exited, is generally unknown. This suggests a distribution of possible expiry dates should be considered to fully assess the value of gamma. This accounts for the evolution of forward implied volatility. We do not develop these ideas further as they represent rather advanced concepts, and they enter the more quantitative, stochastic realm, but it is highlighted to the reader because these are the considerations that quantitative funds may well make, in the context of theories of the term structure of IRs, and in advanced portfolio management theory.

22.10 Appendix

22.10.1 Estimating the gamma of IRSs

A simple formula

Suppose that the delta of a par IRS is known, $\frac{DP}{D\mathbf{r}} = S$. Furthermore suppose this is known to be separable into the discounting and forecasting basis risk,

$$\frac{DP}{D\mathbf{r}} = \frac{DP}{D\mathbf{s}} + \frac{DP}{D\mathbf{z}} = S_s + S_z .$$

Now apportion the risk equally across the tenor, i, of the swap, so that,

$$\frac{\partial P}{\partial s_j} := \frac{S_s}{i}, \qquad \frac{\partial P}{\partial z_j} := \frac{S_z}{i} .$$

Each instrument is assumed to be an annual instrument so $d_j := 1$, and the quantities $\frac{\partial \bar{s}_j}{\partial s_j} := 1$ (although 99%, 98% etc. may be suitable for some level of rates). Acknowledging the triangular and diagonal patterns of the cross-gamma grids[6] we have developed in this chapter we produce the estimate,

$$\frac{D^2 P}{D\mathbf{r}^2} = G \approx \frac{1}{10,000} \left(-2 \frac{(i+1)i}{2} \frac{S_z}{i} - i^2 \frac{S_s}{i} - i \frac{S_s}{i} \right) = -\frac{1+i}{10,000} S .$$

Thus for example 22.8 the estimates of the 29Y and 30Y IRS gamma were, simply, $\frac{-30S}{10,000}$ and $\frac{31S}{10,000}$ respectively.

This estimate can be extended for fwd IRSs with just a little more consideration for the patterns of the cross-gamma grids. For indices, h, i, as defined in table 22.4, then we can use the following estimate for gamma, which collapses to the above form for par IRSs when $h = 1$.

$$G \approx -\frac{h+i}{10,000} S .$$

It might be tempting to think that this formula is not good because it doesn't explicitly depend on DFs or the level of rates. But, in fact, this information is incorporated into the delta component, which is itself dependent upon rates, so remains valid in this respect.

Example 22.9.
To estimate the gamma of a 5Y5Y whose delta is $50,000 pv01, use the formula where $h = 6$ and $i = 10$, such that,

$$G \approx -(16) \frac{50,000}{10,000} = -\$80 \ \text{pv01/bp}.$$

To estimate the gamma of a 30Y10Y whose delta is $20,000 pv01, where $h = 31$ and $i = 40$,

$$G \approx -(71) \frac{20,000}{10,000} = -\$182 \ \text{pv01/bp}.$$

---

[6]easily seen through empirical study

Improvement to the simple formula

We can improve the above estimate without much additional work. Previously we assumed that the total delta risk, S, was uniformly distributed across each annual fwd. If instead, we choose to distribute this risk accounting for term structure, then we are forced to introduce DFs, and use analytic deltas.

The analytic deltas, A_j, of a unit notional in each annual fwd is given by the DF, $A_j = d_j v_j$ ($d_j \approx 1$). For any unit notional swap, with total analytic delta, A, we can use this information to define a better distribution of total risk. The proportion of risk to assign to each annual bucket is given by, $a_j = \frac{A_j}{A} = \frac{v_j}{\sum_{k=h}^{i} v_k}$.

Under this distribution of risk and from the simple formula we know that the gamma estimate for the j'th annual fwd is then, $-\frac{2j}{10,000} S a_j$. Thus, for a general IRS, the gamma can be expressed as the linear sum of all annual fwd gammas apportioned correctly,

$$G = -\frac{2S}{10,000} \sum_{j=h}^{i} j a_j = -\frac{S}{10,000} \sum_{j=h}^{i} \frac{2j A_j}{A} .$$

This reduces to the simple formula when the DFs are all assumed to be equal to one.

Example 22.10.
We re-estimate the gamma of a 5Y5Y whose delta is $50,000 pv01.

j index	A_j	$\frac{2j A_j}{A}$
6	0.990	2.432
7	0.985	2.823
8	0.980	3.210
9	0.970	3.574
10	0.960	3.930
	4.885	15.97

The result of $-79.8 pv01/bp is obtained by multiplying 15.97 by $\frac{50,000}{10,000}$. This is not significantly different from the previous simple estimate (<0.5%). Longer tenor swaps in greater discounted (higher rate) environments show larger differences (c.10%).

22.10.2   STIR Futures convexity adjustment (FCA)

The FCA represents the value of gamma of portfolio consisting of STIR futures and a single period IRS (with the same DCFs on each leg) over the dates of the the i'th IMM. We will construct that portfolio here and derive a formula for the PnL. In this section and the next, we will use the segregation of curves from the book's notation section, that is quite familiar now. We will also define some further symbols to simplify formulae (where capitals are constants and lowercase are variable);

$$r_j = R_j + \delta r_j, \qquad \text{where } R_j \text{ is the mid-market } r_j \text{ rate at time, } t = 0$$
$$s_j = S_j + \delta s_j, \qquad \text{where } S_j \text{ is the mid-market } s_j \text{ spread at time, } t = 0$$
$$A_j = 1 + d_j R_j$$
$$B_j = 1 + d_j(R_j + S_j) = A_j + d_j S_j$$
$$x_j = d_j \delta r_j$$

$$y_j = d_j \delta s_j \implies v_i = \frac{v_{i-1}}{(B_i + x_i + y_i)} = \prod_1^i (B_k + x_k + y_k)^{-1}$$

To set the direction suppose the futures are sold and the IRS received, respectively, at mid-market. The PV of this portfolio is then,

$$P = P^{\text{IRS}} + P^{\text{STIR}} = v_i N d_i (R_i - r_i) + N^* d_i^* (r_i - R_i) \, ,$$

This portfolio is required to be delta hedged at inception, i.e. at time, $t = 0$, which gives,

$$\left. \frac{\partial P}{\partial r_i} \right|_{t=0} = 0 \implies N^* = N \frac{d_i}{d_i^*} v_i|_{t=0} = N \frac{d_i}{d_i^*} \prod_1^i B_k^{-1} \, ,$$

so the required notional on the futures is the discounted notional of the IRS adjusted for the different DCFs on the two instruments over the same IMM period, and thus the PV reduces to,

$$P = N \left(v_i(d_i R_i - d_i r_i) + v_i|_{t=0}(d_i r_i - d_i R_i) \right) = N x_i \left(v_i|_{t=0} - v_i \right)$$

We can state the Taylor series, from [63], of v_i about zero as,

$$v_i \approx v_i|_{t=0} \left(1 - \sum_1^i \frac{x_k + y_k}{B_k} + O(x^2, xy, y^2) \right)$$

which implies the PV of the portfolio to second order, noting that the the first order terms cancel since the portfolio is perfectly delta hedged,

$$P \approx N \prod_{k=1}^i B_k^{-1} \sum_{k=1}^i \frac{x_i x_k + x_i y_k}{B_k}$$

In the case of RFRs where the discount curve is identical to the forecasting curve and therefore $S_j \equiv y_j \equiv 0$ and thus $B_j = A_j$,

$$P \approx N \prod_{k=1}^i A_k^{-1} \sum_{k=1}^i \frac{x_i x_k}{A_k}$$

This expansion gives the daily PnL of the delta hedged portfolio given the daily market movements, δr_j's. A no arbitrage argument would suggest that there must be a consideration that would preclude any PnL being generated over the lifetime of the portfolio. This is precisely the upfront FCA. Taken upfront, this adjustment represents the expected amount of PnL that would be generated by having this portfolio and holding until the futures and IRS matured, where the price of the IRS and STIR futures must converge. That is, accounting for all daily PnLs until the portfolio matures.

To calculate the full FCA this must be made in consideration of time passing, IMM dates falling due, potentially changing volatilities and correlations between each rate and daily delta hedge rebalancing to capture any PnL. This makes this problem a stochastic equation with many random variables having distributions of varying degrees of uncertainty the longer these products have until settlement[7]. However using expectation alone we can use the above formula to derive an approximation for FCAs of a set of STIR futures. Suppose we wished to calculate the FCA of the first contract under the following assumptions;

(i) the date is 16th March 22 with the EDSP on the H2 contract due (after all RFR fixings published) on 15th June 22, and we assume 63 business days in the period.

(ii) the PnL of the portfolio is measured on a daily basis with respect to expected daily market movements and re-hedged daily on close at nil transaction cost,

(iii) the expected market movement, $E[x_i]$, on any day is zero,

(iv) as time passes and the fixings of the compounded RFR rate are published the volatility of the rate declines, as well as the RFRs potentially becoming stable due to known central bank policy rates. Never-the-less we assume a constant daily vol σ_{BP} of 3bps.

So for the single contract over the three month term the expected PnL is,

$$E[P] \approx 63 * N \frac{d_1^2 Var(\delta r_1)}{A_1^2} = 63 * 1bn * \frac{0.25^2 * 0.0003^2}{1.005^2} = 354$$

354 on a notional of 1bn equates to about 0.014bps worth of risk, which is very small, and this is typical of the front contract. If we considered a three monthly period on the second contract,

$$E[P] \approx 63 * \frac{Nd_2}{A_1 A_2} \left(\frac{d_2 Var(\delta r_2)}{A_2} + \frac{d_1 Covar(\delta r_1, \delta r_2)}{A_1} \right)$$

$$= 63 * \frac{1bn * 0.25}{1.005^2} * \left(\frac{0.25 * 0.0004^2}{1.005} + \frac{0.25 * 0.0004 * 0.0003 * 0.95}{1.005} \right) = 1063$$

which is worth a bit more; around 0.043bps. For the latter three months of its life we can assume the same conditions as above and therefore add the previous 0.014bps to get a total 0.057bps for this contract.

As we look to calculate subsequent contracts we have to make future assumptions about forward volatility and forward correlations between instruments for each three monthly period that the particular STIR future has left until expiry. In the case above we just assumed static economic conditions. Whilst the whites tend to have convexity values in the range 0 to 0.5bps, the greens can assume between 1.5 and 12bps, so this effect can add up.

22.10.3 Zero coupon swap convexity adjustment (ZCA)

Suppose a portfolio is composed of a single ZCS and equivalent series of fwd IRSs hedge, and to set the direction suppose the ZCS has been paid and the IRSs have both been received, so that:

$$P = P^{ZCS} + P^{IRSs} .$$

Using similar techniques for FCAs the notional of each IRS is determined from the notional on the ZCS ensuring the portfolio is delta hedged initially. Following the same technique of using

---

[7]the following citation gives a more technical treatment but without the consideration of including discounting basis [64]. This is also an example of the effect of the volatility smile on the value of gamma, see section 22.9.1

a Taylor series expansion to express the daily PnL of the portfolio, it can be shown[8] that the only terms are of second order (neglecting higher orders) and offer high accuracy:

$$P \sim N \frac{A_1..A_n}{B_1..B_n} \left(\sum_{k=1}^{n} \sum_{l=1}^{k-1} \left(\left(\frac{1}{A_k} - \frac{1}{B_k} \right) \frac{x_k x_l}{A_l} - \frac{x_l y_k}{A_l B_k} \right) \right),$$

This expansion highlights a number of features about ZCSs hedged with IRSs. Firstly, the dominant term is the delta/ discounting basis cross-gamma term. The delta/delta cross-gamma term is much smaller in comparison. Secondly, it shows that if the discounting basis spread is zero and likely to remain at zero, i.e **with an RFR curve**, then there will never be any expected PnL. So in that scenario ZCSs are an indistinguishable product to IRSs.

22.10.4 Impact of IRS risk rather than zero coupon deposits

It has been an inherent assumption of the mathematics of this chapter, that the risks, $\frac{\partial P}{\partial r_i}$, $\frac{\partial P}{\partial s_i}$, $\frac{\partial P}{\partial z_i}$, are, in fact, to **fwd zero coupon deposit rates**. A reminder that a zero coupon deposit rate, r_i^Z, can be easily determined from initial and end DFs of a period with the formula,

$$r_i^Z = \frac{1}{d_i} \left(\frac{w_{i-1}}{w_i} - 1 \right).$$

For single period IRSs, the zero coupon deposit rate is the same as the IRS rate, so every calculation is valid provided that risks are measured against single period swaps.

However, when there are multiple swap periods that make up the single period that spans that of a zero coupon deposit rate, we must make an adjustment. For example if the zero coupon deposit was, say, 15Y5Y, the traditional RFR IRS in the same 15Y5Y would be an annual-annual IRS with 5 periods contained within. Or even if the zero coupon deposit spanned a 1Y period and the conventions of the RFR IRS were quarterly-quarterly there would be a mismatch.

Traders' risk views, particularly those created numerically from systems processes, are often expressed in terms of IRS and not fwd zero coupon rates. To give some historical context, once the formulae of this chapter were developed and implemented at Barclays, we noticed a regular small mismatch in our PnL explain numbers and, after some consideration, realised it was this adjustment that was needed to reconcile our formulae with the risks we were using within the formulae spanning n periods, as a simple annualisation,

$$1 + r_i^Z \simeq \left(1 + \frac{R_i}{n} \right)^n.$$

This implies an approximately linear scaling factor, β_i, for each instrument to determine the relationship between risks and market movements,

$$\frac{\partial P}{\partial r_i^Z} = \beta_i \frac{\partial P}{\partial R_i}, \quad \Delta r_i^Z = \beta^{-1} \Delta R_i, \quad \text{for} \quad \beta_i \simeq \left(1 + \frac{R_i}{n} \right)^{1-n}.$$

Generally, zero coupon deposit risks are smaller than, and zero coupon market movements are larger than, their respective IRS risks or market movements.

We now use this relationship to put the theory of this chapter in context. We make explicit, the nature of analytic cross-gamma in terms of zero coupon deposit rates, and IRS rates. Notation wise, we distinguish between zero coupon deposit rates and IRS rates with lower case

---

[8]the extended material [63] shows this derivation and further analysis of importance to ZCAs

and upper case letters respectively. We group the instruments, $\mathbf{r}, \mathbf{s}, \mathbf{z}$ and $\mathbf{R}, \mathbf{S}, \mathbf{Z}$ into $\mathbf{x}$ and $\mathbf{X}$, respectively, as we have done in preceding sections.

The determined linear function, $\mathbf{G}^{\mathrm{Z}}\left(\frac{\partial P}{\partial \mathbf{x}}\right)$, is the result of a calculated method of constructing a cross-gamma grid using zero coupon deposit, first order risks (delta and basis). It returns zero coupon deposit, first order risk *changes* if the zero coupon deposit market movements are given. This is our starting point, being the fundamental theory of the chapter,

$$\boldsymbol{\Delta}\frac{\partial P}{\partial \mathbf{x}} = \mathbf{G}^{\mathrm{Z}}\left(\frac{\partial P}{\partial \mathbf{x}}\right)\boldsymbol{\Delta}\mathbf{x}\,.$$

If, on the other hand, IRS first order risks are used in the construction of $\mathbf{G}^{\mathrm{Z}}$, which are an approximate multiple of the zero coupon deposit risks, then in order to obtain the change in IRS risks **we must still use zero coupon deposit market movements**, since,

$$\boldsymbol{\Delta}\frac{\partial P}{\partial \mathbf{X}} \quad \simeq \quad \boldsymbol{\beta}\boldsymbol{\Delta}\frac{\partial P}{\partial \mathbf{x}} \quad = \quad \mathbf{G}^{\mathrm{Z}}\left(\boldsymbol{\beta}\frac{\partial P}{\partial \mathbf{x}}\right)\boldsymbol{\Delta}\mathbf{x} \quad \simeq \quad \mathbf{G}^{\mathrm{Z}}\left(\frac{\partial P}{\partial \mathbf{X}}\right)\boldsymbol{\Delta}\mathbf{x}\,.$$

If the IRS market movements are used, in place of zero coupon deposit market movements, then the risk changes produced will be incorrect, by a factor of $\boldsymbol{\beta}$, as we adjust below.

To obtain an estimate of the cross-gamma component of the PnL, if the IRS risk changes have been determined then those equivalent market movements must be used, so that **valid PnL estimates are either**,

$$P \approx (\boldsymbol{\Delta}\mathbf{X})^{\mathrm{T}}\,\mathbf{G}^{\mathrm{Z}}\left(\frac{\partial P}{\partial \mathbf{X}}\right)\boldsymbol{\Delta}\mathbf{x},$$

$$P \approx (\boldsymbol{\Delta}\mathbf{x})^{\mathrm{T}}\,\mathbf{G}^{\mathrm{Z}}\left(\frac{\partial P}{\partial \mathbf{x}}\right)\boldsymbol{\Delta}\mathbf{x}.$$

To obtain PnL estimates and market risk changes using *exclusively* IRS first order risks and market movements, we have that,

$$P \approx (\boldsymbol{\Delta}\mathbf{X})^{\mathrm{T}}\,\mathbf{G}^{\mathrm{IRS}}\left(\frac{\partial P}{\partial \mathbf{X}}\right)\boldsymbol{\Delta}\mathbf{X} \simeq (\boldsymbol{\Delta}\mathbf{X})^{\mathrm{T}}\,\boldsymbol{\beta}^{-1}\mathbf{G}^{\mathrm{Z}}\left(\frac{\partial P}{\partial \mathbf{X}}\right)\boldsymbol{\Delta}\mathbf{X}\,.$$

This implies a cross-gamma grid produced with IRS risks, using the formulae and construction method designed for zero coupon deposit risks in this chapter, must be scaled by a factor of $\boldsymbol{\beta}^{-1}$. This produces a cross-gamma grid exclusively compatible with IRS market movements. Another way of describing it is a cross-gamma grid determined with a calculation methodology derived specifically for IRSs,

$$\mathbf{G}^{\mathrm{IRS}}\left(\frac{\partial P}{\partial \mathbf{X}}\right) \simeq \boldsymbol{\beta}^{-1}\mathbf{G}^{\mathrm{Z}}\left(\frac{\partial P}{\partial \mathbf{X}}\right)\,,$$

where,

$$\boldsymbol{\beta} := \begin{bmatrix} \beta_1 & 0 & \dots & 0 \\ 0 & \beta_2 & \dots & 0 \\ & & \ddots & \\ 0 & 0 & \dots & \beta_N \end{bmatrix}\,.$$

22.10.5   Synthetic gamma with a discrete swaption series

Pursuant to section 22.9.1 we calculate here the notionals, $N_1, \ldots, N_n$ of a series of payer swaptions struck at different strikes, $K_0, \ldots, K_{n-1}$, where K_0 is the ATM or initial mid-market rate.

If the underlying rate at expiry falls inline with any of the given strikes, K_j, the PnL attributed to the assumed gamma position is,

$$\Delta P = \frac{1}{2} G \left(K_j - K_0 \right)^2 .$$

The respective cumulative PnL from the series of payer swaptions that are ITM is,

$$\Delta P = \sum_{i=1}^{j} N_i A(K_j) \left(K_j - K_{i-1} \right) ,$$

where $A(K_j)$ is the analytic pv01 per unit of underlying swap for the respective level of rates at expiry, K_j.

Equating the two gives a recursive formula for assessing each swaption notional, N_j.

$$N_j = \frac{1}{2} \frac{G}{A(K_j)} \frac{\left(K_j - K_0 \right)^2}{\left(K_j - K_{j-1} \right)} - \sum_{i=1}^{j-1} N_i \frac{\left(K_j - K_{i-1} \right)}{\left(K_j - K_{j-1} \right)} .$$

The process should be replicated to calculate the notionals for receiver swaptions for the left-hand side.

22.10.6   VBA code for cross-gamma of compounded trade types

Every compounded trade type is made distinct by its start point and end point. This makes it impossible to accurately determine cross-gamma for a portfolio of compounded trade types without that specific information of each trade, which also cannot be ascertained simply from first order risks of portfolio. To design an algorithm, however, **we make the assumption that all compounded trade types start immediately**.

With this assumption, the portfolio of trades that give rise to the compounded forecasting basis risk can be deconstructed into a series of ZCSs, each starting immediately, that replicate the risks of the portfolio. Then, the individual forecasting basis risks of each deconstructed trade can be ascertained - which are of course then needed in the algorithm to determine the cross-gammas.

The below methods calculate **discounting / forecasting basis cross-gamma** and **forecasting / forecasting basis cross-gamma**, respectively. The discounting / discounting basis cross-gamma algorithm previously given also works for compounded trade types.[9]

---

[9]These functions use `Option Base 1`, $\mathbf{Z}$ is the forecasting basis risk strip of length N, $\mathbf{d}$ is the array of DCFs of length N, $\mathbf{v}$ is the array of DFs of the discount curve of size $N + 1$, $\mathbf{x}$ is the array of DFs of the forecasting curve of size $N + 1$

```
Function XGam_sz_1(Z, d, v, x, N As Integer)

Dim j As Integer:  Dim k As Integer:  Dim Ztemp as Double
Dim XGam():  ReDim XGam(N, N)
Dim Notn():  ReDim Notn(N,1)
Dim ZMat():  ReDim ZMat(N,N)
'First calculate the notional of the longest ZCS
Notn(N,1) = Z(N,1) * x(N,1) / (x(N+1,1) * v(N+1,1) * d(N,1))
'Now put forecasting risks of that ZCS into N'th col of Zmat(NxN)
For j = 1 To N
    ZMat(j,N) = d(j,1) * x(j+1,1) / x(j,1) * v(N+1,1) * Notn(N,1)
Next j

'Now iterate backwards to determine previous ZCS notionals
For j = N - 1 To 1 Step -1
    Ztemp = 0
    For k = j + 1 To N
        Ztemp = Ztemp + ZMat(j,k)
    Next k
    Notn(j,1) = (Z(j,1) - Ztemp) * x(j,1) / (x(j+1,1) * v(j+1,1) * d(j,1))
    'Now put the forecasting risks of the j'th ZCS into j'th col of Zmat
    For k = 1 To N
        If k > j Then ZMat(k,j) = 0
        If k <= j Then ZMat(k,j) = d(k,1) * x(k+1,1) / x(k,1) * v(j+1,1) * Notn(j,1)

    Next k
Next j
'Now calculate the cross-gamma given deconstructed forecasting risks
For k = N To 1 Step -1
    Ztemp = 0
    For j = N To 1 Step -1
        Ztemp = Ztemp + ZMat(k, j)
        XGam(j,k) = -d(j,1) * v(j+1,1) / v(j,1) * Ztemp / 10000
    Next j
Next k

XGam_sz_1 = XGam

End Function

Function XGam_zz_1(Z, d, x, N As Integer)

Dim j As Integer:  Dim k As Integer
Dim XGam():  ReDim XGam(N, N)

For j = 1 To N: For k = 1 To N
    If j = k Then XGam(j,k) = 0
    If j < k Then
        XGam(j,k) = d(j,1) * x(j+1,1) / x(j,1) * Z(k,1)
    ElseIf j > k Then
        XGam(j,k) = d(k,1) * x(k+1,1) / x(k,1) * Z(j,1)
    End If
    XGam(j,k) = XGam(j,k) /10000
Next k:  Next j
XGam_zz_1 = XGam
End Function
```

Constructing Trade Strategies

This chapter discusses some of the considerations that should be made in the design of trade strategies. We cover hedging trades for directionality as well as the basic definitions of cost-of-carry, roll-down, expected PnL, volatility of PnL and conclude with the familiar concept of the Sharpe ratio.

We also reference other sections of the book, as there have been other examples of trade strategy building techniques already shown in some other examples.

23.1 Hedging trade directionality

A common stratagem when constructing an RV trade is to try to minimise, or hedge, the directionality aspect of the trade. If the trading view is specific enough, a large directional market movement may sufficiently engulf the RV aspect rendering losses even if the fundamental trading view was correct in the first instance. There is not a unique method for doing this and we will present different calculations, albeit these calculations all use the same underlying historical data and have interconnected results.

23.1.1   PCA hedging

Directionality is often assumed to be the major factor explained by the first PC. So the concept under this approach is to adjust the underlying trade strategy to ensure that the risk, as measured against PC1, is zero.

Example 23.1.

*A trader chooses to pay 5Y against receiving 2Y and 10Y as a RV trade. The benchmark combination would be to pay twice as much 5Y as he receives in either 2Y or 10Y (a 2s5s10s butterfly), but he designs the weightings of each trade so that his risk to PC1 is zero, assuming that this removes directionality. To do this he takes his initial benchmark trade weightings, which sum to zero total risk, and **divides them by the instrument weighting in PC1:***

$$\mathbf{S}^{\mathbf{ini}} = \begin{matrix} (2Y) \\ (5Y) \\ (10Y) \\ (30Y) \end{matrix} \begin{bmatrix} -1 \\ 2 \\ -1 \\ 0 \end{bmatrix}, \qquad PC1 = \begin{bmatrix} 0.65 \\ 0.59 \\ 0.44 \\ 0.20 \end{bmatrix}, \qquad \mathbf{S} = \begin{bmatrix} -1.55 \\ 3.38 \\ -2.27 \\ 0 \end{bmatrix} \propto \begin{bmatrix} -0.89 \\ 1.94 \\ -1.30 \\ 0 \end{bmatrix}.$$

This provides target risk proportions for his chosen RV trade, which can of course be scaled to reflect a target VaR but when viewed in terms of PC risk will always show zero for PC1:

$$\widetilde{\mathbf{S}} = \mathbf{E^T S} = \begin{matrix} (PC1) \\ (PC2) \\ (PC3) \\ (PC4) \end{matrix} \begin{bmatrix} 0 \\ -1.88 \\ 1.90 \\ 3.44 \end{bmatrix}.$$

Example 23.1, which **uses the same covariance matrix and PCs determined in chapter 15**, is a simple calculation and **only works** in the case that the sum of risks, $\sum \mathbf{S_{ini}}$, is zero. For this benchmark trade of 2s5s10s that is true.

An alternative method which is a more generalised mathematical approach is preferred. The complete derivation is explained in appendix section 23.4.1, as well as the generated code. The general idea is to propose an optimisation problem where $\mathbf{x}$ is a minimal adjustment to the initial risks with the constraint that risk to PC1 (or other PCs) is zero.

$$\min_{\mathbf{x}} \|\mathbf{x}\|_2 = \min_{\mathbf{x}} \mathbf{x^T I x} \qquad \text{subject to} \qquad (\mathbf{S^{ini}} + \mathbf{x})^\mathbf{T} \mathbf{I e_1} = 0$$

```
1  >>> S_ini = np.array([-1, 2, -1, 0])[:, np.newaxis]
2  >>> S_ini + portfolio.pca_hedge_adjustment(Q, S_ini, L=[3])
3  [[-1.07],
4   [1.94],
5   [-1.05],
6   [0]]
```

Notice how the code example, which finds a minimal adjustment, has a trade representation which is closer to the original 2s5s10s trade than in example 23.1.

To track and analyse strategic trades that have been PC weighted, we can use residuals to examine the relevant part of the move that has actually contributed to PnL, and, in a sense, strip out the move contributed by PC1.

Example 23.2.

Suppose the trader adopts the above risk proportions, calculated with minimal adjustment method, and suppose the market movements after ten days are shown below. He calculates his PnL estimate:

$$\mathbf{S} = \begin{bmatrix} -1.07 \\ 1.94 \\ -1.05 \\ 0 \end{bmatrix}, \qquad \mathbf{\Delta r} = \begin{bmatrix} +17.2 \\ +18.1 \\ +12.5 \\ +8.1 \end{bmatrix}, \qquad \mathbf{S} \cdot \mathbf{\Delta r} \approx \$3.70$$

The PC multipliers for the move are calculated and the residual is assessed ignoring every PC except the first. **Since the risk to PC1 is zero** *the same PnL estimate (subject to rounding) is given by substituting these residuals for market movements. The residuals reflect the market movements having removed the natural directionality so provides a visible way of analysing the RV aspect of the trade:*

$$(\mathbf{h})^{\mathbf{T}} = \begin{bmatrix} 28.9 \\ 1.39 \\ 2.41 \\ 1.21 \end{bmatrix}, \quad \widetilde{\mathbf{\Delta r}} = \begin{bmatrix} +18.7 \\ +17.1 \\ +12.7 \\ +5.7 \end{bmatrix}, \quad \mathbf{\xi} = \begin{bmatrix} -1.48 \\ +0.97 \\ -0.22 \\ +2.45 \end{bmatrix}, \quad \mathbf{S} \cdot \mathbf{\xi} \approx \$3.70$$

The above two examples indicate there is not a unique way to adjust or devise a trading strategy which is hedged to a given PC (there are infinite solutions). This is why the alternate approach is preferred because it gives a defined formula yielding a unique solution with practical constraints and optimality in the proposed context of adjusting the underlying trade to the least extent possible.

23.1.2 CoVaR hedging

CoVaR minimisation trades were introduced in section 14.6, which described how one can analyse the impact of new, specific trades on the VaR of the existing portfolio risks. This is useful for hedging when it might not be able to hedge the exact buckets. We can also frame the question differently to build weightings for trade strategies. Again, we use the covariance matrix, **Q**, from chapters 14 and 15.

Example 23.3.
A trader chooses to pay 5Y against receiving 2Y and 10Y as an RV trade. He configures an initial risk specifying 2Y and 10Y and then uses VaR minimisation to determine the amount of risk he should pay in the 5Y bucket.

$$\mathbf{S^{ini}} = \begin{matrix} (2Y) \\ (5Y) \\ (10Y) \\ (30Y) \end{matrix} \begin{bmatrix} -1 \\ 2 \\ -1 \\ 0 \end{bmatrix}, \quad \mathbf{S^{trade}} = \begin{bmatrix} 0 \\ -0.344 \\ 0 \\ 0 \end{bmatrix}, \quad \mathbf{S} = \begin{bmatrix} -1 \\ 1.656 \\ -1 \\ 0 \end{bmatrix} \propto \begin{bmatrix} -1.17 \\ 1.94 \\ -1.17 \\ 0 \end{bmatrix}.$$

Alternatively he might configure an initial risk in 5Y and use VaR minimisation to determine the amount of risk in the 2Y and 10Y buckets to minimise VaR.

$$\mathbf{S^{ini}} = \begin{matrix} (2Y) \\ (5Y) \\ (10Y) \\ (30Y) \end{matrix} \begin{bmatrix} -1 \\ 2 \\ -1 \\ 0 \end{bmatrix}, \quad \mathbf{S^{trade}} = \begin{bmatrix} -0.476 \\ 0 \\ 0.616 \\ 0 \end{bmatrix}, \quad \mathbf{S} = \begin{bmatrix} -1.48 \\ 2 \\ -0.38 \\ 0 \end{bmatrix} \propto \begin{bmatrix} -1.43 \\ 1.94 \\ -0.37 \\ 0 \end{bmatrix}.$$

The second case necessarily has less VaR since the degrees of freedom over which the minimisation occurs is 2 instead of 1. The trade, however, is significantly more adjusted from the traditional 2s5s10s weights than in the first case.

23.1.3 Multivariate least squares regression (MLSR)

In this case we propose an initial trade, such as 2s5s10s and then propose hedging away subjectively chosen correlations, such as 2s10s or 5Y. Appendix section 23.4.2 outlines the derivation and the formulae needed for the next examples.

Example 23.4.
A trader chooses to pay 5Y against receiving 2Y and 10Y as an RV trade. He configures an initial risk

then uses multivariate least squares regression to determine adjustments and the final trading strategy. In the first case only the 5Y is regressed.

$$\mathbf{S^{ini}} = \begin{array}{c} (2Y) \\ (5Y) \\ (10Y) \\ (30Y) \end{array} \begin{bmatrix} -1 \\ 2 \\ -1 \\ 0 \end{bmatrix}, \quad [\mathbf{x_1}] = \begin{bmatrix} 0 \\ 1 \\ 0 \\ 0 \end{bmatrix}, \quad \mathbf{S^{trade}} = \begin{bmatrix} 0 \\ -0.344 \\ 0 \\ 0 \end{bmatrix}, \quad \mathbf{S} = \begin{bmatrix} -1 \\ 1.656 \\ -1 \\ 0 \end{bmatrix} \propto \begin{bmatrix} -1.17 \\ 1.94 \\ -1.17 \\ 0 \end{bmatrix}.$$

Alternatively, in the second case, the 2Y and 10Y buckets are regressed.

$$\mathbf{S^{ini}} = \begin{bmatrix} -1 \\ 2 \\ -1 \\ 0 \end{bmatrix}, \quad [\mathbf{x_1} : \mathbf{x_2}] = \begin{bmatrix} 1 & 0 \\ 0 & 0 \\ 0 & 1 \\ 0 & 0 \end{bmatrix}, \quad \mathbf{S^{trade}} = \begin{bmatrix} -0.476 \\ 0 \\ 0.616 \\ 0 \end{bmatrix}, \quad \mathbf{S} = \begin{bmatrix} -1.432 \\ 1.94 \\ -0.373 \\ 0 \end{bmatrix} \propto \begin{bmatrix} -1.43 \\ 1.94 \\ -0.37 \\ 0 \end{bmatrix}.$$

Example 23.4 shows that using multivariate least squares regression gives the same results as the CoVaR minimisation approach. It is well known that solving maximum likelihood estimators under a normal distribution reduces to least squares regression. Thus, in our case of CoVaR where the underlying distribution is an assumed multivariate normal, this is not a surprising result.

It is possible to use Jacobians and transformed covariance matrices to yield adjusted trades, under a CoVaR minimisation calculation, based on other trade combinations, e.g. 2s10s. However, I would argue that the least squares approach here is more flexible in its configuration, if that is the goal. Example 23.5 shows how, as a demonstration of flexibility, we can take elements of the first principal component and regress against those which yields a result very similar to the case of PCA directionality in this instance.

Example 23.5.
A trader chooses to pay 5Y against receiving 2Y and 10Y as an RV trade. He configures an initial risk then uses multivariate least squares regression to determine adjustments and the final trading strategy. The regression is performed against PC1.

$$\mathbf{S^{ini}} = \begin{array}{c} (2Y) \\ (5Y) \\ (10Y) \\ (30Y) \end{array} \begin{bmatrix} -1 \\ 2 \\ -1 \\ 0 \end{bmatrix}, \quad [\mathbf{x_1}] = \begin{bmatrix} -0.646 \\ -0.592 \\ -0.440 \\ 0 \end{bmatrix}, \quad \mathbf{S^{trade}} = \begin{bmatrix} -0.066 \\ -0.061 \\ -0.045 \\ 0 \end{bmatrix}, \quad \mathbf{S} = \begin{bmatrix} -1.07 \\ 1.94 \\ -1.04 \\ 0 \end{bmatrix}.$$

23.2   Carry and Roll

In my opinion cost-of-carry and a separate concept, roll-down, are poorly defined in the IR market, as they might well be in some other markets for that matter. This is not to say that they are misunderstood. Indeed two people, or teams, might understand completely the same concept but one might call it cost-of-carry and the other might call it roll-down, and I have even heard carry-roll used as a bastardisation of terms!

In these sections we will specifically define *our* use of the terms **cost-of-carry** and **roll-down**. We need to distinguish the semantics with a logical approach, and we also aim to align terminology with that present in other financial product markets. This may be at odds with other literature but we will also seek to make that clarification. These two, separate, concepts are important when considering executing trades. Sometimes, even if rates move favourably, these other factors may still leave a trade unprofitable.

23.2.1 Cost-of-carry

Cost-of-carry, or often just *'carry'*, should be a measure, as its name implies, of the cost of holding a derivative trade. By defining it this way it allows for a much better comparison with other products such as equities, bonds, commodities, etc. in terms of the costs associated with holding those trades.

As a simple example consider the case of the spot gold price and the same gold futures contract price with delivery date in one month's time. The usual no arbitrage principle states that there must be a relationship between the spot price and the futures contract price. If a trader buys an amount of gold, at the spot price, there is a cost associated with owning, or carrying, the trade which must then be recouped by the sale of the gold on the date of the futures contract delivery. In the case of gold this cost is two fold; firstly the trader sacrifices some interest, which could otherwise be accrued if the money used to buy the gold was otherwise deposited. Secondly the trader must pay for storing the gold for a month, which means renting a suitable location and paying for its physical security. This results in a futures contract price which is higher than the spot price so that when the trader either sells the gold on the delivery date or physically delivers the gold, as a result of being short a futures contract, the trader has, overall, not made or lost any money. If this were not true, then according to the no arbitrage principle either the futures contract price would either be in such supply or demand that the price would fluctuate to eliminate this arbitrage which could otherwise be exploited. The same type of argument can be made for any commodity or security, be it a bond, equity or otherwise.

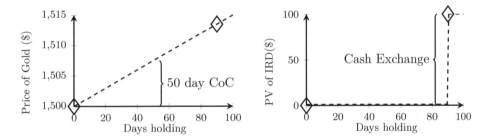

Figure 23.1: Depicting daily cost-of-carry of securities (left) compared with IRDs (right).

The nature of derivatives, though, in particular IRDs, is that they are not securities or commodities, they are two-sided paper exchanges between counterparties. The cost-of-carry that was described in the previous paragraph was the result of a physical outlay of cash and incurring daily costs. For IRDs entered at mid-market the initial PV is zero, and requires no outlay, and the PV does not change daily if the cashflows predicted in the future continue to remain the same as initially forecast. When the IRD has a value other than zero it will experience a form of pull-to-par and a netting collateral cost (if collateralised), as explained in section 5.1. IRDs have a discrete value change on cashflow exchanges (e.g. at day 90 in figure 23.1). But, the net value; cash exchange plus the IRD value change, will remain at zero.

Due to this distinct difference between IRDs and securities we define **the *basic* cost-of-carry of an IRD as nil.** This reflects the gradient of the rightmost chart in figure 23.1. In some literature, a comparison is made between the fixed rate and the current floating period rate (which implies the first cashflow amount), and this value if often given an association to cost-of-carry. However, I do not aspire to naming or using this value at all and have never found a rational use for it.

Comparing physical gold to gold futures also presents an analogy. Suppose purchasing a gold futures contract, with one month expiry, at a price of $1000, when the spot gold price is $995. Each day the spot price will be expected to increase, and the futures price will remain at $1000. By the time the contract expires the spot price will have risen to $1000 and the futures price remains the same and can be sold realising no gain nor loss. No basic monies are exchanged due to the purchase and sale of the gold futures contract being bought and sold at the same price on exchange. The basic cost-of-carry on this gold derivative contract was also nil.

However, even if the *basic* cost-of-carry is taken to be zero, considerations must be made for other peripheral costs related to owning, or carrying, these types of trades. A good example of something that reflects the costs of owning derivatives or futures trades, and which has already been covered in the book, is **margin**. Executing derivative trades through CCPs creates costs related to the margin that must be posted upfront to mitigate that CCP against credit risk. The posting of margin is a cost because it ties up capital that might otherwise be allocated to generate better returns elsewhere in other business ventures.

Another example is regulatory capital. Under the financial regulations laid down by the regulator, certain institutions may have to hold, on account, a certain amount of cash or other assets to mitigate itself against loss due to the potential MTM of any traded derivative[1]. Regulators are keen to implement this kind of requirement because it acts to prohibit excessive trade accumulation and excessive risk taking by appropriating capital usage and therefore increasing cost-of-carry.

Confusingly, some of these costs might be treated differently by different counterparties and thus make for subjective assessments. The way one party chooses to measure their costs, relative to some benchmark for example, might be different to another. Not only this but the costs themselves, borne by one party to hold a trade might not necessarily be the same as another party. This might be due to economies of scale or even mis-economies of scale, where having such large positions might dominate the market and command greater costs, or operating in different regulatory jurisdictions.

Other costs exist as well. There are administration costs associated with booking and settling IRDs, albeit these might be small. Gamma and cross-gamma considerations[2] are usually factored into the original pricing of derivative trades and so are not costs-of-carry per se, but if they are not factored in originally then they become such.

We summarise that the;

(i) **basic cost-of-carry of a derivative trade is nil.** This is based on costs dependent only on theoretical pricing aspects,

(ii) **practical cost-of-carry of a derivative trade must be taken into account.** This is the consideration of margin costs, capital usage costs, or on going trade management costs such as admin, funding and cross-gamma hedging.

Example 23.6.

*A manager wishes to influence the trading decisions of his trading team. He wants them to focus more on trading strategies in which they have stronger conviction and expected likelihood of success. He decides to implement a cost-of-carry charge based on the **total** VaR of any given trader's portfolio, forcing them to eliminate risks in which they do not have strong conviction to maximise their profits. The amount of charge imposed is set to be 10% of a trader's $VaR_{5\%}$. Anecdotally, a concept similar to this was used at Nordea. Table 23.1[3] compares an arbitrary trader's positions before and after the implementation of the charge.*

---

[1] see chapter 17 for capital costs of this nature

[2] see chapter 21

[3] the table assumes each trading strategy is independent and uncorrelated. See chapter 14 for description of the VaR multiplier, c, and a description why the total is not a direct sum

Before implementation						
Strategy index	1	2	3	4	5	TOTAL
c (\$,000s)	100	100	100	100	100	223.6
$VaR_{5\%}$ (\$,000s)	164	164	164	164	164	366.7
Conviction / success rate	50%	60%	70%	80%	90%	70%
$E[PnL]$ (\$)	0	15,960	31,920	47,870	63,830	159,580

After implementation						
Strategy index	1	2	3	4	5	TOTAL
c (\$,000s)	0	0	100	100	100	173.2
$VaR_{5\%}$ (\$,000s)	0	0	164	164	164	284.1
Allocated cost-of-carry (\$)	0	0	-9,470	-9,470	-9,470	-28,410
Conviction / success rate	50%	60%	70%	80%	90%	80%
$E[PnL]$ (\$)	0	0	22,450	38,400	54,360	115,210

Table 23.1: Analysing the reaction of a trader's portfolio to the implementation of imposed leverage costs, where he eliminates strategies with low conviction rates to reduce the overall VaR and forced cost-of-carry.

The manager is pleased with the supposed reaction. The business wide, expected PnL attributable to the trader's actions after implementation of the cost-of-carry is \$143,620 based on a $VaR_{5\%}$ of \$284,100 or approximately 46.5% of leverage, compared to the previous ratio around 43.5%.

This approach, adopted by the manager, forces his traders to utilise their VaR in a more considered ways. Apathetic attitudes towards risk are penalised and thus makes for more effective risk management.

23.2.2 Roll-down

Roll-down is an entirely different concept. It represents the PnL that is acquired if, over the passage of time, **benchmark prices remain static at their current levels**. This is a *specific assumption* about future market movements which directly opposes the no arbitrage principle. As an example consider again the one month, gold futures price of \$1000 with the spot price at \$995. The roll-down quantity here is -\$5 since if the gold spot price remains stable at \$995 then by the time the futures contract expires its price will have fallen (or rolled-down) by \$5 to converge to that recurrent spot price.

Example 23.7.
The current 3M IRS rate is 0.8% and the 3M3M IRS is 1.22%. The current shape of the 3M-RFR curve is depicted in figure 23.2. It is expected, therefore, that future RFR rates will be published inline with these initial forecasts.

After, say, one month the 3M IRS rate is expected to evolve to be 0.98% and at that time the 2M3M IRS would have the same price as the 3M3M IRS rate as measured as of today' date. After another month the rate is expected to evolve to 1.12% and the 1M3M IRS as of that future date is expected to be 1.22%. Finally, after a third month, the 3M rate is expected to be 1.22% in the market, as initially forecast three months ago when the 3M3M IRS rate was initially priced. This is simple pricing theory adhering to the no arbitrage principle.

However, under the assumption that the curve stays permanently the same, regardless of the passage of time, the original 3M3M IRS rate will have to change price, as it 'rolls-down' the curve with each passing day. After one month it has rolled down by 10bps and after two months has done so by 24bps. This gives rise to the calculated value known as roll-down.

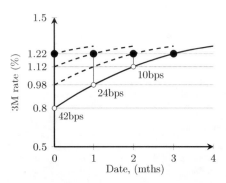

Figure 23.2: Depicting the roll-down on a 3×6 FRA.

Considered from one perspective, roll-down is a quantity dependent upon a hypothetical scenario. The specific scenario chosen is that prices remain constant even though time passes. One could measure a different quantity against an alternative scenario, such as prices double or fall by 20%, but it is simply this scenario, of prices remaining static, that gets the specific name, roll-down.

The example also shows that roll-down (as with cost-of-carry) is calculated with respect to a period of time. One can quote a one month, three month or year long roll-down, for example. The sign given for roll-down might be positive or negative dependent upon the context. Usually a positive value is considered as an advantage so in example 23.7 this roll-down would be considered positive for the receiver of the initial 3M3M IRS and negative for the payer. Expressed in rate terms I would probably express the above roll-downs with a negative sign.

Is the assumption of roll-down valid?

In the years following the financial crisis of '07 and '08 I would argue that this assumption has been completely valid. Central banks cut rates to emergency low levels, always with the inference that they would reverse them when the economy was revitalised. As such, markets priced in higher rates for the foreseeable future. For years, though, the economy grumbled on and central banks refused to hike their rates back. The curve continued to remain broadly static defying the forecasts time and time again. In this environment IRDs with positive roll-down proved continually successful.

Additionally, we discussed in chapter 8 that increased volatility can lead to higher forecast rates. A positive roll-down position in this respect is akin to selling volatility and going long theta. The more time that passes without the expected volatility increasing, leading to asymmetrical market moves, is advantageous for this type of trade.

Other reasons exist to generate positions with positive roll-down. Supply and demand can often move market levels to those which look relatively attractive. For example a large and intensive corporate issuance programme targeting 6Y might result in an IRS curve distorted in that particular tenor. Taking the opposing side of this trade might be attractive relative to 5Y or 7Y (or both) but will entail running some level of market risk until such time as the roll-down has been acquired or market distortion has ebbed.

Psychology also plays a part in the validation of roll-down. Market observers typically use benchmark instruments to gauge levels and sentiment and when one is, say, observing the 10Y IRS rate it will be measured on a rolling basis. There is rarely any consideration that the 10Y IRS rate, which one observed some time last month, is now only 9.9Y long. Taken together, in mean reverting markets, the effect of roll-down will become apparent due to the psychological and systematic bias of the way the market is considered and analysed. As an additional point of explanation, ponder the philosophy of "in the absence of no new information, do nothing". One might also envisage how doing nothing might, in combination with benchmark observation, lead to the result of a static, rolling curve.

On the other hand the central bank tightening cycles of late '21 and '22 did not not permit any of the very large apparent roll-down values to be realised at all. This was essentially an opposite situation to that described above following '07 and '08. Arguably, the market reaction in these times was for all market participants to entirely deleverage themselves against these positive roll-down trades, and as a result market rates may have risen beyond real economic expectation.

Calculating roll-down

In order to calculate roll-down there must be an equivalent rate on the curve that can be compared to provide the calculated value measured over a specific time frame. This is much easier to show for fwd IRSs in the first instance. Consider table 23.2. To calculate the, t-month, roll-down on a fwd IRS compare the IRS rate with the same tenor swap starting t-months prior to original fwd start date.

Start-Tenor	Rate (%)
0M3M	0.80
1M3M	0.98
2M3M	1.12
3M3M	1.22
4M3M	1.30
5M3M	1.34
6M3M	1.35

Table 23.2: Mid-market rates at the current curve

Example 23.8.
Using table 23.2 a trader calculates the following roll-down values (from a receiver's perspective):

  i) 3M roll-down on a 5M3M IRS: 1.34% minus 1.12% (2M3M) is 22bps.

 ii) 5M roll-down on a 6M3M IRS: 1.35% minus 0.98% (1M3M) is 37bps.

iii) 1M roll-down on a 6M3M IRS: 1.35% minus 1.34% (5M3M) is 1bps.

Example 23.8 demonstrates calculations for fwd IRSs. All rates chosen contained floating rates that were able to roll-down the curve. However, once the time limit is reached as to how much rates can roll-down (e.g. 2M3M cannot have a 6M roll-down value), one must maintain the assumption that the current RFR fixing is carried forward to perpetuity. This means that calculating roll-down requires a distinction between whether the trade is a fwd or par trade[4].

Example 23.9.
Consider a 2Y QQ IRS. We attempt to calculate the roll-down as measured over a 3M period.

---

[4]see section 10.4 for an expanded description of this distinction

To do this we will consider the part of the 2Y IRS that is 3M21M, and we will consider the first, 0M3M, period separately. Once we have calculated both roll-down values we will combine them according to proportioned risk. The values we need for calculation are stated in table 23.3

Instrument	Analytic Delta /mm	Rate	Calculation	3M Roll-down
0M21M QQ	–	2.28%		
3M21M QQ	173	2.45%		17bps
0M1D	–	0.70%	-	
0M3M	24	0.80%	-	5bps
0M2Y QQ	197	2.25%	$\frac{173}{197} \times 17 + \frac{24}{197} \times 5$	15.5 bps*

Table 23.3: Calculating the 3M roll-down on a 2Y QQ IRS.

*Note that in the calculation of the 0M3M roll-down we have assumed that the 1D rate of 0.70% is constant everyday for the 3M period, and when compounded up over the whole 3M period yields a rate of 0.75% giving rise to the 5bps roll-down (and not 10bps).

Using roll-down in practice

So what can be said of pursuing roll-down strategies overall? My personal opinion is that, by measuring gains relative to expected market conditions, trades with roll-down can often be very profitable. Conversely, for implementing trades which have a negative roll-down one must either have high conviction of the market move or expect fast liquidation. The latter permits only minimal time for negative roll-down effects to accumulate.

Specific risks exist with roll-down strategies, however. These types of trades are often entered only by specific types of IRD user; hedge funds, asset managers and banks. Other users, such as NFCs, central governments and retail investors, often create the roll-down positions through the supply and demand mechanism outlined in the previous section. This means that those users who typically enter roll-down trades are highly reactive to changing market conditions. The result is that when events occur, which lead to uncertainty and increased volatility, roll-down positions tend to be liquidated at the same time, due to nature and similarity of the users. This represents liquidation risk; the MTM of the trade can become uncharacteristically negative amidst irrational behaviour and stressed markets. Stock market collapses, interest rate and credit sell-offs with respectable rebounds are characteristic of this phenomenon. Another characterisation of this is to say that roll-down strategies are inherently short volatility positions.

Many financial practitioners ascribe to using roll-down across many financial products (even if only periodically) and this can shape financial markets. For our purposes the concept of roll-down exists in all markets, thus it impacts volatility markets, inflation products, single currency IRS rates, XCS rates and FX rates.

We highlight that roll-down is only one metric related to a trading strategy, and others will be touched upon in the next section. Sometimes it might be the reason for the dominant share of profit on any trading strategy and at other times it might be completely irrelevant because the status quo of benchmark prices is not expected to remain. When the IR curve is expected to change dramatically this is precisely the point at which roll-down becomes unappealing.

Example 23.10.

A price-taker has the opinion that the short dated IR curve will steepen due to fiscal and economic conditions. He wants to initiate a consecutive curve steepening trade and analyses the 3M roll-down of various trades to fine tune his strategy. His values are shown in table 23.4.

Instrument	Rate	3M roll-down
6M6M AQ	1.24%	+2bps
9M6M AQ	1.28%	+4bps
1Y6M AQ	1.37%	+9bps
15M6M AQ	1.51%	+14bps
18M6M AQ	1.63%	+12bps
21M6M AQ	1.74%	+11bps
2Y6M AQ	1.87%	+13bps

Table 23.4: Displaying example 6M tenor AQ IRS rates and their respective roll-downs measured by receiving fixed.

The trader considers each consecutive pair, receiving fixed on the first and paying fixed on the second considering the overall trade level and the net amount of roll-down. His consideration is shown in table 23.5.

Instrument	Spread	Net 3M roll-down
6M6M vs 1Y6M	+13bps	-7bps
9M6M vs 15M6M	+23bps	-10bps
1Y6M vs 18M6M	+26bps	-3bps
15M6M vs 21M6M	+23bps	+3bps
18M6M vs 2Y6M	+24bps	-1bps

Table 23.5: Displaying trade combination spread levels and net roll-down values.

The price-taker decides to initiate a 15M6M vs 21M6M spread trade, being the only consecutive combination with net positive roll-down. Arguably the 9M6M vs 15M6M is the worst choice available in terms of roll-down having the most negative net value. The executed choice lends some confidence to the price-taker in the case that the IR curve does not steepen. Indeed in the scenario that it keeps its generic shape then over the course of 3M the trader will still be left with a small profit as opposed to all other trade combinations which would result in small losses.

23.3 Sharpe ratio

The Sharpe ratio[65], named after its author William Sharpe, is a measure of **reward versus risk**. A key metric of a trading strategy by any financial standards. The measure it not without some valid criticism. Specifically this comes due to its inability to consider higher volatility as a positive factor when extreme returns are available in some strategies. Since IRDs are not generally prone to these events - they are mainly caused by jump to default on credit products - we can ignore these and focus on how the Sharpe ratio can be incorporated into trading decisions usefully.

The Sharpe ratio is defined for IRD portfolios as,

$$\theta_P = \text{Sharpe ratio of portfolio} = \frac{\text{Expected PnL of portfolio}}{\sqrt{\text{Variance of portfolio's PnL}}} = \frac{E[P]}{\sqrt{Var(P)}} .$$

A reader already aware of the ratio will notice the omission of a risk free deposit rate in the formula, since IRDs are leveraged instruments requiring no cash investment. We also neglect costs-of-carry.

This ratio should also be put in context with time, since the expectation of PnL and volatility of PnL must be assessed against a timeframe over which the portfolio is likely to be held. Choosing different timeframes can affect the ratio and also affect the potential accuracy of being able to forecast both the numerator and denominator.

Anecdotally, within the fixed income space that I have traded I have, personally, considered a Sharpe ratio of higher than 1.0 a reasonably attractive prospect, although this is of course subjective.

This ratio is *ex ante* (that is before the fact), since both the expected PnL and volatility of PnL are necessarily ex ante, and these are what we will broach in the next sections to hopefully be able to derive a useful metric.

23.3.1   Expected PnL

Any considered trade strategy will have an expectation that it will make a profit. The size of the profit will be dependent upon the movement in rates. How much these rates move is a consideration that must be estimated *ex ante*. The above examples anticipated that the market movement would equate to the roll-down. This is not necessarily a bad assumption, but it is clearly not the only way of determining an estimate.

Depending upon the view of the trader the movement in rates could be estimated in a variety of different ways. We won't cover them all, since they are subjective, but we will highlight major concepts and examples of how to estimate respective market movements. The following items categorise a typical view and a generalised assumption about market movements:

(i) **Maintain status quo:** A trader adopts roll-down as the expectation. Lower volatility is usually favourable for this strategy.

(ii) **Oppose an overbought (or oversold) market:** Here a trader considers recent market-movements to be exaggerated. Often signalled by RSIs (relative strength indicators). One approach to estimate market movements is to target a recent level to which the market will return and calculate the difference between that and the current market levels. Usually this is brought about by higher volatility.

(iii) **Continued momentum:** In this instance a trader expects the trend of a market to continue as it has for a similar period. Momentum oscillators can be used to identify this dynamic. A way of estimating market movements is to replicate the same movements that have been seen over the past period.

(iv) **RV:** A trader might believe specific rates are high or low relative to others, determined perhaps through PCA residuals or deviation to a standard analytical curve model. The expected market movements would be classed as those that bring these 'distortions' back to normality.

(v) **Macro economical environment shift:** Economic environment changes are often the cause of the largest market movements. Arguably these are the most difficult to assess. One might have to revert to previous examples in history or simply intelligent design to estimate them.

Once one has determined a market movement expectation, μ, for a specific timeframe, the expectation of PnL can be determined to first order or second[5], and note these results do not

---

[5]where the second order equation uses the well published result of the **expectation of a quadratic form**

depend upon the distribution of $\mathbf{\Delta x}$,

$$\text{First order:} \quad E[P] = E[\mathbf{S^T \Delta x}] = \mathbf{S^T}\mu$$

$$\text{Second order:} \quad E[P] = E[\mathbf{S^T \Delta x} + \frac{1}{2}\mathbf{\Delta x^T G \Delta x}] = \mathbf{S^T}\mu + \frac{1}{2}tr(\mathbf{GQ}) + \frac{1}{2}\mu^T\mathbf{G}\mu$$

Added to the `Gamma` class we have,

```
class Gamma_:
    ...

    def exp_pnl(self, curve, mu, Q=None, order=1):
        S = self.risk(curve)
        ret = np.matmul(S.T, mu)
        if order == 2:
            ss, sz, zz = self.cross_gamma(curve, swaps=True)
            G = ss + sz + sz.T + zz
            ret += 0.5 * np.einsum('ij, ji', G, Q)
            ret += 0.5 * np.matmul(np.matmul(mu.T, G), mu)
        return ret
```

23.3.2 Volatility of PnL

The volatility of PnL is closely related to VaR. We define the volatility of PnL as the standard deviation of PnL over a specific timeframe, which should be aligned with the expectation. This is also very similar to the CoVaR multiplier, except in this section we actually want to extend the concept of CoVaR to incorporate second order effects.

In chapter 14 we didn't extend the VaR metric to second order for two reasons; firstly because doing this at a portfolio level requires all of the complete information about the gamma of that portfolio, i.e its cross-gamma grid, and secondly because the short timeframes upon which the risk management techniques were needed for were short enough for it to be overlooked.

When we consider trade strategies, however, we can be more thorough. Our limited number of trades means we can effectively estimate the gamma on each trade individually and then factor it into our calculations, although chapter 22 also gives us the tools to efficiently calculate a cross-gamma grid, which is what we will use. Furthermore, the timescales over which trade strategies are held might encompass sizeable market movements, meaning the inclusion of cross-gamma is necessary for accurate analysis.

Covariance matrices are a central ingredient and we have the problem of knowing whether a historical analysis is a reasonable approximation of the future, or whether implied volatilities (from the swaption market) will prove to be realised. Certainly this is one area of fixed income research that is on going; designing systems for optimal covariance matrix estimation. Whatever method is pursued, the reader should always be critical in this regard considering, conservatively, the fact that the volatility might be underestimated.

Similar to the expectation we can derive first order or second order estimates of the variance of the PnL[6],

$$\text{First order:} \quad Var[P] = Var[\mathbf{S^T \Delta x}] = \mathbf{S^T QS}$$

$$\text{Second order:} \quad Var[P] = Var[\mathbf{S^T \Delta x} + \frac{1}{2}\mathbf{\Delta x^T G \Delta x}]$$

$$= \mathbf{S^T QS} + \frac{1}{2}tr(\mathbf{GQGQ}) + \mu^T\mathbf{GQG}\mu + 2\mathbf{S^T QG}\mu$$

---

[6]again using well published results on the **variance of quadratic forms of multivariate normal random variables**

where the second order approximation **requires the assumption** that $\Delta \mathbf{x} \sim N(\boldsymbol{\mu}, \mathbf{Q})$, and G is symmetric, which it is by definition. We also add the below code.

```
 1      def var_pnl(self, curve, mu, Q, order=1):
 2          S = self.risk(curve)
 3          ret = np.matmul(np.matmul(S.T, Q), S)
 4          if order == 2:
 5              ss, sz, zz = self.cross_gamma(curve, swaps=True)
 6              G = ss + sz + sz.T + zz
 7              ret += 0.5 * np.einsum('ij, jk, kl, li', G, Q, G, Q)
 8              ret += np.einsum('ix, ij, jk, kl, lx', mu, G, Q, G, mu)
 9              ret += 2 * np.einsum('ix, ij, jk, kx', S, Q, G, mu)
10          return ret
```

23.3.3   Roll-down / volatility of trade

A common piece of analysis circulated in fixed income markets is the 'carry/vol' matrix. This is a misnomer and a more consistent name by our standards is the 'roll-down/vol of spread trade' matrix. This matrix shows the collection of Sharpe ratios for various spread trades, where the expected PnL is chosen to the be the roll-down and the volatility of PnL is directly proportional to the volatility of the spread trade (which is almost always measured historically). This is equivalent to a first order Sharpe ratio.

Example 23.11.
A trader produces the annual roll-down/vol of spread matrix for EUR IRSs given prevailing market levels and historical volatilities. The direction of this matrix has row instruments as the paid swaps and column instruments as the received swaps.

μ_i (bps)	$\sigma_{i,\text{N}}(bps)$	**Sharpe ratio**	(Rec) 2Y3Y	5Y5Y	10Y20Y	30Y20Y
-9.3	36.6	(Pay) 2Y3Y	-	+0.35	-0.25	-0.25
-20.4	58.6	5Y5Y	-0.35	-	-0.80	-0.70
1.7	68.8	10Y20Y	+0.25	+0.80	-	+0.02
1.4	67.3	30Y20Y	+0.25	+0.70	-0.02	-

Table 23.6: Annual roll-down /vol of spread ratio for EUR IRSs, using data from Aug '16.

The reader is, however, advised to avoid this matrix at all times. The reason being that this first order metric does not account for the gamma of trades, nor the full variation of the PnL of trading strategies. It is a false lure - easy to calculate, available on most providers' RV platforms, and can be misleading by considerably overestimating some of the ratios.

23.3.4   Adjusted roll-down / volatility of PnL ratio

Instead of the above, we suggest the adjusted 'roll-down /vol of PnL' to be much more powerful. This is a second order Sharpe ratio which accounts for the gamma on each trade in a strategy. And by doing this it also factors the overall volatility of the market as well as the volatility of the structure itself, so gives a much more accurate measure of the volatility of the PnL.

Example 23.12.
A trader produces the annual roll-down/vol of PnL matrix for EUR IRSs given the same market levels, historical volatilities, and with assumed correlations of instruments and gamma values of trades.

G^i per 10,000 pv01	Sharpe ratio	(Rec) 2Y3Y	5Y5Y	10Y20Y	30Y20Y
8	(Pay) 2Y3Y	-	+0.39	+0.01	+0.18
11	5Y5Y	-0.39	-	-0.42	-0.10
41	10Y20Y	-0.01	+0.42	-	+0.36
81	30Y20Y	-0.18	+0.10	-0.36	-

Correlation ρ_{ij}	2Y3Y	5Y5Y	10Y20Y	30Y20Y
2Y3Y	1	0.87	0.81	0.81
5Y5Y	0.87	1	0.92	0.89
10Y20Y	0.81	0.92	1	0.96
30Y20Y	0.81	0.89	0.96	1

Table 23.7: Annual roll-down /vol of PnL ratio for EUR IRSs, using data from Aug '16.

Comparing this matrix with the previous, it is clear that receiving longer instruments, which have much more gamma, is more favourable. The bottom left quadrant sees falls in the Sharpe ratio whilst the top right sees gains. The differences are not insignificant either. In fact they are often very pertinent, hence the advice to avoid the former matrix. Of course, the closer the instruments (e.g. 8Y1Y versus 9Y1Y) the less significant the difference, because their correlation is very high and they have approximately the same gamma.

As previously highlighted, we indicate that better ways of forecasting the volatility and correlations of the market, however derived, will produce systematically improved Sharpe ratio estimates over time.

We can add calculations of Sharpe ratios to our code with the use of the previous additions[21, #8df3ab], and we also include a Jupyter Notebook with all examples from this section[21, #5460c6].

```
1   def sharpe(self, curve, mu, Q, order=1):
2       exp = self.exp_pnl(curve, mu, Q, order),
3       vol = np.sqrt(self.var_pnl(curve, mu, Q, order))
4       return exp / vol
```

23.3.5   Efficient frontier and CAPM

The task of maximising the Sharpe ratio, given a set of instruments with assumed correlations was formally documented as the Capital Asset Pricing Model (CAPM), although in that analysis it was placed in a context of equity assets with a cash amount to invest, and with a risk free rate available as a deposit option. Fisher Black extended the concept to exclude risk free rates, and it is in this context that IRD portfolios reside, alongside actually having no cash to invest. His is often referred to as the Black CAPM.

Our goal is the same - maximise reward versus risk. But, this a more difficult problem than that of equity assets due to the non-linearity of our functions for expected PnL and volatility of PnL. Since we don't know what the optimal trade strategy is we can perform a random sample, or more advanced basin-hopping approach, to see which are the best.

A random sample, constructed of any of the four instruments of example 23.12 and using the same parameters, with random risks and directions, gives a generalised strategy. The above roll-down /vol matrices were only produced for 'spread' trades. This is a rather narrow subset of all of the possible strategies that can occur as part of the random sampling. The only constraint used in sampling is to ensure the delta of each instrument is within a range ($-1 \leq S^i \leq +1$, for instance). The results of each randomly sampled trade strategy are shown in figure 23.3.

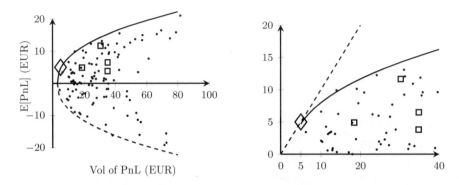

Figure 23.3: Randomly sampled trade strategies combining four instruments producing classical CAPM graphs of reward (annualised expected PnL) versus risk (annualised volatility of PnL).

Searching for the optimum trading strategy produces the familiar 'efficient frontier' shape, introduced by Harry Markowitz[66]. This is the bold line giving the maximum expected return for a given amount of risk of any constrained strategy. The negative PnLs show the same structure and they could of course be made positive (mirrored in the x-axis) by reversing all of the trade directions within that individual strategy.

The four square strategies have been highlighted, and these show the risk and return of the individual trades in isolation. All other portfolios are, in fact, a random combination of these. Overall, the figure highlights the **strength of diversification**, and the diamond marker gives the **optimum** strategy. Any value along the straight, dashed line can then be achieved by increasing, or decreasing, the proportionate trade sizes within this optimum strategy. The Sharpe ratio is the gradient of the line. In this case, and coincidentally, we have found an optimum strategy with precisely a 1.0 Sharpe ratio.

As a more accessible and practical example of the application of diversification, and of Sharpe ratio improvement, consider 23.13.

Example 23.13.
A trader considers the adjusted roll-down /vol of PnL matrix of example 23.12. He observes the three highest Sharpe ratios are to receive 2Y3Y/5Y5Y, pay 5Y5Y/10Y20Y and receive 10Y20Y/30Y20Y. With an assumption that IR curves usually steepen or flatten across all maturities it is likely that paying 5Y5Y/10Y20Y provides some diversification in a portfolio which receives the other two spreads. Indeed, with a small amount of tweaking from the basic 50-100-50% weights to 42-100-86% for each respective spread trade, he manages to achieve a respectably high overall Sharpe ratio of +0.78.

23.3.6   Using other assumptions

The use of the roll-down as the expectation of PnL on a trading strategy is just used for example purposes above. For a strategy based on momentum indicators or mean reversion assumptions it will be necessary, and consistent, to use other estimates instead of roll-down (or additional to roll-down if it is still considered worth including).

The expectation of PnL is *the* most important aspect of the estimation because, firstly, it forecasts the actual profit amount and, secondly, dictates the Sharpe ratio calculation by commanding greatest influence. The volatility of PnL is usually easier to forecast because volatility often averages out over time and correlation has some variability but is usually constrained to ranges. Make sure to be clear about the timeframe of a trading strategy and adopt an appropriate period of volatility measurement that aligns with the timeframe of the expected PnL.

We also highlight that the value of gamma is often skewed to the upside by the effect of the volatility smile (see section 22.9.1). This is the impact of larger kurtosis impacting the possible range of values. In the absence of any formal mathematical adjustments to the second order Sharpe ratio for these effects it might be wise to spare a thought for this effect in certain potential strategies. Generally speaking, being short gamma tends to have a higher cost than initially presumed.

At various stages in this book methods of constructing trading strategies have been exemplified. Those methods rely on the basic principles of trying to target specific views (expectations of PnL) whilst minimising risk in some way (reducing the volatility of PnL). This chapter formalises those ideas and marries it with existing modern portfolio theory.

23.4 Appendix

23.4.1 PCA directionality minimisation

Suppose that $\mathbf{e_i}$ is the i'th PC (column) of $\mathbf{E}$, and, $\mathbf{S^{ini}}$, are the initial supposed risks of the potential trade. We propose an optimisation problem where $\mathbf{x}$ is an adjustment to those initial risks such that the risks to some specified PCs are zero and $\mathbf{x}$ is minimal under Euclidean norm, i.e.

$$\min_{\mathbf{x}} \frac{1}{2}||\mathbf{x}||_2 = \min_{\mathbf{x}} \frac{1}{2}\mathbf{x^T Ix} \qquad \text{subject to} \qquad \sum_{i \in H}(\mathbf{S^{ini}} + \mathbf{x})^{\mathbf{T}}\mathbf{Ie_i} = \mathbf{0}$$

where, H, is a set of specified PCs e.g. $\{1, 2\}$, to which the risk is set to zero. Commonly, this may be just $\{1\}$ if only the principal component is to be hedged. This is a quadratic program with linear equality constraints, solvable via the Karush-Kuhn-Tucker necessary conditions. Let the Lagrangian,

$$L(\mathbf{x}, \lambda) = \mathbf{x^T Ix} + \sum_{i \in H} \lambda_i (\mathbf{S^{ini}} + \mathbf{x})^{\mathbf{T}}\mathbf{Ie_i}$$

$$\nabla_{\mathbf{x}} L = \mathbf{I}(\mathbf{x} + \sum_{i \in H} \lambda_i \mathbf{e_i}) = \mathbf{0}$$

which forms the solvable linear system,

$$\begin{bmatrix} \mathbf{I} & \vdots & \mathbf{E_H} \\ \cdots & & \cdots \\ \mathbf{E_H^T} & \vdots & \mathbf{0} \end{bmatrix} \begin{bmatrix} \mathbf{x} \\ \cdots \\ \lambda \end{bmatrix} = \begin{bmatrix} \mathbf{0} \\ \cdots \\ -\mathbf{E_H^T S^{ini}} \end{bmatrix}$$

where, $\mathbf{E_H}$, is the eigenvector matrix with the selected subset of columns. Although this can be solved with a linear system solver via, for example, Gaussian elimination, block matrix inversion formulae (or inspection) also yield the closed form solution,

$$\begin{bmatrix} \mathbf{x} \\ \cdots \\ \lambda \end{bmatrix} = \begin{bmatrix} \mathbf{I} - \mathbf{E_H E_H^T} & \vdots & \mathbf{E_H} \\ \cdots & & \cdots \\ \mathbf{E_H^T} & \vdots & -\mathbf{I} \end{bmatrix} \begin{bmatrix} \mathbf{0} \\ \cdots \\ -\mathbf{E_H^T S^{ini}} \end{bmatrix} \implies \mathbf{x} = -\mathbf{E_H E_H^T S^{ini}}$$

where we note that, $\mathbf{E_H^T E_H} = \mathbf{I}$, but, $\mathbf{E_H E_H^T} \neq \mathbf{I}$.

One issue with the above solution is that the neutrality adjustments, $\mathbf{x}$, are permitted to vary any risk bucket within the PCA framework. This is not always desired. For example if one seeks to adjust a 2s5s10s trade, neutralising the risk to the principal component, one may legitimately seek adjustments that **only** affect the relevant 2Y, 5Y, and 10Y buckets. In a simplistic way, one could select from the covariance matrix, $\mathbf{Q}$, the sub-matrix containing only data relevant to the 2Y, 5Y and 10Y buckets and then perform the above optimisation problem. The problem with this approach is that it is inconsistent with the overall PCA framework. By subsampling data, the eigenvector values for these chosen buckets change since they no longer need to account for the wider set of information and correlations with other, excluded buckets.

   An alternative approach is to include additional linear equality constraints to the optimisation problem setting specific variables to zero, which leads to the additional term in the Lagrangian,

$$\sum_{j \in L} \nu_j x_j = 0$$

where, ν_j, are additional Lagrangian multipliers, and, L, is the set of indexes of risk buckets which are *not* permitted as variable quantities. If we repeat the above analysis we obtain the linear system,

$$
\begin{bmatrix}
\mathbf{I} & \vdots & \mathbf{E_H} & \vdots & \mathbf{L^T} \\
\cdots & & \cdots & & \cdots \\
\mathbf{E_H^T} & \vdots & \mathbf{0} & \vdots & \mathbf{0} \\
\cdots & & \cdots & & \cdots \\
\mathbf{L} & \vdots & \mathbf{0} & \vdots & \mathbf{0}
\end{bmatrix}
\begin{bmatrix}
\mathbf{x} \\
\cdots \\
\mathbf{\lambda} \\
\cdots \\
\mathbf{\nu}
\end{bmatrix}
=
\begin{bmatrix}
\mathbf{0} \\
\cdots \\
-\mathbf{E_H^T S^{ini}} \\
\cdots \\
\mathbf{0}
\end{bmatrix}
$$

where, $\mathbf{L}$, is a matrix of zeros and ones corresponding to the set of indexes determining which x values are constrained to zero.

We add the following code to our repository[21, #595164],

```
def pca_hedge_adjustment(self, Q, S_ini, H=[0], L=None):
    """defaults to hedging directionality: PC1 is set to zero"""
    lambd, E = self.pca(Q)
    n, n2 = len(lambd), len(H)
    E_H = E[:, H]
    if L is not None:
        n3 = len(L)
        L_ = np.zeros(shape=(n3, n))
        for row, col in enumerate(L):
            L_[row, col] = 1.0
        A = np.block([[np.eye(n), E_H, L_.T],
                      [E_H.T, np.zeros((n2, n2)), np.zeros((n2, n3))],
                      [L_, np.zeros((n3, n2)), np.zeros((n3, n3))]])
        b = np.block([[np.zeros((n, 1))],
                      [-np.matmul(E_H.T, S_ini)],
                      [np.zeros((n3, 1))]])
        return np.linalg.solve(A, b)[:n, :]
    else:
        return -np.matmul(E_H, np.matmul(E_H.T, S_ini))
```

23.4.2 Multivariate least squares regression

Assume an initial trade strategy, for example a benchmark 2s5s10s,

$$
\mathbf{S^{ini}} = \begin{matrix} (2Y) \\ (5Y) \\ (10Y) \\ (30Y) \end{matrix}
\begin{bmatrix} -1 \\ 2 \\ -1 \\ 0 \end{bmatrix}
$$

If $\mathbf{\Delta r^c}$ is the, n, datapoint by, m, instrument matrix of centralised daily market movements then,

$$
\mathbf{y} = \mathbf{\Delta r^c S^{ini}}
$$

is the vector of centralised daily market movements for the initial trade strategy - the so called *dependent variable*. Now propose a number of *independent variables*, in our case we use 2; 2s10s and also 5Y, which have the representation,

$$
\mathbf{x_1} = \begin{bmatrix} -1 \\ 0 \\ 1 \\ 0 \end{bmatrix}, \qquad
\mathbf{x_2} = \begin{bmatrix} 0 \\ 1 \\ 0 \\ 0 \end{bmatrix}, \qquad \text{such that,} \qquad
\mathbf{X} = \mathbf{\Delta r^c} [\mathbf{x_1} : \mathbf{x_2}]
$$

Here, $\mathbf{X}$, is the matrix of centralised daily market movements of those chosen dependent variables. The traditional least square regression model is then,

$$\mathbf{y} = \mathbf{X}\boldsymbol{\beta} + \boldsymbol{\epsilon}, \qquad \text{with optimal estimators,} \qquad \hat{\boldsymbol{\beta}} = (\mathbf{X^T X})^{-1}\mathbf{X^T y}$$

where $\boldsymbol{\epsilon}$ is the error, or variation, term. In this case, $\boldsymbol{\epsilon}$, is the specific quantity to which we seek trading exposure. If for example, we propose no independent variables then $\boldsymbol{\epsilon}$ simply equals $\mathbf{y}$ and our exposure is to the initial trade itself. On the other hand if we proposed the independent variables 2Y, 5Y and 10Y, then the hedges would completely offset the initial trade strategy and leave no exposure and $\boldsymbol{\epsilon}$ would be zero. With rearrangement we see that,

$$\boldsymbol{\epsilon} = \mathbf{y} - \mathbf{X}\hat{\boldsymbol{\beta}} = \boldsymbol{\Delta}\mathbf{r^c}\left(\mathbf{S^{ini}} - [\mathbf{x_1} : \mathbf{x_2}]\hat{\boldsymbol{\beta}}\right)$$

and therefore the adjustment trade weightings, $\mathbf{S^{trade}}$, are determined from,

$$\mathbf{S} = \mathbf{S^{ini}} + \mathbf{S^{trade}} = \mathbf{S^{ini}} - [\mathbf{x_1} : \mathbf{x_2}]\hat{\boldsymbol{\beta}}$$

Reset Risk

Reset risk was introduced in section 18.2.4. This chapter has been relegated to the end since **after the transition from IBOR it becomes effectively redundant and can be ignored in RFR only cases**. It is still included for historical context, and because other forms of financial fixing risk, can employ similar principles where appropriate.

24.1 Resets and reset ladders

The traditional approach of hedging a reset risk is to enter a new trade exactly as that fixing (and risk change) falls due, or by executing offsetting (spread) trades in advance. However for the majority of reset risks present in an IRD portfolio neither approach is generally possible for two reasons;

(i) transaction costs in terms of bid-offer and brokerage fees prohibit the continuous practice of hedging reset risk as it falls due, or ahead of time through spread trades, for each index, in each currency, each day,

(ii) the FRA market or OIS market is not liquid enough in any currency to execute the required daily trades or spread trades.

How does reset risk build up in a portfolio?

Reset risk is created in a portfolio when trades are hedged with other trades that do not have precisely the same fixing schedule. For example, if a market-maker paid $100mm 10Y SS IRS today but then hedged it tomorrow by receiving $100mm 10Y SS IRS then this would create a string of reset mismatches every six months, separated by one day.

Another example might be a price-taker requesting a trade with specific dates which a market-maker then hedges with standard benchmark interbank trades, which do not in general have the same fixing schedules as the price-taker's requested trade.

Using STIR futures as a hedge for non-IMM IRSs is another common way of accruing reset risk.

Why is reset risk often overlooked?

Reset risk represents a very specific, nuanced type of risk. Reset risk is vaguely analogous to risk bleed[1]; the delta risk of the portfolio changes due to the passage of time. But rather than being a steady and gradual risk change due to interpolation fluctuations, these delta risk changes are due to expiry of trades on fixing publications and are arbitrary and can be sizeable. It **is never captured in traditional VaR**, because reset risk affects delta risk only at specific times in the future, and traditional VaR only measures immediate risks.

Secondly, losses due to reset risk tend to be more accrual based amassing over time. They tend not to be large immediate MTM losses (although this does occasionally occur) meaning the 'shock and panic' factor rarely emerges to force a trader to be more proactive with respect to reset risk management.

Ladders

Since reset risk changes through time, after fixings have been published on a daily basis, one has to devise a way of visualising the information about what are the sizes of the risk changes and when they occur. This is the point of a reset ladder.

In the context of an IRD portfolio with thousands of generic trades it will be commonplace to have some exposure to the fixing of any index on any given day. Most likely there will be lots of trades with exposure to the same fixing. It is sensible to aggregate the notionals or pv01 of the exposure of all of the relevant trades to each fixing on each day.

Example 24.1.
A trader has 3 trades with exposure to the 1st Feb USD 3M LIBOR fixing, he has;
bought a $100mm 1st Feb 3M FRA, with a calculated pv01 of $2,433,
paid a $200mm IRS with 1st Feb rolls against 3M LIBOR, with reset pv01 $4,866,
sold a $320mm 1st Feb 3M FRA, with pv01 of $7,785.
The aggregate notional is represented as -$20mm and the risk as -$487.

Once the trades have been aggregated across each index for each day the results are usually presented in a list, or a ladder such as the following;

Fixing Date	3M	6M
1st Feb	-20	-60
2nd Feb	+40	-30
3rd Feb	-10	-10
4th Feb	+20	+5
etc.		

(a) by notional

Fixing Date	3M	6M
1st Feb	-487	-2,958
2nd Feb	+975	-1,479
3rd Feb	-244	-493
4th Feb	+487	+246
etc.		

(b) by pv01

---

[1]explained in section 9.3.5

This example reset ladder has been chosen to only show 3M and 6M resets in USD, but of course a ladder can be equivalently created for any index in any currency. Larger, multi asset trading portfolios can have an extensive number of columns. This chapter will refer to resets and reset ladders in terms of pv01 and not notional.

24.2 Characterising reset risk

We will presently outline the steps for producing **a VaR multiplier for reset risk**, representing the riskiness of a given reset ladder. As a demonstration of the need for this task consider the four reset ladders below and answer the question: whose portfolio should be classified as the most risky, why, and can the risk be quantified?

Fixing Date	Alpha's 3M	Bravo's 3M	Charlie's 3M	Delta's 3M
t+1	-1,400	0	-1,000	-1,000
t+2	0	-2,000	0	+2,000
t+3	0	0	+2,000	-2,000
t+4	0	+2,000	0	+2,000
t+5	+1,400	0	-1,000	-1,000

VaR based approach

This approach provides a means of more detailed classification. In order to produce a reset VaR metric we need to do a number of things simultaneously. Firstly we need to form an opinion about the expected path of fixings, given known prices in the interbank market. Secondly, using these expectations, we need to be able to apportion specific reset risks into more perspicuous buckets, much like an analogous 4.5Y IRS might be apportioned into 4Y and 5Y risk buckets. Thirdly we need a systematic, on going hedging mechanism reactive to these proportions of risk. Finally we combine all of the individual days' traditional VaRs to give a statistical assessment of the risk over the whole period - an holistic reset VaR.

24.2.1 The expected path of fixings and risk apportionment

[2]The FRA market is sufficiently illiquid that there is often limited information on which to base any expectations about the path of future fixings. Furthermore the only practical instruments with which to perform continuous hedging are IMM FRAs or, equivalently, STIR futures. This is not only due to increased liquidity but also due the cheaper costs of executing these trades relative to the penal cost of specific fixing date hedging.

Here we choose to adopt the simplest nature of IBOR rate progression; linear interpolation between the cash rate (the imminent IBOR fixing) and the next IMM rate. The risk apportionment is also done linearly.

Example 24.2.
A trader's portfolio only contains two resets between today, m_0, and the next IMM date on m_{20}. The total pv01 is zero; the first reset has risk +100, and the second has -100, see figure 24.2. Under the assumption of a linear curve, controlled by the two end points, the trader's aggregate apportioned delta risk strip, with the cash rate and IMM rate as buckets, is as follows:

---

[2]this section references only 3M-IBOR fixings but the concept is designed to be applicable to other tenors with other considerations

Fixing Date	3M Reset Risk, S_i	3M Cash Rate Risk, S_0	IMM Rate Risk, S_f
m_5	+100	+75	+25
m_{15}	-100	-25	-75
Aggregate	delta measured as at m_0	**+50**	**-50**

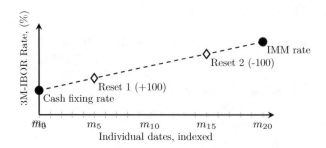

Figure 24.2: Linear model of fixing rates curve before the next IMM rate.

After one, or more days, the apportionment of the delta risk into the two buckets changes, as each reset becomes proportionally closer to the imminent cash rate than the IMM rate. On days m_0 to m_4 both resets will factor into the aggregate delta risk strip for that day. On days m_5 to m_{14} only reset 2 will factor because reset 1 will have already fixed, and after m_{15} no reset will remain so the delta strip will be zero. To give a specific example, on day m_{10} the aggregate delta risk strip would be measured as [-50, -50], where reset 2's -100 pv01 is equally apportioned between both buckets.

24.2.2   Continuous hedging mechanism and overall risk

With the above apportioned risks calculated, each trading day, m_k, will have specific bucket risks for each bucket $S_{0,k}$ and S_f. Assuming we are able to freely trade the S_f bucket, we choose to trade an amount of it to minimise the VaR for each respective trading day. Naturally this involves estimating the volatility of the two buckets and their correlation. This is expanded in the practical example below. This still leaves a residual VaR for that given trading day, essentially the result of the inability to directly hedge the $S_{0,k}$ bucket on any specific trading day.

The overall risk is calculated by accounting for all the individual trading days' VaRs.

24.2.3   Practical example of reset risk assessment

Formal process of characterisation

To be explicit and walk the reader through the process we state procedural steps to take, and give examples how to apply each step:

Step one: calculate aggregate delta risk strips for each trading date, m_k, representing the resets present between m_k and the next IMM date after m_k.

Step two: assume a hedge is permitted at any time using IMM instruments (FRAs or STIR futures) to eliminate all IMM delta risk leaving cash risk (i.e. risk to the movement in the imminent fixing rate) as the only delta risk remaining on any given trading date, m_k.

Step three: establish a measure of volatility and correlation between the cash rate (i.e. the imminent fixing rate) on any trading date, m_k, and the rate on the next IMM date.

Step four: adopting a VaR minimisation approach, hedge the cash risk on any trading date, m_k, by trading the next IMM instrument, in the determined size.

Step five: with all known future daily VaR multipliers derive a single risk metric characterising the reset ladder.

Step one

This step is about systematically calculating what the delta risk of the portfolio will evolve into with each reset falling due, akin to example 24.2. It requires the calculation of aggregate delta risk strips for each trading date, m_k, of all of the resets present between m_k and the next IMM date after m_k. Really, this step could be broken down into three sub steps:

Substep one: for a specific date, m_k, starting with today, calculate the delta strip of each individual reset present between m_k and the next IMM date after m_k.

Substep two: aggregate all of those individual delta strips to produce a total delta strip representing trading date, m_k.

Substep three: repeat the process for the next date, m_{k+1}, to obtain the list of all aggregate delta strips for each date.

According to the linear apportionment the delta, S_i, on any individual reset will be apportioned to the the cash risk bucket, $S_{0,k}$, and the next IMM risk bucket, S_f as,

$$S_{0,k} = \frac{D_f - D_i}{D_f} S_i \, ,$$

$$S_f = \frac{D_i}{D_f} S_i \, , \quad \text{such that} \quad S_i = S_{0,k} + S_f \, ,$$

where D_i and D_f are the number of days from m_k until the given reset date, m_i, and IMM date respectively.

Example 24.3.
Today is 10th Mar, with the first IMM date on 16th Mar.
Using the above method we apportion the pv01 of each reset from the following reset ladder to obtain an aggregate delta strip for date, the 10th Mar.

Fixing Date	3M Reset	$S_{0,0}$	S_f
11-Mar	+3,000	+2,500	+500
14-Mar	-2,400	-800	-1,600
15-Mar	+1,500	+250	+1,250
16-Mar	+0	0	+0
Aggregate		+1,950	+150

We repeat the process to obtain the aggregate delta strip treating 11th Mar as the base day.

Fixing Date	3M Reset	$S_{0,1}$	S_f
14-Mar	-2,400	-960	-1,440
15-Mar	+1,500	+300	+1,200
16-Mar	+0	0	0
Aggregate		-660	-240

And repeat again with 14th Mar as the base day.

Fixing Date	3M Reset	$S_{0,2}$	S_f
15-Mar	+1,500	+750	+750
16-Mar	+0	0	0
Aggregate		+750	+750

The example above shows how to obtain the required aggregate delta strips. The overall information from example 24.3 would be neatly summarised as follows:

Aggregated delta strip by trading date		
m_k	$S_{0,k}$	S_f
10-Mar	+1,950	+150
11-Mar	-660	-240
14-Mar	+750	+750
15-Mar	0	0

Step two

This step is only included to highlight the concept of permissible, continuous hedging with IMM instruments. It could really be combined with step four which is to finalise the delta strip position but it seems simpler to present this concept first. The result of this assumption is that the summary table of step one can be reduced to the following:

Aggregated delta strip by trading date		
m_k	$S_{0,k}$	S_f
10-Mar	+1,950	0
11-Mar	-660	0
14-Mar	+750	0
15-Mar	0	0

Step three

Next we look to establish a relationship between the cash rate and the next IMM rate, in preparation for using it as a guide for how to hedge the cash risk, $S_{0,k}$ using IMM instruments. In this relationship we seek to incorporate the following properties;

  (i) the cash rate always has a constant subsumed volatility,

 (ii) the IMM rate is typically (but doesn't have to be) more volatile than the cash rate,

(iii) the cash rate and the IMM rate are more correlated the closer they are in terms of number of days,

(iv) the volatility of the IMM rate becomes more similar to that of the cash rate the closer they become in terms of days.

It suffices that if we simply assume three parameters; the volatility of the cash rate, the volatility of the start-3M tenor-3M rate, and the correlation between them, then we can derive a covariance matrix between the 3M cash rate on any trading date, m_k, and the next IMM rate as:

$$\mathbf{Q}_{X_1 Z_2}(m_k) = \begin{bmatrix} q_{11} & q_{12}(m_k) \\ q_{12}(m_k) & q_{22}(m_k) \end{bmatrix},$$

where the reader is referred to the chapter appendix for the precise derivation of a model for this matrix using static assumptions.

Step four

Having calculated the cash risk in step two and with the knowledge of the relationship between cash rates and the IMM rate from step three, we look to execute a final IMM hedge in this step which minimises VaR. Look to the appendix for the derivation but here, we state that the hedge is:

$$S_f = -S_{0,k}\frac{q_{12}}{q_{22}} \,,$$

which produces minimum VaR multiplier for trading date, m_k of:

$$c_{k,\min} = |S_{0,k}|\sqrt{q_{11} - \frac{q_{12}^2}{q_{22}}} \,.$$

Example 24.4.
$\sigma_1 = 1.0$: we set the volatility of the cash rate to have a s.d. of 1bp per day.
$\sigma_2 = 1.5$: we set the volatility of the 3M3M rate to be 50% greater than the cash rate.
$\rho = 0.75$: we set the correlation between the above rates at 75%.
Using the formula in the appendix for q_{12} and q_{22} we tabulate the required IMM risk position and the resulting VaR multiplier, c_k, for each trading date, m_k:

m_i	q_{12}	q_{22}	$S_{0,k}$	S_f	$c_{k,\min}$
10-Mar	1.008	1.021	+1,950	-1,926	126
11-Mar	1.007	1.017	-660	+654	36
14-Mar	1.003	1.006	+750	-748	16
15-Mar	1.001	1.003	0	0	0

This table represents the stylised risk on each trading date to minimise on going VaR. To achieve this requires daily hedging of the S_f bucket to attain the correct position.

Step five

Finally we seek to convert our list of daily VaR multipliers into a single metric which represents the overall risk of the reset ladder. A number of assumptions have been used in the model so far and we include one more; daily weighting.

This assumption is included to account for resets further into the future which have a greater chance of being hedged over time, and therefore pose less of an immediate concern. If one makes the simple assumption that each day any particular reset has a specific chance of being hedged, say $x\%$, then the chance of that reset or any subsequent reset still existing by the time the fixing date occurs is $(1-x)^{D_i}$. This suggests an exponential weighting should be applied. Additionally this makes intuitive sense that imminent resets should pose greater concern than those months into the future. I like to adopt $x = 1\%$ as what I believe to be a sensible value, but this is of course very subjective.

The appendix also shows the derivation but in order to finalise this procedure and **produce a single VaR multiplier for the given reset ladder** we calculate,

$$c = \sqrt{\sum_i (w_i c_{i,\min})^2} \,.$$

Example 24.5.
Redrawing the table with the weighting, $w_i = 0.99^{D_i}$, and determining the overall VaR multiplier characterising the reset ladder as $c = 132$. This indicates that with 95% and 99% c.i.s, under

the assumptions of the model regarding volatilities and hedging, the reset ladder will not lose
more than 217 and 307 respectively.

m_i	q_{12}	q_{22}	S_i	S_f	$c_{i,\min}$	w_i	$(w_i c_{i,\min})^2$
10-Mar	1.008	1.021	+1,950	-1,926	126	1.00	15,940
11-Mar	1.007	1.017	-660	+654	36	0.99	1,248
14-Mar	1.003	1.006	+750	-748	16	0.98	255
15-Mar	1.001	1.003	0	0	0	0.97	0
$\mathbf{c} =$	**132**					Total	17,444

24.2.4 Central bank policy meeting dates

One of the biggest causes of PnL due to reset risk are the actions of central banks. Central
bank announcements which lower or raise interest rates have an immediate impact on future
IBOR or OIS fixings. This means then that a reset falling due after a future central bank
announcement is much better hedged with an equivalent reset falling after the announcement
than before it.

The precise nature of these events is difficult to capture. They are often asymmetrical and
the size of IBOR movements are complicated to accurately model the calibration of. We can
proxy a greater risk by assigning more weight to days with announcements and estimating
higher volatilities on those days. This increases those individual days' VaR multipliers.

Example 24.6.
The VaR multiplier is calculated for the reset ladder in each of the two cases where the central
bank announcement day of 3 Mar is firstly ignored, and secondly given a weighting of seven
times more than usual.

Date	3M Reset	c_i	w_i (1)	w_i (2)
2-Mar	-	106	1.00	1.00
3-Mar	+5,000	796	0.99	6.93
4-Mar	-10,000	479	0.98	0.98
7-Mar	+5,000	0	0.97	0.97
		$\mathbf{c} =$	**923**	**5,535**

The reason the VaR is much higher in the scenario is that the reset on the 3rd Mar, which
is visually an offset for the 4th Mar, is published before the central bank announcement. This
means that the risk acquired due to the reset, and that which is outstanding for the 4th and 7th
Mar, is subject to the announcement. The increased volatility then increases the overall risk.

24.2.5 Reviewing

We now revisit the question posed at the start of this section? Whose reset ladder is the most
risky and why?

Date	Alpha's 3M	Bravo's 3M	Charlie's 3M	Delta's 3M
t+1	-1,400	0	-1,000	-1,000
t+2	0	-2,000	0	+2,000
t+3	0	0	+2,000	-2,000
t+4	0	+2,000	0	+2,000
t+5	+1,400	0	-1,000	-1,000

24.3. BENEFITS OF A VAR BASED APPROACH

We are now in a position to begin to answer this. Firstly we should point out that these reset ladders must be considered in conjunction with the distance to the nearest IMM hedge[3]. For example consider the two cases where 't+0' is the 28th Dec and 8th Mar, each of which have the 16th Mar as the next IMM hedge. Using the method the overall VaR multiplier, c, for each reset ladder is shown below:

t+0	Alpha's c	Bravo's c	Charlie's c	Delta's c
28-Dec	1550	1630	1170	1169
8-Mar	95	155	138	99

Two things are immediately apparent. Firstly when the resets are just before an IMM date they pose much less risk. This is due to the quality of the hedge being superior; the cash rate and IMM rate are much more correlated the closer they are in terms of date. Secondly the reset ladders are ordered differently in terms of riskiness dependent upon when these resets are considered. Alpha has the second most risky ladder if it is valued on 28th Dec and the fourth most risky if it valued on 8-Mar. This shows that structure of reset ladders is also important in consideration with placement near or far from IMM hedges.

24.3   Benefits of a VaR based approach

After adopting this model for characterising reset risk, the next logical step is to pose the question, how can it be used to analyse reset ladders in detail? This becomes relatively straightforward, if numerically cumbersome, with the availability of a single VaR multiplier representing the whole reset ladder.

Example 24.7.
Continuing example 24.3, using numerical techniques, such as trial and error, repeated bisection, or datapoint sampling, we can determine the overall VaR minimising trade for each reset date below, and show its impact to the VaR multiplier, c:

Date	3M Reset ($c = 132$)	Minimising trade	Δc	$\left|\frac{\Delta c}{c}\right|$
11-Mar	+3,000	-2,340	-93	70.6%
14-Mar	-2,400	-2,130	-17	12.8%
15-Mar	+1,500	-3,351	-16	11.8%
16-Mar	+0	0	0	0%

Clearly one trade stands out as being the obvious choice for risk reduction. Suppose that it is executed then the after trade position is:

Date	3M Reset ($c = 39$)	Minimising trade	Δc	$\left|\frac{\Delta c}{c}\right|$
11-Mar	+660	0	0	0%
14-Mar	-2,400	+818	-9	23.3%
15-Mar	+1,500	+603	-2	4.3%
16-Mar	+0	0	0	0%

The marginal VaR reduction that can be achieved with further trades is subjectively ignored. The trader is comfortable that the reset ladder poses negligible risk.

---

[3]they should also be considered in relation to central bank policy meeting dates but this ignored in this example

Example 24.7 is a specific case of analysis considering the impact of executing a **single trade**. But of course, through numerical analysis, one can ascertain the impact to VaR of any combination of trades with an appropriate algorithm to run through potential scenarios. This becomes particularly useful when one considers 'spread trades', which is to trade a reset on one date against another date in the same pv01.

24.4 Appendix

24.4.1 Establishing a relationship between the cash rate and the next IMM rate

In the text this represents step three for 3M resets. Where X_1 and X_2 are random variables representing the 3M rate and the 3M3M rate respectively, make the supposition of a constant covariance matrix for any given date, m_k:

$$\mathbf{Q}_{X_1 X_2} = [q_{ij}^*] = \begin{bmatrix} \sigma_1^2 & \rho\sigma_1\sigma_2 \\ \rho\sigma_1\sigma_2 & \sigma_2^2 \end{bmatrix},$$

which indicates X_1 has a standard deviation of σ_1, and X_2, which is usually a bit more volatile, has a standard deviation of σ_2 and they have a correlation ρ, which is usually quite strong, between them.

Now suppose that Z_2 is a random variable representing the IMM rate that falls on date m_f between the start dates of X_1, m_k and X_2, m_{k+3M}. Linearly interpolating let,

$$Z_2 = \alpha X_1 + (1 - \alpha)X_2, \quad \text{where} \quad \alpha = \frac{D_{3M} - D_f(m_k)}{D_{3M}}.$$

We are interested solely in the covariance matrix, $\mathbf{Q}_{X_1 Z_2} = [q_{ij}]$, between variables, X_1 and Z_2, such that from the properties of covariance:

$$
\begin{aligned}
\mathbf{Q}_{X_1 Z_2} &= \begin{bmatrix} q_{11}^* & \alpha q_{11}^* + (1-\alpha)q_{12}^* \\ q_{12} & \alpha^2 q_{11}^* + 2\alpha(1-\alpha)q_{12}^* + (1-\alpha)^2 q_{22}^* \end{bmatrix}, \\
&= \begin{bmatrix} \sigma_1^2 & \alpha\sigma_1^2 + (1-\alpha)\rho\sigma_1\sigma_2 \\ \alpha\sigma_1^2 + (1-\alpha)\rho\sigma_1\sigma_2 & \alpha^2\sigma_1^2 + 2\alpha(1-\alpha)\rho\sigma_1\sigma_2 + (1-\alpha)^2\sigma_2^2 \end{bmatrix}.
\end{aligned}
$$

This relationship has all of the required properties;

(i) X_1 always has a constant volatility of s.d., σ_1,

(ii) as the start dates of X_1 and Z_2 approach they become more correlated and the volatility of Z_2 approaches that of X_1,

(iii) as the start dates of Z_2 and X_2 approach, the covariance matrix $\mathbf{Q_{XZ}}$ tends to $\mathbf{Q_X}$.

Note that $D_{3M} = 91$ days is appropriate for the model.

Other tenor fixings

Similar approaches can be adopted for other tenor fixings such as 1M, 6M and 12M. In those cases one may choose to model individually or combine with other tenors such as the aforementioned 3M. If combining, a larger covariance matrix will be required which documents relevant correlations between the fixings and their respective IMM hedges.

24.4.2 Deriving the IMM hedge for VaR minimisation

This represents step four for 3M resets in the text. Referencing the chapter on VaR let,

$$c_k = \sqrt{q_{11}S_{0,k}^2 + 2q_{12}S_{0,k}S_f + q_{22}S_f^2},$$

$$\frac{\partial c_k}{\partial S_f} = \frac{q_{12}S_{0,k} + q_{22}S_f}{c_k},$$

so that to minimise c_k set,

$$S_f = -S_{0,k} \frac{q_{12}}{q_{22}} \ ,$$

which produces minimum c_k:

$$c_{k,\min} = |S_{0,k}| \sqrt{q_{11} - \frac{q_{12}^2}{q_{22}}} \ .$$

24.4.3   Deriving the overall reset risk VaR multiplier

This represents step five in the text. Let each $U_k \sim N(0,1)$ be an independent, normally distributed random variable with mean, zero, and variance, one. The PnL attributed to the portfolio on trading date, m_k, is, $w_k c_{k,\min} U_k$, taking into consideration the exponential weighting, w_k, of days, prioritising sooner dates over later dates. The total PnL is modelled as,

$$P = \sum_k w_k c_{k,\min} U_k \ .$$

Since P is the linear sum of independent, normally distributed random variables, it has distribution,

$$P \sim N(0, \sum_k (w_k c_{k,\min})^2) \ .$$

Therefore we derive the overall VaR multiplier, c, as the square-root of the variance,

$$c = \sqrt{\sum_k (w_k c_{k,\min})^2} \ .$$

Bibliography

Supporting material for the book

[21] *Code Repository for Pricing and Trading IRDs.* URL: github.com/attack68/book_irds3 (cit. on pp. 74, 143, 144, 149, 150, 156, 164, 167, 174, 177, 179, 183, 192, 197, 199, 200, 213, 219, 279, 283, 289, 295, 298, 346, 348, 350, 377, 381).

[37] L Volpi and Team. *Matrix.xla Addin for Microsoft Excel* (cit. on p. 213).

[63] J H M Darbyshire. "A Preliminary Study on the Convexity Adjustment of Zero Coupon Swaps". 2014. URL: github.com/attack68/book_irds3/files/ZCAderivation.pdf (cit. on pp. 357, 359).

International organisations

[8]   Federal Reserve System (FED). *General Website.* URL: www.federalreserve.gov (cit. on p. 16).

[9]   European Central Bank (ECB). *General Website.* URL: www.ecb.int (cit. on p. 16).

[10] Bank of England (BoE). *General Website.* URL: www.bankofengland.co.uk (cit. on p. 16).

[11] Bank of Japan (BoJ). *General Website.* URL: www.boj.or.jp (cit. on p. 16).

[12] Intercontinental Exchange (ICE). *LIBOR Administration.* URL: www.theice.com/iba/libor (cit. on p. 17).

[13] European Money Markets Institute (EMMI). *EURIBOR Administration.* URL: www.emmi-benchmarks.eu (cit. on p. 17).

[14] Debt Management Office for the United Kingdom. *General Website.* URL: www.dmo.gov.uk (cit. on p. 41).

[15] Debt Management Office for the Republic of Finland. *General Website.* URL: www.treasuryfinland.fi (cit. on p. 41).

[16] Swiss National Bank (SNB). *General Website.* URL: www.snb.ch (cit. on p. 42).

[17] Danmarks Nationalbank (DNB). *General Website.* URL: www.nationalbanken.dk (cit. on p. 42).

Fixed income literature

[1]   D V Widder. *Advanced Calculus.* 2nd. Dover Publications (cit. on p. 1).

[2]   J C Hull. *Options, Futures, and Other Derivatives.* Prentice-Hall, Inc., 2011 (cit. on pp. 1, 251, 298).

[3]   V V Piterbarg and L B G Andersen. *Interest Rate Modeling.* Atlantic Financial Press, 2010 (cit. on pp. 1, 69, 298).

[4]   H Schneider and G P Barker. *Matrices and Linear Algebra.* 2nd. Dover Publications (cit. on p. 2).

[5]   I Griva and S Nash. *Linear and Nonlinear Optimisation.* Society for Industrial and Applied Mathematics, 2009 (cit. on p. 7).

[6]   S Boyd and L Vandenberghe. *Convex Optimisation.* Cambridge University Press, 2004 (cit. on p. 7).

[7]   OpenGamma. *Interest Rate Instruments and Market Conventions Guide.* URL: `tradinginterestrates.com/revised/OGGuide.pdf` (cit. on pp. 10, 15).

[18] J Gregory. *The xVA Challenge: Counterparty Credit Risk, Funding, Collateral and Capital.* 3rd. Wiley Finance, 2015 (cit. on p. 60).

[19] A Green. *XVA: Credit, Funding and Capital Valuation Adjustments.* 1st. Wiley Finance, 2015 (cit. on p. 60).

[20] Basel Committee on Banking Supervision. *International Convergence of Capital Measurement and Capital Standards.* URL: `www.bis.org/publ/bcbs128.pdf` (cit. on pp. 61, 65, 245).

[22] E Gagnon D Bowman and M Leahy. "Interest on Excess Reserves as a Monetary Policy Instrument". International Finance Discussion Papers (cit. on p. 100).

[23] R Litterman, J Scheinkman, and L Weiss. "Volatility and the Yield Curve". based on a Goldman Sachs publication of the same title. 1991 (cit. on p. 101).

[24] D Kim and A Orphanides. "The bond market term premium: what is it, and how can we measure it?" In: *Bank for International Settlements Quarterly Review* (2007) (cit. on p. 101).

[25] V Brousseau and A Durre. "Inferring Volatility from the Yield Curve". In: *Journal of Mathematical Finance* (2015) (cit. on p. 101).

[26] B Bernanke. *Reflections on the yield curve and monetary policy.* Speech. 2006 (cit. on p. 101).

[27] J Cochrane and M Piazzesi. "Bond risk premia". In: *American Economic Review* 95 () (cit. on p. 101).

[28] E Fama and R Bliss. "The information in long-maturity forward rates". In: *American Economic Review* 77 () (cit. on p. 101).

[29] G Duffee. "Term premia and interest rate forecasts in affine models". In: *Journal of Finance* 57 () (cit. on p. 101).

[30] F Messelmi. "Analysis of Dual Functions". In: *Annual Review of Chaos Theory, Bifurcations and Dynamical Systems* (2013) (cit. on p. 146).

[31] J Gilbert. "Automatic Differentiation and Iterative Processes". In: *Optimisation Methods and Software* (1992) (cit. on p. 160).

[32] I J Schoenberg and A Whitney. "On Polya frequency functions. III. The positivity of translation determinants with an application to the interpolation problem by spline curves." In: *Transactions of the American Mathematical Society* (1953) (cit. on pp. 170, 182).

[33] C de Boor. *A Practical Guide to Splines*. Springer, 2001 (cit. on pp. 179, 181).

[34] J D Hamilton. *Time Series Analysis*. Princeton University Press, 1994 (cit. on p. 195).

[35] J Bun, J-P Bouchaud, and M Potters. "Cleaning Correlation Matrices". In: *Risk Magazine* (2016) (cit. on p. 196).

[36] J Danielsson et al. "Subadditivity Re-Examined: the Case for Value-at-Risk". 2005 (cit. on p. 204).

[38] Basel Committee on Banking Supervision. *Compilation of relevant documents*. URL: `www.bis.org/bcbs/basel3/compilation.htm` (cit. on p. 244).

[39] Basel Committee on Banking Supervision. *Basel III Reforms Summary*. URL: `www.bis.org/bcbs/basel3/b3summarytable.pdf` (cit. on p. 244).

[40] Basel Committee on Banking Supervision. *Basel III: A global regulatory framework for more resilient banks and banking systems*. URL: `www.bis.org/publ/bcbs189.pdf` (cit. on pp. 245, 247, 249).

[41] D Diamond and R Rajan. "A Theory of Bank Capital". In: *The Journal of Finance* () (cit. on p. 245).

[42] Basel Committee on Banking Supervision. *The standardised approach for measuring counterparty credit risk exposures*. URL: `www.bis.org/publ/bcbs279.pdf` (cit. on pp. 249, 257).

[43] Basel Committee on Banking Supervision. *Capital requirements for bank exposures to central counterparties*. URL: `www.bis.org/publ/bcbs227.pdf` (cit. on p. 250).

[44] Basel Committee on Banking Supervision. *Review of the Credit Valuation Adjustment (CVA) risk framework - consultative document*. URL: `www.bis.org/bcbs/publ/d325.pdf` (cit. on p. 250).

[45] T Boonen, A De Waegenaere, and H Norde. *A Generalization of the Aumann-Shapley Value for Risk Allocation Problems* (cit. on pp. 254, 264).

[46] "Organising the allocation". In: *Risk Magazine* (2016) (cit. on pp. 254, 264).

[47] Basel Committee on Banking Supervision. *Minimum capital requirements for market risk*. URL: `www.bis.org/bcbs/publ/d352.pdf` (cit. on p. 256).

[48] Basel Committee on Banking Supervision. *Revisions to the Basel III Leverage Ratio Framework - consultative document*. URL: `www.bis.org/bcbs/publ/d365.pdf` (cit. on p. 257).

[49] Basel Committee on Banking Supervision. *Basel III: The Liquidity Coverage Ratio and liquidity risk monitoring tools*. URL: `www.bis.org/bcbs/publ/bcbs238.pdf` (cit. on p. 259).

[50] Basel Committee on Banking Supervision. *Net Stable Funding Ratio*. URL: `www.bis.org/bcbs/publ/d295.pdf` (cit. on p. 261).

[51] Basel Committee on Banking Supervision. *Net Stable Funding Ratio disclosure standards*. URL: `www.bis.org/bcbs/publ/d324.pdf` (cit. on p. 261).

[52] J Boehme. "Aumann-Shapley Values: A Technique for Better Attributions". In: *Society of Actuaries - Risk and Rewards* () (cit. on p. 264).

[53] J H M Darbyshire. *Pricing and Trading Interest Rate Derivatives (v2)*. Aitch and Dee Limited, 2017 (cit. on p. 271).

[54] *EBA/RTS/2014/06/rev1 on Prudent Valuation*. Tech. rep. EBA (European Banking Authority), 2014 (cit. on p. 276).

[55] F Bucci and I Mastromatteo. "Co-impact: Crowding Effects in Institutional Trading Activity". 2018 (cit. on p. 290).

[56] E Said and A Ayed. "Market Impact: A systematic study of limit orders". 2018 (cit. on p. 290).

[57] F Black and M Scholes. "The Pricing of Options and Corporate Liabilities". In: *The Journal of Political Economy* 81 (1973) (cit. on pp. 298, 300).

[58] K Iwasawa. "Analytic Formula for the European Normal Black Scholes Formula". 2001 (cit. on p. 314).

[59] P S Hagan et al. "Managing Smile Risk". In: *Wilmott Magazine* (2002) (cit. on p. 317).

[60] D T Breeden and R H Litzenberger. "Prices of State-Contingent Claims Implicit in Option Prices". In: *The Journal of Business* 51 (1978) (cit. on p. 318).

[61] M Henrard. "Cash-Settled Swaptions: How Wrong Are We?" Open Gamma (cit. on p. 329).

[62] M Lutz. "Two Collars and a Free Lunch" (cit. on p. 329).

[64] V Piterbarg and M Renado. "Eurodollar Futures Convexity Adjustments in Stochastic Volatility Models" (cit. on p. 358).

[65] W F Sharpe. "The Sharpe Ratio". In: *The Journal of Portfolio Management* (1994) (cit. on p. 373).

[66] H Markowitz. "Portfolio Selection". In: *The Journal of Finance* (1952) (cit. on p. 378).

Index

Made in the USA
Monee, IL
18 February 2024

8e4755d1-6ba8-430c-be7d-bc6a8823ad1aR01